The Devil in My Dreams

A Collection of Stories from a Chaplain during the Vietnam War

by
John T. Coleman

ISBN: 979-8-218-23834-6 (Paperback)
ISBN: 979-8-218-23835-3 (Ebook)

The photos shared are from the author and depict his father, Chaplain Clifford B Coleman.

Front cover: Chaplain Clifford B Coleman standing on Monkey Mountain in 1969 in Vietnam during the war overlooking a strategic base camp.

Back cover: Chaplain Clifford B Coleman in his dress uniform while stationed on a marine base in southern California. The photo is a family favorite showing his pride serving as chaplain to sailors and marines.

Dedicated to my father,
Commander Clifford B. Coleman
United States Naval Reserve, retired
served the Marines in Vietnam
as Chaplain
August 1968 – August 1969

"War is an ugly thing, but it is not the ugliest of things. The decayed and degraded state of moral and patriotic feeling which thinks that nothing is worth war is much worse. A man who has nothing for which he is willing to fight, nothing he cares about more than his own personal safety, is a miserable creature who has no chance of being free, unless made so by the exertions of better men than himself."

-- John Stuart Mill*

On the battlefield of war lay the dying and wounded,
the ultimate sacrifice to preserve and shield the freedom of others;
In harm's way, marines battle to defend freedom and land beloved.
A marine falls from enemy fire soon to be held in the loving arms of a
chaplain as he takes his last breath;
the chaplain comforts him in his last moments of this life,
who implores the Lord's prayer with the dying
marine as he enters eternity with God;
When he awakens, he discerns the presence of Jesus, who with open
arms, welcomes him home in Heaven with an assuring "Semper Fi!"

Cast of Characters

Navy Chaplains

Lieutenant Daniel Fontaine Anderson – from Manchester, Georgia, whose family owned a peach orchard. His religious affiliation is Southern Baptist.

Lieutenant Charles Brennan – a New Yorker from New York City. His family owned a pizza business. He came from a conservative Irish Roman Catholic background.

Lieutenant Junior Grade Brian Kensington – former attorney from a lawyer family in New York City. The troops loved him. His devotion to his faith, the Roman Catholic Church, showed through his commitment to the Lord.

Lieutenant William Tecumseh Taylor – from Lancaster, Ohio and a staunch Lutheran. His family owned a farm and excelled as a star football player at a major university in southeastern Ohio.

Rear Admiral Lower Half John White – a Charlotte, Virginia native with Thomas Jefferson in his family tree. The family owned a tourist business and is Roman Catholic.

Commander Sterling Wynn – known for his laid back approach and well liked by the men. His family numbered many educators and physicians located all over the Hoosier state. His religious affiliation, American Baptist, went back generations in his family tree. He swelled with pride as a citizen from Jeffersonville, Indiana.

Lieutenant Commander Larry Earnest Thompson – a conservative Episcopalian and a North Dakota native. His family made a living in the grain and barley business.

Lieutenant Commander Dwight Maher – came from a long tradition of Methodist ministers in the family tree. The remaining portion of the family made an income in the aluminum siding business. The steadfast chaplain was born and raised in Anniston, Alabama.

Lieutenant Melvin Abrams – from Philadelphia, Pennsylvania and a Jewish chaplain. He came from a very prolific tradition of military service. The marines and sailors loved the compassionate and caring Abrams.

Ensign John Campbell – born and raised in Pike County, Kentucky. He came from a family of a long line of tradition working in the coal mines. He arrived in Vietnam as a reservist from Lexington, Kentucky, pastoring a Presbyterian church in Georgetown, Kentucky.

Lieutenant Leon Kingslerly – African-American and from Los Angeles, California. He ministered as a staunch Lutheran from a long line of ministers in his family.

Lieutenant Scott Lumberton – an Inter-denominational minister. The Vietnam War interrupted his acting career. As a reservist from Denver, Colorado, he found himself called up for active duty to serve in Vietnam.

Lieutenant Commander Jacob Marino – came from Italian descent. He was born and raised in Chicago, Illinois, in a traditional Roman Catholic family. His family owned a book business, including book binding.

ENLISTED PERSONNEL

MARINE AND NAVY

Corporal Kenneth Kowslowski, Chief – a member of the Roman Catholic Church and owned a tree grooming business in Minnesota. Native American Indian blood flowed in the veins of his family tree, triggering high levels of pride in his demeanor due to his care for nature and the ecosystem.

Sergeant Adrian Lipstone, The Hammer – dirt poor and African-American from Milledgeville, Georgia. His family were some of the best carpenters in middle Georgia. Though a high school dropout, he obtained an IQ of 132. His affiliation on his enlistment card declared himself following the Baptist faith.

Sergeant Carl Remington, Hunter – a Kentuckian and owned a 'Mr. Fix-It-Shop' in Louisville, Kentucky. His specialty fixed grandfather clocks and is affiliated with a Baptist tradition.

Lance Corporal Fred Jones, Coal – a Kentuckian from Pike County and a coal miners' family. He dropped out of high school and from a staunch Presbyterian family.

Private First Class Michael Dobbs, Trouble – from California and quit school in his sophomore year. He had a history of getting into trouble with the law and with the military police. He did not believe in God and made it known to all he confessed to be an atheist.

Corporal Michael Jaworski, Father – a Polish 1st generation farmer from Pennsylvania. As a devout Roman Catholic, he considered the Priesthood after his service in the marines.

Staff Sergeant Frank Smith, Boone – came from a long rich tradition of an aristocratic family in Williamsburg, Virginia. His family soared in success in the distribution business and large farms. His religious affiliation declared himself as an Episcopalian.

Private Joseph Varnes, Pizza – an 18 year old from New Jersey and from a Jewish family history, who owned a chain of grocery stores. The family specialty prepared sandwiches in the deli of the stores. The family owned a subsidiary business in pizza shops.

Corporal Adolphus Skawinski, Farmer – his family owned a farm in Preble County outside of Dayton, Ohio. His family is staunch Lutherans and found himself in the middle of getting his degree from a prominent university in western Ohio until he volunteered for the war.

Gunnery Sergeant John McElrath, Texas – from Dallas, Texas and his family owned a beef cattle business. He affiliated with the Baptists, but adhered as a nonbeliever.

Private Leonard Shaw, The Law – an African-American from St. Louis, Missouri whose family owned a small family restaurant and affiliated with the Methodist church. His family tree extended itself in St. Louis as lawyers and district attorneys.

Private Benjamin Kiehl, Sharpshooter – a reservist from Kansas city, Missouri, whose family were electricians and worked for the city. Everyone who came in contact with him knew of his Lutheran pride and his staunch Democrat membership.

Private Miguel Rodriquez, Vet, was short for veterinarian – before the war, he worked as a janitor in a department store. A San Diego, California native, struggled economically from a Mexican descent. Prior to being drafted, he found himself trying out and winning a spot on a minor league baseball team. His dream to become a vet and own his own pet supply business inspired him to push forward during his tour and survive the rigors of war. His faith of living a strict Roman Catholic life is first and foremost in everything he says and does everyday he gets up in the morning.

Private First Class Christopher PoKorny, The Painter - from a Polish background. He owned a paint business back home in Bismarck, South Dakota, whose family religious background comprised of traditional conservative Roman Catholics.

Private John Sims, Taxi – an African American from Los Angeles, California. Working as a cab driver before the war, he was very astute as a skilled painter; he sold his work for profit. Sims declared himself a non-believer.

Staff Sergeant Frank Burnside - from a Pittsburgh steel mills background. Born and raised in Pittsburgh, Pennsylvania, his religious background is Quaker and showed a passive demeanor toward war.

Corporal Michael McMillan, Wildcat - a Baptist, but antagonistic toward organized religion. He worked in ordinance and owned a gun shop in Paducah, Kentucky. His favorite sports team was the major university basketball team in the state.

Petty Officer 1st Class Earnest Jackson – from Gatesville, Texas and Baptist. His family owned a department store in his hometown, specializing in men's sports coats and dress clothes.

Chief Petty Officer John Dingus – a staunch Episcopalian and made the Navy his career. The family business back home in Eddington, Maine, composed of antiques. As a corpsman, he served in World War II and Korea.

Petty Officer 2nd Class Philip Jenkins – from Albany, Oregon. His family business thrived in the melting and formulation of metals and alloys. His family lived a strict faith in Methodist doctrine and originally from Ohio being born in Dayton, where his father served while in the United States Air Force.

Petty Officer 3rd Class Daniel Adkins – predominately a Baptist in his background, he attended a Methodist church in California near the El Toro Marine base. His family made a living in the tourist business back in Cleveland, Tennessee.

Petty Officer 3rd Class Lawrence Sigmanson, Preacher – a preacher's kid from Miami, Florida. His affiliation on his enlistment card read non-denominational, and he proved himself as a superb corpsman in combat situations.

Senior Chief Petty Officer Carlson Gross, Surfer – his family served as career Navy. His parents were both corpsmen. Because of his military parents, his birth certificate came from Hawaii and he lived all over the world. The family originally came from White Bear Lake, Minnesota.

Petty Officer 2nd Class David James Crowley – from Mount Airy, North Carolina. His high level of education boasted of a Bachelor of Science degree and an associate degree. His IQ, when tested, scored a 152. He ended up popular with the men.

Gunnery Sergeant Richard Neville Warwick Jurgensen – a Roman Catholic. He fought fiercely and wildly in combat. The enemy feared him as he gained a reputation as a ferocious hand to hand warrior. However, his civilian background portrayed nothing close to his combat service. His father held a history professor and archaeologist position at USC. He himself taught school on the college level before his Vietnam service. He served active and reserve duty in the past. His reserve center is in Los Angeles, California.

OFFICERS

NAVY AND MARINES

Lieutenant Nancy Burleson – was basically non-religious. She came from a nursing family and a native of Las Vegas, Nevada.

Lieutenant Commander John Adkins – originally from Omaha, Nebraska. His family tree extended back for generations as long time farmers and well known for their corn. His affiliation came from a Baptist background and a staunch conservative.

Marine Lieutenant Lance Thomas Rockford – he declared himself a conscientious Presbyterian, but known to break the denomination rules from time to time. His family business thrived from a long line of 18-wheeler truck drivers in Erie, Pennsylvania, owning their own trucker business.

Marine Lieutenant Lawrence Jones – the family earned a living in the wine business, making Jones a popular officer in Camp Love, Vietnam. He lived a devoted life as a Roman Catholic and claimed Spokane, Washington, his hometown.

Marine Lieutenant John Nathan Frost – his hometown of Detroit, Michigan provided his family work in the automobile business for decades. Though he tended to be non-religious, he did attend Methodist church services from time to time and attended Methodist services.

General John Sands – originally from Camden, Arkansas. His religious affiliation is Baptist. His family operated a well-known fishing and hunting supply business.

Lieutenant Commander Veronica Reagan – coming from a family of nurses, she entered the Navy with a great compassion and care for human beings. Originally from Provo, Utah, she grew up Roman Catholic placing her in a small religious affiliation in her home state.

Lieutenant Junior Grade Jennifer Glenn – possessed a strong calling to be a nurse reflective of her strong Catholic faith to serve others. Born and raised in Phoenix, Arizona, she later moved to California after she achieved her nursing degree.

Major James Burns – a music teacher at a major university in West Virginia before the war. A staunch Presbyterian from Winfield, West Virginia.

Lieutenant Lawrence McInally - originally from Wilmington, North Carolina. His devotion and commitment to his Jewish faith served as a spearhead to get him through his tour of duty. His family profited in the real estate business, working with antiques on the side.

Marine Captain Bernard Johannsson – many of his family perished in the Holocaust during World War II. His Jewish parents escaped Europe when he turned 6 years of age. His parents chose New York City to be home, which his family established a law firm known for a unswerving reputation in the state of New York. He served as commanding officer in Charlie Company.

Lieutenant Colonel William "Bud" Lucas – his family background were blue-collar workers working for Goodyear. The family were conservative Baptists in Cleveland, Ohio, where he was born and raised a Buckeye and it showed in his demeanor.

Major Vincent Carroll – one of the few non-denominational service personnel in the 7th Engineering Battalion. From Biloxi, Mississippi, his family started a fishing business. He served as the executive officer of Camp Love.

Marine Captain Theodore Case – his family in Louisville, Kentucky were wealthy and owned many businesses, including a horse farm whose horses raced at the track. As a Roman Catholic, he attended the Catholic schools in Louisville. His aka in Camp Love was "The Scrounger."

Major Michael Porch – the most arrogant officer in Camp Love, 7th Engineering Marine Battalion. From Huntley, Illinois, he grew up in the Roman Catholic Church. His family owned distribution centers for retail companies.

Major Michael "Mickey" Sanborn – from Iowa City, Iowa, his background growing up in a traditional Lutheran family set high standards to live a Jesus like life. His background in farming provided great pleasure teaching the Vietnamese to cultivate their land.

Lieutenant James Delaney – grew up in Dallas, Texas, serving as the battalion surgeon. He graduated from the University of Texas coming from a prominent physician family. The men loved him and enjoyed his presence when mingling with the troops.

Major Harley Stewart – born and raised in Lowgap, North Carolina, his family owned several antique stores, including one in Mount Airy, North Carolina. He became a master silversmith and his family owned a couple of farms. His proudest achievement came in writing a small history book on the Shawnee Indian Tribe.

Preface

John T. Coleman

War.

What, if anything, can be thought of as good with such a notion as war? The word itself is a detestable, abhorrent word. An ugly, offensive word. A word in the English language my family loathes, and for good reason.

For decades, my family observed the effects of war and combat on my father's psyche. War has haunted my father since August 1968.

From the day Clifford B Coleman arrived home from Vietnam, he grappled with the scars and pain of war and the violence that stems from it. He served as a Navy chaplain with the 7th Engineering Battalion 1st Marine Division in Vietnam between August 1968 to August 1969. War was not kind to my father. It did nothing but plaster memories of death and agony into his mind. An imprint of memories no one else can explain but him.

I witnessed firsthand how war affected my father. The occasional nightmare waking up the whole family in the middle of the night. A nightmarish memory of young men possibly dying in his arms and praying as they breathed their last breath. Or the precious Vietnamese children blown apart stepping into a booby trap or onto a land mine. If he could, he would wash those memories away, permanently. I'm sure memories he wants to forget if he could. Unfortunately, our brains do not function to forget or remember by flipping a switch off and on. A delete button to eliminate our memories is absent from our biological makeup. His memories are never-ending.

The slightest little thing could set my father off, though major flashbacks would falter as time passed. He suffered from PTS ever since he returned in 1969, with an occasional and serious flashback. In fact, he thought about the war every day (a fact my family was unaware of until the mid-1990's). My family helped him with his struggles. We would avoid watching television shows with a war theme in his presence to shield him from a scene that could trigger a flashback. Shows that seem harmless too many, but not for my family. One evening, my mother and I were watching a detective show based out of Hawaii and the character experienced a flashback in the episode with a Vietnam War theme. We were playing rummy, which was often, and my father arrived late one night from a meeting with other ministers. "Turn the channel. Turn the channel. Hurry. Hurry." said Mom. She insisted that I immediately turn the channel to prevent Dad from experiencing a possible emotional incident. Over time, we would avoid watching even movies centered in on Vietnam. Even viewing television shows with an educational emphasis about the Vietnam War could ignite something inside his mind, causing him to be melancholy. I, along with my mother and two sisters, did everything we could to assist him to avoid a flashback. With time and age, I understood the line you never crossed with Dad when protecting him from his war experience. A combat question out of the blue about Vietnam was *not* a good idea. Questions such as "Hey Dad, how many Viet Cong did you see get killed in the battle?" or "Did you see any VC attack a Vietnamese village?" These sorts of questions would definitely trigger deep emotions. Asking questions about Vietnam could set off a memory that would upset him very much. Mom would constantly remind us kids growing up not to upset him, saying, "Remember to be careful what you say in front of your father about the war." We would keep our questions and thoughts about the war pretty much to ourselves. If he wanted to talk, we would listen.

To this day, I still have not grasped how war and combat could affect a human being as it did my father. I wish I possessed the power to erase all the terrible memories of his experience as a Navy chaplain and keep the good. Unfortunately, I can't.

For many of my Christmases growing up, a common gift unwrapped every year had been a historical set of toy soldiers from a company who manufactured historical toys. I collected Revolutionary War, Civil War, the Alamo, and World War II soldiers, amongst others. After unwrapping gifts on Christmas day, Dad spent time with me setting up battles on the living room floor with the new soldiers. As a youngster, I grew up oblivious my father painfully struggled with war memories as he played war with me. I imitated the sounds of war - gunfire, explosions, men being killed and wounded in battle. I spent time with my father out of touch something as trivial as my reenactments of battles could cause my father to fall into a depressive state. I considered my father brilliant keeping his emotions within his inner self. On other occasions, I played out a battle from a war movie I watched on television. I set up the toy soldiers in battle formation and relive all the glory and triumph of war from the movie. When Dad returned home, I proudly showed him how I carried out the movie scene. I set up historical engagements, playing out the strategy and tactics of the battle. I still own those toy soldiers from my childhood. Sometimes I pull off the shelf the boxes they are stored in, open them up on the kitchen table, and reminisce of all the fun Dad and I had playing as a youngster. As a boy, though, I never understood the reality of war and the severe outcomes on those who took part in the killing and maiming of human beings. As I played with the plastic soldiers, I lived my young life unaware of the ugliness and pain of war. As I grew into adulthood, I longed to understand the causes of war and the justification of war. Dealing with Dad's PTS through the years as a family, we knew the trials and tribulations families will experience when a loved one returned from combat. We prayed for the troops and their families when our country found the need to send military personnel into a combat zone. As a family unit, we prayed for them. We knew what the future might hold and the aftermath of the effects of war had on the individual psyche. When I have time out of my busy schedule, I read everything

I can get my hands on to get a better understanding of Dad's attempt to grapple with his memories.

As a social science teacher, I love the study of military strategy and tactics. Quotes often seem to help me understand human being's idiosyncrasies, vulnerabilities, and failures when they are in a combat zone. Sebastian Junger said, "The only thing that makes battle psychologically tolerable is the brotherhood among soldiers. You need each other to get by."* I like that quote. Listening to Dad's stories of Vietnam and his ministry to the 7th Engineering Battalion in Camp Love reflects Junger's quote. The brotherhood present within the 7th Engineering Battalion enabled the men to endure the day-to-day sufferings of combat. My father made himself completely available to the men for ministry, as a bond emerged between Dad and the men. His personality reflected a "people oriented" chaplain. His approach bared a constant contact with the troops. On his own initiative, he visited individual platoons and departments in Camp Love, promoting an open door policy. This policy of the day manifested a typical trait of Vietnam chaplains. The men loved him. He loved them. The marines insisted he go with them in the bush in case the unfortunate might happen and fate come to one of the young men. Many of his flashbacks came from his bonding closely to a marine in the camp only to be wounded or killed in action before his very eyes or possibly die in Dad's arms and presence.

The possibility of Dad experiencing a serious flashback was 24/7. He could view something on television, read something in the newspapers or a book, or enter a conversation with a fellow veteran about the war, which could trigger a serious memory. I possess in the back of my mind two distinct memories of Dad having such a serious flashback in my presence.

The first experience, as a teenager, revealed how seriously the war affected my father. I remember my first memory at either 13 or 14 years of age. My older sister moved out of the house and her old room had a small television set in it. Occasionally, any one family member would watch television in her old room. My father and I watched John Wayne's film on Vietnam one evening and we were at the tail end of the movie. Dad, an ardent John Wayne fan, introduced me to Wayne at a very young age. His movies, his patriotism, the man John Wayne – all introduced to me at birth. Dad loved him and thought of him as a great American. In fact, his love for John Wayne influenced me greatly. The Duke became my favorite actor. Lying on the bed watching the tail-end of the movie, one of the main characters stepped onto a booby trap, slamming him into a wall of punji sticks, killing him. My father and I viewed the entire movie up to this point and thankfully no flashbacks! Dad experiencing a flashback at any point during the movie had been a worry in the back of my mind throughout the film. But when viewing the booby trap scene, he went ballistic. The scene sparked an uncontrollable fire within him. He began screaming uncontrollably. Falling onto the floor into a fetal position screaming, he held onto his knees, stiff as a brickbat. The solitary words I remember him yelling were "no" and "Mom." Downstairs in the kitchen, Mom heard screaming and, at the spur of the moment, bolted upstairs to inquire of the shouting. The bedroom location is at the top of the stairs and she practically fell on top of Dad entering the bedroom. I hopped down onto the floor to console Dad, which did absolutely nothing to relive his agony in his mind. At this point, he ceased screaming and uttered quiet grunts repeatedly. Stooping down toward the floor, Mom placed her right hand on his shoulder, expressing to him things were going to be alright. She frantically attempted to redirect his thoughts or to contemplate of something else other than Vietnam. "You're in Ohio." "You're with J.T." "You're preaching in Portsmouth this Sunday, 'member?" Nothing verbal seemed to help. The grunting turned more erratic and rapid. I patted his shoulder (as if this made everything OK!) to carry out my part in consoling him. Mom continued to converse with him, informing him everything is OK. "Everything is going to be OK. It's OK." she repeated excessively. His grunting slowed down, beginning to relax. I next heard a sound from my father I had never heard before. He cried like a baby. His excessive weeping echoed throughout the room, upset from his war memory. The night had turned into a gut-wrenching memory for my mother and I. Finally getting him up off the floor, we sat him on the edge of the bed, as he calmed down. My mother and I walked him into the hall down to the master bedroom as he finally settled down. A rare moment occurred this might for my mother and I. Occasionally, Dad opened up with gruesome accounts of Vietnam, and tonight is one of them. He informed us of what could've caused such a commotion. His memory had been of a young kid (I remember him from Kentucky or the Appalachian Mountain range, or at least the deep south) who went out hunting every morning from Camp Love. The marine became close to my father, a chaplain who cared for his "flock" of military personnel. Besides, as a former enlisted man, he knew the vital importance of chaplain leadership. The two men shared many things in common, acquiring a great rapport with one another. One morning the marine, 19 or in his early 20s, failed to return from hunting. Worried, Dad and a contingent of marines went searching for him. In no time at all, the marines located the young marine whose fate ended with capture, torture, and death at the hands of the Viet Cong. They placed his mutilated torso and detached limps at intervals, leading on a path to the marine's impaled head on a pike. The discovery of the young marine devastated my father and the contingent of marines. Popular within the 7th Engineering Battalion, the young marine's death immersed the battalion into deep depression. The young marine's murder turned out to be one of two instances in my memory bank in which my father informed me he felt so enraged, he considered taking up arms and fighting the enemy himself. Whatever memory had been stored within his mind which triggered the flashback, he only knows. The fact is, Dad saw or heard something in the movie which instigated his flashback. My mother and I were flabbergasted with the account of the young marine.

I experienced a dream the night of the flashback, which recurs from time to time. In the dream, I am in my room constructing a Medieval castle with over sized tools. As I was building my castle, I heard blood curling screams coming from my sister's old bedroom. Our rooms were next to each other, and I ran to the door of the bedroom. When I reach the bedroom entrance, Dad is standing at the entrance begging to be let out of the room. The entrance had plexiglass in it, preventing him from exiting the bedroom. Glancing at the television set, it was repeating the booby trap scene over and over and over again. Dad is extremely terrified and distraught at hearing and seeing the scene over and over. My efforts to free him from his torment undertook pushing through the glass, crashing through with a sledgehammer, and even cutting through with an axe, to no avail. Running back to my room, I attempted to use the over sized tools I used to build my Medieval castle to knock down the plexiglass. That, too, failed. Nothing seemed strong enough to crash through the plexiglass. Hurrying back once again to my room, I climbed out my back window onto the flat roof permitting me to examine my sister's window, only to discover there is plexiglass in it as well. My mother and two sisters finally made their way to the bedroom doorway. In one last desperate attempt, we pushed onto the glass to release my father from his pain. This, too, failed. Still entrapped in the bedroom, begging excessively to be let out, Dad shrieks to the top of his lungs, eventually falling onto the floor, leaning on the plexiglass crying excessively. In a helpless, feeble, debilitating state, he's never freed from captivity in my dream. I always wake up from the dream with Dad, forever imprisoned in his torment. I consider my dream a constant reminder that Vietnam will always haunt him.

The second instance was a trip to Kentucky, in which I accompanied him as he moderated a church business meeting. I was maybe 14 or 15 years of age. After the meeting, we stopped at a convenience store and purchased a snack and a pop and conversed on everything *but* Vietnam for miles. On our way home on Route 93 from Ironton, Ohio, we traveled on a black night in southern Ohio. Route 93 is full of curvy roads (though today, many parts of the road have been straightened out) and in the pitch dark, Dad began to talk about Vietnam on his own. Everything seemed OK, and I even felt safe to ask him some innocent questions about his experience in Vietnam. But as we approached Oak Hill, Ohio, which is about 10 miles from Jackson, Ohio, my hometown, he uttered some quirky statements.

"Son, keep your eye out for the enemy. They're sneaky and can attack us at any moment." "Don't let'em capture you. They'll fight till the death." and "Watch out for those snipers." He asked me to look for the enemy in the darkness. I glanced at him in the corner of my eye to check on him, to see if he was OK. He seemed a bit irritated and startled. He asked me to be prepared to fight if we were confronted with the enemy. I was a little alarmed and jolted with his behavior. He spoke as if the VC and NVA were all around us. We finally arrived at home and drove into the driveway. He drove straight into the parking space, an unusual move on Dad's part. He taught us kids to always back into the space in case of snow. When we stopped, he would not permit me to step out of the car. When I did attempt to leave, he went berserk and begged and begged me to stay in the vehicle. "Son, please don't let the VC get us. They'll kill us." I asked him, "Why are there VC in the bushes?" He responded abruptly, "The VC kill chaplains. They hate us." We just sat there for a few minutes and he was very confused. I attempted to explain to him, "Dad, we are not in Vietnam. We're in Jackson. I'm not a marine and you're not sitting in a jeep in Vietnam." He got emotional. All he said was "I'm sorry, son." At this point, I heard the back door of our home open and it was Mom, stepping onto the back porch. She wondered why it was taking so long for us to come in. As I was rolling down my window to ask her for help, she said, "Are you coming in? I have something for y'all to eat." I rolled my window down a bit more and explained why we were sitting in the car. "Mom, Dad is having a flashback. He thinks there's Viet Cong in the yard. He's scared to get out." She rushed down the back porch steps and to the driver's side of the car. By the time she got to the driver's side, Dad explained to her, "I'm alright. Really. I think I'm OK now. I was just disoriented for a while."

We found ourselves once again leading him through the house and putting him to bed. We donned his night clothes on him and again he told us a story which caused the flashback in the car. One night in Vietnam, he was out with a company of marines and it was a night of total darkness. He was in his usual position marines placed the chaplain in the bush to keep the chaplain safe in a combat zone. Dad somehow wandered outside his comfort zone and found himself isolated in the deep darkened jungles of Vietnam. He was utterly terrified the Viet Cong would bump into him in the darkness prior to the marines locating him. If a United States military chaplain was captured, the VC would not hesitate to kill the chaplain. He knew this, and the thoughts of what they might do to him horrified his inner heart and soul. He prayed for safety. The VC considered a chaplain a source of great morale and boosted discipline for United States military personnel. Two general rules marines insisted the Navy chaplains carry out in case any of them ever found themselves isolated in the jungle – 1) don't attempt to find the marines, lay down and permit them to find you and 2) don't yell out where you are. Keep your mouth shut and be still. My father had patience and did what the marines told him to do – stay put and remain silent. The marines finally found him. Dad suddenly felt a full fill of elation of inner joy. He learned quickly to be more careful of his bearings after that night in the jungle, though. After discussing what happened later on that night, my mother and I assumed that the innocent conversation concerning Vietnam that he started in the car and the darkness of the night spurred on a memory of fright for my father. After he told us the story about his isolation from the marines, he closed his eyes and went to sleep. I will never forget that night. We sat on the bed, praying to the Lord Dad would experience pleasant dreams of comfort and consolation.

There are many reasons for writing this story. In the first place, I am very proud of my father's service to his country. I know no one else who loves his country more than my father. He believes in America. He believes in its values and principles. The freedoms, liberties, and rights the Constitution provides in its tenets and constructs. He treasures the liberty parents have to raise their families with little interference from outside forces. My sisters and I were fortunate to have parents who went out of their way to provide an upbringing that reflected love, forgiveness, caring for one another, and an incredible sense of belonging. My parents instilled in us kids a passionate love for our country. They taught us that when we became adults, we were to be mentors for the next generation and to be an inspiration for future generations. His generation is one who treasures the freedoms and privileges we have and are meant to be protected. His Vietnam experience reinforced this conviction for him. Second, this present generation is in need to hear how a man, full of love and energy, gave himself as a great sacrifice to our military personnel. My father is a Baptist, and for Baptist ministers, those who enter the office of ministry are called to serve. My father's call from God to minister to marines in the 1960s required him to put his life on the line in order that service personnel would have opportunities to live out their faith and to exercise their constitutional right of freedom of religion.

My story is of a man willing to put his life on the line as a Navy chaplain and to provide the freedom of expression and freedom of religion in Vietnam. My father's story is one of many positive narratives that places itself within all the turmoil and chaos of the war which he found himself in the midst of. With all the negativity we have today in the media, both social and mainstream, his story has always been one to inspire others to love their country and its principles.

Every man and woman has a story. Clifford B Coleman's story entails a man who conquered many obstacles thrown his way in life, beating the odds which were heavily against him. The fictitious chaplain in *The Devil in My Dreams* reflects attributes of my father, though many were fabricated to generate my fictitious character. His spiritual testimony led many a person to the Lord. Cliff's story proved without a doubt Jesus can turn anyone's life around, even a man destined to drink himself to death. Cliff survived and conquered obstacles thrown his way each and every time. As a youngster, I imagined in my mind a caricature of Cliff as a conquering warrior hero type of character overcoming the trials of life with his right foot pressed down on an image of each obstacle he conquered in life, a battle within between two wills and a sword held high in his right hand, winning each confrontation piecemeal. The swelling of self and ego of conquering all the obstacles thrown his or her way in life is a temptation for any human being. A mindset many people take hold of when overcoming hardships in life is a 'I overcame' *all* the barriers preventing success in life and give in to the temptation of self-gratification. Cliff brushed aside that temptation and credited his victory over his hardships to Jesus. The singular and exclusive cause of Cliff's change in his life came from one source, and one source only - Jesus. The Savior turned his life around - nothing more, nothing less. His change reflected Christ penetrating a heart longing to experience love and joy in life. And Cliff found the love and joy he longed for in Jesus Christ.

The pages within this historical narrative is his story of Vietnam.

Refer to the notes page at the end of the book for any asterisks within the narrative.

Author's note: all the characters in this historical narrative were created from the author's imagination and events the author's father witnessed in Vietnam. The characters are entirely fictional. The names, traits and characteristics, locations, and events are originated from the author. Any similarity to a real person, past or present, experiences, places and sites is completely unintentional.

Eternal Memories of War

May 17, 1978

Thousands upon thousands of bamboo vipers and boa constrictors converge upon Camp Love, 7th Engineering Marine Battalion, slithering and scurrying along on their bellies out of the jungle, longing to slink in and slaughter United States marines. Thousands and thousands of snakes, with the heads of demons and a blind loyalty to the Devil. Flicking their tongues with the sense of urgency, the lateral undulation is of determination. Wild and side winding perfectly in form, the snakes cover the entire perimeter of Camp Love with anticipation of entering the camp. An aerial view of the perimeter revealed a mixture of brown and black blended with a beige sprinkled throughout with the bright green, yellowish purple of the bamboo viper. The snakes curling over one another with the anticipation of infiltrating the camp, devouring the life out of marines and sailors within. As snakes gather outside the camp, a lone Viet Cong officer steps out of one hootch, skipping along ever so happy and humming a cheerful tune. Skipping and humming the whole way to the camp's gate, the VC officer lollygags his way to let the snakes in to snatch the life out of the marines. The officer takes his time skipping to the gate, intentionally teasing the snakes into a frenzy. Finally, making his way to the gate, he reaches out with his right hand to unleash the latch. As the officer's hand reaches for the gate latch, his hand transforms into a drawn-out, elongated form with long fingers and long nails, boney and disfigured. In time, the officer utterly transforms into the Devil. He leisurely lifts the latch up with his hand, and as the gate opens ever so unhurriedly, snakes pour into the camp, thousands upon thousands twisting and curling round one another, fighting to reach the doomed marines sleeping in their hootches. Bamboo vipers enter hootch after hootch piercing venom into the marines with fangs and boa constrictors squeezing the life out of marines and sailors. The Devil sprints a frenzy to a single hootch, snakes slithering behind him, determined to carry out evil intent as the Devil and snakes converge on the hootch. Within the hootch sleeps a Navy chaplain. The Devil set aside the chaplain last to kill, as he transforms ever so soundly into a massive boa constrictor with his head attached onto his body. As he enters the hootch of the chaplain, he slithers around the hootch as if sizing up his prey. Slithering ever so slowly over to the chaplain's cot, he curls himself underneath and above the chaplain and cot, entirely encompassing the chaplain. Completely encircling the cot, the Devil places his head perfectly above the chaplain's, an inch from his nose. Smiling wide, many arms emerge from his snake's underbelly, in one hand grasping a knife, the other pulling the chaplain's head back, stretching his neck long and wide for the Devil to slit his throat ever so clean. The Devil, with a knife in hand, sharpens back and forth on his neck, smiling ever so wide, restraining himself from slicing the skin. Licking the edge of the knife, he measures up the neck with his knife. The Devil, chock-full of hate and now impatient, has had enough playing and toying with the chaplain and places the knife just under the Adam's Apple to cut his throat. The evil consummation for the Devil taking the life of this menace and ridding himself of a man struggling to spread peace in a war will now end. But just as the Devil puts pressure on the skin of the neck – a chaplain wakes up from a dream in rural southeastern Ohio, panting uncontrollably, screaming - "Ah!"

"Will it ever end!?!?!" came a scream in a strong, deep Kentuckian accent.

The chaplain, still after 10 years from experiencing combat, dealt with the struggle of war heightened from nightmares and flashbacks.

The disturbance caused quite a stir in the chaplain's house, causing his whole family to awake.

"Ah!!!! No!!!" "I'm dead! I'm dead!!!" came more screams.

Following a brief pause, the chaplain says in a softer cracked voice, "Will these... dreams ever end?"

All in the house were woken with the commotion. His wife, kids, and the three family dogs – Dachshunds, who were sleeping peacefully downstairs in their dog beds.

His wife consoles him, holding his nearest arm. "Are you alright? Was just one of your dreams? You're OK." She pauses. "You're in Ohio, not Vietnam. OK, babe....you hear me?"

The chaplain nods yes, collecting his bearings and recognizing his surroundings. With energy his wife turns, switching the light on on her side of the bed.

The children rose from a restful night of sleep, dashing to their parent's bedroom. They converge around their father in bed, who sweats and pants from such a horrible nightmare, staring down at him with sympathy and worry in their eye!

Along with the children came the sudden rush of three fawn colored Dachshunds. With ears perked and tails wagging elatedly, the dogs displayed concern and jumped onto the bed to comfort their loving and gentle owner. Sniffing his hands, the pooches licked and smiled wide, wagging their tails wildly as if to say, 'It's going to be OK.' The chaplain grins slightly at the dogs, petting them on their heads.

The chaplain, waking up from the recurring dream, began to feel much better with the help of his understanding wife, wonderful but bewildered kids, and his loyal canine friends. Overwhelmed to no end he woke up in southeastern Ohio, he sighed heavy. He is ever so grateful he did not wake up in the jungles of South Vietnam. But the dream felt real to him, one which put him back into a gruesome, agonizing setting in his life never capable of shedding from his memories.

The forever imprint of war memories chiseled on his mind, never to forget in his lifetime.

A Bumpy Ride

October 1, 1968

October 1968.

The height of the Vietnam War.

The year began with Peace Talks in Paris. A year ravaged with war as many Americans wished for a speedy peace, bringing soldiers and marines home for Christmas. Vietnam, however, is far from peaceful. In fact, 1968 will see the height of violence in Vietnam since the war began. The year saw an attack on a United States military base ending an attempted peace by Pope Paul VI, and the North Vietnamese Army and Viet Cong forces launched the Tet Offensive at the end of January 1968.

The Battle of Hue, a victory won by the Army of the Republic of Vietnam and United States marines between January 30 and March 3, came at a heavy cost of lives. A victory boosting morale, but with a bloody cost of United States marines. House to house and street fighting brought about brutal violence to a war already stricken with death and destruction. It ended up one of the bloodiest and ferocious engagements of the war.

The infamous footage of a Viet Cong prisoner, Nguyen Van Lem, executed by South Vietnamese General Nguyen Ngoc Loan took place on 1 February 1968. On 16 March 1968, the My Lai incident, which hundreds of civilians were killed, generated a significant lack of support for the war back home in the United States. These two incidents plastered the television screens and newspapers.

Two incidents of anti-war sentiment used to generate even more animosity toward the war.

In 1968, President Johnson delivers a speech on television announcing plans to limit the war and that he will not seek a re-election bid. Though Johnson promises limiting the expansion of the conflict and to downsize the war effort, the year of 1968 finds the highest number of troops totaling 550,000 military personnel in Vietnam.

May 1968 brought a second offensive started by the communists in Tet II, or the May Offensive. That same month would bring the first peace talks in Paris, which involved American withdrawals.

The summer of 1968 propelled an effort of peace talks, starting a summer season of less fanfare with the war.

Beginning in October through December 1968, the United States and South Vietnamese troops conducted a counteroffensive against the Tet Offensive named Operation Toan Thang I. The aim of the counteroffensive intended to counterbalance the attack during the Tet offensives by the Communists the previous January and May.

The month of October found the United States Navy assisting the South Vietnamese Navy with Operation Sealords, beginning on 8 October 1968. The operation's objective centered in on disrupting North Vietnamese supply lines around the Mekong Delta. The two-year operation conducted simultaneously by United States and South Vietnamese forces, as the South Vietnamese took full rein of the operations of the campaign after two years.

The year of 1968 ended with the highest number of Viet Cong killings, murders, and abductions in a single year, totaling over 14,000, including the Massacre at Hue and the Son Tra Massacre. The avoidance of reporting such atrocities of the Viet Cong baffled military leadership and supporters of the war.

Within the jungles of Vietnam, the 7th Engineering Marine Battalion supporting the III Marine Amphibious Force (MAF), part of I Corps Tactical Zone served proudly. The battalion's history in Vietnam started with Company A, attached to the Regimental Landing Team 7 who on 1 June 1965 departed for the Republic of

Vietnam. In August 1965, the 7th Engineering Battalion was ordered for service in Vietnam, arriving on the 24th of the month. Out of Da Nang, the battalion supported III MAF which in 1966 made history by constructing an M-4 aluminum pontoon bridge extending for 1,478 feet over the Da Nang River. The bridge constructed will be listed as the longest crossing constructed during the entire war. The battalion's missions in 1967 were constructing bridges, aluminum and pile bent bridges, maintenance and improving roads. In 1968, the battalion constructed a coffer dam, while Company D engaged in Operation Mameluke Thrust, a spoiling attack operation to counter attack the loss of Kham Doc. The battalion served through 1970 by upgrading and maintaining roads, furnishing general engineering support, and mine-sweeping. The battalion returned to California at Camp Pendleton in September 1970. The 7th Engineering Battalion in Vietnam displayed a history of vitality full of pride and honor.

The year 1968 for the 7th Engineering Marine Battalion began with violence, horror, and agony serving in southeastern Asia. Though serving in a depressive and overwhelming war, the battalion pushed forward with confidence and determination.

Amidst all the violence of 1968, an anxious Navy chaplain, Lieutenant Robert James Buchanan, was aboard a Huey helicopter, heading straight toward Camp Love - the 7th Engineering Marine Battalion base of operations in the jungle.

Buchanan, resolute and self-assured, sat in his buckled seat on his way to fulfill his call of ministry with marines in his only tour of duty. The camp measured approximately 6 miles north of the air base in Da Nang, Vietnam. Ministering in Da Nang the previous 6 months equipped Buchanan for ministry to meet the wants and needs of the marines in the deep jungles of the bush.

The anticipation of arriving in Camp Love overwhelmed Buchanan, who glanced down at his watch, which read 0800 hours in the morning.

Enthusiasm of ministering to marines stood first and foremost on his mind. As a Baptist, he believed people of God were called into service, and his calling of ministry to the marines in the bush was coming to fruition.

The chaplain, fervent with his upcoming ministry, suffered from nausea because of the helicopter flight. Never riding in a Huey helicopter, it shook him up something terrible. The sensations felt as if he was on a roller coaster, without the liberty of stepping off the ride. His strap on glasses prevented him from losing them over the jungles of Vietnam. He felt fortunate to possess a second pair, but he did not want to take any chances, so he wore his strap on glasses.

The Huey helicopter descended left and right, awkwardly ascended upward, descending straight down, taking a sharp turn, along with the usual turbulence of a Huey helicopter. While sick to his stomach, Buchanan's ride was tolerable because of his two friends, Lieutenant Commander John Adkins and Sergeant Philip Jackson. Adkins, a Navy Seabee, discovered his assignment to a construction unit to build bridges and complete projects, including the maintenance of roads two weeks ago. Jackson, Buchanan's chaplain assistant and bodyguard, worked jointly with Buchanan in Da Nang the past six months to marines in the III Marine Amphibious Force (MAF). The three men worked for six months in Da Nang within their respective departments.

The pilot, smirking, thought it a treat to transport a first timer on a Huey.

Buchanan held on to whatever he could get his hands on in the helicopter, holding on for dear life.

The roar and noise of the helicopter practically muted voices, forcing all to yell to communicate.

"I'm going to be sick!" Buchanan yelled.

"You'll live! You'll get used to it!" responded Adkins.

Buchanan shouted, "John, this is crazy! I'm sick. I'm going to puke!"

Adkins laughs. "If you puke, make sure you lean over the side of the helicopter and don't do it in here!"

A proud Midwesterner and a fellow Baptist, Adkins lifted Buchanan's spirit in times of need.

Adkins and Jackson were beginning their third and last tour of Vietnam. The two men were immune to the bumpy helicopter rides. Adkins epitomized a hard-nosed Seabee officer and, as a Baptist, integrated a natural bond with Buchanan, becoming lifelong friends.

"Robert, the shakeup will do you good. It will break you in to the rigors of war."

But Adkins knew better.

Adkins knew exactly what was in store for Buchanan. He knew his chaplain friend had yet to witness a man killed or wounded in battle. He knew Buchanan sat clueless about the horrors of witnessing a man lose his life in a war. It changed a man forever, laying his eyes on a casualty for the first time, and Adkins knew it.

He knew Buchanan never laid his eyes on a human being ripped apart from shrapnel and enemy bullets.

He knew he never caught the screams from young men calling out for their mothers or calling out for God to relieve their pain and soothe the agony experienced from head to toe.

The bumpy helicopter ride will amount to nothing but a drop in a bucket compared to what Buchanan will face in actual combat.

Buchanan glanced over at his chaplain assistant, Sergeant Jackson, grinning from ear to ear. Still shaken, he looked forward to placing his feet back on solid ground.

Just 4 miles now to Camp Love, which felt like an eternity for Buchanan.

"Philip, this is -" Buchanan interrupted himself, reaching into his pants leg pocket, showing Jackson his tobacco pouch which he dropped onto the helicopter floor, "- my tobacco!"

With a firm jolt of the helicopter, Buchanan lost his grip on his tobacco.

"Sergeant Jackson, my tobacco!" yelled Buchanan.

Buchanan stuffed a second pouch of chewing tobacco in his side pocket of his fatigues for a backup and yearned to avoid losing his first pouch because of a bumpy ride on a Huey helicopter. He had not touched tobacco products since his spiritual experience 13 years earlier, and he absolutely had no desire to gain tapeworms, something he avoided like the plague. The scuttlebutt spread throughout the ranks convinced many that tobacco juice killed off tapeworms. Whether true or not, he wasn't taking any chances. He's going to chew tobacco, regardless.

The tobacco fell at the edge of the helicopter entrance - one quick turn and the tobacco would find a new home in the jungles of Vietnam.

"I'll get it, chaplain!" shouted Jackson. He unbuckled his seatbelt, stooping down from his seat while holding on to a metal bar, grabbing the tobacco with his right hand. Lifting himself up, he smiled from ear to ear. The veteran marine handed the tobacco back to Chaplain Buchanan. "Didn't know you were a dipper, chaplain?"

"It's 'uh, a health precaution, that's all. You know, tapeworms." replied Buchanan, in his strong Kentuckian accent.

Jackson laughed at Buchanan's notion of tobacco as a remedy for tapeworms. "It's not 100% guaranteed, you know. The juice, sir? To kill off the tapeworms!"

"Well, I'm not taking any chances. Those things are disgusting. I've seen some of those tapeworms back in Da Nang and I'm not taking any chances. Hundred percent or not – I'm dipping!" Buchanan boasted.

Adkins yelled, "I've never touched the stuff in my first two tours, and I never got'em!"

"You're lucky! Maybe it's because you were cautious and didn't expose yourself to the possibility of getting worms. You ever think of that?" Buchanan yelled.

Adkins grins at the notion.

A smiling Buchanan glanced toward Jackson. "Besides, if I had tapeworms, my height would cause me great harm. I'm short, ya know. I don't have as much to fall back on."

Jackson laughs. "What in the world does that have to do with anything?"

"Taller people have more body weight and have more to feed off of for the worms." Buchanan exclaimed. "And besides, tall people have more intestines!"

Jackson just laughs more exuberantly, nodding his head, bewildered. He knew Buchanan is naïve, having much to learn of war and the violent ends it throws at those who take part in it. He noticed a demeanor out of Buchanan, of nervousness entering an extreme and volatile war zone.

Jackson quit using tobacco products the previous year when he became a Christian and now, as Buchanan's chaplain assistant, is zealous to live the Christian life. The fact Jackson is still a young Christian, he, like many new converts to one's faith, are zealous than most believers. Buchanan and Jackson did not look down upon those who did smoke, they just quit for religious and practical reasons. Smoking damaged one's health, and they felt Christians were to take care of their bodies as Temples of Christ.

"It's a good thing you didn't put any tobacco in your mouth. You might have swallowed some of the juice! It would've made you even sicker!" grinned Jackson.

Buchanan humored him. The green chaplain viewed Jackson as a source of energetic life who considered life worth living. For Buchanan, every minute of life is a minute given by God and human beings were to make the best of those minutes. Jackson enjoyed Buchanan's presence, considering the chaplain a positive source for coping with the horrors of war.

The journey to Camp Love will soon to be over with just two miles left until their arrival. Buchanan felt his heart beating faster and faster with the anticipation of beginning his ministry to the marines of Camp Love.

While the helicopter continued to fly toward Camp Love, Buchanan noticed for the first time the vast greenery of Vietnam. The jungle featured Asian geographical features of dense vegetation. He noticed the beauty of Vietnam almost from the start of the helicopter trip, but really did not appreciate it until he got used to the bumpy, physical ride. The jaded Asian vegetation presented nothing but a solid layer of green with an occasional color of a flower native of the country and plants of the region. He noticed hard working, committed Vietnamese farmers working the rice patties with water buffalo. He observed a stream or creek with a steady current and meanders distinct and impressionable, dividing the dense jungle with many switchbacks. Buchanan sat enthralled at God's beautiful creation, impressed beyond words. He never set his eyes on Vietnam from an aerial view until today, and he is overwhelmed by its grandeur.

All the beauty of Vietnam created by God. And yet a violent war overshadowed it.

All the beauty controlled by God. Buchanan never saw such beautiful rivers. He admired the beauty of the country and the central highlands of Vietnam. For a moment, it seemed to Buchanan that God put forth more effort into His creation of Vietnam than the rest of the world put together. It seemed as if God took something away from the rest of the world during the Creation and put it into Vietnam. Buchanan knew that all the beauty had been overshadowed by a horrific war. War or not, nothing would take away the natural beauty of such a magnificent landscape.

Buchanan noticed something else mixed in with all the beauty of Vietnam - there is a war on. He noticed occasional burned-out vehicles and houses from the ongoing conflict. Houses hit from a rocket or bomb. Military vehicles left along the side of the road, possibly from a booby trap which exploded under a truck or jeep or possibly from an enemy rocket or missile from enemy fire. The remnants of nothing more than a skeleton of the vehicle.

Jackson noticed Buchanan admiring Vietnam. "Beautiful, isn't it chaplain?" Buchanan smiled, nodding in agreement, still nauseated from the ride.

"This country sure is beautiful. I'd never seen such a landscape and so much variations of green before. It's a sea of all shades of green." commented Buchanan.

The helicopter now approached Camp Love. They were about 1 mile from the camp. As they encroached the camp, the men noticed 20 to 30 metal roofed structures with sandbags on top of them. The Seabees and marines cleared out a space of 200 or more yards surrounding the encampment. Two rather large buildings stood out amongst the others - the mess hall and a multipurpose building or conference hall. Few trees and brush are noticed within the perimeter from the Huey. The marines dispersed the enlisted hootches throughout the compound, but many were on the eastern perimeter toward Da Nang. The officer's hootches, including Buchanan's next to the battalion doctor and the med station, were mostly in the center, adjacent and distant from the chow hall.

The dirt surfaced camp had been leveled off on a hill for defensive purposes in order for the camp to overlook any movements outlying the boundary between the treeline and camp. The location of the site reinforced the marine's sense of safety and security inside the perimeter.

Camp Love's name honored a marine killed on the hill earlier in the war.

The helicopter landed in a field next to the camp, as the camp lacked a landing pad. As the three men reached back into the helicopter to retrieve their gear, two marines rushed upon the new personnel to assist the new arrivals, offering to carry their gear into camp. Chaplain Buchanan possessed two seabags worth of personal and military gear. A small pickup truck drove up with a driver to transfer the three men to their quarters.

The party looked over their shoulders, noticing another helicopter in the air approaching the field. The three newcomers, along with the two marines placed their gear into the truck. The helicopter Buchanan rode in flew off, turning back toward the airbase in Da Nang. The second helicopter was coming in swiftly toward the field to drop off its passengers.

"Good morning. Chaplain Buchanan? Lieutenant Commander Adkins?" asked the marine private driving the pickup truck.

"Yes, I'm Chaplain Buchanan," responded Buchanan as he shook the marine's hand.

"Good to meet ya, sir. I'm Lance Corporal Fred Jones."

"And I'm Lieutenant Commander Adkins, here to join my Seabee Unit."

"Yes, sir. Been expecting ya." the marine replied in a deep Appalachian mountain accent. "I'm going to take you to your quarters.

You're going out in the bush, ain't you chaplain to conduct 1100 hours' service out in the bush? Isn't that right, sir?"

"That's right, marine. I scheduled a service out in the bush. Your name is Jones?" asked Buchanan.

"Yes, sir."

"Where are you from, Corporal?" asked Buchanan.

"Pike County Kentucky." replied Jones.

"I can't believe it! Born and raised?" asked Buchanan.

"Through and through chaplain!"

"I was born and partly raised in Pike County!" declared Buchanan.

Jones responded, "Wow, chaplain! I would have imagined you being from some place close to home."

"Well, I would've known you being from the mountains for sure. Especially with that accent of yours." said Buchanan.

Just as Jones was about to ask a question, the helicopter following Buchanan suddenly exploded in midair.

The five men turned abruptly, inquiring of the explosion. Just as the men turned, the helicopter dropped in mid-air, halfway down to the ground. Gravity pulled the fireball down onto the earth, hitting the ground violently, causing the earth to tremble and quake.

Buchanan stood speechless, catching flies.

The party of five stared intently toward the flaming helicopter and the debris all about. None said a word. No one knew the identity of those in the helicopter that blew up, except the killed pilot, and the incident gnawed at Buchanan those in the helicopter would never be identified. Buchanan just witnessed his first MIA's in the bush. No one said much on the way to their quarters. The men just drove off.

Jones dropped Jackson off at his quarters and the three new personnel agreed to meet each other at the commanding officer's office the next day to check in with the CO, who was in Da Nang for a meeting. Jackson reminded Buchanan he would proceed him to the rendezvous point for the services. Buchanan thanked Jackson, saying their goodbyes until meeting in the bush. Jackson cordially offered his acknowledgments to Adkins and his appreciation of support for the chaplain. The remaining party drove off toward the field hospital where Buchanan's quarters were located.

The three arrived at Buchanan's hootch and Jones offered a hand, getting the two officers' gear into their hootches. Adkins' quarters are within walking distance to Buchanan's. Jones would pick up Buchanan later on to transfer him to the bush for the 1100 hours service. Jones went his way and Buchanan entered his hootch for the first time, located alongside the doctor's hootch and field hospital in case a marine needed the last rites. He will find himself called upon in the next year to the field hospital to pray and quote scripture with wounded and dying marines frequently.

Buchanan secured his gear before heading out to the bush for his first services.

All the while, no other thoughts absorbed the minds of Buchanan and his friends but the military personnel on board the helicopter. The explosion of the Huey ended up a forever memory for him and his friends.

Coming to Vietnam

October 1, 1968

After dropping off his gear in his quarters, Buchanan waited patiently outside his hooch for Jones to transport him to the bush. Following the service, Buchanan and his loyal chaplain's assistant would ride 'shotgun' back to Camp Love.

Buchanan swelled up inside with a bundle of nerves confronted with his first Communion service in the bush.

October 1, 1968, began Buchanan's first day of ministry in the bush to the marines. He initially scheduled services in the jungle for 1100 hours on weekdays. His services, regardless of setting, were conducted as if he were leading a Baptist service back home. A nice perk Navy chaplains possessed had been the liberty of conducting services in a manner of their own choosing, and as many times as they so desired during the day. The specific denomination of each chaplain dictated the decorum of services. Buchanan took advantage of the freedom granted to chaplains with his diverse personal background in the bush.

The service conducted measured close to three miles away from Camp Love, smack dab in the center of the thick brush of southeastern Asia. While in Vietnam, the seclusion in the bush seized the conveniences of a sanctuary and a pulpit, but Buchanan made do with whatever was available during his tour.

Jones picked Buchanan up, driving him into the bush, and the two Kentuckians engrossed themselves in conversation about their home state on the three-mile trip to the rendezvous location to meet Jackson, patiently waiting for the chaplain.

Sergeant Philip Stephen Jackson served as Buchanan's trusted assistant and bodyguard in his third and final tour. His foremost responsibility called him to keep Buchanan alive. His second role served to don the service kit for Communion services and support Buchanan's ministry. Jackson's hearth and home lied in Cincinnati, Ohio and a fellow Midwesterner. The born and raised Cincinnatian was a good-looking, young, 24-year-old man. The 6'3" blonde haired, blue eyed Ohioan gave Jackson the appearance of a typical model type, a 'pretty boy' as Buchanan referred to tall, good-looking males, though Jackson certainly did not have the smug demeanor male models display and pretty boy's exhibit. Buchanan loathed 'pretty boys' for good reason. He never preached good looks will get you into Heaven. Passage through the Pearly Gates is determined of what's in one's heart, not with the exterior of a human being. Jackson had the heart of Jesus. He towered over Buchanan, who was just a mere 5'4". Jackson was far from being the pretty boy model type, as his character displayed the Spirit of a believer in Jesus. Though a devout believer and good looking, he displayed many scares and cuts from earlier combat experiences. In the middle of his third tour in Vietnam, the experience for him was different - he volunteered for his third tour. He now was a Christian, becoming a believer in his hometown in between his second and third trips from Vietnam on leave. He found peace in his new life and faith. His inner self found new reasons to live. He and Buchanan developed a great relationship and the rapport between the two men was evident in their ministry to the marines. In fact, Jackson became a spiritual mentor to the men just as much as Buchanan did. As Midwesterners and fellow Baptists, a strong bond emerged between them.

"Well, our first service together in the bush, chaplain," said Jackson enthusiastically.

"Yes, a long time in waiting for us to finally provide spiritual guidance and ministry to marines in the field. Not just out of Da

Nang, but in the field. It's exciting, isn't it?" remarked Buchanan. "The Lord is going to use us here, I'm sure."

An enclosure of bushes along a small knoll of compacted soil was selected for the service for protection suitable for the marines to sit comfortably while Buchanan conducted the service. Jackson came across an abandoned ammunition crate to use as a communion table, a crate used for the duration of the war. The crate eventually being sent back home in the mail to his wife in California his last week of his tour. The piece of wood served as a memento of their ministry in Vietnam.

While in the bush, Jackson took responsibility for the service kit containing all the components essential to conduct services. The kit included a chalice, wafers for communion, crucifix, 2 candelabrum, two trays with "HIS" engraved on the surface – one for salt and one for cotton, a bottle for Holy water, a spoon cup, and a brush. Depending upon circumstances and the area of ministry, a chaplain could go through thousands of wafers in one tour of duty in Vietnam.

As Jackson donned the service kit, he reminded Buchanan, "You know many of the men already from the ministry outreach from Da Nang. Now you're here in the bush - in the deep jungles of Vietnam, guiding them spiritually."

Jackson paused, declaring "It's all beautiful isn't - Vietnam. The mountains. The trees. The emerald and jade color of vegetation….." Looking up, he said, "…. even the blue sky above it all."

Buchanan pondered Jackson's thoughts, noticing he was irritated from within.

Jackson cautions, "One thing's for sure though, there's Viet Cong all over the place. All around us here in the bush. The VC's out there somewhere, sir. As you always say - 'you can bet your bottom dollar' – they're out there. That's what makes you want to look over your shoulder at every turn…doesn't it?"

Contemplating his thoughts, Buchanan said. "Yes. Yes!" He paused. "You OK, Philip?"

"I'm fine, sir. Just a little edgy."

Jackson sensed the enemy's exact presence of the enemy in the bush and how dangerous open fields in Vietnam posed many dangers to combatants. Buchanan was clueless. Soon, the chaplain will feel the sting of battle and experience violent combat.

"You sure you're alright, Philip?" Buchanan asked.

Jackson nods, grinning with confidence and asserts, "Looking forward to motivating and encouraging the men, sir. All of our training now to be put to good use. Our work will be a source of relief and spiritual encouragement for the men. You can be assured of that. You'll see. This tour for me is different this time around."

"Amen to that, Philip." said Buchanan undoubtedly. "I want to be that source of relief and spiritual encouragement. The Lord helps his servants who are faithful to His Word."

Jackson grins, completing the donning of the service kit.

A jeep had yet to be issued to Buchanan for ministry and to transport equipment. Until then, the spiritual team were forced to hump it and carry the service kit and equipment. The back of a jeep would be utilized as a communion table, but with no jeep – no communion table. Buchanan had been promised a jeep in Da Nang, prompting him to look forward to having his own transportation.

1045 hours came fast as marines on patrol began to trickle in from the bush off from the road leading back to Camp Love. As usual, Buchanan greeted the men as they congregated. With the Communion kit donned, the spiritual team visited with marines until all were present coming in from patrol.

The new chaplain at Camp Love has arrived. A good first impression of meeting new people mattered to Buchanan in life. First impressions set the tone for Buchanan when meeting people, and besides, he wanted to set a foundation for great rapport.

Buchanan knew quite a few marines from six months behind fierce battle lines. A few engineering ratings were scattered within the group, but most were regular grunt infantry assigned to the 7th Engineering Battalion to patrol and keep the area secure when accompanying combat engineering teams. Many chaplains in Vietnam were mistrusted by troops. Chaplains were sometimes seen as aligning with psychiatrists and military psychologists. A substantial number of marines considered chaplains as just sources for the military to encourage the men to get back into "the game" and kill again, and not to be trusted. Chaplains were thrown into the same boat, the same category as psychiatrists, as part of the 'establishment'. Buchanan longed to reach out to those skeptic marines and penetrate those barriers perceived as negative. But for many other marines, chaplains were a substantial source of guidance and direction, hope, and encouragement.

As men continued to trickle in from the bush, Buchanan recognized many marines from his six months behind the lines in Da Nang. The men were from Bravo Company and a couple of platoons from Alpha Company of the 7th Engineering Battalion. Buchanan's reputation as a trusted chaplain spread throughout the ranks in just six months. The scuttlebutt amongst the troops was Buchanan was genuine; that he cared for the troops. The men sensed a bona fide caring and loving heart in Buchanan. He actually cared for the wants and needs of the men, the families of each marine, their financial situation, and their spiritual and emotional conditions.

In six months, Buchanan established a rapport with the marines that developed into a bonding relationship lasting for the duration of Buchanan's tour. The men knew, regardless of the severity of a situation, he committed himself to extend a hand to marines in a time of need.

As Buchanan greeted the last of the men as they approached the hillside, the men sat down, exhausted, worn out, and waited for the service to begin as the men take a quick water break. Though a temporary pause from the war, many marines desired church services. Religious services provided normalcy to the marines' lives.

Buchanan, glancing to his right, spotted a separate group of marines, a motley crew, who chose not to attend the service. Sitting on a hump of ground opposite the service site, the marines presented themselves, reflecting the 'beatniks' of the patrol. The men displayed a grudge upon each face, slothful, angry, and defiant body language.

Buchanan thought to himself, 'Wow! What a group!' as he engaged in 'fellowship' with the men.

Pausing in conversation with the men, Buchanan motioned for Jackson to step toward him and said, "Sergeant, those marines there, they didn't come for the service."

"So?" said Jackson, shaking his head and flippant with the defiant marines.

Buchanan questioned, "What sergeant?"

"Yes sir, I noticed, they didn't. And?" responded Jackson.

"Go over - invite them."

"Are you sure, chaplain? Those marines over there, well they're - well, you know, sir."

"They're what Philip?" asked Buchanan.

"Sir, they won't want to..." Jackson paused, noticing Buchanan's desire to invite them to the Communion service.

Hesitantly, Jackson nods and said, smiling, "We'll do, sir."

Buchanan grins, saying, "Thank you, Sergeant."

Jackson turns, and with confidence walks over to the 'motley crew' and motions toward Buchanan saying, "Men, the new chaplain over there, Chaplain Buchanan, well.....he's here on his first day to conduct services for you. Come, join us."

The stoic stares Jackson received spoke volumes - he thought, 'Hell itself will freeze over before they attend any religious service'.

Jackson, noticing one marine in particular, with the demeanor of condescension and smirks, looked at Jackson as if he had invited him to the gardening club for senior citizens. Private First Class Michael Dobbs was a ferocious fighter in battle, but a constant troublemaker with officers.

Still, not a peep from the motley crew.

While no one replied to Jackson's invite, he made his way back toward the makeshift Communion table when Dobbs snarled, "I'm not coming to your service. I don't have any use for it. Or for *youuuu*. It's silly and stupid!"

Jackson turned to one side and looked back at Dobbs. He barked, "It's for weaklings and the weary.....that I'm not!" Jackson heard and sensed antagonism in Dobbs, and politely responded with a bit of annoyance, "OK. But if you ever need any help or just want to talk, the chaplain has an open door policy. You're always welcome anytime, day or hour."

The stare down of Jackson toward Dobbs was stern and unyielding, never coming across such a rude marine in his career. The sergeant vowed to be a burr in his saddle.

Jackson pushed Dobbs further by saying, "Services will be in the main hall in camp every Sunday at 0900 and 1100 hours and services in the field three days a week at 1100 hours and again on Tuesdays and Thursdays at 1300 hours in the conference hall."

Dobbs rolled his eyes.

Infuriating Dobbs, Jackson says with a smile, "Devotions held in the conference hall on Tuesdays and Thursdays in the evening at 1900 hours, as well as at the chapel in Da Nang when scheduled. Hope to see you there. Have a blessed rest of the day and God Bless you all."

Jackson turns to make his way back toward Buchanan, as he looks over his right shoulder and noticed Dobbs and his friends smirking, mocking Jackson's little speech he just delivered.

Dobbs yells, "Have a blessed day, men!" in a contemptuous like voice, mocking Jackson.

A roar of laughter was heard from the group.

"Did you write those service times down, guys?" said another marine.

Boisterous laughter came from the group once again, heard loud and clear.

The marines who *did* choose to attend the service glanced over to Dobbs' group sternly, especially the officers.

Dobbs and his friends slowly quieted down.

Prior to Jackson becoming a Christian, he might have whipped Dobbs' behind for the behavior displayed by he and his friends. The Spirit spoke to Jackson to show love toward those who work for the Adversary.

His demeanor was of a different person now. He had the Spirit of Jesus in him.

Jackson thought to himself, 'there is no way in Hades any of those men will ever come to one of our services!' Turning back towards Dobbs, Jackson smiles and nods, as he joined Chaplain Buchanan for the service.

When finished poking fun at the 'Christians,' Dobbs and his friends stared stoically back at Jackson. Dobbs, unaware Jackson was serving in his third tour in Vietnam, treated him as if he was green in his first tour. Clueless of the fact, he killed just as many of the enemy in his own right on his first two tours. Ignorant Jackson proved himself a battle hardened marine. He stood confident, capable of taking care of Dobbs single-handedly, let alone laying out Dobbs and his friends simultaneously, with ease. Jackson had won one bronze star and a silver star in ferocious firefights and hand-to-hand combat. His background provided a perfect fit to be a chaplain's bodyguard in his third tour as a Christian. However, his mission in his last tour will have a different aim.

While Jackson dealt with Dobbs, Buchanan had been visiting with the troops. Getting to know the men a little better, Buchanan passed out the service manuals, and as Buchanan put it, having 'fellowship' with the men. Oblivious of the confrontation between Jackson and Dobbs.

Jackson said softly, "Chaplain, those knuckleheads over there are going to be a challenge."

"Maybe."

Buchanan motioned toward his heart and said, "And remember, it's all about what's in here. If this is Jesus like, others will see Him."

Jackson nods and says with skepticism, "They will not be easy to win over to our side, sir. I don't think they want any pastoral care - at all! You might as well just give up on 'em. They're what you call hard hearted."

An intrigued Buchanan proclaimed, "We'll stretch out our hand, and if they respond, 'Glory to God.' If not, we'll just dust the dirt off our feet, then pray the Devil will let go of 'em. And besides, there was someone in your life who didn't give up on you - right? Think about the person who didn't give up on you?"

Pondering the thought, Jackson admits, "Yeah, chaplain, you're right." He paused and noted, "Yeah. *Yeah*." He smiles towards Dobbs.

With a snarl, the unbeliever Dobbs glanced toward the religious 'fanatics' with nothing but disdain. Dobbs considered religion nothing but the pampering to the poor and fragile of the world. He thought of Christians as hypocrites. Religion for him was nothing more, nothing less than an emotional tool that pandered to citizens rejected by those in society with the power to control their lives.

The spiritual team turned toward the marines, eager to worship. Their first Communion service was about to begin.

The Service

October 1, 1968

Buchanan's first day in the bush and he looked over the congregation of 75 marines or so, who were out for 2 days patrolling several possible VC threats in the area.

What a sight they were. Muddy. Sweaty. Exhausted. Uniforms ripped and torn, bloodstained from war.

Of the 120 men present, half of the marines felt a deep dependence on their faith to mentally cope with war.

The heavy firefight the marines encountered the past two days was beyond the description of words.

As Buchanan stood before the marines as their chaplain - he had never seen such worn and weary men. Marines in the bush were keen for some normalcy and spiritual guidance after such engagements with the VC.

The men were a mess - but set for a moment of peace and contemplation. Most notable were of Bravo Company. Men of diverse religious backgrounds and belief systems. Different, but common with one aim in the bush – staying alive. Personalities poles apart, but one's Buchanan will minister to, according to each individual temperament. Kowslowski, a rifleman known as Chief as he had Native American blood running through his veins, was Catholic, but found religion to be useless. Lipstone, a radioman, who was dirt poor and black, found religion to be established to keep the "black" man in his place. His nick name was The Hammer for his carpentry skills, while possessing an IQ of 139. Remington, a sharpshooter, whose by name was Hunter for his love of hunting, had much in common with Buchanan – he was Baptist and a fellow Kentuckian. A devout Baptist, but a rigid espouser of predestination, a concept Buchanan vehemently rejected. And then there was Dobbs, another rifleman, an atheist and hated religious people. Innate animosity ingrained in his heart, even hatred. Dobbs considered Buchanan nothing but a jester, a laughable joke. With an attitude such as Dobbs, his by name from the marines was Trouble. And then there was Jaworski, a machine gunner, was Roman Catholic who possessed a lofty opinion of his religious affiliation. Though he was a pushy adherent of his faith, the men respected him with a moniker of Father. Next was Sergeant Frank Smith, a platoon sergeant, or known as Boone, because of linked family ties to Daniel Boone, a proud and pompous member of an aristocratic family and was Episcopalian. He considered Buchanan, a Baptist, nothing more than a Methodist who could read. Shaw, a superb rifleman, who was Methodist in his military files, referred to himself as a "believer." From the segregated city of St. Louis, Shaw, who was black, held an opinion of religion as separating people in society by class. For Shaw, religious people were snub and rude. Protesting the oppressed in St. Louis were forgotten by the religious, which Buchanan ashamedly agreed. Shaw was from a professional family of lawyers, most holding district attorney positions. Shaw would eventually joke with Buchanan that DAs were sent by God to shake things up in the world. The men called him Lawyer with Shaw's family background. And then there was Kiehl, a staunch Lutheran and loyal Democrat who viewed government as a pathway to fulfill God's will. A thought Buchanan considered a silly idea. Regardless, Kiehl, part of the weapons platoon, was a staunch supporter of President Johnson to stop Communism from spreading in Southeast Asia. His skills with weaponry landed him a handle of 'Sharpshooter'. Rodriquez, a reliable rifleman, was a strict Roman Catholic, mesmerized by the company with his daily ritual routine, a means of protective guard from God. With the aspirations of one day becoming a veterinarian, the men referred to him as 'Vet'. PoKorny, one of the platoon's messengers and proud of his Polish decent was devoted to Roman Catholic doctrine. Buchanan bumped into many devoted conservative Roman Catholics like PoKorny – a devotion of one's faith he yearned for his fellow Baptist to possess. Pokorny enjoyed painting and set his skill in painting religious works. This awarded him the moniker 'The Painter'. Next was Sims, a rifleman and firing the mortar known as Taxi, an atheist and an intellectual who believed in an intelligent design and a scientific view of the universe, which Buchanan vehemently opposed. Oddly, Buchanan and Sims connected. Both were learners and sought to enhance their knowledge and they talked frequently. Sims guaranteed Buchanan a taxi ride anywhere in the LA area when they returned home. Sims preached a taxi ride is to be a rewarding experience for patrons - not a terrible memory to suppress for all time. After getting to know Chaplain Buchanan in Vietnam, Sims thought it was a privilege to take Chaplain Buchanan anywhere in southern California in the very best taxi.

Though religious and social differences laid heavy, the marines leaned on one another to stay alive. One common trait for all in Company B was if a member of the company was killed in action, the marine would meet his Maker, regardless of demographics. Death did not discriminate in Vietnam. Buchanan was there in case that might happen.

Buchanan adhered to a strict protocol or order of service every single communion service, with exceptions such as special music or special times during the month such as Mother's Day or Easter. Buchanan would have a short welcome, prayer, a hymn, scripture reading, a brief message for the men, communion, and then a closing hymn and prayer. Short and sweet. This was the standard and he would usually not change the order of service. Jackson, from time to time, led the hymns and prayed. Buchanan chose a Protestant and Catholic lay reader to read scriptures. An Old and New Testament reading provided an ecumenical service as to include everyone's denomination represented in the service. Buchanan insisted on inclusion and found it a key to reach unbelievers. The fact Buchanan grew up Presbyterian, attended a Lutheran seminary, led by a Southern Baptist layman to

Salvation, and was now a Southern Baptist minister attributed to the ecumenical spirit in him.

His time in Vietnam was not to convert marines in becoming a Baptist. His purpose was to protect the freedom of religion of marines and to minister to their wants and needs. And if ministering to the troops led to a convert to Jesus – then "Glory to God."

Buchanan started the first service with a prayer as he recited a prayer by Peter Marshall, one of his favorite authors and mentors.

"Good morning, men." began Buchanan after praying.

The marines responded, "Good Morning"

"Let us begin by singing Great is Our Father out of the service manual." instructed Buchanan.

As the men sang, a marine sergeant drove up driving a jeep, parked, and stepped out, walking up to an officer sitting on Buchanan's left handing him a message, which he read silently. The sergeant whispered an inaudible message in his ear, which the officer turned quite red in the face. Angry and obviously frustrated, the officer, Lieutenant Lance Rockford, commanding officer of Bravo Company, obviously was not happy with the news on the note. Buchanan noticed an immediate agitation from Rockford, slightly shaking his head out of aggravation.

The service continued as the last verse of 'Great is Our Father' ended. The spiritual team completed the remaining order of service up to the message.

Buchanan delivered his short message, searching for the forgiving God when lonesome and disheartened, and his words were exactly what the men needed after a hard firefight.

Time for serving communion arrived, presented to all willing men, Protestant and Catholic alike, intentionally welcoming Roman Catholics to take part in the service. Many Roman Catholics attending took part in and received the elements from him during his tour in Vietnam. A remembrance he held fondly through the years.

Closing with a hymn and prayer, Buchanan reaches towards his heart and says, "Remember, men, what's in here is most important."

With services completed, Jackson gathered up the service manuals and secured the service kit.

Buchanan greeted the men after the service as he always did and stepped toward Lieutenant Rockford.

"Lieutenant, what's wrong?" asked Buchanan. "You looked rather agitated moments ago reading the message the sergeant handed ya."

"I'm not agitated or disappointed. I'm damn angry." replied Rockford.

Abruptly walking away from Buchanan, Rockford said not a word until he felt as if he should say something to this new, though odd, but friendly chaplain.

He turned moments later back toward Buchanan and said, "We've been ordered to reconnoiter section 49 near Route 4 at coordinates 932625 for VC activity."

Rockford added angrily, "We are going to have to walk back to camp."

Pointing his finger at Buchanan and the Gunnery Sergeant of Bravo Company - Richard Neville Warwick Jorgensen, said, "And I can tell ya one thing - the major is going to hear from me when we get back to camp."

Section 49 was one and one-half miles further away from Camp Love.

Buchanan dropped the conversation, knowing Rockford was in no mood to talk.

Buchanan looked over his shoulder and noticed Dobbs with a condescending expression on his face. He knew Dobbs' thoughts - "Here you Christians are praying and singing, and there's no transportation back to camp. So much for your God. So much for your prayers. They're nothing."

Jackson felt a powerful urge to march himself over and punch Dobbs smack dab in the jaw, hard enough to knock a tooth or two out of his mouth. But he thought better of it – he was a unique human being. He reckoned the Lord spoke to Dobbs in the past and would continue working with Dobbs to change his heart. Dobbs was a matter Jackson was pressed to pray about. The marine got under his skin and Jackson loathed encompassing ill feelings contrary of a believer.

Buchanan didn't care about how Dobbs felt. He was going to love Dobbs and his friends, regardless. With a genuine Christian smile he says, "God be with you men!" Dobbs and his friends smirked, shrugging their shoulders. Turning their backs on him, the recalcitrant marines continued to lounge around till the order to saddle up, don all gear and prepare one's self to move out, was barked out.

"Saddle up." ordered Rockford, as the marines set the company in a defensive patrol position. The maddened officer ordered Private First Class Christopher PoKorny at the point.

The patrol headed two miles to section 49 to search for VC, taking two or three hours to patrol, partly through the jungle. They tacked additional time to getting back to camp.

Buchanan was given five months of intense training at the Da Nang base, which included combat situations. There were three main things a chaplain needed to remember in the bush. If a chaplain got lost, he was not about to yell out. The marines would find the chaplain. If the chaplain yelled, the Viet Cong would locate the chaplain and kill him. Second, the chaplain was not to walk or move about and attempt to find the marines. The marines would find him. And third, do not make any movements. Stay perfectly still. Any sound a chaplain started showed movement in the jungle and a signal for the enemy. The Americans were in the enemy's home field, and the enemy knew the jungle better than the visitors did. It was their country, not the Americans.

The patrol paced to section 49 to search for the enemy. Private First Class Christopher PoKorny was still at the point and there was no evidence of enemy activity. They patrolled for two or three hours and came up empty. The order for silence was given - no conversation until Rockford gave an order otherwise.

Rockford gave the order to halt for a 10-minute break along an embankment with a stream underneath. He thought the noise from the water might hide any noise of the marines from the enemy. It was roughly 1900 hours in the evening and sunset was upon them.

The spiritual team stopped and took a seat on the cool ground near the stream. Jackson leaned back onto slanted ground, placing his weapon beside him in case of an unexpected ambush. Buchanan just sat with anticipation.

A lone marine came up from behind them and sat down beside Buchanan.

Corporal Sebastian Gordon, from Iowa, was about to advance to sergeant, and his record exhibited great potential as a leader and marine. The two men introduced themselves and talked of home, which was near for Gordon, having only four more days before departing for Iowa. As a short timer, he was ecstatic, looking forward to a steak at a famous steakhouse in his hometown.

"I love steaks as well, Corporal Gordon." Buchanan said.

"I'm going to get a T-Bone with sautéed onions and mushrooms." responded Gordon.

"I love a T-Bone with sautéed onions and mushrooms myself." said Buchanan. "With a huge baked potato, with butter and sour cream."

"Don't forget the salad, chaplain."

"*Yeah*. The salad is a must."

Gordon paused and changed the subject. "Chaplain, this place - well...it does things that change you. It, well - is depressing. I dream of that steak. Sitting down with my mother and father and eating dinner has been, well - something I have been looking forward to for a long time."

He paused and said, "I'm also going to go to my-my home church again. I've missed church. I miss the sermons from my pastor. The choir specials with the solos. Solos in a piece of music with the choir is, well - my favorite. By the way Chaplain, your message this morning – great! God does indeed forgive, even though you might – well, might seem to think that your actions......." Gordon pauses, "don't deserve to be forgiven - God does indeed forgive."

"Amen, Gordon."

"Going back to school, too. I'm a junior at Iowa University as a business major. Got two years under my belt. Going to start my classes back up again when I get back home. Isn't that great?"

"Amen.' responded Buchanan. "Great major - business. And a great work ethic is a plus and knowing you for just this moment of time, I know your work ethic isn't anything to be ashamed of."

"I'm looking forward to Big Ten football again, too, sir."

"Yes, me too. I love football." Buchanan expressed with great enthusiasm. "I'm from Ohio and I know the entire state is decorated all over with scarlet and grey this year. Ohio State is still unbeaten, ya know."

"I know." said a dismayed Gordon looking off to his side, smiling.

Sensing Gordon's disgust for Ohio State, Buchanan rubs it in and says, "This is going to be the greatest year in Buckeye football history. I just have a gut feeling about it. Iowa and Ohio State still have their game to play in November and it's at Iowa. Should be a great game. I'm hoping the Armed Services Radio will broadcast it." Buchanan swelled with pride in his heart.

"Hawkeye pride's strong too, sir. Studying is scarce on Saturday afternoons in Iowa." responded Gordon.

"Ya have a noble life awaiting you, Corporal Gordon. Your pursuit of education is admirable. I think it's phenomenal. Education is important. You can pick up where you left off in life. Finish your education, get married, a life of fulfillment."

Buchanan had no idea what he was saying to Gordon.

Gordon looked up into the dense jungle with a sad expression on his face. He glances toward Buchanan and says, "I might-might pick up my life from where I was in college and *even* get my part-time job back, but my life - it's anything but the same."

Gordon paused, glancing down to the ground. He grabbed hold of a stick, poking it into the ground as if to avoid the subject.

"I've done many things - here in Vietnam. Things I'm going to have to deal with when I get back home. I've seen many things here that will always be well - imprinted upon m-my mind. I will never be able to shake them off."

Gordon paused again and looked up into the thick foliage of the jungle. He smiled and looked back at Buchanan with emotion, and said grinning, "I've just John Wayned It."

"Yep. John Wayned it." agreed Buchanan.

"I'm worried though about those things I've done and seen, but, my mother and father – I hope will help me with my problems coping with combat. I-I wish I could spend more time with you, chaplain. I think you could help me. I liked what you said today about forgiveness. God does indeed forgive us for our actions."

Gordon paused yet again, then said. "I like you chaplain. The men like you too. They might say nothing, but I-I think they like you."

Buchanan sat, listening to Gordon. He knew that his life had changed drastically. He did not know exactly what to say to Gordon.

He just smiled and said, "God forgives, Gordon. And He lives."

Gordon remarked, "And - He lives in me." Smiling, he said, "And he forgives."

"Amen." said Buchanan.

Rockford ordered the men to saddle up and ordered PoKorny once again on the point of leading the patrol.

Buchanan will have to continue his talk with Gordon another day.

Again, the order of complete silence was given to the company.

The patrol traveled close to a mile, and it was getting dark. Sunset was about to set in.

The day was ending, and the spiritual team experienced their first day in the bush.

The day was not yet finished, as the spiritual team prepared for the night, a night Buchanan will never forget.

THE TOLL OF WAR

OCTOBER 1, 1968

"Finally." said Buchanan, following an order from Rockford for a five-minute break.

Not accustomed to the jungle hikes just yet, Buchanan felt the horrid heat of southeastern Asia. His experience in the bush was sparse while stationed in Da Nang behind the lines of fire. Occasionally, he ventured out to conduct services at Command Chaplain's request.

The long trek so far in the jungle accompanying Bravo Company was a drop in the bucket for what was to come later on in Buchanan's tour. He sat with Jackson on a knoll near the center of the patrol. They sat and rested, saying not a word. He glanced around for Gordon, noticing him resting with his friends. It was a long day. Buchanan noticed the stunning sunset through a small, yet discernible, hole in the dense foliage of Vietnam. It was beautiful, a sunset never seen before. He caught sight of a perfect spectacle of God's creation in a world surrounded by a war and violence. In his first six months in Vietnam, Buchanan could not believe how beautiful the sunrise and sunsets were in southeastern Asia. But this first sunset in the bush was one of awe and wonder. The beauty of Vietnam was stunning.

The patrol started out yet again, and by 25 minutes, it was getting dark. The time was 2200 hours in the day. Buchanan felt the eerie, dooming, pitch dark jungle coming onto the patrol quickly, visibility amounting to zilch in front of him. The vegetation of the jungle enclosed the earth as a roof for the earth's surface, forcing the patrol to encounter the great danger of night. The only light shining through the vegetation was stream like rays from the moon, as Buchanan noticed the marines slowly tiptoeing in the shadows through the jungle.

The territory was dangerous and Buchanan sensed dangers afoot.

A marine, Private Michael Jaworski, a 2nd generation Polish farmer from Pennsylvania and devout Roman Catholic, stepped up behind him and spoke in almost an inaudible whisper in his ear, "Remember chaplain, if you get lost, don't yell out. We'll come and get you."

Jaworski asked Buchanan to nod yes if he heard him, and Buchanan nodded in the affirmative.

Walking in patrol formation from the outset, Rockford halted the patrol near a knoll on a hill, a splendid defensive position if the enemy dared attack Bravo Company. He whispered to Gunnery Sergeant Richard Neville Warwick Jurgensen, a Californian, to relay back in Bravo Company they were to make camp for the night. Rockford ordered to partner up and form a perimeter. Rockford, steamed with the order to conduct another reconnaissance patrol so late in the day and no transportation back to Camp Love, sought a brief confrontation so far from home. Darkness forced him to make camp for the night. In the center of the perimeter, Buchanan sensed he was safe and sound. Rockford restricted conversation to a whisper.

Rockford, uncomfortable with his position, sensed vulnerability and susceptibility in the air. The sense of exposure to the enemy out in the open unnerved Rockford. The marines swiftly grabbed their shovels to dig in for the night.

Instruction from jungle warfare experts trained marines going into the bush to dig a hole for the night in case of an attack. The hole required to be deep enough for a marine to be at least 6 to 12 inches, dug deeper if so desired, below ground level when laying down. Though not required, many marines voluntarily dug a hole for protection. Digging a hole delayed possibly additional sleep for an exhausted marine, but proved time and time again the energy exerted digging a hole saved many lives in nightly attacks from the Viet Cong.

Jackson took upon himself to place Buchanan safely in the center of the perimeter with plenty of marines in and about within the outer limits. Jackson took his responsibility protecting Buchanan as his body guard seriously.

The two men started digging their respective holes. Jackson pressed the vitality of digging a hole every night in the bush before going to sleep. He knew the defenselessness of a marine neglecting the time spent to dig an appropriate hole for the night. He witnessed many marines die from laziness and the neglect of preparing for the night.

With expertise in record time, Jackson assisted Buchanan in digging his hole for the night. After 30 minutes, the two were ready to bed down.

The time was 2345 hours.

Buchanan turned to locate Rockford within the perimeter, when he caught a glance of Gordon's face in the little light there was on this black night. Gordon bed down close to the chaplain, wanting to be near in case of a firefight to protect Buchanan. In the dim light, the two men smiled toward one another, though the two men could vaguely see one another in the darkness, acknowledging their newfound trust and support for one another before retiring for the night.

In the habit of digging a hole in the bush every night, Gordon chose not to dig a hole due to exhaustion. And besides, he was almost home. 'What could happen?' he thought.

Buchanan was just about to whisper a question to Jackson when Buchanan heard something he never heard before. A whistling or hissing sound above his head. Then a 'Pow! Pow! Pow!' A sudden crackling sound came next, as limps of trees and heavy vegetation snapped and tore apart, falling to the ground. Then loud bangs, resembling powerful fire crackers or fireworks.

The sounds were far from fire crackers or fireworks, but the crackling of weapons. Within the assortment of clatter, Buchanan faintly heard for the first time men yelling in combat. He first heard yells in Vietnamese. Never before hearing screams from the enemy terrified Buchanan. If war is hell, he now knows the hell of war.

Marines returned immediate M-16 and machine gun fire toward the enemy.

RATATATATATA! BOOM! BOOM! BOOM!

"Get down!!!" ordered Rockford. "STAY IN YOUR HOLES."

Marines who neglected preparing a foxhole fought for cover into holes dug. Two or three marines fought physically tooth and toenail with one another to shield themselves in a hole dug for a single marine. Men fighting each other for cover. Marines are now vulnerable without a foxhole and firing M-16's in any direction confused and disoriented, yet attempting to fire toward the enemy. Many marines were exposed and taking a heavy beating, hit by enemy fire.

Whether or not in a hole, the grunts fired M-16's toward the green tracers of enemy muzzle blasts in the night's darkness. Firing weapons in a prone position toward the enemy not seen, but locating muzzle blasts of weaponry of the VC.

The company switched the M-16's to full-automatic mode for rapid fire and 'Rock 'n' Rolled.'

Popping up and down, the men fired M-16's toward flickering lights of weapons discharged.

RATATATATAT! BLAM! BOOM! BLAM!

Rockford, spotting marines running for a better position, screamed, "GET DOWN! STAY DOWN!"

Rockford yells, "Varnes GET DOWN! Smith - STAY DOWN! Ya get killed, STAY DOWN!"

"Gordon, you know better! GET DOWN!"

As orders were barked, hissing and whistling came from the rear of Rockford. Buchanan felt the whistling from the left and right of him. There seemed to be bullets coming from every direction now.

Bravo Company felt the terror of enclosure.

Marines fought with ferocity and intensity, as weapons blasted away - BLAM! BANG! RATATTA-TATA!

The grunts popped up, exposing themselves to the enemy.

" GET DOWN!!!" Rockford yelled.

Terrified, Buchanan laid numb, petrified. Face down in his hole, Jackson pounced on Buchanan for protection. In the chaos, Jackson noticed a constant barrage of sporadic light from fired weaponry on his right, sighting a severely wounded marine from head to toe. The shock and pain of being wounded caused him to pop up and down, move to his right and left on the surface of the ground in every direction, moving in all kinds of gyrations. Buchanan felt the weight of Jackson lift off of him.

Jackson bellowed to Buchanan, "STAY DOWN chaplain!!"

Peeking to his right over the edge of his hole, Buchanan noticed Jackson run to the wounded, shocked marine.

Buchanan heard Rockford yell out, "Get down, Jackson! Get down!"

Grasping the marine in a prostrate position, he held him tight and secure from exposure to any other enemy projectiles.

Jackson held the young marine down, screaming in pain, as Buchanan looked on. The marine was only 19 or 20 years old.

A thousand thoughts passed through Buchanan's mind. 'Who was this kid and where he was from?' 'His age?' 'His likes? His dislikes?' 'His family life?' All these questions asked as he watched him bleed to death.

"Mom!!" screamed the young marine.

"God! Make it stop!" he screeched.

Buchanan was shell-shocked, his inner being crushed at the sight.

"MOM!" yelled the marine.

Yet another scream, "Want home!"

All the while, Buchanan watched Jackson struggle in his efforts to hold the marine in place to protect him. Buchanan hunkered down into his hole and hugged the ground hard.

RATATATATAT! BOOM! BOOM! BOOM!

Marines continued to fire rounds toward the enemy. Rockford crawled over to Private Leonard Shaw and Private Benjamin Kiehl, who held the grenade launcher.

Sounds of enemy bullets and projectiles, and the small flares from weapons fired from the north end of the perimeter, were heavy in coming. Marines were more secure at this point in the small battle.

Buchanan heard Rockford order, "Shaw and Kiehl, grenade launcher, twelve o'clock! NOW!"

Sounds now emerged from the firefight Buchanan had never heard before. Sounds of screams and pain from the wounded will forever be etched into the uttermost depths of his memory.

Never will he forget pleas from the mouths of marines.

Never will he forget the entreaties of those about to die.

Never will he forget the cries of those who will be forever maimed because of war.

"Mom!" screamed a marine.

"Medic - I'm hit!" yelled another.

"Corpsman!"

"It hurts!" cried out yet another.

"God help me!" was the scream that Buchanan heard the most.

"Mom, make it stop!" screamed another.

RATATATATATA! BOOM! BOOM! BOOM!

The air combined with a mixture of the crackling of weapons fired, the hissing and whistling of steady bullets, the thunder of weaponry, and the terrifying yells and screams of marines wounded by enemy projectiles.

The wounded were scattered all over the ground.

Though weapons blared, all Buchanan could hear was screams of the wounded and dying. All he wanted was for it all to stop. With a vocal prayer, he prayed to God for a quick halt to the violence. The more he prayed, the louder the screams became.

Buchanan peeked once again out of his hole, saw Jackson holding the wounded marine, preventing him from exposing himself to the enemy.

Buchanan prayed vocally, "God, make it stop. Lord, please, pleeeease, let this madness stop."

The skirmish lasted for two minutes, but it seemed like an eternity for Buchanan. Jackson, holding the wounded marine, noticed nothing but horror on Buchanan's face as he peeked out of his hole.

Jackson felt anguish. Buchanan's first firefight, his first day in the bush, and he is all alone to deal with the horror of war.

Jackson yells, "STAY DOWN, chaplain! STAY DOWN!"

Buchanan heard nothing but gunfire and sounds of war. Jackson's warnings came to nothing.

The green chaplain continued to watch and witness war out of his hole.

Jackson's thoughts were 'Here I am to protect Buchanan, and I ran to this wounded marine from exposing himself. Chaplain Buchanan is in his first combat experience and I'm not there to help him.'

Fear and confusion overwhelmed Buchanan. The fear of a little boy lost from his mother – alone, vulnerable.

The marines fought by now to a slight upper hand against the enemy, and Shaw and Kiehl launched grenades into the heart of enemy gunfire.

Buchanan prayed louder, "God help us! Deliver us from the enemy!"

Looking right and left, Buchanan witnessed a ferocious firefight for the first time.

The fighting did not stop, even with the fervent prayers. Screams heightened.

Rockford barks out orders, "Right flank, cover the center!. Enemy fire, two o'clock!"

Motionless, Buchanan notices an oddity.

It first resembled a rock. Then an Edvard Munch caricature in a painting. Maybe an impressionist caricature. In the darkness, Buchanan found it difficult to decipher. Flashing of the gunfire sporadically gave some light to the unidentified object resembling lightening bolts. To Buchanan's horror, he recognizes it for what it was.

The face of Sebastian Gordon from Iowa was not so innocent looking any longer. The kid who started the day as a short timer with just four more days in Vietnam. The kid going home to finish his degree at the University of Iowa. The same kid who loved steaks and going back to his home church. Falling onto the ground on his stomach, he faced Buchanan, with his eyes fixated on his chaplain. Hit in several locations by projectiles and shrapnel, Gordon suffered from a bullet hitting the upper part of his head, causing part of his skull to shatter with brains and blood mashed together. Half of his helmet appeared blown apart.

Buchanan froze in shock, stunned with fright, as he just talked with Gordon of home.

Now…. he was gone.

Dead.

With what was left of Gordon, he appeared shocked, surprised. What the wounds left of his face revealed shock he was not going home to Iowa. In his last seconds of life, he probably regretted the foxhole he neglected to dig for the night.

Buchanan learned quickly human beings revealed on their face the last emotion or thought they were thinking in their last moments of life.

One moment life abounds, and with the next moment life is swept away - abruptly.

Buchanan turns his head back towards Jackson holding the marine, who by now, attempts to struggle with Jackson.

By now, the young marine was spitting masses of blood and bleeding profusely from wounds. Efforts to resist Jackson were gone.

KAWOSH! KABOOM!

The explosions of grenades toward the enemy reduced the number of Viet Cong who attacked Rockford and Bravo Company. The VC were killed or had run away.

The fighting died down. Alpha Company of the 7th Engineering Battalion attacked the VC on the right flank of Rockford's patrol, outflanked the enemy, and pursued the VC into the jungle. The darkness of the jungle made the situation even more dangerous. With flares shot into the air to locate the enemy, two platoons of Alpha Company advanced into the darkness to kill any Viet Cong who might have gotten away.

The silence of gunfire and crackling of weapons magnetized the reverberations of combat. The echoes of combat ringed loud in the jungle's darkness and now Buchanan heard the wounded and dying screaming and pleaded to God to help take the pain away. Screaming and shrieking for comfort from their mother.

Buchanan now heard marines for the first time yelling out into the darkness.

"Medic - I'm hit!"

"It hurts!"

"Help me God!"

"Mom!"

Of all the verbal utterances of the wounded and dying and most difficult to withstand for Buchanan was "Mom!" An utterance which launched Buchanan into a mood of melancholy most of all. It resembled a man yearning for his mother in his last moments of life like a 5-year-old little boy, innocent and defenseless. His last moments of life remembering her holding him in her arms and loving him like there was no other little boy in the world. Buchanan soon learned there is no stronger bond between two human beings than between a mother and her son.

Screams of the wounded were a permanent memory for Buchanan. It haunted him for the rest of his life.

Buchanan was limp from exhaustion. Pulling himself up, he sat on his legs with his feet under his backside, shaken and forever transformed. Buchanan now knew the extensive physical and emotional drain of combat.

Glancing toward Jackson, Buchanan thanked God for sparing him.

Jackson was essential for Buchanan's mental wellbeing, getting him through the next year of harsh months of war.

Jackson no longer held the young marine to protect him, he now held him to give him a presence as he entered through the gates of Heaven. Death was near. He looked into his eyes and recited the 23rd Psalm and the Beatitudes while he fought back tears. The marine attempted to say something, but to no avail. Jackson felt his heartbeat fade away for good.

Remarkably, Jackson had never held a marine at the point of death. In his third tour and now a Christian, it made all the difference in the world holding a human being wounded in battle and entering Eternity.

Buchanan now knows war, nothing but pain and agony. The permanent mental pictures of men dying lay now in his memory bank.

He knew not the horrors of war prior to this day, but now living with the permanent scars is a lifetime. His life changed forever, forced to cope with war.

A day James Robert Buchanan will never forget.

Traits of a Chaplain

October 2, 1968

Company A escorted Rockford's patrol back to Camp Love in the cover of early morning darkness to provide medical treatment for the wounded. The contingent of marines entered Camp Love around 0245 hours. Rockford lost 4 marines killed, including Gordon, and 8 marines wounded in the firefight.

The patrol suffered the worst casualties for the 7th Engineering Battalion in one day than it suffered in several weeks.

Furious and frustrated, Rockford was miles away when ordered to patrol sector 49, ending up further from Camp Love when attacked, a situation no one in their right mind would wish for.

The spiritual team arrived at the field hospital greeted by Chief Petty Officer John Dingus. The spiritual team prayed and comforted the wounded before retiring to their own quarters for the night.

"Thank you chaplain for your prayers." said Dingus.

"You're welcome, Chief." replied Buchanan.

After ministering to the men, the pair prayed as a team before departing for their respective hootch.

Buchanan thanked Jackson for his presence during the firefight, "Your presence tonight, well…it, well - was moving, Philip. It got me through it all. Thank you. Thank ya very much."

"I'm here to support you, sir." responded Jackson. "Whatever you need, I'll do it for you. Ya know that."

"I know Philip. Good night."

"Good night chaplain."

The men turn and walk toward their quarters, and Jackson turns and says, "Sir."

"Yes, Sergeant."

"You'll be alright. Just hang in there. He's with ya." Jackson smiles.

Buchanan returns a forced smile.

Jackson spoke the truth - Jesus will see him through the hard times.

Buchanan volunteered to serve the rank and file of the United States Marine Corps in Vietnam and specifically called to serve the marines as a Navy chaplain. The six months in Da Nang ministering to marines prepared him for his assignment to the 7th Engineering Marine Battalion who had experienced intense, unbearable, and fierce combat while building bridges and completing construction projects for military and civilian people. Buchanan exerted nothing but his best to minister to the men in Da Nang, though he himself had never witnessed the horrors of war until tonight. The closest he came to the horrors of combat was during the Korean War, while he was an enlisted man in the Air Force. He was a sheet metal technician in Japan during the Korean War and he worked on B-29 bombers and fighter jets. When a B-29 flew back from a mission, he discovered an odd object he could not identify in the fuselage's darkness of the plane. When he crawled back out of the fuselage into the light holding the unidentified object in his hand, it horrified him discovering the object was a human limb which had been thrown into the fuselage during aerial combat. It was a frightening experience, but was nothing compared to what he experienced on October 1, 1968.

The men he got to know behind the lines in Da Nang marked a critical period for Buchanan developing a bond of trust and love with the troops which would last for the duration of his ministry in Vietnam. He ministered to men in Da Nang who had altered back and forth from the front lines. Within Buchanan's Baptist mindset, he considered his service in Vietnam a calling from God. A love for Buchanan and his presence was a state of physical ease from the pain & stress of combat for the marines. The typical charm and congeniality of Midwesterners rubbed off onto the marines. The many Ohioans in Camp Love added to the rapport he would have with the men. Hard work in the Midwest was deemed a way of life, and those lacking a robust Protestant work ethic were thought of as lazy and slothful. The work ethic shown from Buchanan was typical of a Midwesterner, evidence of his concern for the troops. He worked all hours of the day, a typical Midwestern trait, to ensure that their wants and needs were taken care of – spiritually and physically.

The marines found Buchanan entertaining. Anything to ease the stress of life in the bush, marines sought it out. He told jokes, stories, encouraged the men to do likewise. Buchanan's demeanor was one-of-a-kind, genuine, and real. His presentation of himself and personality was God's spun. For some, Buchanan was a God sent. By the end of Buchanan's Vietnam tour, many marines considered Buchanan the source of getting through the misery of war.

Buchanan was one of a kind, as people seemed to feel comfortable and at home around him. When entering a room, he brought with him a love of life no one else knew. Life was precious to him and he knew where that love of life came from. It came from the change he had as a twenty-four-year-old when he gave up the things of destruction and the Devil, and became a believer in Christ Jesus. He was destroying himself with alcohol. He drank anything with alcohol in it and became a drunk. When Buchanan served as an enlisted man, the Air Force busted him down to E-1 once and, in another instance, down to E-2 because of his addiction to alcohol. Though he worked his way up the enlisted ladder to E-5 and once to E-6 respectively, his love and addiction of alcohol did him in.

While stationed in Mobile, Alabama, he accepted Jesus as Savior in his life and became a believer, a Christian. The change in his life was genuine and people discovered a new Robert James Buchanan. As an unbeliever, thoughts of abusing alcohol phased him not and displaying a demeanor reflecting life was all about him.

As a youngster, he got in trouble in and out of school and with the law, partly because of his alcohol abuse.

Drinking himself to death was inevitable. At six years old, he took his first drink and his own mother gave it to him, becoming hooked on alcohol. The addiction became a way of life.

His life changed when Jesus entered his heart in 1955, becoming a Christian. Recognizing something in Buchanan directing his life which was not of this world was immediate for the marines.

Stuffy and stiff-necked Navy officers, especially Annapolis grads, thought Buchanan was nothing more than a country bumpkin. Smug officers who thought Buchanan was undeserving of wearing the uniform of a military officer. To them, he's a joker, a funny man. A showboat of a character who wanted nothing but attention. A few military officers thought he was more concerned about being an entertainer or an attention getter than carrying out the duties and protocol of a Navy officer.

Those who favored his personality admired him very much and simply said, "So what if he tells jokes from time to time and he's always looking at the good side of things? He's genuine, and that's what counts."

Buchanan knew some officers loathed his style. But he could have cared less. Besides, he was who he was. Possessing a genuine personality, he wasn't about to change for anybody, especially for a bunch of snobs.

What others thought of him had little bearing on his ministry to the marines. He could have cared less what others thought of him. Before entering the officer ranks, he had served as an enlisted young man. As enlisted, he knew firsthand the wants and needs of rank-and-file personnel and committed himself to minister to them. Regardless of what others thought of him, he was going to live life - 'Jesus like'. Though there were the few officers who stuck their noses in the air, he felt thoroughly supported by the vast numbers of officers who supported his efforts and ministry. The officer ranks knew he contributed to the troops' cohesion and discipline. Love of life was essential for him and he was going to live it. Even in a crummy war, Buchanan believed Jesus could still change lives.

Buchanan considered those who slighted him as bystanders. He felt that if a person forms an opinion of you based on his or her shallowness, then the blame of that person to reform is on him or her, not you. A quote from college he was fond of by Vernon

Howard and quoted often as a reminder of the smug in this world spoke volumes - "A Truly strong person does not need the approval of others anymore than a lion needs the approval of sheep." A lady and member of his church in Columbus, Ohio cross stitched the quote with a rose border and framed it for him. The quote hung on the wall in Chaplain Buchanan's office in California and in Camp Love to remind him the only approval he needed was from the Lord.

Buchanan witnessed serious combat his first day in the bush, a rarity for a green chaplain.

Securing the rest of his gear and possessions not earlier secured set his mind off the death and combat he witnessed earlier, at least temporarily. His quarters furnished a small dress of drawers securing his underclothes and socks, along with some of his uniforms. He had a small couch, a small stationary metal chair, desk and a swivel chair along with his cot. The hootch had little walking space. Confined, but cozy. Gnawing, but comfortable. Acquiring a single hootch served as a perk, he was fortunate. A bookshelf was on the left-hand side of the entrance of the hootch. Buchanan brought along a small collection of western and military history books. His small collection of books filled the bookshelf perfectly.

In addition, Buchanan had a small sink and mirror on the right as you entered the hatchway. The merged shower stall for officers in the center of the officer's quarters served the many staff and line officers. Considering the hootch's foundation stood on blocks and certainly not a five star motel, it was home. It was home until he could get back to his wife and kids.

After stowing away his uniforms, he retrieved his desk supplies and papers from one of his sea bags, placing it all on his desk. The desk opposite the doorway of the hooch sat beside his cot, left of his desk. The couch faced the desk, eventually adding a chair to counsel the men. The couch, a luxury in the bush, he figured Adkins or Jackson handled.

The family pictures he placed on his desk included photos of his mother and father, brothers, his wife and kids. His seven children, five boys and two girls, were a blessing from God each and every one. His kids – Robert James II, John Thomas, James Dwight and Jacqueline Louise – the twins, Kenneth Charles, Joseph Bethel, and Johanna Kathleen were all the world to Buchanan. He loved his wife and children more than anything else in the world. Buchanan and Dorothy, his wife, insisted a family portrait be taken prior to Buchanan's departure for Vietnam in case war took his life, sitting the picture on his desk. When Buchanan switched the desk lamp off every evening for the night's shut eye, the family picture was the last thing he would see every night as the pitch dark within the hootch hid all to see till morning.

Accustomed to large families with many siblings, the young couple decided early in their marriage to have a large family. Fourteen years of marriage brought with it a greater love for one another, which grew deeper and stronger each year. To keep in touch with the family, Dorothy sent Buchanan tape recordings of herself and the children. Along with the recordings, she would send newspapers to inform Buchanan of the news in southern California and of the country. Occasionally, one of his brothers would send him an Ohio paper. Not to catch up necessarily with Ohio news, but to keep up to date with the Ohio State Buckeyes. Communication with Dorothy was vital for Buchanan to deal with the emotional stress of war. His family was a driving force of encouragement. He was determined to see them again.

Last, Buchanan hung four framed cross-stitched quotes, inspiring him daily. The first was Philippians 4:10-14, bordered with Christian symbols and red roses. The second was a John Wayne quote bordered with saddles and horses which read "Courage is being scared to death.....and saddling up anyway."*

The third quote was special to Navy chaplains and medical personnel. The PRAYER FOR THOSE WHO MINISTER TO THE WOUNDED AND SICK inspired Navy chaplains for decades.

Buchanan quoted it often, reminding him of his purpose in Vietnam.

The prayer for those who minister to wounded and the sick set the tone for ministers and the medical field - "O merciful God,

Whose blessed Son went about doing good; Uphold with strength and grace those who do service to the wounded and the sick; grant to the ministers of the Gospel faithfulness and love; to the physicians and surgeons wisdom and skill, to the nurses sympathy and patience; and we beseech Thee to protect and bless them in all dangers, anxieties, and labours, through Jesus Christ our Lord. Amen."*

Vernon Howard and his view of life gave a lasting impression on Buchanan. The fourth cross stitch was a quote by Howard - "A Truly strong person does not need the approval of others any more than a lion needs the approval of sheep."*

Securing his gear and personal items, Buchanan set out for some shuteye.

Combat Fatigue

October 2, 1968

Buchanan's first night in Camp Love met with sleepless hours, compounded by mental attacks from the evils of combat. The memory of the Iowa kid plastered all four corners of his mind. He just couldn't shake off the memory of the imprint of shock on the marine's face. When sleep came, nightmares soon followed. He arrived at his hootch at 0345 hours and 0515 hours in the morning came quickly. At 0515 hours, he was to get up and ready himself for breakfast with Adkins.

Sleep came scarce with jungle patrols, a fact he would learn fast. Shut eye in his hootch came much more effortlessly.

Disconcerted with his first combat experience, Buchanan perceived the ordeal one civilians would discover inconceivable. With sleep at a standstill, he rose out of his cot for the day. Buchanan felt great all over with his shower and shave. Dressing to visit the marines in Camp Love, he still yet found it difficult to brush aside the noises of combat, the terror of death, and the facial expression on Gordon. As Buchanan dressed, he fell numb all over, knowing he will never be capable of brushing the memory of Gordon aside for the rest of his life.

Buchanan's experience had been difficult the past 24 hours, but still had a responsibility as chaplain.

The men Buchanan counseled in the six months behind the lines dealing with battle fatigue did not skim the surface of what they were dealing with inside their hearts and minds. Buchanan now knows. War was not what he could've imagined. He discovered war is serious business.

War was not the movies, and far from the glory of old soldiers' dreams. Nor what Hollywood portrayed it to be.

Warfare is nasty and brutal. It takes the lives of young men and women with their whole life in front of them.

Buchanan expected Adkins to arrive at 0600 hours for breakfast in the chow hall.

While waiting for Adkins, Buchanan attempted to cope with his stress by reading a western novel he began days earlier. Along with loving western novels, Buchanan loved western movies, especially John Wayne pictures. His family and friends knew him as an avid fan of John Wayne since childhood. The 15 or so paperback westerns sitting on the bookshelf provided pleasure reading along with non-fiction books about military history, including his favorite period to study - the Napoleonic wars.

Pulling the western off the shelf, Buchanan stepped to his swivel chair behind his desk to read. As he folded back the pages, he placed a Cincinnati Reds bookmark on his desk and read his novel. In just 5 minutes, the realization hit him this would not work. All his thoughts were of Gordon and the skirmish just mere hours ago.

Placing the western back on the shelf, he stepped back to his desk, sat down, and opened his Bible to read. Surely Scripture would take his mind off things. Reading the Beatitudes was peaceful, but the void was still wide, and the battle within himself continued.

Buchanan pulled out from the middle desk drawer his calendar to set his mind aloof from his fresh mental state. Reviewing his schedule for bush duty seemed to distract his scatter-brained thoughts, at least temporarily. Tuesdays and Thursdays scheduled an officer's call at 0900 and 1300 hours. Several hard corps marine officers frowned upon a chaplain being in the officers call meeting, but he didn't care. With the military matters spoken of in the meetings, the several officers thought it a joke that the chaplain take part. But Buchanan thought of himself as a Navy officer and a Navy chaplain. Buchanan loved the study of military tactics and strategy, and the military mind of the officers in the camp fascinated him.

Sunday services will be in the camp conference hall at 0900 and 1100 hours. Scheduled services in the field were on Monday, Wednesday, and Fridays at 1100 hours, or as many times as Buchanan scheduled. Services again on Tuesdays and Thursdays at 1100 hours in the camp conference hall. A devotion and Bible study on Tuesday and Thursday nights at 1900 in the camp conference hall stood as standing dates.

Last, but not least, Buchanan scheduled on Friday nights a social for the men to generate teamwork and camaraderie. He visited and counseled marines and sailors the remaining part of the day. He threw the schedule out the window when accompanying men in the bush.

A routine schedule for Buchanan gave him structure to carry out the day's activities. A constant schedule came vital in reaching the marines wants and needs. A strict agenda for each day regimented order to include all marines and to avoid exclusion in any 'way, shape, or form'. A Happy-Go-Lucky approach to ministry was far from a Buchanan ministry, except for counseling a marine out of necessity or spur of the moment.

The days in Camp Love were visiting men, making himself available for counseling. The exposure to combat his first night in the bush placed counseling marines with combat fatigue a top priority for Buchanan.

The time was 0600 hours and a sudden knock came from the hootch door, taking Buchanan's attention away from his calendar. Lieutenant Commander John Adkins has arrived.

"Who goes there?" insisted Buchanan.

Adkins chuckles and responds, "It's me. Lieutenant Commander Adkins. John!"

"Come in. Come in, John." said Buchanan.

Adkins steps in and says, smiling, "Who goes there?"

"That's right. We were taught in Da Nang to request identification for all who enter your respective hootch. You want me to do as I'm asked, don't ya?" said Buchanan, with a bit of sarcasm in his voice.

"Sure, chaplain." said Adkins, grinning.

"Well, are you ready?" asked Adkins. "We need to have breakfast and get over to the Colonel's office. You and I have an appointment with him at 0730 hours."

"Yes, John, I'm ready. I'm coming." responded Buchanan, in his heavy Kentuckian accent.

Relieved Adkins' presence in the room, Buchanan felt the loneliness and melancholy mood broken by his entrance.

The Lieutenant Commander Seabee's family roots held firm from Omaha, Nebraska. As a proud son of a hardworking Midwestern family owning a farm, Adkins conducted himself as such. The strict Seabee considered his position as a Naval officer seriously, keeping his uniform in tiptop shape, intolerable of an "Irish pennant" or a stain. As a staunch Baptist, Adkins and Buchanan became friends from common traits. Though Buchanan tended to be a bit less conservative than Adkins theologically and politically, the two men possessed the committed work ethic of Midwesterners, a motivating factor for them in Vietnam. The commitment as Midwesterners encouraged the men to accomplish the roles and responsibilities assigned in Vietnam to complete tasks 110% and considered their commission as a Navy chaplain a calling from God. For Adkins, the Bible set the standard as the only source to guide your life, and nothing in this world took precedence. Adkins rubbed people the wrong way. In public, some people considered him to be a jerk. Informing a perfect stranger back home in California at Camp Pendleton he or she were out of uniform because of an Irish Pennant was normal for Adkins. Buchanan knew deep down inside his friend possessed a caring and compassionate heart. In his third tour, Adkins knew Philip Jackson from his previous two tours and considered him a friend, though enlisted. Jackson chose his closest friends wisely, so if he trusted Adkins, there was something good within him.

Adkins mused Buchanan over and said, "I heard about what happened last night. Sure you're ready to visit the men? You want to sit awhile and mull over last night?" He looked over Buchanan to measure up his emotional state. He himself had already seen plenty of war. Adkins' body language spoke volumes with concern for his fellow brother in Christ, whom he appreciated as a friend.

Buchanan exclaimed, "Honestly, John, I don't know how I'm doing. This business of war – it's crushing. I hate it already. It seems as if I spent the morning with the Devil."

"You have to find ways to cope with it." advised Adkins. "It will never get better. Discover ways to overcome it. I'm sorry you were thrown a blow below the belt from the get go. I know you need to get your feet wet, but last night - well, I know that was a bit much for ya."

"I know so!" exclaimed Buchanan. "I'm a little jittery, but I think visiting the men will help me do just that – cope with it."

"First combat experience causes stress, and a lot of it." said Adkins. "Maybe some chow will do ya good, Robert. Let's go have some breakfast."

Turning off his lights, the two men stepped out of the hootch toward the chow hall located dead center of Camp Love. Their discussion comprised their duties at Camp Love, as Buchanan mentioned a jeep promised him in Da Nang and yet to be issued to him.

Adkins reassured him. "You'll get one to carry out services in the bush. There's a jeep for ya. You'll see."

The pair of friends arrived quickly to the chow hall, entering with a pair of marine officers of Company A just in from patrol. The men were filthy, covered with mud, dirt, spots of blood, and debris. The smell of jungle and sweat reeked with the stench of war from head to toe. With their face paint smeared with dirt and mud.

The men picked up a tray, placing a plate and silverware on the surface to file down the chow line. A moment in time Buchanan found most pleasurable. Never was he so hungry. As hungry people do, he filled his plate with a mountain of solid food.

Finding himself behind the two officers in line, Buchanan greeted them with a broad smile, "Good morning, men."

"Good morning, Chaplain." responded one officer.

With an inquisitive glance toward Buchanan, the officers displayed nothing but a condign mood, having suffered one casualty and one wounded marine on patrol and in no mood for pleasantries. It was natural for Buchanan to be friendly. And in time, he became accustomed to the restraint of marine moods after returning from a patrol or skirmish. The marines in time would get accustomed to Buchanan. The men would eventually understand an innate friendly demeanor from Buchanan came naturally.

The men continued down the line, choosing from the various pans of food for breakfast.

The first officer was Lieutenant John Frost of Alpha Company. His 6'1" frame intimidated most everyone he first met. Over time, Buchanan learned from Frost the necessity of cohesion and interdependency of marines in the field. A Detroit, Michigan native, Frost sprouted from a hard working blue collar family. The auto industry filled his family tree and was first from his family to graduate from college. In military life, Frost gained a reputation as a brilliant tactician on the battlefield. Buchanan strengthened his military prowess through Frost's battle smarts soon enough. Neither a churchgoer nor an adherent of religion, he admitted there was a place for spirituality for moral's sake. If he attended church services, he felt most comfortable in Methodist services. The Frost family affiliated with the Methodist church, preferring the least liturgical order of service. Personally, for Frost, many Christians were hypocrites, using religion as a source to control people. Frost felt many church people used church for nothing but a place to gain social status in the community. He loathed the notion.

Buchanan attempted to cultivate a relationship and said, smiling in his deep Kentuckian accent, "I'm Chaplain Buchanan. Just arrived yesterday. If there's anything I can do for you, just come by the office. I've an open door policy. Any hour, any time of the day, is just fine. Come by if you just want to talk. Pray. Anything." Frost and his friend gazes at him as if he were crazy, though the men reply graciously with a simple, "Thank you, Padre. We'll do - if a need arises."

Reaching the end of the buffet line, Buchanan pours himself a cup of coffee with tons of creamer and grabs a can of orange juice.

Every day, Buchanan ate the same breakfast items unless the chow hall served powered waffles and pancakes. Buchanan's breakfast comprised two boiled eggs, occasionally scrambled, two sausage links or one piece of bacon if available, one piece of toasted bread with butter, a couple of pieces of fruit if available, and fresh vegetables if available. If there were pancakes or waffles, he would eat them. Meals in the bush, even inside the perimeter of Camp Love, were minimal compared to the meals within the perimeter of Da Nang Air Base. Breakfast reigned as his favorite meal, and it showed. Buchanan wanted a big breakfast to start the day, storing up energy for the atrocious heat of Vietnam and the perils of the jungle bush. Getting sick was the last of Buchanan's wants, but he did not want to take a chance having an empty stomach in the jungle either. Over time, Buchanan learned the balance of the intake of food for jungle patrols.

Turning to speak to Frost once again, Buchanan discovered he was gone, walking in the opposite direction from him to sit at a separate table. The captain sat with fellow officers in an opposite corner of the chow hall. There were no separate chow halls in the bush for enlisted and officers. The chow hall served both ranks. Most tables were enlisted, while the hall reserved a quarter of the floor space for officers.

Buchanan felt he might have been too bold in his initial contact with Frost. The last thing he desired to do was to offend him. Buchanan would befriend Frost another day.

A doctor and dentist from the field hospital sat opposite of Buchanan. The conversation was good and cordial, as Buchanan invited them to the Friday night socials and worship services. The wounded from the previous night were foremost in Buchanan's mind, and the doctor informed him they would heal from their wounds. Pleased to hear good news of the wounded, Buchanan promised to visit the wounded later in the day with Jackson. When finished eating, farewells were given and Buchanan and Adkins departed the chow hall for the scheduled appointment with the commanding officer, as both men detested being late for anything.

On the way out, Buchanan glanced over toward Frost. He looked his way, but ignored him.

Stepping back to Buchanan's hootch to drive to the skipper's office in Adkins' jeep, Buchanan fell into a deep sense of nervousness meeting the Commanding Officer, Lieutenant Colonel Lucas. Buchanan was envious of Adkins' jeep.

Buchanan said sarcastically, "I see you have a jeep?"

"Yes, but I am part of the chain of command for the Seabees working with the marines. I need one." declared Adkins, smiling.

Buchanan stares grudgingly, snarling at his friend.

"You'll get one, you'll see." added Adkins.

Turning the keys of the ignition, Adkins drove toward the skipper's office.

The time was 0715 hours.

Buchanan felt butterflies within the deep crevices of his stomach. Making a good first impression was critical for him. His calling as a chaplain was a serious matter, praying the Lieutenant Colonel was open to him and his ministry.

Many questions arose in his mind. 'What would the colonel think of him?' 'Would the colonel be open to his proposed ministries to the men?' 'Is he going to be thought of as nothing but a country pumpkin?'

He would find out soon enough.

Buchanan was as nervous as a long-tailed cat in a room full of rocking chairs.

Visiting the Colonel

October 2, 1968

Adkins delivered the lowdown on Lucas, informing Buchanan, "Robert - the Lieutenant Colonel is a man who is, well - to put it bluntly, a no nonsense type of guy. Yet, he's willing to bend, fluctuate when the need arises. Military chain of command is expected and tolerates *some* activities allowing men to cope with bush life, but if it impedes keeping the camp safe though, he'll put a clamp on it. You understand?"

"Yeah, I understand. Lucas is his name, right?" Buchanan asked.

"Yep. Lieutenant Colonel William 'Bud' Lucas." responded Adkins.

"Friday night social will be a go, you think?"

Adkins grins sarcastically."Well, you've been telling everyone it's already a forgone conclusion. If the Colonel doesn't permit it, then you will just have to put out a memo, huh?"

"The social on Friday nights, it'll be a pleasant break for the men. I plan on showing John Wayne movies." affirmed Buchanan. "I hope the Colonel likes John Wayne."

"Well, ask him Robert."

Grinning, Adkins cites in jest. "The services haven't been approved, and you've been inviting everyone and their uncle in the camp to attend them."

"Then I can't imagine him denying any requests." Buchanan swore.

Adkins chuckles, advising Buchanan. "Just be yourself with him. But be careful when you ask of the CAP's visiting the Vietnamese villages and the orphanage."

"Why?"

"He doesn't mind contact with the natives, but he is cautious."

"What? We assigned platoons a village to create a base of positive support already. What's the difference?" Buchanan responded.

"You'll learn quick in Vietnam - it isn't easy to know friend from foe. He just wants to protect the men from danger. That's all."

"Could it be a religious CAP?" asked Buchanan.

Adkins glances toward Buchanan and confirms, "Maybe."

The pair finally arrived in front of Lieutenant Colonel Lucas's office. Entering the front door, Secretary Sergeant John Mark Vickers rose out of his seat to welcome the two visitors.

"Good morning, sirs." said Vickers.

"Good Morning. I'm Lieutenant Commander John Adkins."

"And I'm Lieutenant Robert Buchanan, chaplain. Our appointment with the Lieutenant Colonel is at 0730 hours. Sergeant Philip Jackson will join us directly."

"Yes, sir." responded Vickers. "The Commanding Officer has been waiting for you. Take a seat, sir. He'll be with you directly."

As the visitors sat patiently, they heard an officers call in progress, hearing muddled voices from the other side of the door. Half of the conversation heard came inaudible and obvious. Evidently, Lucas felt unhappy about something.

After five minutes, the officers attending the meeting walked out in single file past Buchanan and Adkins in the waiting room. Every single officer humbly walked past Buchanan. Nothing but a demeanor of obliged officers. Next in line for a meeting were Buchanan and Adkins, and all Buchanan could do was pray 'Lord help me.'

Vickers peeked into the office and informed Lucas, "Sir. Lieutenant Commander Adkins and Chaplain Buchanan are here for their scheduled meeting."

With a boisterous, deep voice, Lucas says, "Thank you, Sergeant. Send'em in."

Standing up, Buchanan caught himself catching flies and wide eyed, while Sergeant Vickers motioned for him and Adkins to enter the office and instructed, "The CO will see you now."

Just as the officers were about to walk toward the office, Sergeant Jackson walked through the entrance door.

"Sergeant Jackson," said Buchanan.

"Good Morning, Chaplain," responded Jackson.

"Good to see you this morning, Sergeant. Thank you for helping me when we got back from the bush last night. You'll never know how much I appreciate your patience with me." said Buchanan.

"My pleasure, sir. I'm here to assist you, sir."

Jackson turned to Adkins, "Good Morning Lieutenant Commander. How are you, sir?"

"Great Jackson. Good to see you again." replied Adkins. "We better go ahead with the meeting, gentlemen. We don't want to keep the Lieutenant Colonel waiting."

"Um." Lucas chuckles.

The delay in the meeting welcomed a well-timed interlude for a somewhat nervous Buchanan, who had never proposed a chaplain ministry to a commanding officer for a military base or a combat base.

The men stepped into the commanding officer's office, and with a first glance at the Skipper, Buchanan thought, 'Oh no. The dumb jock type. A pretty boy.' Buchanan loathed the smug of dumb jocks.

Shaking hands with Adkins and Jackson, Lucas turns to Buchanan and delivers a firm handshake to the new chaplain.

"Good morning, chaplain." greeted Lucas. "How are you this morning?"

"Great, sir." Buchanan responded. "Just wanted you to know that -"

Interrupting Buchanan, Lucas asserted, "Just want you to know that I've been looking forward to meeting you. Heard great things about ya. It's about time we get a chaplain with some energy. A man with some go get 'em in him."

Buchanan, humored by Lucas' high standards for the new chaplain, appreciated the challenge from the commanding officer to set forth a successful religious program in Camp Love. With the cold shoulder Frost threw at him in the chow hall, he worried about what might come in the next few weeks.

Lucas continued to speak frankly, "I'm sick 'n tired of the top sending me a chaplain from time to time, who does nothing but sit in his office on his butt all day twiddling his thumbs."

Buchanan and friends sit, smiling, nodding their heads nervously.

Lucas sashays to his window, which descends to the camp entrance and says with his back to Buchanan and friends, "A chaplain who practices his golf swing outside his office. A chaplain who reads Mechanics Monthly or Playboy." Lucas paused, glancing back at Buchanan with a slight smile and says, "Well - I mean Christianity Today the whole day through."

Smiles emerged on the visitors' faces as Lucas corrected himself.

Stepping back to face the visitors, Lucas heeded, "I prefer a chaplain who doesn't care about...well, stepping in some cow manure every once in a while, you know what I mean?"

The men shake their heads in agreement.

Lucas continues to vent, "These chaplains who do nothing during the week and - then turn around, conduct services on Sundays when there are only two, three - four people to serve communion to!"

Buchanan just listened, noticing Adkins and Jackson smiling from ear to ear.

'Well.' thought Buchanan. 'He looks like a dumb jock. But he doesn't talk like one.'

"Please sit down, men." said Lucas.

Each of the men take a seat in front of his massive desk. Lucas took a seat in his wooden swivel chair - his pride and joy. A premiere furniture maker made the desk and chair in the Cleveland, Ohio area. The set was 125 years old, made of the best oak available.

Buchanan, back on his heels from the smell of cigar smoke in the office, surrendered to the heavy odor dominating the room. Lucas had smoked cigars for decades with little restraint. Accustomed to a smoke free environment since he quit smoking 12 years earlier,

Buchanan fought the irritable odor of smoke, but admitted to himself the cigar smoke smelled pretty good.

Buchanan coughed.

"Never mind the cigar smoke chaplain, you get used to it." assured Lucas, laughing.

"These anti-tobacco advocates make me sick to my stomach. If I want to smoke a cigar…," Lucas interrupted himself picking a cigar out of his box on his desk, examining it from one end to the other, and looks back to his new personnel and contends, "…I'm going to smoke a cigar."

Buchanan and friends smiled, nodding slightly.

"My father is eighty-eight years old, and he's smoked'em since he was in his twenties. I'll smoke these dang things till they close the casket lid on me." asserted Lucas, chuckling.

"Hahaha!" laughed the men, more humored by Lucas laughing at his own joke than the joke itself.

Lucas then reached into his right pocket of his uniform and pulled out a book of matches. He looked at all three men and struck one match to light the cigar.

Lucas said, "Look at that cigar, gentlemen."

The men stared at the cigar as if it was an order. Confidently, Lucas asked, "Do you know where this cigar came from?"

None answered.

"Cuba. Yes, Cuba. The best cigars in the world." He lit the cigar with the match and put it in his mouth and took a hard puff. He laid the cigar down in the ashtray and divulged, "I love these things."

Buchanan and the others smiled, shaking their heads in the affirmative.

"If I hear nothing from you about how unhealthy these things are, I won't tell you how to run the chaplain's office. Is it a deal?" asked Lucas, as a slow, deliberate smile emerged on his face.

Buchanan grins, nodding in the affirmative.

All three men were in a chair in front of the colonel's desk, as Lucas caught them all admiring it. The width of the desk stretched wide from one end to the other with a beautiful finish to it. The presentation of the 125-year-old desk presented an enormous display, made of oak.

"I assume you all like the desk?" asked Lucas.

"Yes, sir." answered the men.

"You men are laying your eyes on a 125-year-old desk specially made back in my home state of Ohio." said Lucas, feeling the right edge of his desk with his fingers from one end to the other.

"The desk is my pride and joy. A desk like this shows what kind of leader you are. Portrays a strong sense of business. Reveals your authority over those you are to lead. Gives my visitors great first impressions, don't you think?"

Nodding with a smile, Buchanan swallows hard from nerves.

The desk impressed every visitor. Everything Lucas insisted the desk exemplified, it exemplified, and then some. Buchanan felt mortified at the thought of Lucas ever seeing his desk back home, thinking of him as puny. It convinced him Lucas would take one look at his desk and say, "Yep. The Woolworth special." Buchanan's desk was nothing but cheap wood, beaten up with nicks and crannies.

As Buchanan thought of his puny desk back home, Lucas explains, "My family owns a furniture company back home. The Lucas Furniture Company in Cleveland. A competitor of Fosters Furniture."

"My family's traveled all the way from Cincinnati, sir, to purchase furniture from your company." Jackson proudly informed the colonel. "The best furniture we've ever owned."

"Why thank you Jackson." replied Lucas

Lucas said, "I've read your record, Sergeant Jackson. Your personal presence will be a good thing for Chaplain Buchanan. A chaplain who ministers to the marines like Chaplain Buchanan will be fortunate to have a marine like yourself to protect him. With your record, he'll be quite safe. Whayathink, Jackson?"

Jackson turns to his right, smiles at Buchanan, with embarrassment all over his face. Looking back at Lieutenant Colonel Lucas, he nods his head and says, "Yes, sir."

Lucas then turns his attention back to Buchanan and apprises, "Enough about me. Let's get back to you, Chaplain Buchanan.

Now, I want you to know I've looked at your requests on paper and they're great. Times, days of the week for services all look good to me. Remember, time spent in the jungle bush might alter schedules frequently. Friday night socials, times for counseling are fine. All sound great chaplain! You remember completing the form I sent you?"

"Yes, sir - I do."

"The form, only formality for me. You understand, don't you?"

"Yes I do, sir."

Lucas explained, "Personnel's spiritual care is to be taken care of."

"Spiritual matters are of a top priority with me as well, sir." said Buchanan.

Lucas stepped up out of his swivel chair and walks to the front of his desk. Walking between the desk and his three visitors, Lucas stood, leaning back on his antique, vintage desk, something he would permit no one else to do.

After all this time, Buchanan noticed for the first time three Siamese cats lounging on the lieutenant colonel's book shelves on his right, staring down onto the human beings. The center of attention for the felines focused on the visitors. The jarring of nerves within Buchanan hit hard following the discovery of felines in the office. Loving classical music, Lucas named the cats Ludwig, Brahms, and Hans.

Buchanan deemed himself more of a dog lover, though he grew up with cats in the mountains of Kentucky and the hills of southern Ohio. He did not hate cats, but his wife Dorothy was never comfortable around cats and was allergic to felines.

Lucas said, leaning on his desk, "Fine. However, there is one matter, Chaplain. I want to address a concern of mine that's been an issue with past chaplains."

'What could it be?' pondered Buchanan.

All three visitors glance at one another with anticipation and uncertainty.

Lucas straightened up from his desk, walking over to the bookshelves to pet his cats. The loving attention he expressed to his feline friends resulted in an immediate purring from the spoiled four legged pets.

As Lucas continued to caress the cats, he explained, "Chaplain, we've had problems in the past with men of the cloth who didn't show respect to all the personnel's choice of faith. You know what I mean?" Lucas pondered his thoughts. "Our last chaplain was great. A Lutheran from Iowa, a fellow Midwesterner like yourself. The men loved him. Great chaplain! But some other chaplains here in Vietnam and in other combat bases didn't amount to nothing. You understand?"

"Yes, sir. I think I do." responded Buchanan.

"Well, let me clarify it for you. Jackson, you listen as well, since you'll be working with Chaplain Buchanan for the next twelve months. Adkins, you're a friend and supportive of him 110%, so you keep your ears wide open for my little spill we well. I uh - I just want you all to know I've, in the past, experienced some chaplains – well, to put it bluntly, haven't been good to God…themselves… or the Marine Corps. In fact, to put it bluntly weren't worth the sweat off my dog, Checkers, back home. And yes, he's named after President Nixon's dog."

Lucas smiles.

All three men shuffle in their seats, thinking of the dog's name, with noticeable smirks plastered all over their faces.

Lucas continued, "If I hear of anyone feeling as if their spiritual needs are not being met, I will not be a happy camper. You understand? But I have a gut feeling I will not have a problem with you, Buchanan. This isn't going to be an issue for me like in the past, is it?"

"No, sir. It's not." answered Buchanan. "An open door policy to my office is the standard, sir. Anyone of the day or hour can come by my office. When enlisted in the Air Force, I had a chaplain who had an open door policy. Every one knew he cared for men and women in uniform. I've modeled myself after him. Whatever problem we had, we knew he'd be there to help us solve our problem - if he could."

"Well Chaplain, I feel confident after meeting you today, reading your service record, hearing the scuttlebutt about ya, you're going to be something positive for the men." said a convinced Lucas. "You occasionally will hear from my mouth a word of profanity once in a while, but think nothing of it. Probably coming after some hose head or grunt does something stupid."

Lucas heard chuckles from the visitors as if agreeing with the commanding officer with a grunt deserving a good dressing down after committing something stupid.

Buchanan says, "I won't think anything of the profanity, sir. I hear it all the time."

"And by the way, chaplain. I love John Wayne. Showing John Wayne pictures on Friday night, well, a substantial source of boosting morale. It was one of the first things that caught my eye in your request sheet I sent you." commented Lucas.

"Great! You're invited sir." replied Buchanan.

"I'll be there Chaplain - for sure."

Lucas knew immediately Buchanan's presence was a blessing to the troops. He further discussed the religious program for a few more minutes, pivoting the discussion toward Adkins' role and responsibilities with the Seabees as their executive officer.

"Well gents, our meeting can end now. I feel comfortable with your leadership here is going to be successful." exclaimed Lucas. "Sergeant Vickers will hand you a check-in sheet. You'll visit the departments and officially be a member of Camp Love and the 7th Engineering Marine Battalion."

"Thank you, sir." said the visitors.

"Thank you gents, have a good day." responded Lucas.

"Good day, sir." responded the visitors.

Stepping out of the office, Sergeant Vickers distributed the check-in sheets to each of them, turning the sheets in after visiting the departments within the camp.

Buchanan felt satisfied with his presence. There was apprehensive at first, but now confident with no end departing the CO's office.

Walking from department to department, the men sought the signatures required from each superior in each office.

Buchanan appeared head over heels with confidence as he left the Commanding Officer's headquarters, but left falling short of acquiring one essential piece for ministry - a jeep.

During the meeting, Lucas fell silent with the requisition of a jeep to carry out ministry, promised to Buchanan in Da Nang.

The determination for Buchanan to own a jeep strengthened his resolve. And nothing was going to stop him from getting his hands on one.

Music Soothes the Soul

October 2, 1968

Most of the day resulted in visiting the camp's engineering departments and infantry companies. Adkins walked Jackson to his quarters, then marched off to Buchanan's hooch. The men discussed checking in with the camp's departments and the ministry to the marines. Adkins returned the next morning to pick Buchanan up for breakfast.

The late hours approached quickly, and all needed a good night's rest.

Buchanan stepped up into his hooch for the night at 2000 hours.

Buchanan suffered a long, first full day in Camp Love. The day started with breakfast and ended checking in the departments in the camp. Exhaustion hit him hard. Buchanan looked forward to a restful second night. He longed for a calmer night, not one of nightmares full of death and violence. The search and discovery for the means to cope with war as Jackson and Adkins suggested he do would come in time. Visiting each department at least twice a week, he figured, would be a good means of coping. He started the day visiting the medical aid station, and end the day with the car pool - no talk of war, just visiting and cultivating relationships with the men.

Though his thoughts were of war, he hid his innermost feelings for the whole day. Stomach cramps gnawed at him, causing a drainage of his emotions, leaving him physically fatigued. His thoughts were still of Sebastian Gordon foremost. The kid was a mere four days away from going home, and Buchanan thought of his death as calamitous.

Buchanan thought of Gordon and his family. He thought of his parents who were waiting for him patiently at the farm, only to see from a living room window a Navy chaplain emerge from a vehicle, walk up to the front door of the family home only to inform his parents he was never coming home again. He thought of his friends at Iowa University who fed off Gordon's intellect and learned from their academic friend, never again to admire his brain power. Last, he thought of his childhood friends he grew up with, never again to reminisce about the memories of being young. Gordon's siblings will never again tell their brother, "Stop bugging me." They will mourn his death for the rest of their lives.

Buchanan knew Gordon for a mere few hours, but he admired him. He found himself fond of Gordon. The young marine haunted him for the rest of his life.

The first night in the bush and the cruelty of war hit him like a ton of bricks. The end of Gordon's life arrived too early, angering Buchanan, a trait uncharacteristic for him. From time to time in Vietnam, war caused him to lose his temper. War did that to people. War pushed people to get angry, even hateful.

Regardless of the fact Buchanan considered anger and rage a sign, even a trait, of the Devil - he witnessed time and time again marines and sailors hate and even find themselves in a bit of frenzy and rage. Buchanan will discover himself occasionally in a state of exasperation and frustration. War did that to people. Nonetheless, he felt strongly and theologically that anger, hate, and envy were all from the Devil.

The battle within Buchanan to fight hate, anger, and envy began his very first night in the jungle bush. A continuous battle ensued within Buchanan on every patrol he would accompany marines into the bush during his tour.

Nonetheless, Buchanan considered hate a weakness.

Witnessing young men's lives taken so early hurt Buchanan's most inner self while in Vietnam. He attempted, with the best of his ability, to think God's permissive will occur for a reason and that God is in control of all things in life. Being a Baptist, the strong adherence to God's hand in human beings' lives came proven in history books. God's permissive will ultimately brings good out of evil.

Though it was difficult for Buchanan to accept the fact God has a reason for everything in life, including Gordon's life taken so early, he would not question the permissive Will of God, regardless of how difficult it was to accept. Buchanan was a Baptist through and through and believed all things in life have a purpose. God's will is perfect, and it is not Buchanan's business to question it. Man's sin and selfishness caused many evils in life, not God. And war is certainly one of the many evils in the world.

His thoughts turned to Deuteronomy 29:29. "The secret things belong to the Lord our God, but the revealed things belong to us and to our children forever, to observe all the words of this law." The words touched him deeply. Buchanan accepted "secret things" in life human beings can never understand. Even reason and logic cannot answer the mysterious questions humans have in this life.

Education and knowledge will only take a human being so far in answering questions about this life. After that, intelligence gained can go no further in discovering the full knowledge of God. Buchanan struggled with the pain of war.

Buchanan attempted his entire tour to cope with the loss of young lives. He theologically understood St. Augustine's argument of a justified war, but he grappled with the loss of life and how a loving God permitted such violence and destruction. In the end, he held to his convictions that God is in control, that the fall of man corrupted the world, and people of God were to bring peace in it.

He prayed for peace and a quick conclusion of the conflict.

Buchanan sought to hit the sack and pursue some shut eye. A shower and shave prior to going to sleep made him feel good all over. The reading of Scripture and part of the western novel temporarily took his mind off of his traumatic experience.

Buchanan slipped into his nightclothes, which were always a pair of sweats, underwear, and a t-shirt. He wore his combat boots every night out of fear of snakes, airing out his feet in the evenings prior to getting shut eye. Adkins thought wearing sweats was crazy, but Buchanan did not care. He wore the sweats for the duration of his tour, whether he sweated or not. Wearing the sweats decreased exposure to any dangers the jungle might throw at him, especially snakes, to his legs. Again, Adkins thought it was asinine. Silly or not, Buchanan was bull headed and never experienced the jungle in a war zone.

Finished reading his Bible and western novel, Buchanan read and researched his military books. But he was tired, and the hour called for some shuteye. He climbed into his small cot, laid down on his back, and stared straight into the ceiling of his hootch. For minutes on end, he laid on his cot thinking of nothing but Gordon. The young marine filled his thoughts. When finally closing his eyes, Buchanan laid on his cot, too distracted mentally to go to sleep. Frustration set in, so he rose, grabbed a military history book on the grand strategist Napoleon attempting to brush aside thoughts of the horror of Gordon and set his mind on rest and shut eye. But to no avail. He read a little more of his western novel, and he finally felt a little drowsy.

Lying back on his cot, Buchanan closed his eyes, ready for some sleep. Still yet, all of his thoughts were of Gordon.

The fears of nightmares, which he dreaded most, confronted him as he closed his eyes. Adkins warned him of the nightmares.

As the time set at 2130 hours, he opened his eyes and laid on his cot. At the point of giving up, and knowing he was a heavy sleeper, his first night of war and his first experience of combat posed him with a problem he never faced before in his life.

As Buchanan thought of a solvent for his problem, a sound came ringing through the air, something which echoed throughout the entire camp. The hums and pulsations of the sounds bounced off one building onto another in concert, bouncing off one surface onto another. Coming in from all directions were the odd resonances, odd sounds, but peaceful and gentle. Spirited with a passionate resonance, Buchanan could not figure out the vibrations at first.

The sounds passed in just a mere few seconds, but he finally recognized the hums, pulsations, echoes, and resonances – it was classical music - of a soothing calmness.

Music of a assuaging temperament.

"It's beautiful!" admitted Buchanan. He loved it, as it pleased his heart. The music filled the camp, giving him peace.

Many questions arose in Buchanan's mind.

'Who played the music?' 'Did Lucas approve music this late?' 'How could someone get away with playing music this loud at this hour?' Buchanan reasoned the sheer noise tipped off the VC.

For the moment, he brushed aside such questions which mattered little. What mattered most for Buchanan had been he finally found something to help him cope with war - music.

Buchanan loved the piece of music reverberating throughout the camp. The music eased the pain, at least temporarily. He enjoyed the music. Lying on his cot listening to the music, Buchanan remembered being introduced to classical music from time to time growing up, but it was not a genre his family listened too much. In fact, his family was not avid classical music lovers hardly at all. His first exposure to appreciating classical music as a serious form of art would be in college. He loved music and listened to many sorts of genre. He basically grew into a gospel and country music fan peppered with some popular music. His favorite country singer from Alabama had a knack of singing with an astounding ability to probe the deepest of human emotions using the language of ordinary people in his lyrics. The singer's life ended up a sad one, he lost his life young in an automobile accident. When life got tough, Buchanan listened to him when hitting rock bottom. When in the mood, he listened to country rock or a popular vocalist, such as a popular English female vocalist he enjoyed, or music stressing brass instruments.

The piece of music this night was nothing he had heard before. All the essential components of classical music rang in the piece, drawing him closer to the auditory sensation. He instantly fell in love with a genre of music he never really paid much attention to.

He discovered the power of classical music, which affects the heart and mind of a human soul.

Buchanan brushed aside the memory of Gordon and the battle from listening to the music, at least for the moment. Of all things, therapy to cope with war discovered in music. Buchanan closed his eyes, creating within his own mind images drawing parallels along with the music. He discovered himself thinking of the notes and the musicians playing the notes. Buchanan, reminded from college of the power and symbolism of classical music for human beings, created in his own mind pictures and visuals he imagined using his own creative spirit listening to the music.

Buchanan was determined to locate the marine responsible for playing the music the next morning. He sought to know the composer, the title of the piece, everything of it. The aspiration to know everything about the music seemed to give him a means of coping with war was pertinent.

Morning would have to wait as he fell asleep listening to music. He was totally exhausted.

God's presence added to a restful night.

A soothing night.

Meeting Major Burns

October 3, 1968

The next morning, Buchanan prepared himself for a second day of ministry in Camp Love.

After a shower and shave, he waited for Jackson to head for the chow hall, which gave him a chance to hammer out in his mind his better, more restful second evening in Vietnam.

A sudden knock on the door shifted his attention.

"Who goes there?" asked Buchanan.

Jackson responds, chuckling, "It's me, Sergeant Jackson."

Stepping into the hootch, Jackson said, grinning, "Good morning, Padre. Are ya going to say 'Who goes there?' for every visitor?"

"Yep."

"Why, for Heaven's sake?" asked a probing Jackson.

"Security."

"Psst." replied Jackson. "'Who goes there?' is for men on duty, sir. You know that. You were once enlisted."

A smiling Buchanan reminded Jackson, "Listen, we were told in training to identify all entering your area for security's sake."

"Ok, sir." said Jackson, raising his hands and looking off to the side, then dropping his hands next to his legs.

Changing the subject, Jackson asked, "How was last night? Was it better?"

"Wasn't as bad as I thought, Philip. In fact, it wasn't a morning with the Devil like yesterday morning!"

"Oh? Well, Amen to that!"

"Yes, Amen! The music. You heard it - didn't you?" said Buchanan enthusiastically. "I loved it."

"Music's played every night, sir." Jackson explained further, "Men aren't bothered, it's therapeutic. Though most of the marines hate classical music, it well - gives troops a mental break. For that, they love it."

"Who plays the music? You know him?" asked an inquisitive Buchanan.

"Yeah. Can't remember his name, but I'm sure we can find him. Are you ready for breakfast? I'm hungry."

"Yeah. Me too."

The men started out for the chow hall, and conversation quickly turned to the night before, the violence of war Buchanan witnessed for the first time.

"Can't explain my emotions, Sergeant." commented Buchanan.

Glancing toward Buchanan with concern, Jackson asked, "You're going to make it, chaplain. You have a strong faith. You care for the men. You have a strong backbone. That counts a lot here. You'll see."

Almost to the chow hall, Lieutenant Commander Dwight Maher, a friend and Alabama native, came walking out of the chow hall, a man Buchanan held high in regard.

"Good morning Chaplain Buchanan, Sergeant Jackson." said Maher.

"Good morning Chaplain Maher," responded the spiritual team.

Maher, a Methodist chaplain, ministered to the 1st Marines Division, 7th Marines 3rd Battalion, a neighboring unit in Quang Nam province. Maher came to visit a friend in Camp Love who succumbed to enemy fire a few weeks earlier.

"If you need anything Chaplain Buchanan, let me know." said Maher.

"We'll do, Chaplain Maher. Thank you."

Two six shooters hung on Maher's belt, taking Buchanan and Jackson aback, thinking George S. Patton was standing in front of them. Buchanan considered chaplains non-combatant as did the Navy, and he thought to himself, 'Will he ever use those things?'

Chances of Maher aiming and discharging his weapons toward the enemy were null to void. Most of the Navy chaplain corps cohort, including Buchanan, insisted the demeanor of Navy chaplains was to impart peace making, not participants of war.

"Heard of your first night in the bush. Hope you're doing alright? It's rough, Robert. It's gut wrenching. I'll be praying for you." commented Maher.

"Thanks, Chaplain." said Buchanan.

Buchanan thought to himself - 'Wow! Word sure spreads fast around here!'

"Good day, gents. Gotta get to my own men." said Maher.

"Thanks Chaplain Maher," responded the spiritual team.

As the spiritual team journeyed toward the chow hall, Buchanan asked Jackson, out of earshot of Maher, "Are you kidding me?"

Buchanan gestured with his fingers the peace sign and said, "*Twoooooo*. Two six shooters? Will he ever use those things, you think?"

"He thinks he's Wyatt Earp." said Jackson as they laugh. "I don't think he's going to have a western showdown anytime soon, sir."

"I don't think so either, buckaroo." quipped Buchanan.

The men chuckle with amusement.

Jackson said, "I do feel safer with John Wayne here in Vietnam."

Buchanan thought it a compliment.

Stepping into the chow hall was too long in coming. The passing through the entrance door was a relief of sorts with hunger calling.

Turning to the left, Buchanan with anticipation grabbed a place in line for breakfast. The officer in front of him was Major Vincent Carroll, Camp Love's executive officer. From Biloxi, Mississippi, he lived as a true southerner through and through whose family thrived in the fishing business.

Turning to one's side, he smiled at Buchanan, and nodded, smiling toward Jackson with a recognition of knowing him.

"Chow hall here's for both enlisted and officers, Padre." said Carroll. "But yesterday, Jackson here sat in the corner of the chow hall reserved for officers only."

"Yes, major, I know." Buchanan asked his name, "And your major -?"

"Major Carroll." Carroll abruptly answered.

"Well, Major Carroll - it's a beautiful day, isn't it?" Buchanan wasted no time ignoring the issue at hand. He asked the base commander for permission for Jackson to sit in the officers' corner of the chow hall, and permission was granted. Buchanan knew there would be hoopla from the stiff necks.

In line for chow stood another officer - Major Michael "Mickey" Sanborn from Iowa City, Iowa. A Lutheran and noted to bend military rules from time to time, he trained and supported the South Vietnamese farmers in cultivating crops, his expertise. Along with Carroll, Sanborn adhered to a staunch Lutheran faith in life. The rank and file highly admired him.

"Heard you attended a Lutheran seminary, Padre." said Sanborn.

"Yes sir, I did,"

"You're a Baptist, and you went to a *Lutheran* seminary?" asked Sanborn.

"Yes, sir. And raised Presbyterian." added Buchanan, grinning with the broadest ecumenical smile possible.

Sanborn laughs and said, "Sounds like you have a spiritual identity crisis chaplain."

Buchanan chuckles and says, "No, nothing like that. It's a long story, though. I'll tell ya of it on another day."

"I'd love to hear that story one day, chaplain. Regarding Jackson here, you go ahead, sit with the officers, Sergeant." said Sanborn.

In his second stint, Sanborn knew Jackson from previous tours.

"How you doing, Jackson?" asked Sanborn.

"Great, sir."

Unbeknownst to Buchanan, Jackson saved Sanborn's life in February 1967. The Viet Cong ambushed Sanborn and Jackson's patrol on the way back to base. Sanborn, shot up and disoriented, became isolated from the patrol, exposed to the VC. Jackson searched and located Sanborn, carrying him back to camp and out of the Viet Cong line of fire.

"Good to see you, Sergeant. Come to my quarters, we'll catch up on things." encouraged Sanborn.

"We'll do, sir" said Jackson.

Arriving at the end of the mess line, Buchanan chose his usual breakfast with a little extra this morning - two pancakes. When available, he would get a bowl of strawberries and peaches if they looked fresh.

Buchanan searched for two empty seats in the officer's corner, locating a couple of seats after scanning the corner for space.

The only empty seats found by the spiritual team were the center of the officers roped off portion of the chow hall. The mess crew set the table for ten and they sat right across from Major Michael Porch, finishing up his breakfast. As a 'gun ho' officer, Lucas assigned Porch double duty in Camp Love - personnel and part-time security. Porch, conducting himself strictly by the book, reasoned a wide gap between officer and enlisted personnel instilled intangibles and discipline amongst the troops. Enlisted personnel quickly came to hate him.

"Good Morning, Major." said Buchanan, offering a friendly handshake, returned with nothing but a stern stare, followed by a soft handshake, and nodding in the affirmative. As Buchanan conversed with officers at the table, a tense couple of minutes passed as Porch paid no attention to Buchanan, when Porch finally conveyed a show of condescending expressions of body language. Porch leaned slowly over the table toward the spiritual team.

Lowering his voice hushed enough for the spiritual team to hear, Porch exerts himself, "Let me tell ya something, *chaplain*. Your style of ministering is a cancer for the chain of command. I know it. You know it. You bring your assistant in here throwing military rules and regulations out the window. You already parade yourself around here as if you're a mere preacher. I observed you back in Da Nang from time to time. This isn't church Buchanan - it's a war zone. Don't...you....forget it. Conduct yourself as a *Navy* officer - not some happy-go-lucky circuit preacher. You don't - you'll live to regret it."

The spiritual team stare stoically.

Porch continued, "I don't like your country preacher bit. Your mountain wit. Your southern accent. Your little jokes and laughing all the time. You might fool everybody else, but you don't fool me. I'm fore warning you - conduct yourself as a Navy officer....or else."

"Or else?" asked a sarcastic Buchanan, glancing over to Carroll and Sanborn, then back at Porch sternly and with concern.

Marines in close vicinity longed to hear what he said to Buchanan. Porch went on and on, and practically no one could hear anything. His tirade laid upon Buchanan is not appreciated by many of the officers sitting at the table, whatever was inaudibly said to Buchanan.

An officer or two heard parts of Porch's tirade, but did not quite make out what he said to Buchanan. The men well liked the chaplain and would remember Porch's tirade, audible or not.

Buchanan sat patiently as Porch spout off the mouth, thinking for wise words in response to the major. When Porch finally ended his utterances, Buchanan lowered his voice, leaned over the table, and came as close to Porch as possible.

Out of earshot of the officers, Buchanan asserted himself, "Sir - *Major*. I'm here to meet the physical and spiritual needs of *all* Navy and Marine personnel, including *yours*. My duty as a Navy officer and a Navy chaplain is to meet the wants and needs of the troops. And nothing – *nothing* - is going to get in the way of that. Don't lecture me. I know the appropriate separation between officers and enlisted personnel."

By now, Porch's face was full of flushed red anger.

Buchanan continued, "Don't lecture me, *Major*, of military bearing. I learned military bearing when enlisted in the Air Force, *sir*, and I know what is appropriate and what's not. These men's spiritual guidance and needs are going to be met, and that's exactly what I intend to give'em. They go out and fight, kill, and put themselves in the line of fire every day. I'm here to get 'em through it. You don't like my style - then go to the skipper with your beef. You might not care for me, but don't get in my way when I'm doing *my* job."

Porch's blood vessels popped out. Never had a junior officer or even a chaplain spoken to him as Buchanan just did. One man at least heard Porch spout off the mouth to Buchanan - Sergeant Jackson, smug and smirking all the while.

An austere Porch sneered, rose from his seat, staring at the spiritual team intensely as he left the chow hall. Some officers, embarrassed by Porch's behavior, apologized immensely.

Buchanan knew paths would cross with Porch again in the months ahead.

Jackson reminded Buchanan of an Abraham Lincoln quote he once read and said, - "I would rather be a little nobody, than to be an evil somebody."

"Don't worry about it, Sergeant Jackson. There's people in this world who's just downright mean." claimed Buchanan.

"Chaplain, someday that officer is going to need you and you're going to be there." insisted Jackson.

"That's right, Philip. Someday."

"He's nothing but ate-up, sir."

"Sure is. Sergeant." responds Buchanan.

Conversation at the table continued, as Buchanan overheard officers discussing music at the opposite end of the table.

An officer spoke of the music played last night, "I played Johan Strauss's The Sleepwalkers Waltz last night. One of my personal favorite's. It's a work I based my last piece of music on when composing a musical play for a company back home in Huntington, West Virginia."

Major James Burns, a university music teacher in West Virginia, featured many connections with Buchanan - the Tri-State area, Ohio, and his wife, a fellow West Virginian.

Buchanan moved closer toward the middle of the table and listened intently to Burns as he talked about music and of West Virginia.

As he listened to Burns, he waited for the right moment to ask him a question. Finally, when there was a long pause, Buchanan asked, "Can I ask you a question?"

Burns looked toward him with merriment in his eye and says, "Sure, chaplain. Go 'head."

"Are you the marine who played the music last night?" asked Buchanan.

"Why, yes. Yes, I am, I -" Buchanan interrupted Burns and said, "Let me tell you I've never been so enlightened in my life. Your music touched me like no other music I've ever heard. I really appreciated it."

"Well, thank you. Thank you, sir." responded Burns.

"I just heard you're from West Virginia." asked Buchanan

"Yes, I am."

"Amen!" roared Chaplain Buchanan.

"My wife was born in Huntington, West Virginia, and a proud West Virginian." commented Buchanan. "Were you born in West Virginia?"

"Yes, born in Winfield, West Virginia."

Buchanan stretched out his hand, introduced himself. "I'm Chaplain Robert Buchanan."

"I know. Glad you're with us, chaplain."

Burns returned a firm handshake, smiled widely and with exuberance.

"Sergeant Jackson, my chaplain assistant." said Buchanan.

"You're Sergeant Philip Jackson?" pointing his finger ever so slowly toward Jackson, and asked, "Who knows Major Sanborn?"

"Yes. Yes I am, sir." Jackson quickly changed the subject and said, "You're Major Burns."

Buchanan, noticing the change of conversation, grins and nods at Jackson.

"Yes. Major James Burns. Good to meet you gentlemen. I work in ordnance. Sorry for your confrontation earlier. Porch can be pretty obnoxious. He's a little too military, if you know what I mean? I already appreciate your presence, chaplain. I'm Presbyterian, so if you need any help, just let me know. I heard of your work in Da Nang the past six months and you're OK."

Buchanan said, "I'll call you, if needed. Thank you."

Burns admitted, "The men are going to respond to you well. They'll appreciate your presence here in camp. You too, Jackson. I know your record from your previous two tours - you're loyal, a disciplined marine. The men are going to appreciate your efforts as well."

"Thank ya, sir," replied Jackson. "Chaplain Buchanan was raised Presbyterian."

"Well, I know you're going to work out chaplain." said a cheerful Burns.

Buchanan professed, "Major Burns, you probably already heard my first night in the bush was one to remember. An emotional night. A difficult time getting shut eye. I tried everything. Reading my history books. Even reading the Scriptures. *Nothing* seemed to work. But you know something? When your music started playing, it did some good for me. Helped me fall asleep. Just wanted you to know that. Thank you."

Satisfied with the fact his music soothed a soul and eased the pain, Burns smiled from ear to ear.

Burns said, "Great. *Great*! What ever normalcy can be felt out here, the better. Calming the mind, soothing the soul. The marines and sailors enjoy it every night. Even the kids who *claim* they hate classical music - well, come to me all the time to - well, to inform this *boring* classical composer from West Virginia they loved the piece of music played the previous night."

Burns chuckles and, in a stern and serious manner, acknowledges the spiritual team with a firm and somber expression and empathy in his eyes. He insisted, "It's oblivious to many of the men how powerful classical music can be to the heart and soul - the wonder of it, the power of it. There's a transcendence of culture within classical music, and it breaks down generational barriers. There's a story behind every piece of music - whether it is a symphony or just a simple quartet or a piece for chamber music. It has something to give to the human heart, chaplain. My music at night is therapeutic to the men as they bed down for the night. The commander knows it. Besides, he enjoys it himself."

Burns smiles, slowly standing up.

"Good to meet you, chaplain. Good to meet you, Sergeant Jackson."

Burns reaches out, acknowledges Buchanan and Jackson with a firm handshake.

"I've got to get to work." said Burns. "Either of you ever want to come by my hootch and just listen to some music - feel free. Door's always open. Sure of one thing, chaplain - I'll be in attendance for Sunday services. Count on it. Don't miss a Sunday."

"Thank you, sir," responded Jackson.

"I'll be over for sure, Major Burns," acknowledged Buchanan. "I'll be looking for you in service as well. Good to meet you."

"Likewise chaplain."

Burns steps up from the table to go to work.

The spiritual team set out for work as well on this third day of ministry. There was one vital tool to deliver and conduct church and Communion services, but still not in the possession of the spiritual team. On this third day of work in the bush, the 'spiritual team', as Buchanan would refer to themselves, were out to gain that vital tool in delivering services to the men - a jeep.

Jeeps were akin to gold. Everyone desired a jeep, but not everyone was a privileged one.

Buchanan had a schedule and services were an essential part of the weekly agenda. To carry out the services in the bush, the spiritual team necessitated a jeep for ministry. The team loathed the thought of depending on riding 'shotgun' everywhere they traveled.

The spiritual team yearned for a jeep - and nothing standing in their way will deter them from laying their hands on one.

The Jeep

October 12, 1968

Nine days since meeting Burns and still no jeep.

The past nine days found the spiritual team humping the service kit and equipment from and to Camp Love while in the field, and the team was sick and tired of it.

As long as they were without a jeep, the dependence on someone else's mode of travel to and from camp was a reality and had to ride shotgun for every destination in the field.

Buchanan was weary of it. He was determined to have services in the bush every week, possibly every day. And nothing was going to prevent him from doing so.

Buchanan received the run around for nine days from everyone, and it gnawed at him.

Dependence on someone else's transportation got old quick. However, one of the few perks of riding shotgun came in getting to know the man. The few perks certainly did not outweigh possessing a jeep. A jeep or truck driver would transport Buchanan to the bush to hold services, but without a return trip. The team was then reliant on another driver. The fact numerous vehicles consistently traveled back and forth on all local routes in the vicinity assured Buchanan riding shotgun was a steadfast means of transportation, but one neither Buchanan nor Jackson cared to depend upon for an entire year of ministry in the bush.

Buchanan believed whole-heartedly in capitalism, and supply and demand were in the air.

On the demand side stood Buchanan and Jackson, and the supply was somewhere in Camp Love. The spiritual team set out to find the supply in camp.

The time was 0600 hours, and the search for a jeep will come after breakfast.

Jackson dropped by Buchanan's hootch to pick him up for chow. After breakfast, the spiritual team discussed the predicament they were in, the vitality of a jeep to provide ministry in the bush and setting out to find a jeep in camp.

For nine days, Buchanan requested from the chain of command in Da Nang for a jeep they promised him in the six months stationed on the air base and for nine days, he received the runaround from the chain of command. Buchanan would ask, "I *am* going to have a jeep in the field, right?" He received nothing but a hearty and assuring, "Aye, Aye, chaplain."

Still nine days and no jeep.

Buchanan even reminded Lieutenant Colonel Lucas of a jeep. Lucas answered with, "Extra jeep comes our way - it's yours chaplain."

Buchanan thought, 'An extra jeep? You mean *a* jeep.'

Feeling the brunt of the runaround, the spiritual team split up and searched for a jeep in camp, visiting each department in camp to speed up the process. The two asked each department if there was a spare jeep available, then meet back at Buchanan's hootch and give a full report.

When back at the hootch, the spiritual team discovered the team came up dry locating a jeep. The men visited one department after the other - and no jeep. Logistics. Medical. Headquarters. Chow hall. Communications. Ordnance. Everywhere. They verbally listed one by one the departments visited from each other, and discovered they visited all the departments except for one: automotive.

"Well, let's go visit automotive," smiled Buchanan.

So off they went.

The time was now 0845 hours.

Walking to automotive, Jackson, amused, said in jest, "Wouldn't it be hilarious if we find a jeep in the last department visited - automotive?"

Laughter came abundantly to the two spiritual leaders. When composing themselves from the laughter, they stopped and Buchanan prayed seriously for a new jeep. He lifted up a prayer and requested, "Lord, our last department to visit is automotive. Lord, if it is Your will, let automotive have a jeep." Buchanan fought the urge to laugh. "Philip and I need a jeep to do your work in the field. Be with us now as we go. Bestow upon us confidence and strength as we do your work. Amen."

"Amen," affirmed Jackson.

Smiling, the team continued to walk toward automotive close to Buchanan's hootch.

Arriving, Buchanan turned to Jackson, asking him what to say.

Jackson looked directly at Buchanan and said, "Just simply ask – you got a jeep?"

"OK." said Buchanan.

Chuckling, the men entered automotive and walked straight to the service counter. The team noticed immediately a sergeant sitting at a desk behind the counter. His feet were on the desk and dressed in a dirty tank top shirt with civilian shorts. Wearing cowboy boots with no socks, the sergeant wore an apparent day's worth of a five o'clock shadow.

The fact all were in the bush and a constant beat down of horrid heat made it unbearable, wearing a skimpy layer of clothing was understandable, but the sergeant's appearance presented himself a bit too much for the spiritual team.

Saturating every page and every word of his men's magazine, and barely paying any attention to the spiritual team, Jackson says, "Uh-um."

"Yeah, whayawant?" asked the sergeant.

Looking over the counter, the spiritual team gave the most stern stare down at the sergeant.

Slowly, the sergeant eased his magazine down onto the desk face down, noticing chaplain bars on Buchanan's collar.

"Sergeant, you need to do something about your uniform, don't you?" said Buchanan.

"Uh....yeah. Y-Yes-Yes sir. I guess so. Yes, sir." responded the sergeant.

Jackson had had enough of the shag nasty sergeant. With a rough tone, he said, "Listen, sergeant, if you don't start showing us some proper respect, I am going to jump over this counter and kick you around a bit. You'd better straighten up right now."

The sergeant stood short, scrawny, and a measly 5'4". Jackson towered over him at 6'3".

The sergeant swallowed hard, muttering inaudible words.

"What's your name?" asked Jackson.

"My-My name is Michael Mc-McMillan. I come from Paducah, Kentucky."

With raised eyelids, an astonished Buchanan stared straight at McMillan and said proudly in his deep Kentuckian accent., "You're from Kentucky? And you conduct yourself in a manner like this? Your demeanor is just unacceptable, son. I'm from Kentucky. That's right - Kan-tuc-kee."

Buchanan paused and said, "Kentuckians are better than this."

Embarrassed, McMillan said, "I-I'll try, sir."

"Aren't you a little young to have the rank of sergeant, McMillan?"

"Well, sir." said McMillan. "My MOS is a demolition expert, one of the best in the Corps. I, well - have a reputation as being one of the best and I guess rapid promotions come with it."

McMillan chuckles. Clearing his throat, asks, "What can I do for you, sir?"

As Buchanan was about to speak, a large robust staff sergeant steps through the door behind the service counter, standing in front of Buchanan.

Working on paper work behind the wall divider and hearing the entire conversation, the staff sergeant greets Buchanan, "Good morning, sir."

"Good morning, Staff Sergeant." said Buchanan. "This is Sergeant -"

Interrupting Buchanan, the staff sergeant declared, "I know Jackson. How you doing?"

Jackson nodded nervously in the affirmative.

The sergeant looked Jackson down one side and down the other and said with a broad smile, "I see you're spreading love this tour instead of being the killing machine you're known for, huh?"

Looking at Jackson, a puzzled Buchanan mulled over what 'killing machine' might confer.

Jackson obviously withheld some of his past from Buchanan, keeping to himself what might be self-conscious and bashful for Jackson to render of his years prior to becoming a Christian. There were facets within his past he was not proud of and wanted to keep those things from Chaplain Buchanan. New converts of a faith are embarrassed and ashamed of things of the past. All Jackson wanted Buchanan to know of him was his new life as a believer in Jesus and as a person of compassion and love.

"It's Staff Sergeant Frank Burnside, right?" asked Buchanan.

"That's right chaplain." said Burnside. "Jackson and I know each other from his first two tours, don't we, Jackson? We have great memories don't we? Vietnam won't be the same after we've been here, will it?"

A grinning Burnside gives a stern glance toward Buchanan and Jackson.

Nervous trepidation plastered itself all over Jackson's face as he stood in front of the two men. Jackson prayed his friend would not spill the beans to Buchanan of his past behaviors.

Jackson remained silent.

Buchanan asked, "You're from the Steel City, aren't you? We met in Da Nang back in the summer. You remember?"

Burnside nodded in the affirmative.

"Your family's in the steel workers industry. Aren't they?" commented Buchanan.

"Yes, sir." answered Burnside.

"Well, a family who works in the steel industry and from the Steel City. Great combination, don't ya think?" asked Buchanan.

"I seem to think so, sir. You have a good memory chaplain. And you're from Ohio?" asked Burnside.

"Yep. The Buckeye state."

Burnside once again looked over Jackson down one side and down the other with a broad smile on his face.

Glancing toward Buchanan, Burnside says, "You know what a buckeye is, sir."

Buchanan sighs. And says with a smirk and half-hearted, "*No*, sergeant."

Burnside glances back at Jackson, knowing he's a Buckeye and said, "A worthless nut." He chuckles at his own joke.

Jackson shakes his head, smirks grudgingly and changes the conversation.

"Frank, we're here for a favor." entreated Jackson abruptly.

Burnside ponders what it could be and asks, "What can I do for you, chaplain?"

"Well, truth is - I need a jeep."

Burnside scoffs, then chuckles.

Buchanan leans closer to Burnside and says, "Need a jeep Sergeant. Jackson who wants to spread love now -" as Buchanan grins, says, "can't if he's minus a jeep. The transportation to reach men in the deep crevices of the jungle bush at a moment's notice, Sergeant, well - is absolutely necessary for us to hold services out there."

With a momentary pause, Buchanan leans back and asks in his Kentuckian accent, "You have a jeep sitting around for us to do our job?"

Slowly, Burnside smiles from ear to ear.

"Chaplain, jeeps are hard to come by." commented Burnside.

Buchanan asked, "Well, what if I do something for you? I can see if, well - I can get you a pass, cigarettes, maybe some extra rations, anything you want."

Nodding no the whole time spent while Buchanan was wheeling and dealing, Burnside smiles and says bluntly, "I can already scrounge for any of that. All that's penny ante."

Jackson offered, "What if we'd wheel and deal for some automotive parts to work on vehicles?"

"No deal. Friends in Da Nang can get me anything." responded Burnside. "Philip, I'll tell you what I really want and could use."

"What?" responded Jackson.

"Well Philip. I need, well uh, I need, well - 4 AK-47's. That's, well - what I want." answered Burnside.

Buchanan smiled, chuckled, and thought to himself, 'Yep. This is a marine. A real marine.'

"You have a jeep or not?" asked Jackson. Pointing with his thumb toward Buchanan says, "Needs a straight answer, Frank."

Burnside glances toward Buchanan. "Chaplain, you find me 4 AK-47's and I'll get you a jeep."

"Well, Burnside, we're going to get you those AK-47's. You can count on it. If it's the last thing I do, I'm gonna get you those weapons." said Buchanan with a bit of assurance in his voice.

For whatever reason Burnside desired the AK-47's, Buchanan didn't ask. Buchanan quickly discovered you asked little fool hardy questions in Vietnam when wheeling and dealing supplies.

"We'll be back Sergeant. Have a good day." said Buchanan.

"See you around Frank." added Jackson.

"Yeah, we'll see you Philip. Now the Jesus person. Haha hahaha!" quipped Burnside.

Jackson grins.

The spiritual team turns, exiting automotive set out for ordnance with great enthusiasm and determination.

The day embarked on coming across a jeep and the reality of attaining a mode of transportation was one step closer.

SERGEANT MCELRATH

OCTOBER 13, 1968

Discipline and professionalism depicted Gunnery Sergeant John McElrath - most senior marine in ordnance and 'gun ho' representing the esprit de corps of the United States Marine Corps. Requesting from him, 4 AK-47's stood comparable to asking an exterminator for rat poison, but possessing their own jeep was well worth the petition. A no-nonsense marine veteran for 29 years, he saw action in World War II and Korea embedding a salty, pungent war veteran. Eyeing retirement just around the corner from the military was coming soon for McElrath. As a disciplinarian, he insisted first and foremost strict military bearing in the ordnance office. The danger of one knucklehead's mistake could cause marines getting killed in handling arms and munitions. Armament was not the department for hose heads or lamebrains to hang around.

Jackson and McElrath were good friends from days past. It will help matters asking for the weapons. Regardless of an age gap, a friendship widened from common interests.

Acquiring weapons from McElrath presented a task reflective of climbing Mount Everest and Jackson knew it, but manageable if offered the best possible deal.

An AK-47 was a Soviet manufactured semi-automatic and fully automatic weapon. An assault weapon, it fired 600 rounds per minute with a 7.62-mm projectile with the capacity of inflicting heavy damage upon the enemy if used properly. The AK-47 was the basic weapon of the NVA, and its distinct crackling burst of fire recognized when fired.

Arriving at ordnance, between the center of camp and the back side of Camp Love, the spiritual team takes a deep breath, as Jackson hinted, "Well, here she goes, sir."

As they entered the front entrance of ordnance, a service counter identical to automotive stood smack dab in front of them, with two desks sitting behind the smooth service counter.

Buchanan noticed immediately adult posters and calendars plastered all over the walls and profanity scribbled from one corner of the room to the other, something he could do little about. The adult material and profanity seemed trivial compared to the bigger picture – the war. Nonetheless, in Buchanan's estimation, it displayed an unkept office, and exhibited space neglecting military bearing.

A private, John Sims, known as Taxi, stood up and welcomed the visitors.

"Good morning, chaplain, sir. Sergeant, good morning. How can I help you all?" asked Sims.

"Yes, we're here to ask a favor, private." responded Jackson.

Sims smiled and asks, "What do you want, Sarge?"

Struggling with the words to say, Buchanan said, "Well, uh, w-we need - well. We need -"

Buchanan motioned towards Jackson who requested, "Can we speak to Gunnery Sergeant McElrath?"

"He isn't here?" responded Sims.

"Where is he?" asked Jackson.

Buchanan interjected, "We need to talk to him, Private. To ask a favor of him. You see-" interrupting him, Jackson nudged Buchanan with his elbow and said, "Uh-um."

"Well, he should be back from…." Sims paused as he heard the side door open in the back of the ammo room, with a loud, solid hit of wood coming together as the screen door closed shut.

Taking off his cover, McElrath hangs it on the hat rack behind the wall in the ammo room and walks down to the entrance into the service room. Entering the room, he steps behind the service counter and notices Jackson immediately. Shocked from his different outward appearance, McElrath caught his mouth wide open, catching flies.

With a deep, commanding, steely voice, McElrath asks, "Jackson? Is *that you*?"

"Yes, it's - it's me." responded Jackson.

"What the heck happened?" McElrath knew Jackson as a non-believer.

"Well, I - I changed a bit." responded Jackson.

"*A bit*? How 'bout a whole lot from where I'm standing." proclaimed a surprised McElrath.

Bewildered, Buchanan again ponders Jackson's life prior to his conversion.

"I can *see* a change, Philip." exclaimed McElrath.

"I suppose it'd be loft for me to ask if you want some beer tonight and get drunk, huh?" inquired McElrath.

Buchanan grins as Jackson stands silently still.

"Let me take a look at you." said McElrath. The Gunnery Sergeant steps out from behind the counter to get a better gaze at Jackson.

Looking from top to bottom at his friend, McElrath expressed nothing but delight in his demeanor with Jackson's new appearance.

At first, Buchanan thought of McElrath as mocking, but realized the old, salty Gunny genuinely received what stood in front of him.

Clean cut all over, Jackson exemplified impressive military bearing and a sturdy confidence in himself. McElrath had never seen Jackson so imposing.

"Well, well. What do you know? You look so, well - so..."

"Well - so *what*? What John?" asked Jackson curiously.

The gritty gunnery sergeant pondered a moment for the correct words.

"Different. No, that's not the word - new. Yeah, that's - no, that's not it either. Not the same? Distinct? No, that's not it either." pondered McElrath.

Thinking with a pause - "Genuine. That's it! Genuine. Authentic."

Jackson sighed and smiled with pride at the assessment of him from his friend.

"Yes, John. Genuine. And believe me, it's real. I never been more satisfied with life than today." replied Jackson.

McElrath said with conviction, "I'm pleased. Very pleased. If you didn't start taking care of yourself, you were going to drink yourself to death. But please, don't start into me. Christianity's for some, but not me. I like my life just the way it is, thank you very much." commented McElrath with affirmation.

Listening to the conversation, Buchanan observed Jackson and now realized his life in the past was destructive, useless. He interrupted the reunion of old friends and said, "I hate to break up the reunion Gunny, but Jackson and I have some business to take care of."

Buchanan leans toward McElrath and asserts, "OK, let's get to the business at hand. We need something, and we need it fairly quickly."

"I don't think we've met, have we? Chaplain -" McElrath noticed Buchanan's name on his uniform, "Buchanan, is it?"

McElrath then set his personal perimeters and delivered a tangent, "Well, chaplain, *sir*, Sergeant Jackson here can tell ya I've lacked quite a bit of luck with chaplains in the past. They've been, well, most annoying to me. They're a pain in the neck. I've met chaplains for 30 years, wouldn't shut up about becoming a quote unquote 'believer.' Chaplains have been the worst magpie's I've known in the military. If I were you, I would just turn around and get out."

Buchanan sighs and is about to say something, when McElrath beat him to the punch, "I don't mean to be rude, sir. But I'm an independent thinking man, and nobody -" McElrath glances toward Jackson pausing says, "and I mean, nobody is going to order me how to live."

Jackson sighs and petitioned, "Look, John, all we-"

"No, wait." interrupted McElrath. "I need to tell you all this. Since we'll be seeing each other from time to time here in the camp. You see, *sir*, I smoke, drink a lot o' beer, and especially, *especially* love women, and I don't want some stiff-necked chaplain to tell me how horrible a person I am. So Philip, my friend, you and your chaplain friend can just leave. If that's your purpose, you can just forget it.

Good to meet you *sir*, but I like beer and my love for the opposite sex. Good day, sir."

McElrath turned, stepped around the other side of the service counter, and Jackson clarified his role - "John, I work with Chaplain Buchanan. My third and last tour, and my MOS is being the chaplain's bodyguard and his assistant. And we're not here to 'convert' you."

"You're not?" asked McElrath.

"No, we're not. Gunnery Sergeant." added Buchanan. "What we're here for is to ask for - "

"Uh - chaplain, please." interrupted Jackson. "John, what we need is - well. To be quite frank, we need 4 AK-47's. That's right - 4 AK-47's."

Smiling slightly, the spiritual team showed anticipation for an answer. Private Sims scoffed and chuckled.

McElrath, stoic with the notion, stared at Jackson. He shifted his eyes back and forth onto the spiritual team. Finally, setting his eyes on Buchanan, who had nothing but anticipation and worry on his face.

Buchanan waited patiently for an answer.

A slow, methodical grin emerged upon the face of McElrath toward the chaplain, turning into a deliberate smile with purpose. A friendly grin on Buchanan's face emerges with an expectant answer.

With a smirk, McElrath asked, "Let me get things straight in my mind. You're not here today to convert us sinners here in the ordnance department? All you want is 4 AK-47's?"

McElrath laughs slowly, turning into an immense, uncontrollable laugh which Taxi joins in laughing, dropping his head onto his desk. McElrath flops back into a swivel chair behind a second desk.

Perplexed, Buchanan finds himself bewildered of what sort of spark could ignite such behavior. The spiritual team glance at each other, shrugging their shoulders, and grimacing from sheer frustration.

Was it a bad sign? What did this peculiar behavior mean? Was the spiritual team getting the weapons or not?

Fixated on McElrath and Sims laughing exceedingly, the spiritual team found themselves impatient. The spiritual team sought to seriously wheel and deal for a jeep, and these two 'yahoos' were making a joke out of it.

Jackson, the gritty, combat experienced marine, discovered a rage building within himself which he gave up when becoming a Christian. The rage spoke volumes to beat the crap out of both men. However, his new found patience believers give talked him out of beating the boorish behavior out of both of them.

The laughter seemed an eternity. The unpredictable, baffling behavior finally ended, and McElrath and Sims calmed down.

As the two easily humored marines quieted down, Buchanan expected a negative response for his request.

McElrath stood up leisurely from his swivel chair, still snickering, and asked the chaplain, "Chaplain, can I tell you something?"

"Sure, McElrath." said Buchanan.

"Do ya know what you've done for me today, sir?" asked McElrath.

With a temporary pause, Buchanan softly uttered, "No."

"You've restored my deep, strong conviction in human beings. Ya really have."

"How's that, John?" asked Jackson.

"Philip. Chaplain. Human beings are innately selfish and brutish. Hobbes was right, wasn't he?" stated McElrath. "Yes, I'm self educated. I know who Hobbes is."

Taken aback, Buchanan knew exactly what McElrath meant.

"Sergeant." Buchanan looked at him with a stern glare and a slight grin. "Can we have those AK-47's?"

McElrath chuckled a bit and asked, "Why?"

"Why what, John?" asked Jackson.

"Why do you need the weapons?"

Buchanan answered, "Well -" he paused, looking straight into McElrath's eyes quipped, "why ask such brutish human beings such a question?" Buchanan paused and added, "What do you use weapons *for*?"

McElrath smiled from ear to ear. "I like you, chaplain. I really do. You come into my work space, asking for weapons to kill other human beings, and not once an attempt to convert me. That's a first, sir." He turns to Sims and admitted, "No other chaplain has ever done that before, have they, Taxi?"

"No, they haven't Gunny." confirmed Sims.

McElrath revealed, "I *like* you, Buchanan. You're going to work out, sir." He paused and thought for a moment. "I tell you what, since you've made my day humoring me and you're a friend to someone who I consider one of the most trustworthy men I've ever known. I'm going to get you those weapons, chaplain. I don't know why you need 'em, but whatever the reason, I know you will put them to good use."

"Really? You're really going to get them for us?" Buchanan asked.

"Amen!" said the spiritual team as they shook each other's hands.

The spiritual team extends their hands to McElrath and Sims out of gratitude, as the marines reciprocate the handshakes. McElrath said, "I'll have the weapons for you tomorrow. Taxi, ya know what to do. Get the ball rolling."

"Yes, sergeant." replied Sims.

"That soon? Tomorrow?" inquired Buchanan, surprised.

"Yes *sir*, chaplain. You're going to learn fast out here in the bush: it's don't ask, don't tell." declares McElrath.

"Besides, I owe this mutual friend of ours. I owe him, well, more than this. This little favor will not even come close to owing him what I do."

Jackson glances nervously toward McElrath and said, "You're my friend, John. Thanks! And in the past, well - I'd do it again. You know that."

McElrath nods and smiles, shaking Jackson's hand once again.

Jackson shared a past with McElrath as an unbeliever in a far-away place, in a faraway culture. Some things in life are best not to speak of again.

For now - all Buchanan cared about was getting the 4 AK-47's, and he got them.

All extend good byes and handshakes and the spiritual team thank McElrath for the AK-47's for the last time.

Exiting ordnance and far enough from earshot, Buchanan disclosed with a smile, "Ya know Sergeant Jackson, I think that if we went in there attempting to convert that marine, we wouldn't have gotten the 4 AK-47's."

"You know something chaplain, you're right." responded Jackson.

Pinching tobacco out of his pouch and placing it in his mouth to chew to his heart's content, Buchanan adds, "No telling what he'll think of me once he sees me put this in my mouth."

Chuckling, Buchanan lifts his tobacco pouch up in front of them.

"You know something else, Philip?" said Buchanan.

"No, sir."

"The marine back there doesn't know it yet, but I think we're going to convert him one day." said Buchanan with a smile. "Maybe, even Taxi."

Grinning, Jackson affirmed. "Amen chaplain. Amen."

"Yep, Amen."

The next morning, Buchanan woke up, read his morning devotional, prayed, and prepared himself for a day of ministry. The last two weeks in the bush had amounted to riding 'shotgun' to and from the camp. He was sick of it. Mobility was key in delivering appropriate Communion services for the men. And the fact he lacked a jeep for independent mobility gnawed at his gut to no end.

He was to meet Jackson for breakfast, then set off into the jungle with a caravan of troops to conduct services for Delta and Alpha Companies, again having to ride shotgun. He grabbed his cover and his chaplain's manual and turned the knob on his hootch door, and upon exiting the hootch, sitting in front of him was a sight which overwhelmed him inside.

Smack dab in front of Buchanan sat a jeep, a beautiful, gorgeous jeep. Leaning against the engine hood posed a smiling Jackson, with folded arms and crossed leg.

Grinning, Jackson said, "No more shotgun. It's nothing but 24/7 service from here on out."

LIZARD FRIENDS

OCTOBER 15, 1968

The time for Major Burns to play his selection for the night has arrived deciding to end the day playing the Septet in E-flat major for winds and strings by Ludwig Von Beethoven.

A perfect piece of music to end the day. The piece did nothing but soothe the heart and speak to the mind. The night ended up as an evening tranquil, peaceful.

Buchanan's day ended as a taxing 24 hours. He prayed the music will generate tolerable dreams and prevent waking up with the Devil.

Casualties filled the day. Company A suffered one killed and 14 wounded while on patrol. Buchanan hated casualties. The marine killed came from Topeka, Kansas. Buchanan will miss him. He enjoyed his company and presence. The young marine had been popular in camp and will be missed.

Incident after incident, one after the other, came from all directions, leaving Buchanan exhausted. A day Major Porch complained to Lieutenant Colonel Lucas that Buchanan sought to proselytize marines, attempting to further 'Southern Baptist membership' - a notion which infuriated Buchanan.

If a marine became a believer through ministry, Buchanan declared 'Glory to God'. As a firm advocate in religious liberty, he guided the new believer to choose membership of a Christian denomination based on individual choice. The young marine declared a denominational affiliation when joining the military, and usually attached himself to that faith group when becoming a believer.

If a marine found Salvation in Jesus and it offended someone, Buchanan thought, as a good sailor would say, "Oh well." If not, at least he planted a seed.

Buchanan listened to Beethoven's septet, intentionally to ease tension in camp and eradicate an irritable mood.

Enjoying the music, Buchanan retrieved his Bible for his daily reading and devotion for the evening, followed by a prayer. Finishing his devotion and Bible reading, he pulled off the bookshelves a western novel.

Buchanan read for about 40 minutes, as the septet was about to end. He immensely enjoyed the western novel, but exhaustion set in and his cot called for him to rest. The novel will have to wait. Besides, he didn't want to finish the novel drowsy.

He donned his sweats and night shirt for the evening, along with his boots, to protect him from the dangerous, natural elements of Vietnam.

For some odd reason, a creepy, crawly feeling in the air came over him. Buchanan hated snakes and this night he bordered on the paranoia that snakes were about. The hatred for snakes, especially the bamboo vipers, set loose too many day dreams this night for him to lie down comfortably and fall asleep. As a believer, the word hate came as a four letter word in the Buchanan house. Within the family unit, words such as dummy, moron, stupid, idiot and others, including hate, were prohibited from saying. However, Buchanan boiled it down that the toleration for even the utterance of the word hate came down to two uses of the expression - snakes and rival sports teams. Bamboo vipers were most deadly, and he had already seen a couple of marines killed by the snakes in the bush.

Marines dying because of a venomous snakebite occurred from time to time, with death after a snakebite. The phrase "two-step" in Vietnam referred to a snake bitten serviceman who took two steps before collapsing and dying.

Flipping off his ceiling and desk lights, he crawled into his cot, listening to the last bit of the septet.

As the music ended, Buchanan closed his eyes and attempted to gain some shut eye. Enjoying Beethoven's septet, he rendered it once again as best he could in his mind. Thinking of the music, he attempted to block the day out of his memory. However, he suddenly heard something move about in the darkness. A sound he had not heard before, a distinct sound coming from the floor of his hootch.

"Oh my Lord." he whispered in horror, "I hope and pray it isn't a snake. I *hate* those things."

Raising himself up, he cowered on his knees on top of his cot. He reached over toward his desk, which was at arm's length, and searched in the darkness for his desk light. Entering a nervous night, he felt all thumbs - knocking over practically everything on his desk. Pushing his calendar and a chaplain's instruction manual off the side onto the floor, he finally found the desk light, turning it on.

With the shedding of light, he cautiously stepped off his cot, searching for the intruder. He glanced under his desk, then around his bookshelf. He heard yet another small, but unnerving sound in the darkness. He's convinced something is in the hootch.

Buchanan cautiously steps to the upper right-hand drawer of his desk, retrieving his .45 caliber pistol.

He heard yet another movement on the surface of the floor, abruptly glancing at his metal chest he had brought along and nothing there.

Another thud, then a pause, and yet another bump heard. The space between thumps became shorter, closer together. Buchanan looked right and left haphazardly and still saw nothing.

He then examined the corners of his couch, bending down on all fours to take a peek underneath, discovering nothing!

Finally, in the corner of his eye, he spotted what appeared to be a reptile sticking out from under the desk. A green, long tail appeared clear. Buchanan definitely identified a reptile invading his domain.

Terror overwhelmed him.

Pointing his weapon toward the apparent green snake, he second guessed himself and thought otherwise of firing his weapon. Chaos would follow if he discharged his weapon, causing the marines to be disoriented, creating an illusion of enemy infiltration, arbitrarily and at random, firing their weapons in all directions, killing each other with friendly fire. He certainly did not want to be responsible for something so grave.

Buchanan laid his .45 caliber on his desk. He thought to himself - 'the doc can help me.' So he sought the help of the field hospital doctor to lend him a hand.

Lieutenant James Delaney administered his skills as the battalion doctor, a very proud Texan and a member of a traditional physician's family. As a superb physician and surgeon, the marines and sailors in camp had all the confidence in the world in Delaney.

Buchanan spoke softly. "Doc. Doc! Get over here." Again, movement in the dark, but still hidden from sight.

"Doc. Get over here." insisted Buchanan softly, in his strong Kentuckian accent.

Again, no response from Delaney's hootch, in earshot of Buchanan's domain.

"Dooooc. Please - wake up. Wake up! Get over here." pleaded Buchanan.

Still no response from Delaney.

"Doc, there's something in my hootch. A snake - a snake. There are vipers in here!" he whispered.

Buchanan reached over onto his desk to retrieve his letter opener for defense against the reptile. As he reached nervously for his letter opener, he knocked his desk lamp onto the floor and broke the bulb. "Rats!" Buchanan fumed.

Buchanan grasped the letter opener. With all means of light gone, he felt blind, feeling even more vulnerable. The letter opener, designed with a marine insignia on the handle end, made with solid steel and trimmed with marine corps colors, made Buchanan, as silly as it seems, feel safe, protecting him from any intruder.

He stepped back up onto his cot.

Nothing else to do now but cry for help. Whispering, Buchanan said, "Doc. Doc!" He continued with his soft pleas for Delaney to wake up.

Buchanan finally heard a drowsy response from a man waking up from a good night's sleep, "What? What is it? Who - what's the matter? What's that noise?"

"Doc, it's me, it's me. Chaplain Buchanan. Get over here. I got snakes." whispered Buchanan.

"What? Who? Is that you, Padre?" answered Delaney softly. "Snakes? What? Seriously? I'm on my way."

Discombobulated, Delaney slipped on his combat boots, grabbing his machete. Quietly walking over to Buchanan's hootch, he slowly makes his way up the steps to the entrance, and slowly opens the hootch door.

With the near full moon shining through the window, Delaney had enough light to recognize Chaplain Buchanan cowered on his cot, chuckling at the sight. "Chaplain Buchanan, you look scared stiff."

Smiling, Delaney flipped his small flashlight on.

"I've got vipers all over the place in here. I'm telling you the truth." whispered Buchanan boldly.

"OK, OK chaplain. I'll look." said Delaney quietly.

Sizing up the place, he combed the room with his flashlight, locating under the desk not a snake, but a lizard, possibly a Chinese Water Dragon. Not only did the Doc discover one reptile - but two!

"Chaplain." uttered Delaney. "It's not snakes, it's reptiles, possibly Chinese Water Dragons. You know, lizards."

"Lizards? You're kidding? No - No!" Buchanan answered with defiance. "A reptile is a reptile. No reptiles period. Get those things out of here. Get 'em out."

Delaney fights back his laughter. Smiling, Delaney advised his friend, "Listen to me, Padre. They're your friends. They'll deter other reptiles from hanging around the hootch you don't want. Like vipers. Besides, they eat tons of insects and worms - who are, as you and I both know, are just one thing - pests. Now, what do you want hanging around in here? Reptiles? Or insects? Or vipers slithering around?"

Buchanan paused, pondering the circumstance he was in. "I don't know, Doc. A lizard for a pet? I've never had one. I'd be afraid they'd try to gnaw on me at night!"

Delaney chuckles softly. "I have a giant house gecko and a couple of Chinese Water Dragons that hang around my hootch myself. Listen chaplain, get down off the cot and come look at 'em. They're harmless."

Buchanan stepped cautiously onto the floor of his hootch, slowly peeping around his desk, catching his eyes on the two robust reptiles. Swallowing hard, he takes a good hard gander at them. Buchanan didn't care if the geckos were plain ordinary lizards. He thought, 'reptiles are reptiles. Period.'

"Why haven't I seen them before?" inquired Buchanan.

"They're diurnal."

"What?" asked Buchanan.

"I said - they're *diurnal.*" answered Delaney.

"You mean, Doc, they're only active in the daytime?"

"Yep. You probably never saw 'em until tonight because you're hardly ever here. You're out ministering to the troops."

"Yeah. *Yeah.*" pondered Buchanan.

Intrigued, Buchanan asked Delaney, "And ya say they'll take care of the insects and the vipers?"

"Yep. Well - the insects. The vipers might be more of a challenge, but their mere presence is a deterrent."

"I suppose they're better than the vipers and the insects." said Buchanan. "And I suppose if they're going to be part of the family, I might as well name 'em."

"Listen, chaplain. I've got to hit the sack, man. We've had a long day, remember? Good night chaplain." said Delaney. As he turns, he looks over his shoulder, and informs Buchanan, "Don't forget to wear your boots at night, chaplain. The dragons love human toes." Noticing a terrified grimace on Buchanan's face, he walks quietly back to his hootch, grinning the whole way.

Grinning, Buchanan sighs heavily, knowing Delaney is egging him on.

Delaney laughs heartily before falling to sleep. Plastered all over his mind were images of Buchanan crouched on top of his cot, terrified.

Buchanan, sitting on the edge of his cot staring at the reptiles for at least 5 minutes, debated on whether to keep'em. Regardless of the fact the lizards guarded Buchanan from centipedes, insects and vipers - the wary sense for reptiles he sustained within himself stood in the way as a drawback to permit the lizards to live and roam in his hootch.

Pondering a short time longer, he kept them. The thought of vipers, centipedes, and creepy crawlies running around in his hootch determined for him in his mind the lizards were worth keeping.

The deliberation considering two names for the dragons took some thought, as Buchanan finally decided on Arthur and Churchill. He chose his two favorite English generals, The Duke of Wellesley and The Duke of Marlborough. He held high their military accomplishments and sense of tactics and strategy, admiring them greatly. He reflected on the dragon's prowess of defending the hootch against snakes and insects were as good as The Duke of Wellington's and The Duke of Marlborough's military prowess.

Buchanan swept up the broken glass from the light bulb and changed the bulb in the desk lamp. He crawled back into his cot and constantly popped up to see where the 'critters', as he occasionally referred to them, were. As he popped his head up for a few minutes, thinking where the dragons were, he found himself nervous and antsy knowing the reptiles were in the hootch with him.

He thought - 'if the dragons were in his hootch for two weeks, unaware of their presence as the doc said, he might as well relax and go to sleep.'

As Buchanan fell asleep, the reptiles were now here to stay. Overtime, Arthur and Churchill became pets and friends to Buchanan, becoming part of the family so to speak, and living in Buchanan's hootch until his very last day in Vietnam. Fruit, wrapped up in a napkin from leftover scraps from Buchanan's plate from the chow hall, served as treats for his new found reptile friends. The lizards, overtime, will be treated as family dogs back home. Dachshunds they were not, but would do until he got home.

Buchanan gained with confidence a sense of protection from snakes, centipedes, and insects with Arthur and Churchill in the hootch. A sense of security and comfort set in for Buchanan, especially for the centipedes, huge and intimidating - reflecting a small animal to Buchanan. Arthur and Churchill served as a natural exterminator against the "bugs" as Buchanan referred to them, and as a great means of coping with the war. One fear, however, his newfound friends were incapable of ridding Buchanan of – his constant fear of nightmares.

THE VETERINARIAN

OCTOBER 16, 1968

After eating breakfast at 0730 hours with Jackson, Buchanan made his way back to his hootch to do a little reading prior to visiting the departments in camp.

Vivaldi's *Four Seasons,* one of Burns' favorite pieces of music, ended up last evening's piece to soothe the soul and soften the heart. The camp's mood certainly softened, lightening the men's hearts prior to falling asleep listening to Vivaldi.

Pleased with waking up minus the nightmares, Buchanan felt grateful for the welcomed distraction of the music.

Buchanan's dreams were of home. The setting of the first dream centered on the Great Depression. A young Buchanan stood fishing along the banks of the Ohio River below a bridge he occasionally jumped off of into the river in Middleport and Pomeroy, Ohio, which crossed over into beautiful West Virginia, the city of Mason. If discovered by his father he took part diving off the bridge, harsh punishment followed as a result, and deservingly so acting in such precarious behavior. In the dream, he caught an enormous fish large enough to feed the people of Middleport and Pomeroy for months. The dual riverfront towns were of poor, hardworking to middle-class people, and evidence of an impressive work ethic enabling them to overcome the Great Depression.

His next dream found yet another setting during the Great Depression. The Buchanan clan packed up a picnic meal, traveling a short distance southwest down Route 7 adjacent to the Ohio River to Gallipolis, Ohio to a popular state park along the river bank. The abundance of picnic food, even for the Depression, consisted of hot dogs, hamburgers, chips, potato salad, and so forth, the typical picnic food for the Buchanan clan. The setting of the dream proved an oddity due to many family members in the dream were born after the Depression. His children, his brothers and their children, and other family members were present, eating and enjoying one another's company. Abruptly in the dream, individual strangers came joining the picnic, then whole groups of families welcomed to eat at the Buchanan's table. The strangers were raggedly and scantly dressed, all hungry for food to consume in the middle of the Great Depression. Droves of families and individuals seemed to gather around the family. The family continued to provide sustenance for those who were hungry. The family handed hot dogs, coming from nowhere, to one person after the other from a line that never seemed to end to those with empty stomachs. Buchanan distributed a never ending supply of bagged chips to every man, woman, and child in need of nourishment.

The night's end of odd dreams ceased only when reveille came calling.

'Why these dreams?' he asked himself.

One plausible explanation might be the constant everyday observation of the hunger and struggle of the Vietnamese people to make ends meet in South Vietnam. Experiences most Americans will rarely undergo.

Leaning back in his swivel chair, Buchanan stared out the side window of his hootch, thinking of the previous night's dreams and how great it would be to drive to Da Nang, hop on a plane, and fly to Ohio and fish in the river as he did as a boy.

His mental state imagined himself in Ohio sitting on the front porch taking in the cool breeze of the October cool air, reaping the benefits of fall of the Tri-State area while being forced to tolerate the horrid heat of South Vietnam. He envisioned the beautiful brown, orange, red, and yellow colors of leaves on tree branches along the rolling hills of the Ohio River. And the cool air flowing in the crisp, comfortable morning temperatures carrying over into the late afternoon.

Buchanan found himself in a deep reminisce of his Ohio days growing up, when a loud, firm knock on the door interrupted his concentration.

'Who could this be?' he thought. It being rare anyone came this early in the morning to visit.

"Chaplain Buchanan?" came an unfamiliar voice.

"Who goes there?" ordered Buchanan.

With a quick chuckle, the stranger says, "It's Private Miguel Rodriquez. I'm Private Rodriquez from Bravo Company. Can I come in, sir? Sir, I can come later, sir."

"Yes, Private Rodriquez. I'm here. Wait just a minute. The door's latched and locked."

Leaping up from his swivel chair, Buchanan stepped over and unlatched the door fastener, welcoming Rodriquez, standing in front of him smiling from ear to ear, and thrilled to no end to be in Buchanan's presence.

"Well, Private Rodriquez, what can I do for you this morning? Ya look as if you're excited about *something*? Well, come in. Come in."

As Rodriquez stepped into the hootch, he explained, "Well, sir. I-I am. I mean - I am excited. The two lizards you have living with you, well, that's why I'm here."

"The lizards? That's why you're here? Well, I - why?" asked Buchanan.

"Doc Delaney sent me over. He briefed me on your two new friends living with you. I know a little about animal behavior. I worked part-time back home in California for a veterinarian. That's what I want to be someday - a vet. If I get out of Vietnam in one piece, that is." grins Rodriquez.

"I love animals. Doc Delaney thought I might be of some help to you." added Rodriquez with some urgency in his voice.

"Oh, OK. Yes. I'm thrilled you're here, Private Rodriquez. I could use some pointers." Buchanan mentions in jest, "I've never believed in my life I'd be living with reptiles."

The men chuckle at the thought.

Rodriquez observed everything he could lay his eyes on in Buchanan's hootch, inquisitive on the contents of the chaplain's office. Glancing at all four corners of Chaplain Buchanan's quarters, he noticed most notably the pictures of his family and his bookshelf. Rodriquez lifted his right eyebrow from surprise, noticing the military history books and western novels, as Buchanan noticed the surprise in Rodriquez's eyes.

"I've never been in a chaplain's hootch before. It seems quite normal." said Rodriquez. "I've been told since I've been a youngster, 'the contents of a man's abode expose the mind a man possesses.' It's reveals what is in the inside of a man, you know - in his heart."

All the while, Buchanan stares straight at Rodriquez.

Embarrassed, Rodriquez attempts to change the subject. "Well, sir - the lizards. Where are the lizards?"

Guessing Rodriquez's thoughts, Buchanan asked with a grin, "What'd you expect in a chaplain's hootch, private?"

Rodriquez shrugged his shoulders, grinning, and humbly answers, "To be honest, sir. I didn't exactly know what to expect."

"You know, Private. I notice you run the play dumb bit with your fellow marines. You're a lot smarter than what you want them to know. Aren't you?" asked Buchanan.

Pausing, Rodriquez admits, "Well, sir. Well - yeah, I guess I do. I prefer the low profile status. I'm a little like you, sir. You don't like a lot of attention, either. Though you get some, it's just because of who you are."

Buchanan turned his head toward the right, smiling, as if impressed by Rodriquez's observation.

"Like me?" asked Buchanan.

"Sir, I notice you. You don't mind me saying sir - you do the same thing. The other officers, you know, the ones who point out how everyone else looks bad in order that they look good. I know you loathe the very thought of what they do to others - hurting someone else just to get ahead."

"I'll tell you the truth, Private Rodriquez. I wouldn't give ten cents for the rude, obnoxious men within the enlisted or officer ranks I've met through the years."

"Me neither, sir. Me neither."

"I've always attempted to keep an arm's length from people who work for the Devil. People who are arrogant." added Buchanan.

"Me too, sir. Me too."

"Well, enough for now of how we despise the total depravity of man. The lizards, remember?" said Buchanan.

"Yes, sir. The lizards. Yes, that's right. What do they look like?" asked Rodriquez.

Buchanan pondered the question for a moment and answered, "Well, I saw 'em in the dim light. It was dark, so to identify them will be difficult. But here she goes. They were large, but the length was maybe 20 to 25 inches or *more*, including the tail. From the snout to the, uh - what do you call where the torso of a lizard ends and the tail begins?" asked Buchanan.

"The vent, sir. The vent." answered Rodriquez.

"OK. Well, that might have been maybe 10 to 12, maybe 15 inches. The rest of the length was the tail. They were maybe green and red, with a little orange. Maybe a shade of black on both of them. Or was it brown? Anyhow, there was a dark color. Their underbellies had a shade of maybe blue or purple with even some white, along with its throat being black or blue." said Buchanan.

After Buchanan's brief description of the lizards, Rodriquez contemplated what the lizards might be.

"Did the reptiles have high horn scales running from its head to the base of its lateral tail?" asked Rodriquez.

"Why yes. Yes, they did."

"Did the tail seem flattened to you?" asked Rodriquez.

"That I couldn't tell. There wasn't enough light. But the tail was very long."

"Well, that's not a lot to go on, but what you have given me based on size and color, I would say they are just simple Chinese Water Dragons."

"That sounds very dangerous. They will not eat me at night, are they?" asked Buchanan in all seriousness.

Rodriquez smiled, holding back his laughter, declaring, "I doubt it, sir. Don't worry about 'em, sir. We're not on their menu. Their diet comprises eating insects, such as cockroaches and crickets, rodents, smaller lizards, even some birds and fish. They even cater to some vegetation and eggs. Besides, their presence might scare off some snakes at night."

"Some snakes?" questioned Buchanan, with some misgiving.

"Well, they definitely will not take on a boa constrictor, sir." joked Rodriquez, laughing. "But smaller snakes will reconsider coming into your quarters with a reptile who can defend itself fairly well. Anyhow, Doc Delaney sent me over here to reassure you the presence of the reptiles is a great help here in the jungle, sir."

"Well, if you say so, Rodriquez. Since I decided to keep'em, I've given them names, Arthur, after the Duke of Wellesley and Churchill, after the Duke of Marlborough. Two eminent men of military strategy and tactics." insisted Buchanan.

"Yes." bragged Rodriquez with conviction. "Wellesley had the smarts to outsmart Napoleon and Churchill, who led a victory against the French in the last attempt to invade the British Isles."

Impressed and pleased with Rodriquez's assessment of his two favorite military tacticians, Buchanan beamed with excitement. "Well, you understand military science. I love it."

"I've read the new book by David Horwarth, *Waterloo: A Near Run Thing.** It's comprehensive and informative." divulged Rodriquez with pride.

"Well, Rodriquez, I already knew you were ahead and above the rest, but I now know after your visit here today, you're foremost on my list to give you a little more room than others. If you know what I mean?" proclaimed Buchanan, with a smile.

Rodriquez smiles, shakes Chaplain Buchanan's hand and confirms, "Yes, sir, I do."

The two sit in Buchanan's two chairs chatting about military history for an hour, the love of animals, spirituality, the war, and families back home. Anything that came to mind.

Homesick for family and San Diego, California, his hometown, Rodriquez lacked a circle of friends in Camp Love.

Buchanan knew from experience, people who are lonely talk. And he talked. And talked and talked.

Buchanan just listened and occasionally got a word in. He didn't care, the thrill itself providing a brief space in time for Rodriquez to enjoy life and socialize amounted to all the gold in the world for him.

Jackson finally arrived to visit the camp departments, as Rodriquez's visit came to an end.

Jackson greeted Rodriquez with small talk, as Buchanan invited Rodriquez back to talk again one day.

"I'll be looking forward to it, sir." vowed Rodriquez. "The men I share a hootch with, well, we have little in common. They care for nothing but drinking, getting drunk, and listening to pop music on the radio all day."

Rodriquez added, "The visit really gave me a mental release. A chance to talk of things that intrigue me. I really appreciate you spending time with me, sir."

"You're very welcome, Rodriquez." commented Buchanan.

"Goodbye, sir. Goodbye, Sergeant." said Rodriquez, shaking hands with Buchanan.

"So long, Rodriquez." Buchanan responded.

Rodriquez departed Buchanan's hootch on his way to supply as Camp Love issued Bravo Company new equipment.

"That kid, as you would put it, sir, gets picked on something terrible." commented Jackson.

Buchanan, unyielding, gave Jackson a stern glance and pointed out, "Well, that kid, as you refer to him, is going to get some constructive attention from us. And *I* swear, if I hear one of the 'bully' marines, and there's plenty of 'em all over, call him anything but his name or something else or put his hand on Rodriquez.....I'll kick his backside myself."

Jackson noticed a look in Buchanan's eye he's never seen before. An expression of determination, temper, and resolve.

Jackson knew Buchanan meant it.

If a marine crossed him regarding Rodriquez, Jackson knew Buchanan could take care of himself.

If not, Jackson, in his own words, would "kick his ass."

SKAWINSKI

OCTOBER 18, 1968

When long away from home, human beings gravitate toward one another with basic common traits. A birthplace, origin, or region of the country are typical traits to pull together individuals into one group. Religious background, age or education level might contribute to the cohesion of strangers becoming friends. Even an interest in history, science, or sports adds to the gravitation of individuals coming together in a strange place. Regardless, human beings feel secure when grouped together based on related common traits.

One marine in particular, who loves his state and upbringing, will connect with Chaplain Buchanan immediately.

Corporal Adolphus Skawinski, born and raised in Preble County, Ohio outside Dayton, exemplified the typical Midwestern farm boy. His family-owned farm, one of the most productive dairy and vegetable farms in western Ohio, led the Midwest in innovative and pioneering cultivation and dairy farming technology. Cultivation ran within the bloodline, as his family farm goes back for three generations. His family were staunch Lutherans, especially his mother, who considered most other Protestants as "phonies". As a junior in college attaining his degree in engineering from a major university in the Miami, Ohio area, he volunteered to join the marines in 1965 to fight, as he would refer to them, the 'commies.'

Growing up on the family farm, a routine insisted on an early morning rise for the Skawinski clan to go to work. Habits are hard to break, whether in Vietnam or Ohio. Skawinski, up and at 'em every morning in Vietnam, welcomed every day greeting the sun with a cheery 'Good Morning'. Today was no different. The urgency to meet Buchanan ran high since arriving back into camp from a long, drawn out combat engineering patrol. Skawinski implored a staunch support of the chaplain's office. Center stage for the Skawinski clan revolved around church life, including Skawinski singing in the choir and volunteering in community involvement programs, such as feeding the poor and reaching out to young people as a mentor at the homeless shelter. His affiliation with the Lutheran Church strengthened his commitment and devotion to Jesus, strengthening his dedication and faithfulness to serve Christ, his Lord and God, through denominational efforts. Family tradition of military service shined brightly as his father served in the Army proudly during World War II, influencing Adolphus the vitality of the chaplain in the military, an essential source for creating high morale for the troops.

Skawinski ate an early, cheerful breakfast. He exhibited the most confident, forthright constitution for a young man, on his way to Chaplain Buchanan's hootch to introduce himself to the new chaplain. He arrived for his third tour in Vietnam a week earlier than Buchanan, and a tour requiring a three-week extension which bypassed Buchanan's departure date.

As he walked the short distance toward Buchanan's hootch, his thoughts turned to chaplains in the past he encountered in the marines. One Baptist chaplain did nothing but read his boating magazines and theology books in his office sent to him from home, hang out with fellow officers, and listen to Armed Forces Radio. Skawinski remembered on his way to Buchanan's hootch what his mother maintained concerning non-Lutheran Protestants, especially Baptists, that they are 'phonies', Methodists who could barely read. He wanted to know for himself if Buchanan was 'phony' or not. Skawinski himself did not really deem non-Lutheran Protestants as phonies, but he dearly loved his mother and didn't want to show any disrespect toward her. Being away from home long enough, Skawinski discovered genuine, 'born again' believers in all denominations, including Baptists denominations. Skawinski wanted to determine for himself the authenticity of Buchanan, now just moments away.

In the days Buchanan had been in Camp Love, Skawinski's demolition team completed a long patrol in the bush.

The young marine arrived at Buchanan's hootch at 0645 hours sharp, knocking on the door, and hearing a voice render, "Who goes there?" Grinning, he nodded his head in jest and announced, "A fellow Buckeye. Good enough?"

With raised eyebrows and bewildered, Buchanan failed to recognize Skawinski's voice.

Opening the door, Buchanan sets his eyes for the first time on Skawinski, standing in front of him on the top step, bearing a grin from ear to ear.

"Come in. Come in, marine."

Smiling, Skawinski extended his hand to Buchanan, introducing himself, "Good morning, Chaplain Buchanan. Good to meet you. I'm Corporal Adolphus Skawinski."

Shaking hands, Buchanan looked over the marine standing in front of him. Hiding his humor looking over Skawinski, Buchanan thought of him as a cross between a famous red headed puppet on a children's show of the 1950s, a smug teenager character from a late 1950s and 1960s television show of a young boy growing up, and one of Buchanan's favorite actors who usually played a tough guy and from a bounty hunter television show. Though tall and slender, Skawinski lacked the physique of a lanky young man. His keen intellect, added to his muscular frame, complimented the holistic human being he amounted to. His appearance lacked the display of the brawny, beefy, arrogant muscle builder type with no brains. He certainly wasn't the dumb jock type. Though an odd appearance to Buchanan, he still portrayed a handsome appearance and seized an interior of intelligence and aptitude. And yet, Buchanan took a quick notice of his eyes and the contour of his face. The young man presented a battle hardened, experienced marine of war.

"Good to meet you, Corporal." expressed Buchanan with a resilient mountain accent.

"Just wanted to come by and welcome you, chaplain."

"I appreciate it."

"Well, I hang out in the chaplain's office from time to time, if that's OK?" asked Skawinski inquisitively.

"Certainly is, Skawinski. I would appreciate the company."

Skawinski opened up, "Church life, well, it's an important part of my life, and, well, supporting the chaplain gives me some encouragement, a purpose while on duty. Helps me get through, well, the hardships of the day, so to speak."

"Well, thank you for your support, corporal. I agree - depending upon God's presence in a war zone helps matters, physically and emotionally. Have a seat, son."

Skawinski took a seat in front of the desk, while Buchanan stepped behind his desk, sitting in his swivel chair.

"Chaplain. I hope not to bother you. But just wanted to meet you. I want to support you in any way I can. To attend services, assist in any CAPs you might support. Whatever the need is."

"Well, thank you corporal." said Buchanan. "I've some chaplain friends who have a CAP or two already in place and set to support their CAPs. You can have some sort of role with them."

"Sure thing, chaplain."

The two conversed on the potential success of the CAPs.

Skawinski changed the subject and asked, "If you don't mind me asking, sir, but what denomination are you affiliated with again, sir?"

"Not at all Skawinski. I'm Baptist. Southern Baptist." Buchanan disclosed with confidence and conviction.

'Uh-oh!' Skawinski thought. 'The camp's got one. A 'loud mouth'. A 'You're going to go to Hell if you don't convert to my doctrine and theology.' A 'neo-Baptist' with no thought for anyone else.'

Skawinski, never taught to be rude, gave the nod, "Great Chaplain. I always welcome diversity in my religious life. The benefits of serving with other Christians in other denominations is a healthy endeavor."

"Amen!" said Buchanan.

Skawinski expected a long, drawn out explanation and received a simple 'Amen' instead.

Skawinski listened intently to Buchanan's answer to his probing question concerning Buchanan's approach as a chaplain and ministry to the men. Sensing Buchanan's sincerity as a chaplain acknowledged Skawinski's confidence in Buchanan, reaching the wants and needs of not only himself, but the entire camp.

Buchanan sensed Skawinski's query into his personal theology and approach to ministry. To ease his mind, he briefly offered Skawinski a personal history of his spiritual life, hinting at the notion of his firm conviction of ecumenicalism.

Skawinski heard the lowdown of Buchanan's life starting with his rough upbringing in Ohio and Kentucky. He began with his strict Presbyterian rearing during his childhood, along with his teenage years peppered with rebellion toward authority. The young Buchanan got in trouble in and out of school when finally the judge gave him an ultimatum, granting the young man a choice, "Robert, it's the Army, Navy - or jail." He certainly didn't want to sit in the middle of a reform school, so he chose the military. When entering the Air Force as a young seventeen-year-old, he discovered discipline and purpose in life. While in the military, a Southern Baptist, while stationed in Alabama, led him to the Lord, and he became a believer in Christ. Skawinski discovered Buchanan quit drinking and smoking, turning his life completely around for good instead of destructive behavior. While in the Air Force, the Lord called him into the ministry, and started college, though dropping out of high school at 17 as a sophomore, without a high school diploma. Completing his GRE prior to entering college, Buchanan discovered a whole new world in academia. What significantly intrigued Skawinski most came when Buchanan enrolled in the Lutheran seminary in Columbus, Ohio, graduating with a Master of Divinity in Theology from his own denomination's School of Theology. Buchanan's Lutheran training enthralled Skawinski to be the most impressive.

As Skawinski noticed Buchanan's wide experience and background, he discovered a man he could trust. In the past, Skawinski bumped into too many Baptist chaplains presenting themselves as exclusionist and "landmark" type of Baptists, and now thrilled to no end knowing Buchanan was far from attaining a smug attitude.

"You're alright, chaplain." boasted Skawinski. "Your background isn't typical, is it? Raised in one denomination, finding Jesus in another, and attending a seminary from a third not of your own. I don't think I've met a chaplain with that kind of background. No offense, sir, but I love it!"

"None taken, corporal. Thank you. My background helps when addressing the troops. And, I guess in my lifetime, I've found believers in all Christian denominations. But I *also* know for a fact there are church goers sitting in the pews every Sunday of all denominations who are as lost as a person in a raft in the middle of the Pacific."

The two laugh and nod in agreement.

Skawinski only wished his mother was sitting in Buchanan's hootch to soak in all of his personal life, his genuine persona. Skawinski heard a witness of Jesus through Buchanan's voice and words. Maybe hearing the chaplain's story might help her shake off her stereotypes of non-Lutherans.

A natural and immediate friendship between the two emerged, chatting about home and Ohio. The reminiscing of the Buckeye state sealed an immediate bond. And of course, the talk of football bonded any Ohioan away from home.

"I go to Ohio State football games frequently with my father, chaplain. It's a lot of fun." Skawinski informed Buchanan. "Have you ever been to a game, sir?"

"No. But I have family, a brother in particular, and friends who go from time to time." answered Buchanan.

"Maybe Dad and I can take you when we get back home."

"I'd like that."

"The Buckeyes have a chance to win it all this year and maybe end up voted number one. I'm excited." cheered Skawinski.

"Me too, Skawinski. Me too."

As the men enjoyed the football talk, Skawinski changed the topic and proudly talked about his family farm.

Buchanan listened intently to Skawinski's description of the farm. The shudders on the home resembled a Midwestern farm house out of a Norman Rockwell painting. The red barn sparkled for every visitor without a trace of chipped paint. The perfect rows of crops, representing various sorts of vegetables, aligned perfect in form and placement. Skawinski described every farm animal imaginable which walked the property of the farm, dozens of them, including horses, chickens, goats, and pigs. And, of course, the hundreds of dairy cows with a dozen or so employees to carry out the daily chores of a farm of such size and significance of the Skawinskis.

"My father owns the most productive dairy farm in the Midwest chaplain. It is the proudest part of my life, sir. If you ever get to see it, you'll see. It's beautiful!" boasted Skawinski.

"Amen!" added Buchanan. "I certainly want to see the farm someday, Skawinski. I'm sure it's land and a farm many long to acquire if so desired."

As a young man, Skawinski possessed the innate skill of a good judge of character and integrity of another man. After visiting Buchanan, he determined within himself Buchanan owned Christian character and integrity, along with a sincere desire to see the best for the troops.

"Well Chaplain Buchanan, I must go. Good to have met you. Thank you for your support to the men so far. I appreciate it. Great chaplains in the bush is a uplifting motivator to a marine, sir. Thanks again." encouraged Skawinski.

"Thank *you*. Have a great day, Corporal Skawinski."

Skawinski left Chaplain Buchanan's office, knowing he met a new friend he could depend on to lead him spiritually.

Sticks and Stones May Break My Bones, but Names Can Never Hurt Me

October 19, 1968

Listening to Antonio Vivaldi in the Tri-State area back home came across as nerdy as nerdy could get. The new found love of classical music pushed Buchanan to the limit to dive into deep waters, expanding his desire for more classical music. Day after day, Major Burns introduced Buchanan to oodles of new pieces of classical music and the musicians who wrote them. Since Buchanan arrived in the bush, Burns has exposed to Buchanan to pieces of music such as Vivaldi's 'concerto for guitar in D major', Vaughan Williams' 'Fantasia on a Theme by Thomas Tallis', Bizet's 'Carmen Suite', Tchaikovsky's Piano Concerto No. 1, and Arne Rodrigo's 'A Fantasy of a Gentleman.' Burns' nightly broadcast of classical music provided a whole new education for him. Nerdy or not, Buchanan enjoyed the fun every night at 2130 hours listening to the genre. He discovered a whole new world in his life. The Enlightenment, alive and well, again pushed itself deep into the 20th century to inspire yet another heart and mind to open up to the better things in life.

Buchanan had been vaguely familiar with Antonio Vivaldi before his Vietnam tour. Buchanan recognized the Four Seasons written by Vivaldi, hearing them from time to time to emphasize the four seasons in church or at a seasonal event.

The love of Vivaldi's music heightened for Buchanan. The month of October for Burns focused on Vivaldi, thinking no other composer showed forth the beauty of God's creation but through Vivaldi's music. In Burns' estimation, the splendor of God's design showed forth in October more than any other month. The variation of colors and the distinction of the fall showed no better than in the great state of West Virginia. For a West Virginian, nowhere else on the globe embodied the beauty of the stunning, beautiful, and breath-taking fall colors than a drive in the depths of the West Virginia mountains in the peak of fall. The breath-taking experience of emotions for a first timer laying their eyes upon the Creator's love of color in the mountains set a permanent mental picture.

Last night's selection featured *The Concerto for Two Violins in A Minor RV522*. Again, Buchanan seemed enlightened with the proficiency, brilliance, and skillfulness Vivaldi possessed within his heart and mind, along with the God given talent of composition. Music flowed within every vein of Vivaldi's body, attached to every molecule of his chemical makeup. The concerto had been foreign to Buchanan until last night, falling in love with what he heard.

The concerto consisted as a part of a collection of orchestral concertos called "Lestro Armonico". The collection turned out to be one of the most significant set of collected works in the first half of the Eighteenth Century. *The Concerto in A minor, RV 522*, the eighth concerto in the collection, composed of a three-movement piece of music focused on two violins comprising an orchestra emphasizing violins, violas, cellos, and the bass. The opening Allegro, commanding and energetic, displays soloists alternating in play with each other, but reflective of one another within the musical notes. The middle of the concerto, the central larghetto, written as a march, emphasized chords of the violin soloist in three romantic and expressive movements. The final allegro of the concerto proved the most moving for Buchanan. The end played out fast, full of sequences played simultaneously, leading to a climax of a sturdy and muscular tempo and pace. The succession of exchanging of instruments and notes serve as a final theme, with the two soloists feeding off of one another pushing toward a final immense cadence.

Buchanan gained a liking for Vivaldi. The composer calmed his nerves, and he longed for anything to deflect from all the rainfall for the month, flooding many areas around Camp Love. Buchanan never saw rain come down as hard and heavy since his arrival in April. The typhoon season in Vietnam lasts between July to November, while the heavy rainy season lasts between mid-April to mid-October. The dry season usually occurs between October to April. Hanoi in the north could have 68 inches a year, while the mountains received an annual average of 160 inches, and exceeding a peak of 160 inches from time to time. In Vietnam, Buchanan experienced monsoon type rains in which he could barely see 5 feet in front of himself.

Buchanan scampered off to Burns' hootch at 1730 hours to catch him before he left for duty. He wanted to know every detail of last night's piece of music. Who wrote it, the emphasis of the theme, and the climax of the last movement of the music. Buchanan had plenty of time to speak with Burns about the details of the piece of music.

Due to the heavy rain, the 7th Engineering Marine Battalion duties had been severely hampered. 16 inches of rain poured down on Camp Love in the past three days, preventing the battalion from carrying out their duties. Roads and bridges in the Da Nang TAOR (Tactical Area of Responsibility) were flooded out and impenetrable because of the heavy rains. The pouring rain completely washed away a fixed span bridge with trestle assemblies crossing the Cam Lo River.

On the 16th of October alone, 10.73 inches of rain fell onto the camp. The 17th and 18th marines received 3.24 and 3.00 inches, which created a muddy camp and practically called for a halt on engineering duties for Camp Love.

The Battalion, however, accomplished minor operations. Salvage operations continued with the Seabees and combat engineers installing and fixing span bridges at AT 946777 and AT 919598, with a new span bridge over the existing structure for AT 946777. However, bridges at AT 945695 and AT 957718 were completely washed out.

One of the most important means of transportation incapable of operating because of the rains in the Da Nang area was the Song Thu Bon Ferry northwest of Da Nang and northeast of Camp Love. However, combat marine and sailor engineers could place 240 cupid yards of 6 pound rocks behind abutment for a bridge at AT 945694.

The camp stood at a standstill. Dormant. Not much to do.

Sidelined as well were the combat marines who accompanied combat engineers on patrols because of the rain.

The 19th of October brought an additional 1.38 inches onto the camp, and the surrounding area of Camp Love an additional two or more inches closing many roads in the Da Nang TAOR. However, Alpha Company ventured out in the hazardous terrain to accompany Seabees to reconstruct two head walls at AT 907755 and AT 906762.

When Buchanan arrived at Burns' hootch, he found it empty. So he moseyed his way over to Lucas' office, asking permission to travel to An Ngai Dong and check in on the orphanage, assuring himself things were safe and sound. Buchanan received a big fat 'no' from Lucas.

Practically stranded in Camp Love, Buchanan sought to find Jackson to visit the hootches and departments to fill in time, inquiring about how the men were coping emotionally and spiritually during this unexpected hiatus.

Stepping into Jackson's hootch, Buchanan greeted his bodyguard, "Good morning, Philip. Missed you at breakfast."

Buchanan walked in on Jackson writing letters to his mother and friends back home in Ohio.

"Morning, sir." replied Jackson, glancing up at Buchanan as he resumed finishing up his last letter.

"Sorry I missed breakfast with you, sir. I wrote Mom a return letter from the letter I received from her, couple days ago. She wrote to me some time back. Cincinnati has a new television station, WKIO Channel 8 out of Cincinnati-Newport, Ohio. She said it was up and running in August and will cover news in the Tri-State area. The city and Northern Kentucky have needed a new station for years." expressed Jackson.

"Yeah, the city needed a new station. The growth of Northern Kentucky, north of Cincy. The area has seen a lot of growth."

Jackson sighs heavily and moaned, "I miss home. The river. The Reds. The food. The *weather*."

"Whew. Me too. It's so blasted hot. Miss the air conditioning. I think I've lost weight just from sweating." Buchanan chuckled at the thought.

"Then there's the new football team. The inaugural year for the Bengals, and I'm here sitting in southeast Asia. Gosh, I'm missing out." grumbled a disappointed Jackson.

Buchanan reassures him, "The Bengals will be there when you get back."

Pausing, Jackson informed Buchanan, "Already, my cousin's gone to a game. Cincy beat the Broncos." Contemplating, he hinted of the future, "A team I feel someday I might have a reason to hate."

Grinning, Buchanan chimed in, "*Yeah*. Maybe."

Jackson finished writing the end of his letter and sealed it for mailing.

"Well, I'd love to talk, lift up the beauty of Cincinnati with you all day, and talk sports, but let's go visit the men. I think they need it today. It's rained and rained and rained. A visit from the chaplain will do 'em good. Whatyathink?" asked Buchanan.

"I think so too, sir. Let's go."

Jackson grabbed his cover, donned his dungaree shirt over his already sweat filled green under shirt, and off they went to visit the men. The spiritual team first walked to the mail room to drop off Jackson's letters and visited with the marines in the postal room since they were there.

Buchanan insisted the spiritual team's first hootch to visit would be Rodriquez's. Buchanan vowed to return the hospitality shown to him and the aid given with the care of the water dragons.

The walk toward Rodriquez's hootch, a hundred feet on the other side of the camp, entailed a hot day. The young marine shared a hootch with four other men: Private First Class Dobbs, Corporal Kowslowski, and two other marines the spiritual team vaguely knew, members of Alpha Company, a Corporal Lawrence Patrick Jansen and Private John Thomas McElwaney, from Michigan and not particularly religious.

The spiritual team arrived at Rodriquez's hootch, catching him and others in the final stages of cleaning their weapons. The maintenance and upkeep of weaponry required a constant routine for marines, especially during the full swing of the monsoon and typhoon seasons. No service personnel in Vietnam - a marine, soldier, or sailor wanted his weapon to jam on him in a tight spot in the bush. The constant regularity of cleaning weapons demanded the utmost priority for combatants.

Within earshot of the hootch walking toward the entrance, the spiritual team heard, "Shut up, Rodriquez! We don't give a crap about caring for these stupid animals in the jungle."

Buchanan softly touched Jackson's right arm as if to stop. As they paused in step, the pair listened for a bit of the conversation in Rodriquez's hootch.

"Listen, if you had a heart, you would care for these animals' natural habitat. Our fighting is disturbing their indigenous confines." imparted Rodriquez.

"I don't care. And I *know* Jansen doesn't care either." blurted a marine.

"No. I don't!" blabbed another marine.

Listening to the conversation, the spiritual team expressed disgust at the rude, and as Jackson would refer to such marines, 'jackasses'.

"Leave him alone, he has done nothing to you." appealed Dobbs.

Shocked, the spiritual team leans their heads back in astonishment, surprised at Dobbs' comment, coming out of the mouth of 'Mr. Self Absorbed', the 'Mr. It's All About Me.'

Maybe Dobbs has recently tilted a little more on the spiritual team's side of the intangible, spiritual world of Christ. At least that's the spiritual team's hope and prayer.

"*Yeah.* Next time I see a wild animal, I'm going to blast him." yelled the second marine.

"HAHAHAHAHAHAHAHA!" laughed the marines with demented, fiendish laughs.

"Let me tell you something, Rodriquez. You're nothing but softy and a whip. Go back to California." hounded the first marine in a demeaning manner.

The spiritual team heard next from the hootch a derogatory term used towards Rodriquez's ethnicity, infuriating the spiritual team. The name calling pushed Buchanan over the top. Looking down toward his feet listening, he abruptly fixed his eyes on Jackson hearing the disparaging term thrown out of one of the marine's mouth. His face turned as red as Jackson's Cincinnati Reds hat in his hootch from anger. This sudden fury within Buchanan he knew from his past days and imparted to others from time to time, including a clod in Alabama, beating the poop out of a fellow airman when referring to a dear, devoted black friend a derogatory term Buchanan also loathed.

"Will the two of you shut the hell up? Leave him alone. He loves animals. So what?" said Kowslowski, defending Rodriquez.

Patting Jackson's shoulder, Buchanan spoke softly, "That's it. That's enough for me. Come on."

Buchanan's face turned not only red, but hot.

Buchanan, followed by Jackson, briskly walked through the entrance and boldly announced, "Hello, men. Good Morning."

"Uh. Hello, chaplain. G-Good Morning to you. s-sir." said Kowslowski, a faithful participant in Buchanan's communion services.

"Morning, sir." said Dobbs, standing up respectfully, acknowledging Buchanan's presence.

"Morning, sir." said Rodriquez.

"Morning. Arthur and Churchill are doing well. You're right. They love fruit and veggies from the chow hall." commented Buchanan.

"Told you so, sir." answered Rodriquez with a smile.

"Good Morning Rodriquez." said Jackson.

"Morning Sergeant." responded Rodriquez.

"Have you gotten good use with the book on the care of conifers and true mosses I brought you?" asked Jackson, peering toward the Michiganders with a seething expression on his face.

"Yes, yes, sergeant, I have. It's very informative. I can use it when I get back home. The trunk is a very volatile part of the tree and must be cared for in order for a tree to have a healthy life." commented Rodriquez.

The smirking Michiganders giggle, glancing toward Buchanan. Aghast with the Michiganders behavior with the presence of an officer, he stares intently, sending a message to straighten up, to conduct themselves with a military bearing.

Neither Jansen nor McElwaney acknowledged the chaplain in any respectful manner.

"You think Ohio State is going to beat Michigan this year?" asked McElwaney with a bit of cynicism. "I've heard your talk around camp. Ohio State this. Ohio State that. *Pleeeease*. They're going to get their *butts* kicked. You'll see. And finally, you can shut your *stupid* mouth about Head Coach Barnes and Ohio State and the whole bit."

Jackson sternly glares at McElwaney to stop the disrespectful tone.

"Yeah. I bet Michigan wins. The game is at Ohio State and that ain't even going to help'em. Ohio State is *waaaaaaay* overrated." implored Jansen.

The Michiganders brushed Buchanan aside. They considered him a mere Baptist preacher. The scuttlebutt in camp spread: the pair are nothing but mean spirited, disrespectful marines toward chaplains, regardless of denomination. In fact, disrespectful for any religion.

"I'll tell you the truth, chaplain. I don't like people who try to intimidate. *Especially* religious fanatics like you all, *sir*." provoked Jansen, changing the subject.

Jackson grew ever more irritated, growing less patient with the Michiganders. Jackson's body language spoke volumes, displaying tight lips, along with his hands on his hips.

"I've watched you with your country bumpkin show. Your mountain accent. It's nothing but a farce and you're just in it to please the officers in order to get us to obey orders. Yep. That's it. It's all to treat us special into obeying orders. And besides, I've killed so many of Charlie, I don't need no help from no chaplain to do that." added

Jansen as he arrogantly takes a quick glimpse over toward McElwaney, as soft chuckles emerge from the rabble-rousers.

No one had talked to Buchanan in his 12 years of service like Jansen and McElwaney just did, either enlisted or an officer.

As Buchanan was about to lay into the two Michiganders with a tongue lashing, Jackson abruptly threw his hand up for the Michiganders to shut up.

The hootch fell silent, quiet as a mouse.

McElwaney thought twice to open up his trap to say something, when Jackson extended his index finger to his mouth, staring captive into McElwaney's eyes.

McElwaney said not a word. Jackson's physique and demeanor mirrored one of intimidation, speaking volumes of Jackson's experience in combat. The glare given to McElwaney exhibited one he saw only in combat situations.

Jackson stepped angered, as red as his reds hat, in front of Jansen a foot away, grabbed his t-shirt, pulling Jansen face to face who is only 5'7" and with a methodical and slow flow of words threatened the Michiganders, "Ya talk to Chaplain Buchanan like that again... and I'll *kill* you."

Jansen swallowed hard, shaking in his boots.

A veteran of three months in Vietnam, he knew enough now of a combat zone. Jackson meant what he said, solely in the tone of his voice.

Flabbergasted with the sight, Kowslowski, Dobbs, McElwaney, Buchanan, and Rodriquez stare catching flies.

Buchanan saw for the first time behavior out of Jackson with the intent of literally taking the life from another human being, without hesitation. His eyes are acquainted with the fact war brings about behavior out of the ordinary. In Jackson's last tour, he would've encountered Jansen differently. Buchanan shuttered with the thought of what Jackson would've done to Jansen in his last tour.

The 6'3" Jackson pulled Jansen inches off the floor to pull him up face to face. He snatched his t-shirt tight, tearing the collar of the shirt.

Kowslowski knew Jackson from past tours, knowing he meant every word he said.

With a glare of repulsion in his eye, Jackson ripped into Janson, "I've never seen you take the life of anybody, you little runt. If you knew the enemy killed on my KIA list, you'd know it wouldn't be nothing to take your worthless life away right here, right now. So shut...up. You're nothing but a talker. A big mouth. The type who gets killed easy 'cause of their stupidity."

The complete past of Jackson's life continued to be hidden from Buchanan, and intentional on his part.

McElwaney froze stiff. Staring wide eyed and catching flies.

With no doubt, Jackson convinced the men of his resolve.

Jackson, unrelenting, held Jansen off the floor face to face, tearing his t-shirt, demands with an unyielding conviction in his voice, "Before we leave, you're going to apologize to Chaplain Buchanan. If not, I'm going to kick your asses right here, right now. Kowslowski knows I will. He knows me, you don't."

Jansen swallowed hard, uttering a wimpy, "Yes. Yes, I will."

Jackson lowers Jansen back onto the floor gently, but firm.

Looking over toward McElwaney, Jackson makes the point. "All the chaplain wants to do is to care for your spiritual wants and needs."

"Y-Yeah." said McElwaney nervously.

Giving Jansen an abrupt intimidating glance, Jackson says with contempt in his voice, "I don't care if you care about *that*. But I *do* care if you mistreat the chaplain in any way....shape...or form. You hear me."

Jansen responds with a wimpy, "Yeah. I mean, yes."

Still shocked with the sight in front of him, Buchanan now knew his body guard was God sent, one who shielded the chaplain even from those who were supposed to be on their side.

Buchanan noticed Dobbs staring the whole while with a gratifying, almost of retribution and vengeance, expression on his face. Dobbs sat on his cot satisfied somebody finally gave Jansen and McElwaney what they always deserved - a good dressing down.

"Now apologize to Chaplain Buchanan. You first." ordered Jackson, pointing his finger at McElwaney.

"I'm-I'm sorry for my disrespectful behavior sir." pleaded McElwaney without condescension.

"Now you." as Jackson motions with his hand to Jansen.

"I-I'm sorry too, sir." whimpered Jansen a sorrowful apology.

"Good. We're leaving." barked Jackson.

The moment stood as grandiose. A moment defined by war. A mere few minutes exposing how war will change a human being's innermost self. A moment shared by a few men in camp, isolated far from home, and which people back home, living the rules of a more peaceful and civilized world, would never understand. A brief moment reflecting the abhorrence and enmity of war.

Grinning, Buchanan says, "Good day, men." He leisurely dons his cover, places a pinch of tobacco out of his pouch into his mouth, and walks out of the hootch, exhaling a long sigh, "Whew!"

Jackson follows Chaplain Buchanan out of the hootch, turns back toward Jansen and McElwaney, and with a grimacing smile, says with a bit of sarcasm, "I too happen to be from Ohio. And Ohio State is going to kick that state up north's ass all the way back to the lake shore."

Jackson sneers, walking out of the hootch, leaving Jansen and McElwaney at the mercy of the other men, all knowing now that the pair is all mouth, hoseheads, and empty within of fortitude or resolve.

Respect will be shown to a man Jackson knows to be a Godly man.

The sergeant served Buchanan as his bodyguard, committed to guard him.

PLAYING WITH EXPLOSIVES

OCTOBER 20, 1968

The duties of a combat engineering team in Vietnam consisted of stressful, dangerous, and hazardous situations. The dangers confronted encircled every patrol when stepping into the jungle for defensive sweeps. The threatening situations encountered by combat engineering teams were everyday occurrences and the Viet Cong were ever present crafting new means to disrupt everyday living for the innocent South Vietnamese, placing horrid booby traps in the most unexpected locations of routine everyday life. The VC's intent to construct a device to take the life or to maim a marine or friendly civilian revealed evident with the horrid booby traps laid in the most unexpected locations of routine everyday life.

Adolphus Skawinski served proudly in 3rd Battalion, 2nd Platoon combat engineering team. A tedious and meticulous worker, he developed a master skill of talents. An engineering team required a high level of dependency and trust in one another. One slip up from one incompetent knucklehead and a person's life is cut short.

Combat engineers took the responsibilities and duties assigned seriously and were anything but shoddy with their trained skills. Nincompoops were quickly turned away serving in the combat engineering corps.

For a 20-year-old, Skawinski exhibited advanced maturity with his skills as an explosives expert. Few men are born with leadership qualities showed by Skawinski at such a young age, and along with his intelligence and candidness, set himself forward in life to achieve great things. As a young man, his pride swelled working alongside his parents in building one of the most profitable dairy and vegetable farms in the Midwest. As a single child, he beamed far and wide, bursting with pride with the success on the farm.

The pleasure of one particular skill as a combat engineer he possessed bordered on sheer sin and self-satisfaction in the arming of booby traps. On top of the many responsibilities of a combat engineer required to disarm booby traps. But Skawinski took great pleasure in setting booby traps and Claymore mines within the defenses of the perimeter surrounding Camp Love, serving as a buffer between the bush and the safe haven of Camp Love. Skawinski immensely enjoyed setting a death sentence for the VC in the perimeter. His disdain for the VC bordered on sheer hate. A hate gained from firsthand experience witnessing the aftermath of the Viet Cong torturing prisoners of war and the treatment of pro-American South Vietnamese. The VC enraged his inner self and his feelings toward the VC, conflicting with his deep convictions of his strong, ever present Christian conscious.

Along with his fellow combat engineering team members, Skawinski's training provided setting explosives and disarming them. When his team set booby traps in the perimeter, they served as a defense against the VC infiltrating Camp Love. The perimeter of the camp ran to the edge approximately 200 to 300 yards wide that surrounded the camp. An additional 100 to 200 yards between the edge of the perimeter and the jungles of Vietnam ran a mere 15 feet away from the treeline. Barbed wire, approximately 12 to 20 inches off the ground, laid atop of the service of the perimeter. The barbed wire laid elevated off the ground from being attached to wooden stakes driven into the ground 10 to 12 feet apart. Within the barbed wire, booby traps were set, scattered throughout the perimeter to take the Viet Cong into the next life.

One booby trap Buchanan found most fascinating contained fuel with a contraption dousing Viet Cong infiltrators with gasoline, triggered by a spark from a flask. The VC found himself "lighted" up, engulfed in flames.

The Viet Cong's intent stemmed from cutting a pathway through the barbed wire within the perimeter to crawl on the ground to the edge of Camp Love at night. Once they reached the edge, the VC set forth, killing the sentries on guard duty, enabling the VC to swarm into the camp without difficulty. All done, of course, with little or no noise.

At night, the camp knew a Viet Cong met his death, being "lighted" up and engulfed with gasoline from the small fireball emerging in the darkness. The VC bore the resemblance of being "cooked" from the booby trap, his skin singed with a heavy black residue.

In the morning, in the shadow and sunrise of the sun, the blackened remains of the "fried" Viet Cong laying on his back would soon be discovered by marines. Many a time, the VC grasped the very wire cutters or pliers he held as he attempted to cut the wire for a pathway of infiltration.

For the average American, the ghastly sight seemed unfathomable. But for the marines in Camp Love, waking up with the discovery of a blackened VC corpse in the perimeter delivered an additional sense of buoyancy and a sense of security. Viewing the corpse within the perimeter of the camp added a victory for the marines, whether a grisly sight or not. The discovery set a common denominator in camp: the defenses of the perimeter solidified a common sentiment of impressive accomplishment.

Buchanan welcomed as many layered obstacles as possible to prevent the Viet Cong from infiltrating the camp. In fact, the booby traps served as a mental picture of chain mail of armor for Buchanan.

The very first sight of a "fried" Viet Cong, waking up from a good night's sleep, hit Buchanan with an abundance of horror, a crushing mental memory of the stench of death.

After the short stare of one corpse, Buchanan slipped back into his hootch, retrieved his camera, and took several slide pictures of the 'charcoal' remains of the Viet Cong.

The slides of the dead Viet Cong served as a testament to others war wasn't to be taken lightly. A testament from Buchanan that war is to be avoided if all possible.

Buchanan wasn't necessarily frightened of the Viet Cong as a fighting force. But his experience of combat in his tour exemplified the VC will fight to the death. Most times, he witnessed a high level of bravery from the VC and the NVA. But as a fighting force, however, and rightly so, Buchanan witnessed the firefights between the VC and the marines, with the marines inflicting far more casualties on the VC than they did on United States forces. What Buchanan feared most was the possibility of being captured by the Viet Cong. Seeing with his own eyes the torture and dismemberment of prisoners of war and pro-American civilians, he loathed the possibility of capture. The high degree of brutal torture by the VC inflicted upon a chaplain, if caught, became unimaginable to Buchanan. A military chaplain furnished a source of inspiration for military troops, and if capturing and torturing to death a Navy chaplain demoralized American forces, the VC definitely considered a chaplain a prize capture which they looked out for in the jungle. Sticking to Jackson like glue in the bush to avoid falling into the hands of the VC became a top priority for Buchanan.

The most rage and resentment boiled up inside of Buchanan most of all came from the experience of witnessing the treatment of children and elderly from the hands of the Viet Cong. The memories will last a lifetime.

Though the booby traps were violent and gruesome, Buchanan felt grateful for the extra layer of security for himself and the camp.

The morning of October 20, 1968, marines woke up to five "blackened" VC who had attempted to cut a pathway within the perimeter and into camp. Skawinski had set every booby trap.

Waking up, Skawinski walked out of his hootch toward the edge of the perimeter where the five 'torched' VC were discovered. Looking out toward the corpses, his soul swelled, full of overwhelming satisfaction. Comprehending the intent of the VC and personally encompassing a part in halting a potential and deadly attack, Skawinski tabbed the morning with a moment of personal pride and accomplishment.

Skawinski, a devout Christian with great regret, gave rise to feelings of guilt taking another life. But again, a permanent imprint upon his mind of the tortured remains of those at the mercy of the Viet Cong gave justification for actions to a marine in a combat zone. Besides, as a man of astute intelligence, he became well versed in the Augustinian theory of a just war, falling politically into it well.

War demands a strenuous undertaking, executing actions a human being normally wouldn't take part in. Protecting life takes top priority, as there are a few hundred yards away in the jungle, an enemy who hates and despises those within the perimeter. An enemy who is ready, willing, and able to slit a marine's throat when given the opportunity.

For Skawinski, the continuous conflict within himself between his Christian convictions versus the demands of a marine in a violent, tumultuous war laid heavy on his heart. Skawinski justified his actions with the fact the Viet Cong hated him and he had grown to hate the VC. Besides, seeing with his own two eyes the gruesome death of friends from crafty handiwork of VC booby traps pushed his incredible drive to defeat the VC even more within himself.

Skawinski, like all service personnel, searched for means to cope with war and violence that comes with it. One means for him surfaced with the personality and presence of Buchanan.

Yes, there were other chaplains, but Buchanan emerged as a vital component for Skawinski, keeping his sanity in Vietnam. Skawinski sighted many tools of ministry Buchanan gave upon the men to lighten obvious and stressful conditions of war in Vietnam. The John Wayne movie nights provided the men much needed confidence. Buchanan showing attention to a marine, possibly neglected his whole life, giving him a birthday party. The counseling of men dealing with issues such as death, suffering, and depression. Possibly the most crucial trait of Buchanan in Skawinski's estimation came in his willingness to address issues with the marines as men, and not just as enlisted men or a peon inferior to an educated lofty clergyman with many letters behind his name.

Skawinski perceived the first day he met Buchanan his personality manifested a natural, uplifting person to counsel the depressed, down trodden marine after a major firefight. The new chaplain embodied a genuine and authentic magnetism. His unique, trustworthy manner connected with people's problems, generating avenues to solve problems proving to be a great strength for Buchanan. Skawinski detected a strength within Buchanan the very first day he met him in his hootch. He discovered Buchanan's past experience piecemeal, explaining the knack of connecting so strongly to the men. Buchanan could bond by means other chaplains were incapable of achieving.

The stress level sat on high for Skawinski with the duties and responsibilities placed on him, pushing the young man to stopover frequently to Chaplain Buchanan's hootch to seek counseling with the dangers of a combat engineer. The many visits resulted in an impenetrable bond between Skawinski and Buchanan. He exalted Buchanan as a father figure.

The Christian bond between the two men forever changed their lives.

The Orphanage

October 22, 1968

For ten days, the spiritual team, thrilled from head to toe, now traveled in their own jeep to minister. The team were now spoiled, and Buchanan even insisted on stopping by to visit Adkins and the Seabees re-constructing the bridges washed out a few days ago along the Cam Lo River. With a jeep, the world itself seemed wide open for ministry. The two men were so spoiled to the degree of craving a country road ride in the jeep just for the sheer joy of taking a pleasure trip, soaking in the temptation of site seeing. Of course, Jackson knew the danger of taking such a ride, and thought better of it.

Nonetheless, no more bumming rides. No more riding shotgun. No more asking for favors. No more walking and lugging the service kit by foot. Buchanan traveled where he wanted, when he wanted.

The spiritual team started the new day after a hearty breakfast on a spiritual high.

At 0730 hours in the morning, the schedule ahead fell full for the day. A 1900 hours devotion in the camp conference hall will follow the 1300 hours Communion service.

The day's schedule included Jackson to drive Buchanan to visit a friend, Chaplain Lieutenant Junior Grade Brian Kensington, two and a half miles southwest of Camp Love. The officer's call, scheduled at 0900 hours, will be scratched off the agenda due to the extensive list of duties of the day.

Chaplain Kensington supported a Catholic orphanage through a CAP (Civic Action Program) which Buchanan wanted to throw some support toward with the 7th Engineering Battalion personnel.

In 1967, Buchanan attended chaplaincy school with Kensington in Rhode Island. A staunch Roman Catholic from New York City, his family gained a reputation of character and integrity as lawyers. The Kensington clan also owned a pizza franchise which grew with prominence throughout the Tri-State area. The marines loved Kensington, treating the men with the utmost compassion and love. In his second consecutive tour in Vietnam, Kensington set his sights on the Catholic Church's emphasis of nurturing and caring for the downtrodden resulting from the war.

"What are we meeting Kensington about, sir?" asked Jackson.

"The orphanage school about two to three miles from Camp Love." answered Buchanan.

"The An Ngai Dong school? The Catholic school?" asked Jackson.

"Yeah. Ya know about it?"

"Yes, I do." answered Jackson. "The school takes in children whose parents the enemy have killed because of the war. The children are innocent. Some of the sweetest children you'll ever meet."

"Well, Philip, we're going to help Chaplain Kensington. It'll be a CAP for us and Camp Love."

Grinning, Jackson said, "Good. Lieutenant Kensington's been working with the orphanage for some time now, hasn't he?"

"Yes, since December, 1966. But as priest prior to his commission as a Navy Chaplain."

"I remember him on my last two tours." remembered Jackson. "I've never met him, but I've heard him give some devotions before I became a Christian. He's great. He reminds me of you."

Buchanan grins, glancing toward Jackson and asks "How?"

"He loves the men. He, well, cares. Like you."

Buchanan smiles wider and responds, "Thanks."

Nodding in the affirmative, Buchanan says, "You'll like him very much, Philip."

"I already like him, sir."

The spiritual team drove closer to the orphanage. Buchanan encouraged as many Civic Action Programs as possible and, in his sights, standing in front of the orphanage stood Kensington. However, just a half a mile from the orphanage, the remnants of war laid evident left and right of the roadway. A truck sat alongside the road, blown up from a land mine concealed from a driver who never knew what hit him. The presence of burned and blown out houses 15 to 20 feet from the road's edge from the result of rocket or artillery fire, or possibly Viet Cong terrorism inflicted upon a Vietnamese family simply living as farmers and attempting to make ends meet. The natural habitat, trees and vegetation, dead from either a fire or Agent Orange. The ghastly sights of a horrible war.

The ravages of war apparent in and around the one-mile radius of the orphanage were obvious signs of violence and hostilities.

In the distance ahead of them, Buchanan saw evidence of a different sort. The abundant signs of concord with recently constructed, freshly painted, spacious, accessible buildings in the distance reflected a more joyful life.

"I think that's it, sergeant. It is! It is! Amen! We're here!" said an elated Buchanan.

Kensington, a priest, and two Catholic nuns greeted them as Jackson drove up near the administration building of the orphanage school.

Stepping out of the jeep, Kensington greeted them with a firm handshake grinning from ear to ear and very excited with the potential ministry to the children from the 7th Engineering Marine Battalion.

Jackson sensed great admiration in the air between the two chaplains.

"Chaplain Kensington." greeted Buchanan.

"Chaplain Buchanan! Good to have someone present who doesn't mind getting his feet dirty." replied Kensington.

As Navy chaplains, the two Navy officers shared a mutual effort as ministers - a commitment to Jesus, to minister to the weak and forgotten.

"Well, it's good to be here. Brian, this is Sergeant Jackson."

"Good to meet you, Jackson." replied Kensington.

"Pleasure to meet ya, sir. I've heard you speak in my previous tour. I appreciate your words. You're an inspiration to the men."

"Well, I try Jackson. I speak what I need to say and - hopefully, my words will sink in. You know what I mean?"

"Yes sir, I do." said Jackson.

Kensington said, "I remember a Shakespeare quote, 'Men with few words are the best men.' I say what the men need to hear." He added in jest, "Can't be too long winded in the bush." added Kensington with jest.

The men chuckle.

"Enough about me." insisted Kensington.

Kensington introduced the nuns and the priest to Buchanan and Jackson.

Undertaking the role of head schoolmaster, the priest knew how to read, write, and speak English and attended Catholic parochial schools in the United States.

"Chúc mọi người một ngày tốt lành," as Buchanan gave his best shot, attempting to articulate 'Good day everyone' in Vietnamese. Grinning, all were humored with the attempt of language. Buchanan studied Vietnamese to communicate an affable manner and to cross the barriers of culture to express a welcome civility.

Kensington, possessing a knack for learning languages, knowing several native tongues, including Vietnamese.

After introducing themselves, the nuns and priest showed the utmost appreciation to Buchanan for the interest in supporting the orphanage and school, excusing themselves to carry on their duties in the orphanage.

Kensington walked the spiritual team to benches parallel to the school, as he discussed the school and the ministry to the children. He changed the subject with consternation.

"Robert, I asked you to come to see if your people at 7th Engineering can help us here at the orphanage." asserted Kensington. "My commanding officer, a hard nose, is anything but thrilled about the school. He's new - doesn't like too many CAPs. He maintains

CAP's occupy too much time away from the duties of being a chaplain. He insists I spend too much time here. It's only 2 or 3 times a week and 3 or 4 hours total, tops a week. He loathes the support of the marines sponsoring the kids. He insists it makes them soft in combat - somewhat sympathetic to the communist cause. He sat in his office the other day, and I heard him spill all this crap out of his mouth, gibbering. I'm asking myself, 'Is this man for real? Has he ever needed any help in his life?' I had an afterthought, 'You skinny, turtlenecked, hard-nosed ring-knocker.' I pictured myself jumping the table and wringing his skinny, little neck."

The men chuckle, remembering past officers with skinny little necks, hard-nosed ring-knockers, with little to no compassion in their hearts for anybody but themselves.

As the spiritual team listened, Kensington commented, "He will not permit them to come here much more in the future. I can come, but not the men."

"How is it sympathetic to the communists?" asked Buchanan.

Kensington explained, "I don't *really* know. He doesn't want them too close to the native people, I guess, because it will cause a blur to the marines' sight of the purpose of being here. I suppose he thinks if marines became too involved with the locals, they'll question orders and begin to slowly question our intent, our mission here to stop South Vietnam to be overrun by the Commies. We're here to stop the Communists, aren't we? You know that. And I'm all for it. The people around here are scared to death of the Communists, of the VC. My commanding officer informed me he didn't want his men to become too 'Christianized.' Yes, it's true. Can you believe it? That's the way he put it, 'Christianized.' All of his words, which spouted out of his mouth, that offended me more than anything else."

Sitting patiently, the spiritual team listened and in total disbelief at the 'Christianized' comment.

Kensington continued, "You would think the Lieutenant Colonel would consider that if marines got close to the children, well, it would fire the marines up, not make 'em soft. Anyway, it was the Communists, the VC, who killed their parents. You'd think it'd create a desire in the marines, to fight with more intensity after seeing with their own two eyes what the VC did to the children's parents. Robert, Sergeant, some of these precious kids saw their mother *and* their father tortured to death. Yes. S-Some of 'em raped, while the other parent suffered a tortured death simultaneously. This *angers* me. That *really* angers me, Robert."

Kensington smacks his fist into his other hand. "The children didn't ask to be tortured. They didn't ask to witness the murder of their parents. Those blood thirsty Communists did it to 'em. We must stop the Communists from being capable of carrying out these atrocities. They must not take this country. If they do, they'll kill the rest of them. They'd kill so many people. It'll be a bloodbath if they take the south. I've got to do my part to stop 'em."

By this time, Kensington came close to tears.

Buchanan saw the determination in Kensington's eyes. He meant every word spoken.

"You desire the men of Camp Love to sponsor the school?" asked a compassionate Buchanan.

"Yes." responded Kensington.

Jackson interjected, "Well, that would be something Lieutenant Colonel Lucas would have to approve."

Kensington added, "And the chaplain chain of command as well."

"That's right, Brian." added Buchanan.

"Well, can you ask him?" What's this Lucas like? Is he, well - a reasonable man - or a hard nose?" asked Kensington.

"Well....." spoke Buchanan, rubbing his chin with his fingers, "to be honest with you, Brian. H-He's approved everything I've asked him of so far. I don't know how he'd respond to this, but we can ask him. With my persuading, I think it'll be alright."

Buchanan paused and asked, "Why don't you tag along with us, go back to Camp Love with us, ask him yourself?"

"Well, these kids need attention and care. I just might go back to Camp Love with you." insisted Kensington.

"Good." confirmed Buchanan.

The men stand up from the benches, ending their conversation. Kensington walked the two men on a tour of the school and campus with the first stop in the two main classroom buildings of one room enclosures, each educating 50 children at a time, with lessons taught from the nuns. The education comprised a Neo-Classical tradition mixed in with a Socratic approach. Of course, education in the primary and secondary schools complimented religious Roman Catholic courses and curriculum. The next stop introduced the spiritual team to the administrative building for priests and nuns, with a kitchen built on the backside next to living quarters for faculty for additional priests and nuns for the local Catholic church. The fourth building of the tour housed a large living space for the children furnished with bunk beds and a few furniture pieces.

Last in the tour introduced the spiritual team to the play area on the backside of the school with rusty and depleted swings, sliding boards, and monkey bars for children to play on. The playground reflected anything spectacular, but it was better than nothing.

In a world of war, pain, and agony - the only setting these children ever knew - anything, including the rusty swings and monkey bars, equaled all the gold in the world to ease the pain of the war for the children.

After the tour, the spiritual team headed back home to conduct the 1100 hour service in the bush, with Chaplain Kensington tagging along to meet Lucas in Camp Love. Besides, the trip offered Kensington an opportunity to lead Roman Catholics in Communion.

Wearing White Can Get You Killed

October 22, 1968

Services in the bush on October 22,1968 will end up a lasting talking point years later when reminiscing of amiable memories of Vietnam. The memory of conducting simultaneous services transpiring within the deep jungles of Vietnam led by two friends, one Protestant, one Catholic, will typify Ecumenicalism as Navy chaplains set out to accomplish.

Combat engineers and marines on patrol were ordered to secure a rather large perimeter southwest of Camp Love centered on sweeping the area to start a new road project to interconnect the infrastructure of territory. United States military strategists ordered to secure the area due to the fact the Viet Cong increased terrorist and infiltration activities in the past two weeks. The marines were exhausted and in need of taking a 'breather', to take their minds off the war, and what better way to do it but to participate in a Communion service. Most of the marines knew Buchanan, and as a bonus for Catholic marines, a priest will lead in Catholic Communion.

For a mere few moments in time, the men will experience peace from the war. Buchanan discovered quickly Communion services in the bush for military personnel during the war served as an instant semblance of normalcy like no other. A mere moment in time to reflect and acknowledge God, even amid a horrible war.

Chaplain Kensington, inspired and motivated to carry out God's Will, donned all the vestments required for Communion - white alb, amice, orphreys, chasuble, maniple, his chimera, and stole. Buchanan, with his back to Kensington, talked to the marines, 'having fellowship', getting to know them a little better. As Buchanan fellowshiped with the men, he took a glimpse over his shoulder and noticed Kensington donning his entire worship attire.

Buchanan abruptly excused himself, walking briskly over to Kensington and objected, "What in tarnation are you doing, Brian?"

Smiling, Kensington boasted, "I'm donning my worship vestments to give Communion. What do you think I'm doing?"

"You're going to get yourself killed. Don't you know there's a sniper all over the place?" adduced Buchanan, with alarm in his deep Kentuckian accent.

"Robert, I'm a Catholic priest called by God to serve. He'll protect me. The Lord has placed an armor of steel upon me, to get me through this hell we're in every day. I'm in His hands. My Saint Christopher around my neck has a purpose. Besides, I must continue the work of Father Capodanno. It's important to me to finish what he started." professed Kensington with confidence.

Buchanan nodded with affirmation, "Listen, Brian. I'm called from God too, as you are, but you're taking on a monumental risk, exposing yourself to danger - to unnecessary danger - worries me. Have you always conducted services in the bush donning your vestments?"

Pausing, Kensington stated, "Yes, and I'm *still* alive - aren't I? The Lord protects me."

As Jackson completed donning the service kits, he motions to the chaplains - one Protestant, one Roman Catholic - the services were set to lead the men in Communion.

The simultaneous services occurred in rural flat land with sparse trees and foliage interspersed within the open space.

Marines attached camouflage netting to jungle trees to block any attempt of Viet Cong snipers to kill Kensington behind ammunition boxes used for Communion tables.

Simultaneous services, one Catholic, one Protestant. Years later, discussion of the service entailed one of pride and accomplishment for Kensington and Buchanan. No two chaplains in Vietnam could've boasted of such a feat meeting the essential wants and needs of the men in the bush than this day. Buchanan took great measures to fulfill ministry to meet the wants and needs of all the men, along with accomplishing the Navy chaplain motto in Vietnam - 'cooperation without compromise' without conflicting upon his own Baptist convictions.

Buchanan strived toward Ecumenicalism, convinced the concept appeared indispensable to completely meet the wants and needs of the marines. His Presbyterian upbringing and Lutheran seminary training contributed to his proper approach of recognizing common theological convictions of Christian denominations without modifying his own Baptist convictions. To serve communion in terms of Catholicism definitely went too far, however, and definitely compromised his personal convictions. He preferred to stress the similarities of Catholicism and Protestantism, advocating Ecumenicalism, producing brotherly love and not divisive mind-sets. Besides, as a man in his late 30s, he had by now become a staunch and conservative Baptist in his own right. His Baptist stance on serving The Lord's Supper grew into a stern stand. Holy Communion for Catholics advocated a conviction of transubstantiation - in which the bread and wine actually become the body and blood of Jesus Christ. The point of transubstantiation generated a strong opposition for Buchanan as a Baptist, amounting to one reminding him of Martin Luther's courage and conviction reflecting his most famous quote, 'Here I Stand'.

Regardless of Buchanan's Baptist convictions, he loved Kensington. Catholic friends Buchanan knew growing up were minimal due to the demographics of rural Ohio and Kentucky. Catholic membership in rural areas comprised low numbers compared to Protestants, of which ninety percent of Catholics in Ohio and Kentucky lived in urban and suburban populations of the two states. Buchanan grew to love and appreciate the countless numbers of Catholics he met as an enlisted man in the Air Force. He held them high in regard, observing their devotion to the Lord, witnessing to others the Salvation and love of Jesus, and dedication to living out Jesus' commands and instructions of living life.

Buchanan noticed the radiant personality of Kensington, visiting and joking with the men, carrying out Jesus' call in his life. Kensington personified one of the greatest Christians he had met in the Navy Chaplain Corps. Buchanan thought, 'if any human being on earth God's gonna to protect in a war zone, it's Brian Kensington.'

Kensington began with the Liturgy of the day of the Catholic Church, while Buchanan read a passage of Scripture laid out for Protestants in the chaplain manual.

A stickler to detail, Buchanan conducted his customary order of service. A prayer, a spoken welcome, scripture reading, one hymn, a short devotion for the men, communion, and closing with a prayer. As usual, Buchanan finished in sturdy fashion, a 20 minute service. The men, as usual, gained a greater insight and a better understanding of how to live Jesus' life from a direct and astute Buchanan.

With the conclusion of the Protestant Communion, Protestants, enticed by Chaplain Kensington's presence, listened intently to Kensington lead the Catholic Liturgy. Protestants slowly took interest in the Catholic service. Gradually, Protestants sitting on the ground pivoted an angle for themselves toward Chaplain Kensington for earshot to hear the final stages of the Catholic Communion service.

Buchanan made his way to sit with the Protestants and show support for his friend Kensington.

When the time came to serve Communion, humor fell upon Kensington as Protestants remained seated while Catholics, one after the other, jockeyed to get in line to receive the elements. Buchanan intently observed Kensington offer the elements to each marine standing in line to receive the bread and wine.

Marine after marine, received the bread and wine from Kensington who had blessed the elements and presented them to God. All the while, Protestants sat patiently, respectfully till Communion ended. The two sets of marines may have experienced a different religious world growing up, poles apart theologically regarding the Lord's

Supper or the Eucharist, but a common trait all held in a war zone beheld the trust in one another to keep each other alive. Esprit de corps thrived, a common thread in all marines seized in boot camp, the fiber bonding marines together, and the dependence on one another to keep one another protected and alive in war. A brotherhood like no other in the armed services. The grunts supported one another with the esprit de corps of the Marine Corps, though proud and thoroughly devoted to their polarized religious beliefs.

Kensington spoke, "The Body of Christ" as he laid a wafer on each tongue of the marines. Every marine responded with a confident "Amen." The chalice full of wine followed, sipped by each believer, as Kensington utters "The Blood of Christ." The men replied with a convincing, "Amen."

Theological convictions of the meaning and the conducting of Communion or the Eucharist in history have moved human beings to go to war and kill each other over such issues as the Lord's Supper. The two friends were staunch believers in their own faith, but respect for one another overflowed with love and appreciation for one another.

There was no doubt Buchanan and Kensington were fellow conservatives in their respective faiths, but nothing would allow their belief in the Lord's Supper or any other theological point come between their friendship for one another or the mission each felt they were called to do in Vietnam. Their mission to minister to marines the love of Christ served as a top priority, and given the chance to minister to the Vietnamese people Christ's love.

As the last Catholic marine received the elements, Kensington prayed and ended the Roman Catholic service.

To greet marines after Communion services established a routine for the pair of chaplains. The marines this day requested a last prayer with the chaplains for them to complete a vital, but dangerous patrol to start the new road project. The two friends stood as each grunt in line received a prayer of blessing and laying of hands for the protection of God's armor to be given upon each marine.

Jackson secured the service kits, jumped back into the jeep with the chaplains, and continued the journey to Camp Love. The mutual admiration for one another instantiated a bona fide presence. Though obvious theological differences spoke loud and clear, love and admiration melded the relationship together as Christian brothers.

As fellow brothers in Christ, God rendered foremost in their lives. And, as Christians, centered on God and sought God's will in their lives.

As Navy Chaplains, God's will lead them to seek means to meet the wants and needs of marines.

And fulfilling God's will in their lives proved most pertinent.

Oh Rats! Trapped in Booby Traps

October 25, 1968

The human body can only endure a beating for so long till the pounding whittles away the strength and stamina of the human will. The human brain can only tolerate traumatizing experiences for so long till the episodic memories unending dwindle away the sanity and realism of the mind.

Death and violence delivered a constant bombardment upon Skawinski's human will, dwindling away little by little the neurons of his mind. The beatings onto his human will and mental state came from every direction and never ending. He had had enough.

He hoped some shut eye would ease the hammering away of his human will and stop, at least temporarily, the dwindling of a sane mind. Buchanan glanced toward his cot in the dim light, calling for him to catch some shuteye.

Skawinski caught a moment of peace in the war as he accompanied the spiritual team on the first visit to the An Ngai Dong school and orphanage to break in the newly acquired CAP for the camp. Even his deep commitment of benevolence shown to the innocents hampered the beating he had taken mentally, spiritually, and physically because of the war.

The time sat at 0030 hours.

The exhausted Skawinski received a package sent by his mother in yesterday's mail call, a box of homemade caramel chocolates.

He locked it in his air tight sea chest for safekeeping until arriving back from patrol. Knowing the marine in the mailroom, he slipped an unauthorized package through for Skawinski from time to time with a favor in return, of course. Skawinski forked over cash, dealt with weapons, and even dealt cigarettes and beer with the mailroom personnel.

Unlocking the sea chest, Skawinski retrieved his chocolates and placed them on his desk. Exhausted, he sat on his cot, staring down at the box of caramel chocolates. Though he possessed a craving love for caramel chocolates, his love for the sweets failed to move him in diving into his treasure trove of goodies, as he simply fell back on his cot into a deep sleep.

When completely exhausted, human beings let loose all the strength within oneself and surrender to enervation. In such a state, Skawinski fell back onto his cot, exposing his caramels to the open space, and calling for nocturnal pests of the night to pounce on his sugar treats.

His physical state called for shut eye. The caramel chocolates would have to wait till morning.

Skawinski's personal domain he called home beheld very little wiggle room. The hootch comprised a dug in hole inside of a compacted mound of dirt, narrow and rectangular. Bordered inside with wooden planks to serve as a wall of sorts, the hootch occupied enough space to provide a book shelf, a cot to sleep on, and a small desk for writing and reading. Though Skawinski highly valued the book shelf and small desk, they took up a considerable amount of walking space. The time consumed in fighting the war took away from the astute nature within him and isolating himself inside his little cocoon turned out to be perfect for a man who was a bibliophile.

Skawinski comprised an intellectual. He knew how irrational Washington, DC, conducted the war's strategy and tactics and the politicians' approach to winning the war. Talking to his fellow marines, the passive approach to winning the war seemed to get the United States nowhere. Pitching his tent in President Johnson's camp of a containment approach to stop Communism in southeastern Asia spoke volumes to others, bared across his chest. His conviction of the truth behind the domino theory and the spread of Communism initiated enough of a fear in him to fight in order to prevent the spread of Communism at all costs and considered the fight an admirable undertaking. But Skawinski seriously doubted Johnson's refusal to attack aggressively the Communist and the VC in Cambodia. Let alone to attack and annihilate North Vietnam by invading and bombing the north.

Like many serving in Vietnam, Skawinski grew tired of news and reports of how the management of the war came to be selfishly managed by power-hungry politicians and ungrateful Americans ignorant of what actually took place in Vietnam.

Skawinski dreamed during the night of the intentional alteration of war reports by newspaper reporters in print. He envisioned reporters as cackling jokers, laughing with colleagues of the stupidity of the general public concerning the progress of the war and how gullible the public believes anything in the papers. Skawinski woke up momentarily, remembering the content in recent papers, unpleasant reports which he vehemently thought of as lies.

The overwhelming sense of helplessness in the war's conduct served as a heavy weight wearing down on Skawinski's patience in carrying out the strategy and tactics of the war. For Skawinski - the role of negotiating the war falling into the hands of bureaucrats and politicians proved a complete failure. He considered the negotiators as aloof buffoons and callous toward the wants and needs of the South Vietnamese people.

An intellect, Skawinski knew those who conducted negotiations were nothing but nincompoops.

The Communists decreased military movements in October. The NVA withdrew to the borders of North Vietnam and Cambodia to either regroup for a future attack or to decrease the infiltration of South Vietnam, turning the infiltration over to the Viet Cong for a temporary time span.

The October 9-14 negotiations in Paris heard North Vietnam representatives ask Ambassador William Averell Harriman to stop bombing North Vietnam if in return the United States and its allies gave North Vietnam an affirmative simple answer to the question of Saigon taking part in talks. Harriman informed President Johnson of the proposal who asked the advice of General Creighton Williams Abrams and Ambassador to South Vietnam, Ellsworth Bunker. They advised the President that the North Vietnamese meant that the proposal produced a shift of strategy from the battlefield to the "conference table." President Johnson instructed Bunker to relay the proposal to President Nguyen Van Thieu of South Vietnam.

President Thieu insisted that if they were to halt the very little bombing of North Vietnam up to this point in the war, the allied efforts would continue to fight the VC and further military movements of the United States and the ARVN in South Vietnam.

Between October 16-22, a series of meetings were conducted between Ambassador Bunker and President Thieu, in which they demanded three conditions prior to a bombing halt. The three points were: 1) that the DMZ be respected 2) a no halt of bombing South Vietnamese villages, hamlets, and cities supporting the Communists and 3) agree that the Paris Peace Talks include participation of the South Vietnamese government. An additional demand by Thieu insisted the National Liberation Front (NLF), the Viet Cong, be prohibited from any participation in the political negotiations.

The complexity of the diplomatic situation heightened with the Chinese Government on October 1, 1968 declared that they supported the Communists in Vietnam with the "heroic Vietnamese people" in their efforts to establish a Communist state in Vietnam. The declaration by China sent a convincing political message to the western world that Communist China possessed a strong will to establish an oppressive, cruel, and undemocratic Communist state in South Vietnam, infuriating Skawinski and others, including Buchanan.

Militarily, the heaviest air raids in Vietnam began in July 1968 through October 1968. United States planes annihilated 45 supply craft, 31 tanks and destroyed 2 dozen roads in North Vietnam. One of the largest Navy actions in the war, Operation Sealords, launched water maneuvers on October 8, 1968. The action taken consisted of a joint United States, South Vietnamese Navy operation. The enormous action and strategy included Southeast Asia Lake, Ocean, River, and Delta River valleys.

Operation Sealords amounted to a threefold series of actions. First, the United States attempted to cut off every supply line for the Communists from Cambodia into South Vietnam. Second, to destroy supply depots along water ways. And third, to control the Mekong Delta and the major water routes linked to the delta. Three major forces conducted the operation, including the United States 9th Infantry Division Riverine Assault Force, the ARVN, and South Vietnamese Marines. The chain of command called on Skawinski from time to time to aid in the operation. Superior with his skills, he found himself summoned frequently to implement his expertise.

Between October 26-29, a major ground assault of the North Vietnamese Army and the Viet Cong kicked off and lasted for over a month. The enemy attacked the United States 1st Infantry Division in the Tay Ninh Province, 59 miles North of Saigon and near the Cambodian border. In response, the United States bombarded the Tay Ninh area to disperse thousands of North Vietnamese infantry. Unfortunately, marines and army personnel were hindered pursuing the enemy by crossing over the Cambodian border and annihilating the VC or NVA, an agreement the United States had made with Cambodia negotiated by President Johnson's administration. The agreement stated the United States could not bomb the VC and North Vietnamese Army in Cambodia or to cross the border in pursuit of enemy troops. The Johnson administration handed the enemy a ready-made, simple hit-and-run strategy for the North Vietnam forces for the duration of the war. An agreement angering Buchanan, Jackson, Skawinski, and others.

On the home front, protests in San Francisco, possibly numbering in the thousands, but probably in the hundreds, were led by a few dozen soldiers and reservists, along with veterans of possibly all four branches. The protest march set a precedent for the remaining years of the war, for it consisted of demonstrators like no other in the 1960s. The distinct protest featured leadership and organization from former liberal military personnel, many who had served in Vietnam, and encouraged by the Democratic party. The protests in San Francisco incensed Skawinski, Buchanan, Jackson, and many others in Camp Love.

The marines in Camp Love were well aware of South Vietnamese with little to no desire to live under Communist rule. The marines and many South Vietnamese villagers knew good and well the intention of the Communists, and feared atrocities inflicted upon them if the Americans withdrew from South Vietnam. The convenience of life in the United States provided protesters an easy comfort zone, a laid foundation for protesting a war they knew nothing about, and who cared little for the people in South Vietnam. Let alone caring for the men fighting in Vietnam for freedom and to establish a freer society.

Besides, the United States sought to fight and win the Cold War, to halt Communist aggression around the world. Communist worldwide aspired to control the peoples of the world by creating Command economies and governments in less developed countries. Skawinski knew without a doubt the protesters would think twice if forced to live under such a regime as Communism. Calling out the protesters in San Francisco and the country, Skawinski called them for what they really were - selfish and naïve victims of coercion by the far left wing of the Democratic party and politicians who cared nothing for the South Vietnamese who the United States were protecting. Skawinski held the opinion that the protesters and the far left in the United States wouldn't care one bit if the Communists killed every single human being in South Vietnam as long as they could win politically in the United States.

Skawinski's blood pressure skyrocketed thinking of such things concerning the war. An intellectual, he knew without any doubt the government ran a war in irrational terms, driving him crazy.

Skawinski grew grumpy, agitated.

Quickly falling asleep, the young marine had forgotten about his chocolate caramels, wide open on his desk, inviting pests of the night for a midnight snack.

Emotionally and physically drained, Skawinski fell back onto his cot wearing nothing but his shorts, t-shirt, and combat boots. He wore boots often at night, as did his friend Buchanan, out of fear of pests lurking in the darkness of night.

Dreams came frequently for marines in Camp Love, including Skawinski. His dreams waited for nothing, as his head hit the pillow, losing consciousness.

Skawinski dreaded sleep at night when totally exhausted. More often than not, nightmares flowed fluently during the night when dog-tired. Tonight was no different. As soon as his head hit his small pillow, he immediately fell asleep, dreaming plenty, as the last dream turned into a humdinger of a nightmare.

In his dream, Skawinski is catching some shut eye on his cot. The Viet Cong cunningly sneak into his hootch, surrounding him. Encircling him, the VC strategically sit smack dab in the middle of his desk, directly into his chair, positioning themselves on the floor, and leaning ever so quietly on his bookshelf. As the VC giggle, reflective of devilish snickers, they patiently wait for deadly booby traps they set in and all around Skawinski's hootch to blow up the second he trips one off. The Viet Cong can once and for all rid themselves of a marine whose proficiency in combat engineering skills has disarmed so many booby traps they had set in the jungle. The VC glare at one another, cackling fiendishly, rubbing compulsively their hands together for a booby trap to blow up a great adversary into smithereens. The most deadly booby trap set was a 200 pound tree trunk studded with bamboo spikes with a trip wire to swing down and crash into Skawinski's chest as he sat up in his cot. With a constant demonic tone of giggling, the VC, humored with the booby traps set in Skawinski's cot, wait patiently for abrupt movements from him to trigger trip wires, setting the booby traps off, killing and dismembering his body.

From start to finish, the Viet Cong appear in the dream as if their faces are smack dab on top of a camera lens, distorted as if in a house of mirrors at the carnival. Their faces pulled back with demonic smiles. Worse yet, the VC embodied a four-legged animal every marine and sailor in camp loathed - rats. Large, hairy, grotesque rats, as big as small dogs in southeast Asia. In Vietnam, rats were an enemy and menace to United States military personnel, very much like the VC. Marines in camp hated them, as rats were infiltrators just as much as the Viet Cong were. The pests ate and contaminated food. They chewed and destroyed electrical wire. The pests bit and ruined parts of the camp's defenses containing plastic and wood. The sailors and marines in camp came to equilibrate the rats with the Viet Cong.

All the while, attempts of the Viet Cong, or the rats, to cause Skawinski to move abruptly, causing the booby traps to go off, came to a dead end, one attempt after the other. The VC pests each took a stab in causing an abrupt movement. The tickling of Skawinski's nose with a feather came to no avail. The tickling of his feet with sharp claws came to nothing and even jabs into Skawinski's rib cage were ineffective. Nothing seemed to work for the VC.

With the patience of the rats came a more boisterous, demonic giggle in the dream.

The long-suffering of the rats finally came to an end, as Skawinski moved tersely from jabs in his ribs from a sharpened stick, setting the booby traps off, including the tree trunk, blowing Skawinski into smithereens, hurling him all over the hootch. He hastily woke up screaming, "Noooooooooo!"

Rising abruptly, he inspected quickly every inch of his hootch. He slapped and grabbed his chest, assuring himself he's still alive. When reality hits, he's still with the living. He adjusts to the darkness of the night with his eyes. Sitting in a long position with his legs stretched out in front of him on the cot, he discovers he's soaking wet from sweating profusely. Adjusting to the dim light, he grabs a towel hanging on the wall to wipe away the perspiration from his body. After regaining his whereabouts, Skawinski hears the slightest faint of noises in the night's stillness. Detecting noises from the direction of his caramel chocolates on his desk, he centers in on all the racket to identify the source of the noise.

To his horror, he remembered his caramel chocolates sitting on his desk and thought, 'The chocolates. I didn't secure them in the chest.'

Terrified, he felt something heavy between his legs, moving about, kicking the hefty object off his cot.

Glancing toward his caramel chocolates in the few streaks of moonlight into his hootch, he recognized an unwelcome sight incensing him to no end, causing immediate anger.

'Ah, rats!' he thought.

In the darkness, Skawinski discovered the source of the soft, low-pitched noises. He laid his eyes on the ugliest, dirtiest rats he had ever seen scattered all over his hootch, munching down on his caramel chocolates. Spotting the candy box on his desk ripped to shreds with his 20/20 vision, the ugly monsters, the size of small house dogs, found a midnight snack courtesy of Skawinski's caramel chocolates.

The rats invaded every inch of the hootch. Two rats were sitting in the center of Skawinski's desk, staring straight at him with the most satisfied expressions on their hairy faces after ripping into the candy box and consuming several treats. A third rat sat on the edge of the desk munching on a chocolate. An additional rat sat at the foot of his cot on the floor undetected. The first rat discovered between his legs increased the number of invaders to five. One last rat sat his fat self on an empty ammo box Skawinski used for storage and an end table. On top of the ammo box, he placed pictures of his parents, his dogs, one of southern Ohio hillsides, and a photo of his family farm. The rat knocked the pictures face down, gnawing on one edge of a wood frame containing a picture of his parents. Skawinski heard short, pesky squeaks discharged from their mouths.

Six rats in all!

Skawinski's knee jerk reaction enticed him to fetch his .45 caliber in his holster at arm's reach and blow the rats apart, sending them to rat Heaven. Retrieving his .45, he aimed his pistol right between the eyes of one rat. Knowing full well if he fired his weapon, the entire camp would go nuts, risking a chance of marines firing weapons in every direction, possibly killing each other with friendly fire from confusion. Slowly lowering his weapon, he placed it back into its holster. Stepping softly and carefully onto the floor, he reached for his machete hanging on the wall in a sheath.

Pulling the machete out from its sheath, he stepped toward each rat, slitting the throats of each gnawer one by one with one swift slice. Rat squeaks turned into hisses once the rodent sensed the danger it found itself in. The hissing turned into an ominous growl when approached by Skawinski. Slitting the throat of each rat one by one, he flung the rat outside his hooch. The pile of rats accumulated outside the hootch with each execution.

The consternation interrupted his much needed sleep. The intrusion of his abode intensified and amplified his hatred of rats ten fold.

The time sat at 0245 hours. Keyed up from all the commotion, Skawinski paid Chaplain Buchanan a visit in the middle of the night. Grabbing his cover, he rushed over to Buchanan's hootch to fill him in on his nightmare, ridding his mind of such horrors.

Buchanan's open door 'any day, any hour' policy spoke loud and clear for Skawinski, calling him to his chaplain's hootch.

When Skawinski arrived, Buchanan heard a faint knock at the hootch door.

When disturbed in the middle of the night of his beauty sleep, Buchanan found himself initially annoyed. But this night he felt a sudden delight within himself when setting his eyes on Skawinski standing in front of him. He welcomed Skawinski's company at any hour or day of the week, a blessing for Buchanan.

After a bit of small talk, Skawinski laid out in every detail his dream of rats and booby traps. The two talked the rest of the night away. Skawinski did nothing but talk and talk and talk. The men discussed every topic and issue. They talked of sports, Ohio State football, politics, the upcoming Presidential election between Nixon and Humphrey, economics, and vegetable and domestic farming. The engagement of conversation furnished consolation and comfort for Skawinski. The young marine, keyed up as usual following a nightmare, found the usual means of consolation visiting Buchanan in the middle of the night.

Two hours passed as the hands of the clock rested at 0445 hours, and a new day was just about to dawn. Skawinski functioned on a mere two hours of sleep, but time spent with Buchanan seemed, as always, enough to encourage him to push forward the next day.

Skawinski welcomed a new day in Vietnam. Another day as a combat engineer in a combat zone.

Another day to exterminate rats.

AN NGAI TAY

OCTOBER 29, 1968

The past week of ministry had been long and taxing. Within the week, Kensington met with Lieutenant Colonel Lucas, along with Buchanan and Jackson. Lucas supported the Civic Action Program at the orphanage and school, advocating the benefits of a holistic, physiological endeavor for the battalion. Lucas approved the CAP for the orphanage almost straight away. Lucas came across a few chaplains in Vietnam who brushed aside CAPs, thinking they took too much time of ministry from the men. These chaplains had no intention of initiating any new CAPs either, though the Chain of Command of the Chaplain Corps advocated such ministries. Lucas thought the chaplains' reasoning was 'crap' and that marines need exposure to humane endeavors.

Along with the CAP at the orphanage, Buchanan accompanied the battalion doctor with his monthly visits to the surrounding villages, hamlets, and townships. The camp doctor administered his skills within the auspices of a Medical Civic Action Program, better known as a MedCAP to those advancing the efforts of United States Military and political objectives of President Johnson in southeastern Asia. One hamlet the camp doctor visited was An Ngai Tay. Lieutenant James Delaney, a proficient and dedicated doctor, built a successful reputation as a surgeon back home in Texas. An immensely proud Texan, he expressed every chance he got to non-Texans how great Texas is - inside and out. His family owned deep roots in the medical profession, reaching back several generations. The family tree provided documentation his kinfolk provided medical attention to General Sam Houston's army fighting for independence against Mexico, a fact of immeasurable pride for the Texas surgeon. A detachment of corpsmen assigned to Camp Love aided Delaney with medical care in camp and accompanied marine patrols into the mountainsides, deep jungle, and rice patties to administer their medical skills.

Chaplains in Vietnam served as medical aid personnel to the corpsmen. The Navy trained them with basic first aid, assisting the corpsmen with the wounded in combat.

Buchanan discussed the very first day in camp with Delaney if he could tag along with him to the MedCAPs. Adamant of the prospect of Buchanan 'tagging' along, Delaney considered Buchanan a source of moral support to many villagers in the area from his months in Da Nang. He also accompanied Catholic chaplains to villages to assist with Catholic services. Besides, Buchanan begun, with Lucas' approval, a food and clothing CAP in 5 surrounding villages.

When finished with an early breakfast, the spiritual team began their trek into the jungle with Lieutenant Delaney, corpsmen, and two platoons from Companies B and C, led by First Lieutenant Lawrence Jones of Company C.

Buchanan had been in the bush for nearly a month, and he had yet to be immune to the heat of the dense jungle of Vietnam. Admiring the power and beauty of southeastern Asian topography was one thing. But he never appreciated the awful, brutal heat of Vietnam. Today spawned a vicious humid day. Growing up in Kentucky and Ohio, he settled for more of a year round four-season climate.

The spiritual team set out for An Ngai Tay hamlet, a population of about 200. The hamlet held its head high with a new meeting hall, two improved roads leading into the hamlet, a deep water well, and a rice-drying floor, all built by the marines of the 7th Engineering Marine Battalion and Navy Seabees. Often, the Viet Cong cruelly harassed and intimidated the village, putting the people in the village on edge and fearful for their lives. The citizens of the hamlet trusted the marines from Camp Love after a long, enduring process of cultivation from other camps growing into a trusting relationship with the members of the hamlet since 1966. The cultivation of the marines paid off - the villagers of An Ngai Tay hamlet trusted the Americans more than their own fellow Vietnamese, South Vietnamese traitors serving the North Vietnamese Communist within the ranks of the Viet Cong.

Buchanan and Jackson hopped into their jeep, preceded by the doctor and three of the twelve corpsmen assigned to Camp Love in their jeeps. Companies B and C platoons led the convey in trucks, along with an additional truck transporting a combat engineering crew, including Skawinski, at the tail end of the convoy.

Delaney's right arm in the bush served in a sailor's uniform, a Navy corpsman, who provided excellent care to the marines. The dependence upon a corpsman in the bush in case a marine fell wounded in battle placed a high pressured role in combat on the shoulders of corpsmen, and one a marine set into the capable hands of a corpsman to keep him alive. The sailors for the trip to An Ngai Tay were Chief Petty Officer John Dingus, Petty Officer 2nd Class Philip Jenkins, and Petty Officer 2nd Class James Crowley, who served in prior battles and skirmishes under heavy fire and placing themselves with bravery between the wounded and the enemy.

In any war, the rank and file considered United States corpsman life savers. In the jungles of Vietnam, the corpsmen worked in close order with the marines. A Navy corpsman's equipment in Vietnam comprised a 'Unit One' medical instrument set, including medical supplies, issued to a corpsman to implement medical aid. When in the bush, corpsmen stocked additional reserves of medical supplies. Marines held corpsmen in high esteem, regarding them with great respect and admiration.

Held in high regard by the marines, corpsmen served as a 'life line' for the men. Corpsmen in Vietnam ranked the highest with casualty rates in the war, putting their lives in harm's way with a dangerous risk and in frantic and trying situations.

The ebullient devotion of a corpsman never to leave a wounded or dead marine behind in the jungle appeared quite clear during the war. The dedication risked further casualties to retrieve a wounded or killed marine. The NVA and VC acknowledged this commitment and cowardly cornered wounded marines into holes to avoid heavy weaponry against them. Of course, the marines set out to secure the trapped marine, which exposed more marines to enemy attack.

Two corpsmen caught Buchanan's eye, most curious. First was PO 2nd Class Jenkins, who possessed every weapon imaginable attached to him. His arsenal included an M-16, a .45 caliber pistol, a Colt M1911A1, a machete, a hunting knife, several Mk 2 grenades attached to his belt and uniform, two humongous Bowie knifes and a Ka-Bar knife. Jenkins readied himself for action. Buchanan considered Jenkins' presentation as overkill, a burdensome array of weaponry, on the verge of looking ridiculous.

"Did you see the weaponry that corpsman had attached to himself? Isn't it a little bizarre, and considered overkill to you, Philip?" asked Buchanan, as Jackson chuckles.

"*Yeah.*" responded Jackson with a smirk. "His name's Philip Jenkins. Know little about him, though. Regardless of his ridiculous show of manhood, I'd heard he's an excellent corpsman. But, you know, he's hardly ever used any of those weapons, except for his M-16 and .45 pistol."

"You're kidding?"

Jackson smiles and remarks, "Guess if he's ever to use them, he'll be ready, huh?"

"I guess so." responded Buchanan. "What about the other one? Is it Crowley? Looks educated and intelligent. What do you know of him?"

"Not much, sir. You're right, though. He conducts himself smartly, doesn't he?" answered Jackson.

Smiling, Jackson continued to drive toward the hamlet just a few miles northeast of Camp Love. Buchanan observed, as usual, the routine work of the people of Vietnam in the rice patty fields, the beauty of Vietnam, and the remnants of war such as the remains of a jeep after an explosion. The intrigue for the country of Vietnam fascinated Buchanan.

As the convoy stopped from time to time to survey the road for mines and booby traps, Buchanan took advantage to capture some of the culture of the Vietnamese and the aftermath of war by snapping several slide pictures for his record and experience in Vietnam.

As time passed, the convoy finally arrived at An Ngai Tay Hamlet. Platoons of Companies B and C conducted a reconnaissance operation of a wide radius surrounding the village, along with Skawinski and his combat engineering team searching for booby traps and mine sweeps in the rice patties, while Delaney administered his doctoring skills upon the citizens of the hamlet.

The spiritual team stepped out of their jeep, joining the medical personnel.

As Delaney stepped out of the jeep, he immediately noticed the line of Vietnamese needing medical attention. To his dismay, the line before him grew longer than usual, many of them children.

To speed the process, Delaney set up two tables with two separate patient lines. One table manned by himself and one corpsman, the other manned by the other two corpsmen.

His first patient stepped forward, an elderly man suffering from a broken finger. His index finger broken at the middle phalanx while fixing a splintered wooden frame on his home damaged from a severe storm weeks earlier. Delaney and Crowley buddy tapped his fingers and gave him some painkillers.

The second patient Delaney remembered from his initial visits, a girl of 6 or 7 years old and a favorite amongst the children in the hamlet. Her name was Hung, which meant 'pink rose' in Vietnamese. Her humble, gentle spirit exhibited a 'pink rose', though all she knew in life came from a war-torn world. Her beauty shined for all to see and within her innocent self attained peace dogged by war. Her displayed demeanor reflected that of the Vietnamese and the eastern religions way of life.

As Hung's father held her during the examination, Delaney noticed puncture wounds in various locations on her feet. For a better bird's-eye view, he sat Hung on the table to examine her.

Delaney greeted her - "Chao em yeu."

"Chao ban." responded Hung.

"Ban rat dep." added Delaney.

Hung smiled widely and touched Delaney's arm. Patting her soft, gentle hand, he smiled to reassure her of his concern for her health.

As Delaney examined Hung more in depth, he noticed two distinct bruises, an abrasion or two, and many scratches. Examining her feet, several punctures on the bottom and sides of her feet looked suspect. In fact, her severely damaged feet gave the impression Hung stepped onto a punji booby trap of some sort.

Delaney and Crowley doctored Hung's wounds and, when finished, approached her father to ask the liberty of treating her more in depth in Camp Love. If not, infection and gangrene might take hold of Hung's injuries and become sick. Delaney spoke to her father through two interpreters to inform him of her situation and asked him for permission to take her back to Camp Love.

Hung's father gratefully granted permission to treat her back in camp.

45 minutes passed as half of the line received treatment from the medical team. Most patients were children, and problems similar to Hung's, bruises, abrasions, and welts as if the Viet Cong had whipped the children with a branch or whip. To describe the mental state of Delaney as 'alarmed' might be an understatement.

The spiritual team stood in between the tables to furnish a spiritual presence for the MedCAP. While standing in the center of the tables greeting the Vietnamese patients, Jackson reminded Buchanan to discuss the possibility of conducting Catholic services in the hamlet with the elders. Many Catholics in the hamlet fled North Vietnam from cruel Communist persecution in the 1950s. The spiritual desire for Catholic services reached an all-time high, absent from the hamlet for months. The previous two Catholic priests were murdered by Viet Cong insurgents who forced parishioners to watch the execution.

There were too many wounds, bruises, welts, and scratches for the Americans to ignore. The first inclinations for the many and obvious wounds such as these indicated the Viet Cong were responsible for the wounds. The Viet Cong applied physical intimidation on rural villagers almost daily.

Curiosity filled every American heart and mind. 'Who did this?' 'Who committed and carried out such atrocities?'

The spiritual team excused themselves and walked over to converse with elders of the hamlet.

An individual hamlet in Vietnam served as a single part of a village, combining several hamlets together to form a village. Social scientists define a hamlet as a sub-unit of a village with a population of anywhere between 500 to thousands of people, as small as 200. The total number of hamlets in South Vietnam added up close to 17,000, making up a little over 3,000 villages. Part of the United States' strategy in Vietnam sought to politically permeate the hamlets to create a source of intelligence to track Viet Cong and North Vietnam Army movements and to use as bases for military strategy and tactics. Hamlets were protected and fortified, either with barbed wire or bamboo fence with the assistance of the South Vietnamese Army and United States forces. The United States and its allies often implemented Civic Action Programs as incentives for villagers to cooperate with the United States. The VC countered with intimidation and harassing hamlets not to cooperate with the ARVN and United States forces. The VC did not think twice of torturing and murdering villagers if suspected of assisting South Vietnamese or American military personnel.

The United States countered Viet Cong intimidation of villages and hamlets with President Johnson's Civic Action Programs (CAP) in South Vietnam to replicate the Strategic Hamlet Program, which was dumped after South Vietnam's President Ngo Dinh Diem's assassination in 1963.

During the war, Viet Cong forces employed hamlets as cells to conduct ambushes and attacks against South Vietnamese and United States troops. An Ngai Tay supported the United States' efforts to establish a more western type of government based on individual freedoms. The Viet Cong terrorized many hamlets and villages, including An Ngai Tay. The VC would destroy a hamlet if deemed necessary on their part.

Buchanan and Jackson, along with one interpreter assigned to Delaney, ambled their way over to the hamlet elders assembled under the community center. The center, built of mortar and stone bricks, stood as a monument of dedication and service for the marines and Seabees of the 7th Engineering who constructed it. The center exemplified the pride and joy of An Ngai Tay, uniting the citizens within the hamlet. The elders welcomed the spiritual team, and it didn't take long to talk the elders and their chief into having Catholic services. A few elders had converted to Catholicism many years earlier. The spiritual team made their way back to Delaney and the corpsman, about to finish the medical aid to the villagers.

Buchanan, followed by Jackson, walked directly to Delaney, engaged in a tense conversation with First Lieutenant Lawrence Jones from Spokane, Washington, and a member of the Roman Catholic Church. Two other officers were present, Captain Bernard Johannsson, Charlie Company's ranking officer, giving his two cents worth in the conversation, along with Lieutenant Rockford of Bravo Company. The four men were in a fervent discussion concerning the high number of children with similar wounds and injuries. Bruises, abrasions, and serious welts indicated suspicious beatings and torture presenting ample evidence of abuse from the Viet Cong. Jones, the executive officer of Company C, sensed in his gut the Viet Cong had intimidated the hamlet with violence. Rage filled the insides of Gunnery Sergeant Richard Neville Warwick Jurgensen, of Bravo Company, incensed with the injuries and insisted on radioing to Camp Love for permission to go after the VC right there and then.

"Let's go get these VC, Captain Johannsson. Those devils maimed these babies. Look at 'em." insisted Jurgensen, motioning with his hand the children sitting and standing off to the side. "The VC deserves what's coming to 'em."

Few villagers knew English, but reading the body language of any foreigner served an international language, and the villagers read Jurgensen's body language loud and clear. Obviously furious, Jurgensen set out to find the VC responsible for the torture of the children.

"No, Gunny." pressed Captain Johannsson with a tone of caution in his voice. "First, we need permission to conduct such action. Under an immediate life or death circumstance we might go after them, but we have the chaplain *and* the doctor with us, we can't take a chance of putting them in danger. Under normal circumstances, we'd get them."

Regardless, Jurgensen continued his tirade. "But sir, those VC might still be in the area. We've four platoons. Let's go after these thugs. Look again what they did to these kids. Those VC devils, well...I'm sick and tired of seeing them hit and run constantly. Let's show 'em marine grit and determination. Let's radio in and get permission. Send the Doc and Padre back to base. Let's get these animals!"

Johannsson interjected, "I'm all for showing them how much more superior we are to them in fighting, Gunny. But we've got to go with chain and command on this one. I'll report to Captain Case, and he can go up the chain of command, inform superiors of what's happened here and they'll deal with it properly."

Angered, Jurgensen pointed out, "Sir, if VC have spies in the hamlet, they just might snitch on the villagers about us being here today. Might come back and torch the place. We got to do something."

Pausing, Captain Johannsson responded with a simple, flat out - "No."

"Yes, sir." succumbed Jurgensen, reluctantly.

Standing near the officers' call, corpsmen James Crowley spoke up, overhearing the entire conversation.

"Sir, I know I'm only a 2nd Class Petty Officer in the Navy, but, I, well. Can I talk frankly, sir?" asked Crowley.

"Go ahead Crowley." acknowledged Johannsson.

"Well, sir. If the villagers are being threatened by the VC, why don't we radio in, inform chain of command of the situation? Let us transport the severely injured, let us treat 'em back at base and let wounds heal. Platoons here can do their thing, set up a temporary perimeter for the night." said Crowley.

"I think PO Crowley's correct in his assessment of the situation, captain." added CPO Dingus.

Johannsson cocked his head sideways, pondering the notion from Crowley.

Lieutenant Jones stated with some authority, "I'll go back with Doc Delaney, talk to the Skipper in getting a work order in for the engineers, along with Navy Seabees, to construct a perimeter with barbed wire and fortifications within the next few days. The Vietnamese leadership in the hamlet already showed they have absolutely no trust toward the VC and they want to help us."

Rockford inserted his two cents worth and pointed out, "We and the South Vietnamese marines train Vietnamese men all the time in the use and implementation of firearms and weapons, are in villages and hamlets constantly training men to defend themselves. Gunny Sergeant's right, when the VC gets word that we've been back once again to provide medical aid to An Ngai Tay, they just might torch the hamlet. They know when we come, we're out to gain a bit of info on enemy movements."

Every eyeball within the MedCAP brain trust centered in on Captain Johannsson. The decision to deliver all the strength and military might of the marines into the Viet Cong to pay them a lesson in what real military superiority is laid on the weight of his shoulders.

Nervously, Johannsson says, "OK. Let me think about it here for a moment." Turning to his side, he stepped to his right with his back to the others.

Crowley breaks the thoughts of Johannsson and made a point. "Sir, you've been here for a month. And we're here to tell ya, sir, those VC - they're the meanest people on earth."

Crowley's comment caught the ear of everyone in leadership roles. With a nerve-racking moment of silence, he added, "*Really* mean. They'd kill every child in the hamlet if it'd give them a heavier hand on the villagers."

Johannsson mused on the situation and said, "Alright, Corporal Lipstone, radio in for permission, set up a perimeter and send back the most severely wounded to Camp Love. Inform the base of the situation."

Turning to Gunnery Jurgensen, Johannsson says, "Gunny, you and Bravo Company get started setting up a temporary perimeter."

Johannsson barked an order to First Lieutenant Jones. "Take one platoon back with you, guard the severely wounded and I'll stay here to lead the initial steps to jump start the perimeter."

"Lance, allocate between your two platoons of Bravo Company, secure pathways into the village and secure Route 540 coming into An Ngai Tay." said Johannsson to his friend Rockford.

"Will do, sir." replied Rockford.

Johannsson said to Buchanan, "Padre, you and Jackson, along with the Doc, ride back to base with the wounded. Your presence will lighten the mood."

"Yes, sir. We'll take care of morale, you can count on that." responds Buchanan, grinning.

Lipstone, all the while communicating with Camp Love, informs Johannsson, "Sir, base gives the word *go*. We can proceed with the perimeter, Captain."

"Thanks, Lipstone." said Johannsson with great satisfaction written all over his face. "And the wounded?"

Lipstone smiles and says, "Base informs me no one person could be in better hands than in Doc Delaney's. The word's go, sir."

Lipstone loved his role in the Marine Corps. The young marine came from Milledgeville, Georgia. His role and responsibility as radioman for Bravo Company placed him in the perfect position to succeed in the military. He described himself as 'dirt poor' back home and found a home in the Marine Corps. As an African-American, he didn't see any prospects for a high-paying job in middle Georgia, so he volunteered to join the marines. He never studied in high school, but possessed a high intellect. His experience in high school had been dull and boring. School lacked to challenge him to think, to expand his mental capacity. When entering the Marine Corps, the military gave him an IQ test and scored a whopping 132 IQ. When seeing the IQ score results for himself, all he could say was, "Wow!" After the results of a 132 on the test, the marines wanted to place him in an intelligence unit or working in the Judge Advocate office, but he refused. He had no desire to hang around smug turtle neck types and Annapolis ring knockers.

One trait embedded into the Lipstone's very soul comprised his outspoken voice in protecting the locals. Providing a higher standard of living for the Vietnamese sided with the United States personalized a top priority for Lipstone. He might have been a corporal, but he let his voice be heard, including letting the officers hear a voice of reason from time to time.

Buchanan noticed Lipstone's demeanor. He heeded to the wants and needs of other human beings. Lipstone's sincerity came to be quite obvious to Buchanan. He considered Lipstone a future prospect of support for the chaplain's office.

Lipstone held back in An Ngai Tay, assisting in the perimeter's security and as communications liaison for Johannsson and Charlie Company.

The marines loaded up the severely wounded villagers onto the trucks, while those staying behind secured the perimeter.

Skawinski's combat engineer squad volunteered to stay behind and secure the area in case of booby traps.

The next day, Camp Love began assisting and fortifying An Ngai Tay, training the men of the hamlet in using weapons supported by South Vietnamese soldiers and marines.

For Buchanan, his aim of establishing a permanent Catholic service for the citizens of An Ngai Tay fell in place. For the secular realm, An Ngai Tay would be more of a safe haven for citizens in the hamlet. The presence of a secure perimeter and the company of weapons in the hamlet showed a warning of strength and vigor to the Viet Cong.

An Ngai Tay had had enough. If the atrocious treatment of human beings by the Viet Cong reflected life living under communism, the citizens of An Ngai Tay didn't want to have anything to do with the Communist north.

The citizens of An Ngai Tay were now ready to fight back and the Viet Cong certainly would feel the hammer onto the anvil pounding out a strengthened resolve.

SWEET REVENGE

OCTOBER 30, 1968

First Lieutenant Jones, Captain Johannsson, Charlie Company, Lipstone, and Skawinski spent the night in An Ngai Tay holding a defensive perimeter around the hamlet. The large contingent waited patiently for reinforcements to scope and sweep the rather large perimeter desired to eliminate any immediate threat of the Viet Cong to the hamlet.

Finally, reinforcements arrived from division, Bravo Company, an interrogation team, and two sweeper teams from Camp Love.

Time ran fast as the hands of time rested at 0600 hours in the morning.

The 7th Marine Engineering Battalion shared engineering skills with South Vietnamese civilians in strategic villages and hamlets. Part of President Johnson's strategy to win the war hung on the fact he vowed to protect and fight for South Vietnamese with the desire to live a freer life, opposed to being forced to live under Communism.

The battalion engaged itself in several Civic Action Programs within Camp Love's vicinity and encouraged to do so in order to establish support for the United States' effort of stopping Communist aggression in Southeastern Asia. The CAP's of the battalion continued in October, including the MedCAP program, which treated medically hundreds of Vietnamese in the past few months. The 14,500 soil-cement bricks issued and distributed throughout the Quang Nam Province served as a lifesaver for construction projects throughout the province. An additional CAP for the 7th Engineering Battalion,

Tung Son Hamlet, turned out to be time well spent because of the improvements of the livelihoods for the citizens in the hamlet. The elders in the hamlet witnessed in October improvements within their hamlet with 30% construction completed of a two-room school, 3 bath houses 75% completed, and a head 15% installed. The uttermost for the citizens of Tong Son Hamlet in October comprised the construction of a water pump, a hand-type, becoming a monumental addition for the people, changing the lives of citizens in the hamlet. The battalion launched three garden plots in the Hoa Thanh Village and Hoa Ninh Refugee camp, putting to use American seeds and methods in which Major Michael "Mickey" Sanborn proudly made use of his knowledge in agriculture and help establish the garden plots. The battalion recognized the efforts and work of Major Sanborn, teaching the South Vietnamese agricultural skills frequently.

But the pride and joy of the 7th Engineering CAPs centered in on An Ngai Tay hamlet. The battalion in November set goals for defensive measures for the hamlet. The 6 defensive bunkers within the perimeter of the hamlet topped at 90% completed in November and the defensive perimeter improved with establishing abatis, including punji sticks, in and around the perimeter. Major Sanborn presented a plow and a spiked-tooth harrow to the farmers, instructing the agricultural use of the tools. In the past two years, the completed construction of a school building came to fruition, along with completing other construction projects, including a head and a community center.

An Ngai Tay held a special place in the hearts of the battalion. The populace of the hamlet was pro American and Roman Catholic. An underlining motivator of resistance against the NVA and VC forces for the villagers grew out of the possibility of living forcefully under the auspices of an oppression Communist government, which the citizens of An Ngai Tay loathed the thought of. Besides, the immense yearning of a cherished life of religious freedom flowed within the veins of every Roman Catholic heart and mind of the hamlet villagers.

Hamlets and villages hostile to Americans were given very little help, only by order did American forces assist hostile villages. An Ngai

Tay identified itself as pro American and even served as an informant to American forces on Viet Cong and NVA movements in the area.

The evidence of Viet Cong torture and intimidation on An Ngai Tay hamlet inflamed anger of the 7th Engineering Battalion, especially corpsmen and Bravo Company, who aided the hamlet more than any other in Camp Love.

To secure the hamlet with marines from division in a joint effort, Camp Love implemented their competent skills from the efforts of Bravo Company, Charlie Company, Skawinski's combat engineering and demolition teams, the interrogation team, and 2 teams of mine sweepers. The mine sweepers worked a 1500 feet perimeter around An Ngai Nay hamlet for booby traps. Skawinski's team searched and destroyed for Viet Cong tunnels or 'nests' posing an immediate threat to the hamlet.

Villages and hamlets friendly to Americans were threatened by the Viet Cong, vulnerable to receiving a high level of intimidation. What incensed, compassionate, empathetic marines in Camp Love most came from the treatment of children in An Ngai Tay. Many marines had siblings and were uncles to children of similar ages with the children in the hamlet, many of them young girls intimidated and violated by the VC. A few marines were even fathers to girls back home, as young as those in An Ngai Tay.

The marines quickly went to work. Men from division served as guardsmen in and around An Ngai Tay, while Bravo Company and Charlie Company accompanied Skawinski's demolition team and the minesweepers in the bush.

The interrogation team interviewed people of the hamlet to inquire of who might be informants for the VC within the populace of An Ngai Tay.

The effort to find booby traps and search for Viet Cong tunnels would take time. The efforts proved to be well worth it since the hamlet showed to be a loyal supporter and adherent ally with the Americans and an informant of military and enemy movements of VC.

Fortifications built in and around the An Ngai Tay hamlet's perimeter the past two years failed to pass inspection from engineers and construction men. Defenses in the perimeter failed inspection due to neglect and the dilapidated condition of the perimeter.

The new defenses in and around the perimeter encompassed two rather large trenches from 4 to 5 feet deep, surrounding the hamlet with punji sticks emerging from the surface of the ditches. Engineers positioned larger punji sticks on both sides of the ditches, with booby traps placed within the perimeter. Three watch towers were constructed serving as lookouts, with barbed wire placed in the ditches attached to trip wires adding to the potency of the booby traps. United States and South Vietnamese marines trained the men in the hamlet with weapons for protection. The men of the hamlet became exceptionally skilled with weapons given the training from the ARVN. With the layers of barriers to prevent infiltration into the hamlet, the weapons training for the men, and the protection from the Americans, the VC still infiltrated the hamlet from time to time.

The Communists dispersed Viet Cong secret infiltrators dressed in civilian clothes all over South Vietnam. Agents in and around An Ngai Tay must have been present, providing tactical information to the North Vietnamese concerning the hamlet to have been so severely intimidated and pressured the past three months.

Skawinski's team found many booby traps, including claymore mines and trip wire booby traps. He and his team discovered several booby traps secured by secondary traps as well. The Viet Cong would set a booby trap in such a manner that a marine combat engineer circling around to disarm a trap would run into another booby trap. The VC hoped the combat engineer failed to notice the secondary trap setting off both traps, maiming or killing the marine.

Mine sweepers discovered 8 claymore mines strategically positioned around the hamlet. All American M18A1 mines found were stolen, another obvious warning a VC presence loomed. The specifications of the mine were about 3.5 pounds, with measurements of 8.5 inches, 1.5 inches in width, and about 5.0 inches in height. The caliber of the mine was potent, composed of meticulous specifications, including 1/8-inch steel balls that contained 600-700 projectiles in a single mine. Effective firing range of the mine reached 60 yards, while the maximum firing range maxed approximately 290 yards.

Totaling the combined hard work of Skawinski's combat engineering team and the mine sweeping teams, they discovered 15 booby traps walking the perimeter of An Ngai Tay. If the goal of the VC intended to frighten An Ngai Tay into submission, the number of booby traps certainly threatened the hamlet. Undeterred, the citizens of An Ngai Tay fought back.

Evidence ran plenty that the Viet Cong meant business setting 15 booby traps to maim, injure, or kill a citizen of An Ngai Tay. Regardless, the hamlet fought back.

Company C emerged from the bush with 7 prisoners suspected of being Viet Cong terrorists. All their hands were tied behind their backs and tied at the waist, connecting all 7 suspects. With hope, interrogating the prisoners in a neutral location will provide information to lead to those responsible for terrorizing friendly South Vietnamese.

Staff Sergeant Frank Smith of Charlie Company informed Captain Johannsson that Skawinski's combat engineering team and Company C destroyed a Viet Cong tunnel supplying Viet Cong efforts in the vicinity.

The obvious presence of the VC alarmed the marines. The efforts of the enemy to infiltrate the region of Camp Love so heavily signaled a clear red flag of danger for friendly Vietnamese near Camp Love. To avoid future danger, the marines set out to 'nip any threat of the VC in the bud'.

The roads leading to and from An Ngai Tay set as a top priority for the engineers and sweepers of Camp Love in the days and months ahead.

When word of Viet Cong infiltration of An Ngai Tay reached Buchanan and Jackson, they seethed with indignation. The spiritual team met no more Christian, hospitable, and friendlier South Vietnamese than the citizens of An Ngai Tay. It saddened them to no end as the VC beasts terrorized the villagers' lives. A fact of Viet Cong terrorism had no effect on the protesters and liberals back home in the United States, clueless of the atrocities committed by the Viet Cong and the Communists upon innocent victims. Even if the anti-war protesters knew of the atrocities, they could have cared less.

The hamlet longed for religious freedom, a basic western tenet many in the world came short of encompassing, a liberty those in the west were blessed with.

As long as Buchanan and Jackson were present in their lives, and with the collaboration of Navy Catholic chaplains, the spiritual team sought to provide religious freedom for An Ngai Tay.

A BRIDGE TO HELL

NOVEMBER 1, 1968

On his way to conduct services in the bush at 1000 hours, Buchanan sat in the passenger seat of his jeep traveling on Route 540 with his steadfast chaplain's assistant, Sergeant Jackson.

The spiritual team, en route to An Hoa, a strategic marine base in the dangerous Quang Nam province, traveled with a convoy for safety.

The time set at 0730 hours on a Friday morning. The spiritual team refused to piddle deep in the bush. Every Friday stood as a standing date for the social and nothing but success has come from Friday nights. Nothing in the world is going to hinder the spiritual team from arriving back at camp in time for the social.

The spiritual team would return with a second convoy scheduled to travel back across the Song Thu Bon river toward Camp Love and Da Nang Air Base.

If time allotted, Buchanan would take some slide pictures for his personal account of his tour. If not, slide pictures would have to come another day.

The spiritual team had had their fill of breakfast, riding steady in the jeep, set out to conduct services in the bush. Destination of the convoy ended at the marine base positioned next to the city of An Hoa, a city vulnerable to attacks from the VC. Marines patrolling the area for several days usually returned exhausted and sought for some normalcy of life. Many marines killed in Vietnam lost their life in and around the city of An Hoa. The spiritual team's intent centered on welcoming the men home from a long, hard patrol in the bush with Communion services.

The chaplains assigned to An Hoa marine base had accompanied marines on patrol in the area for two weeks, with six more days to go for the patrol.

One of two chaplains assigned to An Hoa marine base featured Lieutenant Leon Kingslerly, an African-American and from Los Angeles, California. A staunch Lutheran owning a heavy presence of ministers and military service members within his family tree. A fact he pointed out and was immensely proud of. The second chaplain assigned, Lieutenant Scott Lumberton, distinguished himself as an Inter-denominational minister. A man of an interesting background, including an acting career, interrupted by the Vietnam War. Lumberton, along with Buchanan, despised the Vietnam heat as a born and raised citizen of Denver, Colorado.

Kingslerly contacted Chaplain headquarters four weeks prior to schedule substitute chaplains to conduct Communion services for the troops while the two were absent on the long patrols scheduled for An Hoa operations. He asked specifically for Buchanan, his friend from chaplains school in Rhode Island, to substitute when he could fit An Hoa into his busy schedule. Buchanan considered it a privilege to contribute and fulfill the concept of 'coverage' chaplains to be carried out, expected of clergy in Vietnam

After traveling a few miles, the convoy approached Liberty Bridge, a vital overpass transporting supplies to marines quickly for military operations based on Go Noi Island. The Viet Cong delivered constant attacks upon Liberty Bridge every week, severely damaging the bridge from time to time. The 7th Engineering Battalion repaired the bridge when called upon, along with the Seabees. The bridge served strategically and tactically as a vital component not only to marine operations, but for overall military operations in the Quang Nam Province Tactical Zone. Besides, the bridge's location stood near Hill 55, a site designated as the 7th Marine Regiment Command Post.

As the convoy closed in on the bridge, Buchanan remained overwhelmed by the size and power of the bridge.

Buchanan commented, "Wow, what a bridge! Look at the size of that thing! We rarely travel this a way, but when we do - it-it always overwhelms me coming this a way! It's incredible, isn't it, Phillip?"

"Yes, sir. Phenomenal. And yes, it's huge. Vital for marine movements. The convoy avoided the ferry down south, takes more time. Besides, you've never taken pictures of the bridge. Today might as well be the day."

"Amen." said Buchanan.

The convoy halted to have an officer's call prior to crossing the bridge. It would be five minutes for the officer's call, which gave Buchanan a chance to capture several slide camera shots of the bridge.

Jackson pulled off the side of the road in front of the guardhouse near the entrance onto the bridge. The chaplains' jeep usually traveled in the heart of a convoy to protect the spiritual leader.

Buchanan stepped out of the jeep with his camera, followed by Jackson, who advised Buchanan good angles and shots to take impressive pictures of the bridge.

As Buchanan took slide pictures, the overall strength and power of Liberty Bridge would impress even the least interested. The skill and competence of the engineers to construct such a wonder impressed Buchanan to no end.

Jackson pointed out, "It's beautiful, isn't Padre."

Buchanan sighs heavily and says, "Sure is, Sergeant. Sure is."

With a bit of pride in his voice, Jackson comments, "The Seabees. Marine engineers. Incredible people, aren't they?"

With confidence, Buchanan agrees. "Best in the world. Hands down."

"Amen to that, sir."

With that, the spiritual team jumped back into the jeep, waiting to cross the bridge over the Song Thu Bon River with the convoy.

Breath-taking beyond words, Buchanan sat in the jeep taking in a panoramic view of the bridge. Taken in totaled embankments along the river, the reflections of the jungle on the water from the sunlight, and the vast beauty of the Vietnam foliage added with the flow of the Song Thu Bon River.

As the officers' call ended, the convoy continued to journey into the deep and dangerous jungles of Quang Nam Province. To cross the bridge itself posed an extremely dangerous endeavor as the NVA and the VC harassed American convoys traveling the bridge.

While crossing the bridge, Buchanan said in his deep southern draw, "That bridge is huge! Look at that thing! Vital for marine operations."

"Sure is." answered Jackson.

"Imperative it's operational and in order." said Buchanan.

Jackson comments, "Well, it maintains crucial supplies to marines at An Hoa, serves to support strategic movements from the Island of Go Noi to attack Viet Cong strongholds and NVA attacks. The marines are isolated when the bridge is out of commission. It's constantly being attacked by the VC. And sir, occasionally, and unfortunately" Jackson pauses, glances over toward Buchanan and says, "suicide bombers blow it up."

Buchanan, shocked and flabbergasted, asks "What? A human being actually killed themselves to destroy the bridge?" Buchanan pondered the thought for a moment and comments, "I still don't understand war Phillip. I-I've been in the bush for only a month and I have seen things and heard things that I still do not understand."

The jeep came close to driving once again onto dry land. Jackson glanced over to Buchanan and makes a point, "Sometimes, and unfortunately, the VC will send - well, a young person with explosives. Explosives strapped to himself, and well....blow themselves up."

Grimacing, Buchanan shakes his head in disbelief.

Once over the bridge and without incident, the spiritual team entered Arizona Territory in the center of the convoy. Marines described Arizona Territory as hell on earth. Considered a free-fire zone, the high command gave marines the liberty to kill individuals who were combatants, were of age, and posed a threat to military personnel without first being fired upon. Buchanan experienced close calls in Vietnam, including one or two in the Arizona Territory.

Evidence of a war and violence waging in Vietnam screamed volumes in the Arizona Territory.

An Hoa marine base was located approximately six miles from the bridge. Buchanan witnessed the evidence of a war being carried out more in Arizona Territory than any other region in Vietnam. The remnants of war bore itself in the territory with burned out huts. The evidence of Agent Orange destroying foliage appeared left and right of the spiritual team. The skeletal remains of what once was a jeep or truck obliterated by a rocket, booby trap, or bomb sat in the middle of a field. The worst for Buchanan were the ghastly remains of the enemy alongside the road.

The enemy human remains sighted alongside the road lasted as an unforgettable memory for Buchanan. For years, Buchanan fell short to wipe away and erase in his mind the horrific, permanent pictures and images of NVA and Viet Cong corpses lying next to the road killed by marine weapons. The remains of the enemy neglected by the VC to give them a proper burial. They simply left them there in the jungle. The remains possessed unusual positions of mangled, torn to pieces human beings, either lying face down or on its back.

The flashbacks over the years came plenty for Buchanan of those killed alongside the road.

Buchanan never understood the neglect of the enemy to simply disregard deceased human remains out in the open. Exposed remains, in which the elements of nature or creatures of the night had the liberty to devour the remains for its own nourishment.

The delight of the convoy turning in a direction with a stunning angle of Marble Mountain came as a welcomed sight for Buchanan after viewing the ghastly corpses of the Viet Cong alongside the road.

Buchanan now sat in the convoy in perfect sight of the breathtaking Marble Mountain. He seized the moment, taking a few shots of Marble Mountain when the convoy came to a stop.

Over time, the convoy reached An Hoa. The spiritual team set the communion services from the back of the jeep, flipping the ammunition box over on its topside to serve as Communion table.

As the spiritual team suspected, laying eyes on a chaplain and chaplain's assistant furnished a welcomed sight for the marines coming in from patrol. The men were exhausted, filthy, and worn out from hard days patrolling in the hillsides.

Practically every marine on patrol attended Communion. More than a hundred men received the elements. Seven KIAs resulted from the patrols were fresh in the minds of the marines. Seven friends lost in combat who will not see home again. Seven men alive and well in the hearts and minds of surviving marines. The men simply participated, asking God to take care of their friends in Eternity.

The spiritual team and the marines will remember the Communion service as emotional and memorable. Buchanan himself felt like weeping, though he would never show it in front of the troops, later perhaps only in Jackson's presence. The strength to contain his inner emotions passed as phenomenal. His composure to hold in all of his emotions had been God sent. The Lord was with him, providing the essential strength to lead the men in such a desperate situation.

Chaplains in Vietnam did not look forward to two responsibilities while in the field, requiring of them a significant stamina to minister to the men. One responsibility called for the leadership of chaplains in leading with KIA memorial services. Emotions ran high during the memorial service. Second, a Communion service following a combat patrol involving casualties usually ended up with emotional marines who lost a friend within the firefight. A chaplain in the bush carefully chose his spoken words to comfort and uplift the hearts and minds of the fighting men in both services.

The spiritual team provided ministry to the marines in An Hoa through Communion. The team consoled and comforted the marines till the returning convoy of trucks were ordered back to Liberty Bridge and towards Da Nang.

The returning convoy began a departure time from An Hoa at 1330 hours.

The six miles back to Liberty Bridge seemed shorter than the trip to An Hoa marine base. Regardless of the time and distance, the gruesome sight of forgotten, deceased VC corpses lying about sickened

Buchanan. Americans never left a fellow member of the military out in the open to rot under the scorching, sizzling sun. Americans leaving fellow service members in the open fields is disgraceful.

Arriving back at the bridge, a bout of trauma hit the spiritual team following a trip through the Arizona Territory. Many visits into the territory came to pass, but this trip sickened the spiritual team the most from the vast sights of the remnants of war. Buchanan experienced a bit more why the marines referred to Arizona Territory as 'hell on earth'. A hell spread all across the Song Thu Bon River Valley.

Buchanan felt the rough drive across the bridge was going to throw him over the side into the Song Thu Bon River. The ride shook him up something terrible. A mutual sigh of relief came upon the spiritual team exiting Arizona Territory.

The distance of the Song Thu Bon River measured approximately 16 miles from Da Nang. Hoi An, the major city on the banks of the Song Thu Bon River, thrived in the era of antiquity as the city of Fai Fo. As a center of festivals and events on the Vietnamese calendar, Hoi An grew into a major tourist city after the war.

The river spoke of calmness and a gentle nature to Buchanan, therapeutic amid a war zone. Far from violent and rough war zone, the aura of the river sustained a pleasant environment. The river, reminiscent of the days growing up in Middleport, Ohio playing on the bridge, reminded Buchanan of his childhood days crossing the Ohio River to picnic in Mason, West Virginia. Buchanan had jumped into the river off the bridge, swam along the shoreline, and fished for fun in the Ohio River. Buchanan's father, however, gave him a good dressing down if caught jumping off the bridge for fun.

Remembering the Ohio River gave Buchanan a pleasant moment of pause from the war.

"You miss the river Philip?" asked an interested Buchanan.

"Which river, sir?" answered Jackson with a grin.

"The Ohio River? The Ohio we grew up with? What other river would I care about?"

Jackson smiled. "Course I do. I love the reflection of Cincinnati's skyscraper lights on the river at night, the riverboats the most. Dinner at night on a riverboat might be my favorite, most memorable fun of the river."

Jackson pauses, reflecting on his growing up in the Cincinnati area and said, "The river's fun."

"I think so too Philip. That's a good way of putting it. It's fun."

The convoy continued on the MSR, main supply route, to Da Nang. The spiritual team set out toward Camp Love on Route 1.

As the spiritual team started for home in the jeep, Buchanan noticed boys on an embankment overlooking the bridge, smiling from ear to ear. The boys ranged from ages 8 to 15, enjoying life, as the marines and Seabees repaired damaged portions of the bridge from the last Viet Cong attack.

Buchanan glimpsed at his watch noticing the time hurried itself to 1625 hours, and plenty of time to arrive back to Camp Love for the Friday Night Social. The spiritual team made great time on the return trip for home.

"Hey, we have any more gum or candy? In the back, Phillip?" asked Buchanan.

"*Yeah*. I think we do, sir."

"Let's stop. Give the kids some candy. What do you think?" asked Buchanan.

"Yeah, great idea. They'll love it, sir."

"Amen."

"Amen, chaplain." answered Jackson.

Jumping out of the jeep, the team reached back toward the floorboard, grabbed boxes of chocolate candy, caramels, and gum.

Eying the sweets, the boys dashed quickly to the jeep.

"Chao ban! Chao ban! Ban Khoe Khong? Ban Khoe Khong?" yelled Buchanan.

"Hey, your Vietnamese is coming along chaplain. That's good." commented Jackson.

"Thanks, Sergeant." Buchanan proudly responded with a broad smile.

"Chao ban! Chao ban!" responded the boys.

Patting the young lads on their shoulders, the spiritual team smiles, handing chocolates, candy, and gum to the boys evenly.

"Cuc keo!" "Cuc keo!" the boys yelled.

Next came, "So co la!" "So co la!"

"You know what that means, sir?" Jackson yelled.

"Yep! Candy and chocolate!" answered Buchanan. The men laugh.

The spiritual team energetically hands the boys a second round of candy and gum, consuming the remaining sum of treats. The candy boxes amounted to zilch. After spending quality time with the boys, Buchanan attempted to speak more of his self taught Vietnamese.

He asked the boys, "Ban co thich bong nhay mua?"

Jackson and the boys laugh.

"What did I say that was so funny?" asked Buchanan, in his strong Kentuckian accent.

"I think you asked them, 'If they enjoyed dancing balls?' They probably don't even know what a dancing ball is, chaplain." said a chuckling Jackson.

"No, I asked them 'if they liked baseball.'" claimed Buchanan.

"Chaplain, baseball is 'bong chay' in Vietnamese. You didn't say that. You said 'bong nhay mua', dancing balls. But you're getting better, sir." commented Jackson, chuckling. "It's time to go, sir."

Bewildered, Chaplain Buchanan repeated over and over again to the boys, "bong chay! bong chay! You know, baseball! baseball!"

The boys laugh and laugh at the strange, short American.

Humored at the funny American, the boys holler out, "Khoi hai!" "Khoi hai".

Buchanan asked fervently, "What did they say? What did they say?"

Jackson grins wide and informs the chaplain, "Those boys said - you're funny."

Buchanan half grins, bemused by the boy's impression of him, as they laugh in jest.

Jumping back into the jeep, the spiritual team wave goodbye to the boys and yells, "thấy bạn lần sau!"

Jackson drives off toward Camp Love.

The boys wave back, humored at the funny man from America.

Arriving back in Camp Love, the spiritual team had plenty of time for the Friday Night Social, the John Wayne movie, and having 'fellowship' with the men. The movie provided the perfect medicine to cure, at least temporarily, a stress filled gloomy, ominous day. The team even had time to spare to go by An Ngai Tay to visit the hamlet, checking in on the progress of fortifications and overall wellbeing of the people.

Buchanan prayed his night of dreams amounted to his day ministering to marines coming out from the bush, the children playing at the bridge eating candy, the good visit at An Ngai Tay, and the fellowship with the men at the social enjoying the John Wayne movie. Prayerfully, the pleasant events would trump any permanent memories of hell in the Arizona Territory.

PROTECTING AN NGAI TAY

NOVEMBER 8, 1968

Friday morning began with Chaplain Lieutenant Commander Jacob Marino, a Catholic Priest, visiting An Ngai Tay. Arriving last night, the spiritual team spent the evening with Marino planning strategically the establishment of Roman Catholic ministry in the An Ngai Tay hamlet, permanently placing a priest in the village with protection from South Vietnamese marines. The Viet Cong murdered the past two priests. Buchanan intended to visit An Ngai Tay hamlet with Marino to provide religious instruction, discipleship training, and catechesis. The An Ngai Tay MedCAP positively benefited the hamlet villagers, reinforcing support for the war effort of the United States. The chaplains ate breakfast with Jackson and Skawinski, who had the day off and tagged along to support the hamlet. Gunnery Sergeant John McElrath, Private Miguel Rodriquez, and Private First Class Christopher PoKorny accompanied the spiritual team, acting as a guard in case of any incidents on the way to or on the way back from An Ngai Tay. Besides, PoKorny and Rodriquez were devout Roman Catholics and wanted to do their part in promoting Roman Catholic efforts in Vietnam. McElrath tagged along out of curiosity into Jackson's new way of life, not out of any religious commitments.

The two chaplains mutually respected one another and thoroughly enjoyed time spent in one's company, sharing much in common. The love of books is most notable. Marino's family, back in the states, owned a book business in Chicago, Illinois, including a book binding repair shop for rare books. Marino's greatest love of reading growing up amounted to military history, a shared trait strengthening his bond with Buchanan. The most noteworthy facts featured the men were common Midwesterners and avid Big Ten fans. Marino, a University of Illinois Fightin' Illini alum, stayed an extra day to listen to Ohio State play the Wisconsin Badgers on Armed Forces radio. No. 2 Ohio State had been tested the prior week squeaking by no. 16 Michigan State Spartans 25-20 in Columbus, Ohio. Though the game will not be much of a contest this week playing the Wisconsin Badgers, the contest still trotted out two Big Ten football teams and home measured thousands of miles away. Listening to a Big Ten game softened things up in a war zone. The Badgers ranked as one of the worst teams in the country and winless thus far in the season. The chaplains were looking forward to listening to the game, but top priorities came first and foremost – An Ngai Tay hamlet.

Marino's visit bore purpose. Command Headquarters initiated the visit to inquire how Marino could assist with the hamlet from time to time via a request from Buchanan. Marino, attached to the 1st Marine Division, 5th Marines, excelled as a Navy chaplain. The people of An Ngai Tay grew to love Marino very much, for he possessed a natural love for people, an essential prerequisite Buchanan insisted on for ministers.

Marino set a top priority in supporting hamlets and villages sympathetic to the efforts of the United States to establish a government based on western liberal ideals and principles. Roman Catholic hamlets and villages terrorized by the Viet Cong who vehemently hated Roman Catholicism were especially concerning to him.

After breakfast, the chaplains, Skawinski, and Jackson jumped into Buchanan's jeep and rode to An Ngai Tay about 15 minutes away. McElrath followed in his jeep with Pokorny and Rodriquez as passengers.

The time to depart for the hamlet was 0730 hours. An early start, but hopefully a productive day.

Visiting the hamlet regularly sat high on Buchanan's priority list. Many citizens suffered from the hands of Communists in the

1950s, witnessing kinfolk murdered by the Communists Viet Minh in North and South Vietnam. Murdered for no other reason but owning membership in the Roman Catholic Church. All seven men traveling to An Ngai Tay valued his religious freedom, and as a Baptist, Buchanan valued even more his religious Constitutional rights. He and his friends set out to lend a hand to those starving for a freer world.

The small party drove through the rural confines of southeastern Asia to the hamlet. Jackson slowly drove up to the gate of An Ngai Tay, as guards opened the gate for the Americans to enter the interior of the small hamlet.

The Americans came as a pleasant surprise for the An Ngai Tay villagers. Especially excited laying their eyes on Marino, who had in months passed conducted Catholic services, establishing rapport with the populace of the hamlet. Following Marino's leading in the Catholic Eucharist, he visited with the citizens of An Ngai Tay with his natural, gracious personality, contagious and naturally innate. As a Catholic priest, he possessed an affectionate longing for Roman Catholics to develop and mature in their faith.

Immediately, the Americans noticed the new fortifications constructed to the hilt. South Vietnamese marines were present in the hamlet, giving instructions to hamlet leaders on military defensive tactics.

The visitors noticed the proficiency and imposing fortifications of the perimeter and trenches encasing the hamlet. Awed with the fortifications, the defenses impressed the Americans, including two rows of bamboo abatis, two 4 to 5 feet trenches with abatis positioned on the edges of the trench, and punji sticks facing out on both sides of the trenches. The defenses added two knee high rows of razor blade barbed wire positioned at the bottom of the trenches, an additional row of razor blade barbed wire between the inner most trench, and several checkerboard positioned punji sticks bordering the edge of the interior of the hamlet. Last, defenses included claymore mines scattered within the perimeter to attach an extra layer of force. Buchanan perceived the fortifications close to overkill.

Overkill or not, when setting traps to keep the rats out of the house, whatever means necessary to avert the pests from invading your abode, you use them.

Two lookout towers built overlooked the perimeter and beyond on one side of An Ngai Tay and open fields of rice patties farmed on the south end. Most nerve-racking and worrisome to security lay at the jungle treeline. The jungle bush, a natural cover and concealment for the Viet Cong, caught the eyeball of every member of security in the hamlet at night, the Viet Cong's favorite time of the day, to slither out of hiding for prey. A third lookout tower, built on the North end of the perimeter, overlooked the treeline of the bush.

Combatant men in the hamlet reached proficiency in training with various weapons from ARVN firearms experts and US marine special forces. The weapons consisted of the M1917 Enfield Caliber 30 rifle, two Browning caliber .03 machine guns M1919A4, U.S. Rifle .30 M1, and various pistols and revolvers.

Villagers manned the towers around the clock with armed guards and sentries. The village positioned additional guards at intervals on the inside perimeter of the hamlet. The combatants, divided into make shift platoons, served duty to stand watch on a week-by-week basis.

Though pleased with the improvements of the perimeter fortifications for An Ngai Tay, Buchanan and his friends still sensed the threat of a Viet Cong presence within the hamlet containing a VC informant. The VC in Vietnam operated as an unseen enemy threatening to strike the innocents when their backs are turned. The threat of attacks occurred anytime, anywhere - including An Ngai Tay hamlet. No one could detect or predict where the enemy might strike next. The VC, hidden and concealed from the public, terrorized and bullied a populace pushed to abhor and detest an enemy willing to kill innocent children and a frail elderly population.

Buchanan's feet hardly hit the ground stepping out of the jeep, when the jolt of children running toward him came from all directions. First to the jeep followed the reward of first dibs of chocolate and candy from the spiritual team. First come, first served. Marino jumped into the fun, delighted to distribute treats amongst the children. The remaining party members, even McElrath, mingled with the children, doling out chocolate and candy.

Contaminated by ants, Buchanan lacked gum to distribute to the children as the tarnished gum lost its value. The immense quantity of ants hid the gum wrappers, hidden under layers of ants on top of the paper wrapping, eventually ripped to pieces. Usually secured in an air tight chest separate from the chocolate and candy, the gum ended up in the chest which Buchanan failed to secure the night before. Buchanan was beside himself. Irate at himself for failing to secure the chest proper.

While in Vietnam, Buchanan noted, written and mental, the many comparisons of home and Vietnam, including the curious, innate and learned behavior of insects in southeast Asia. The insect numbers seemed to unfairly quadruple for Buchanan, and an unwelcomed presence for him. Everywhere he stepped in Vietnam, there seemed to be insects in every direction.

With initial greetings with the elders out of the way, they gave the Americans a complete tour of the new fortifications of An Ngai Tay. The elders impressed the Americans with the new fortifications the marines and Seabees constructed to protect the hamlet from future Viet Cong physical attack.

After the tour and the closing of secular formalities, the eager Americans desired to fulfill the intent of the visit to An Ngai Tay – ministry in the hamlet and the extension of a generous hand of Christian benevolence.

Occasionally, McElrath stepped out of the ordnance office and ventured out of camp to serve CAPs and encourage the bonding relationships with the populace as part of the strategy of the United States in winning the war. McElrath, the salty, rigid marine veteran, along with Buchanan and with an interpreter, visited several adults in the hamlet befriending Americans from past visits.

Chaplain Marino and Jackson, along with an interpreter, visited villagers, while Rodriquez and Skawinski walked about cultivating rapport. but just as vital as stand-ins seeking any danger in the hamlet.

One elderly lady, Bi'hn, whose name meant 'peace' sold canned American pops, along with homemade cross stitching, crocheting, and native Vietnamese clothes. If a natural capitalist existed in the hamlet, she perfectly fit the mold. A favorite amongst the marines, she let the Americans know of her exuberance for capitalism. The marines patronized her small enterprise with every visit, forking over doe to her, owning a piece of authentic handmade Vietnamese merchandise. In jest, she claimed the marines purchased her authentic goods and services for girlfriends and wives back home. Bi'hn, jovial and friendly, came across as easy to talk to. McElrath fell in love with her immediately. He discovered turning away from Bi'hn, denying her a profit did not come easy. Compelled, he purchased a small scarf, sending it to his sister in Texas.

In broken English, Bi'hn showed her appreciation. "Thank you. Thank you."

Next in line for Buchanan and McElrath to visit was a senior citizen, Lanh, who gained a personal interest in Buchanan. He felt an affection for Buchanan, comfortable in conversation with him while addressing theological questions.

Lanh felt at ease around Buchanan, asking him questions such as 'Why does God seem to permit evil ones in the world to succeed?' and 'Where does evil come from?' He might have been comfortable in the presence of Buchanan, but Buchanan found himself taken aback with the curiosity of Lanh. He searched in his mind for answers to these tough questions to provide Lanh with satisfactory theological conclusions. He didn't feel he could answer Lanh in solid Roman Catholic terms. Today Buchanan, thankful for a Catholic presence, motioned for Marino to make his way over to him, permitting Marino to provide an answer from a Roman Catholic perspective. Lanh possessed an inquiring mind, leaning heavily on philosophy to answer the many questions of life within his Catholic perspective. Buchanan loved Lanh, for he desired to learn and he asked deserving questions calling for convincing answers.

Buchanan and Sergeant McElrath continued to visit the hamlet, reassuring the citizens of the government of the United States and its people pitched their tent in their camp for freedom, especially religious freedom.

Though visits in An Ngai Tay drew pleasant outcomes, the villagers' demeanor conveyed a pensive, on edge presence. The appearance and character exhibited by the villagers seemed a bit more secure with the new fortifications, but not entirely convinced Viet Cong infiltration stood null and void. The expressions of villagers still showed evidence of fear and apprehension, though the fortifications spoke loud and clear to the VC to 'keep out'. War is an antagonist, a rival to joy and contentment in life. The result of war is nothing but grief and misery. War is depressive, an antagonist of harmony and peace. The Americans knew it. The Vietnamese knew it.

A pause in the misery in the war for every adult in the village, bringing a illuminating smile to each adult, came from the joy of observing the children's fulfillment and pleasure of receiving treats from Chaplain Buchanan. At least one stimulant of pleasure in the middle of a horrible war came from a simple pleasure of life - candy.

Buchanan and McElrath made their way back to the jeep, reached into the back storage compartment and lifted more candy boxes for the children. A second race to the jeep ensued. McElrath, ever so pleased to dispense more treats, received the most pleasant, precious smiles from the children.

The spiritual team glanced over at McElrath, spending time with the children. The older, maturer marine enjoyed the fun. The salty old marine experienced joy in life, at least temporarily, as if the war existed in the middle of nowhere. Skawinski and Jackson soaked in every second of the sight of McElrath's benevolence toward the innocent.

Rodriquez stepped up onto Skawinski's right and said, "The old grunt has a soft spot somewhere in his heart after all, doesn't he?"

Skawinski glances towards Rodriquez, smiling, "Yep. But I'll never have the guts to tell him to his face."

The marines chuckle.

Jackson struts to assist McElrath by distributing the plentiful candy to the innocents. Buchanan intentionally saved candy for two weeks for the children in An Ngai Tay.

Skawinski and PoKorny moseyed on over to the jeep, taking hold of a box of candy and chocolate. The men distributed candy equally amongst the children with their friends. Every innocent Vietnamese child bore a broad smile. All four enlisted men distributed candy. All four men knew life for a child in Vietnam came with gloom and doom, though the sweet smiles worn on the faces of the children featured anything but a war. Children in the United States were clueless of a hard life. Candy and chocolate came catered to an American kid, only a drive to the grocery or drug store. Candy came as a luxury for the Vietnamese children.

The four enlisted Americans were as high as a kite. The pure joy and elation the candy brought to the children measured radiant in their smiles as the Sun beaming down on a beautiful Vietnam morning sunrise. The fact the enlisted brought comfort and ease into someone's life instead of taking one's life brought upon a deep sense of contentment within each one of their lives. The spiritual team will remember the rare moment for a lifetime.

The moment seemed to brighten up the adults in An Ngai Tay, especially the elders of the hamlet. All seemed to shine with glee as the children indulged in the sweets the Americans shared with them.

The chaplains noticed specifically the jubilant demeanor of McElrath and PoKorny. As the 'Candymen' finished dispensing the goodies, all sat down in chairs under the community center pavilion built by the Seabees. The children followed the marines to the pavilion, sitting on the laps of their newfound friends. The men thoroughly benefited from the time spent with the children. Some children jumped up, rushed to their homes, fetching the few toys in their lives and running back to the pavilion to share with the rough, sturdy marines. The marines and children laughed. They talked and ate candy, giving them a presence of security. The moment will be one of the most revealing points in time for Buchanan in Vietnam.

The chaplains sat while visiting with the elders of the hamlet, glancing occasionally toward the young men taking a pause in the war to dispense charity and Christian benevolence to the innocent children, instead of fighting a war opposite of adults with a different political and economic ideology and poles apart with a set of beliefs contrary to their own.

As time passed, departure for Camp Love came imminent. The spiritual line briefed the elders of the hamlet of Marino's forthcoming return to conduct mass in the weeks ahead with Catholic nuns to assist in a pilot education program for the children.

Buchanan reassured the elders Chaplain Kensington would visit with the MedCAP, delivering educational materials to supplement the teaching instruction of the nuns.

The Americans departed the hamlet with a deep awareness. The Viet Cong threats remained high on the Richter scale, posing an inevitable danger for the villagers in An Ngai Tay. The tainted sense of An Ngai Tay persisted with a VC infiltrator, even after the fortifications, loomed heavy upon the minds of the Americans. With gloomy thoughts on the minds of the Americans, all acknowledged the visit benefited the villagers and confidence rose within the hamlet.

With a most satisfying day of ministry fulfilled, Buchanan will end the day with icing on the cake showing a John Wayne movie to the men. The next day, Saturday, scheduled a day of ministry with Chaplain Marino in Camp Love. Sunday is game day for Buchanan and Marino. Buchanan will remember this weekend fondly, with little war and more ministry. The best weekend for Buchanan in Vietnam as he, Skawinski, Marino, and others listened to the Ohio State Buckeyes blow out the Wisconsin Badgers 43-8.

Ohio State remained undefeated and came closer to another national championship.

His thoughts on Sunday night after listening to the football game dwelled on An Ngai Tay. Marino made his way back to the 1st Marine Division, 5th Marines by shotgun, traveling with a convoy of trucks.

Sitting in his hootch on Sunday evening, Buchanan thought of the citizens of An Ngai Tay and the lives they desired for themselves and how trivial football was in comparison.

The citizens' minds of An Ngai Tay hamlet could have cared less about American college football. Their first thoughts in the mornings getting up from a full night's sleep focused on 'Will a visit from the Grim Reaper come calling at my doorstep this day?' or 'Will I live another day to see another morning?' Questions difficult to answer for Buchanan and even more so for citizen Lanh.

Even with the massive layers of fortifications protecting and defending An Ngai Tay, no one but God knew the answers to such questions.

God Protecting His Own

November 16, 1968

Ohioans in Camp Love ascended to the gridiron mountain top. The spiritual football experience of a national championship the state and fans have longed for year after year has come short to celebrate since 1954 and 1961. Ohio State success transformed Ohioans into confident, self-assured football disciples devoted to a football team, a state, and a state capital city serving the Buckeye state. When Ohio State wins, Buckeye fans feel invincible, supreme. Certainly stronger, and even unbeatable. Ohio State fans simply cheer on the home team. Ohioans, however, fail to see in themselves what others see in them when Ohio State is on a long winning streak. Ohio State haters see smug, cocky, over zealous fans who need humbled with a devastating loss. Truth is, the demeanor of Ohio State in the past few weeks has been a strut of cocky, and rightly so. Head Coach Jack Barnes is having one of the best coaching years in his dominance of the Big Ten and the Buckeyes are on a roll. Ohio State's most recent Associated Poll national championship was 1954, a triumphant record of 10-0. In 1942, Ohio State ranked number one in the polls, achieving the school's first national championship. The last undefeated season for the Buckeyes was 1961, posting a 8-0-1 campaign. Ohio State's claimed national championships ranked number one in other polls in 1957 and 1961 added to Buckeye lore. Ohio State alumni, fans, and the Buckeye state wish to add the 1968 team to the list of national championships. The 1968 Ohio State

Buckeyes squad is destined to be the greatest Ohio State football team in the school's illustrious history.

The day is Saturday and those in camp claiming ties to Ohio are elated again for another Ohio State football game. Tomorrow being Sunday, the marines will listen to another college football game on armed forces radio. Ohio State exhibited championship caliber a week ago demolishing Wisconsin 43-8. Ohio State will travel to Iowa this weekend to play the Hawkeyes for an away game. The Iowa Hawkeyes historically play power house football teams competitively and prove to be a trap game year after year against ranked teams, Ohio State included. Iowa unnerves Buchanan year in and year out, a Big Ten football team who historically plays the Buckeyes close in many a game.

Regardless, the Ohio State Buckeyes are on a roll and undefeated. It's Friday in the United States, and Buchanan knows without a doubt Buckeye Nation all over the country is fired up for Saturday's game.

Ohioans in Camp Love are cocky even to the point of being downright smug. Ohio State has not been in this good of shape of winning it all since 1961, and the 1968 Buckeyes are hungry for another national championship.

The smug smile of Ohio State fans gnaws the insides of marines most of all from other football conferences in camp. Fans from the SEC, PAC-8, ACC, and the Southwest conference. Fans period. It's a 'you're a loser' smirk from Ohio State fans, one that takes great pleasure in everyone else's misfortune and pain. It's a smirk causing people to feel like walking right up to an Ohio State fan and punching him right in the nose. Especially fans from the Southeastern Conference, who in their own right are just as smug and haughty.

The vainglorious smile Ohioans laid onto SEC fans displayed the epitome of a smug smile from ear to ear. In Ohioans estimation, including Buchanan, if it wasn't for Alabama winning national championships over the years, the SEC would be nothing but pitiful and second rate, as the PAC-8 is pitiful absent Southern California.

Over time, Buchanan picked up an Ohio State smug smile himself, wearing it with Ohioan pride. A proud display of one's self wasn't a trait Buchanan possessed. He loathed those who portrayed themselves as a self-saturated, smug, arrogant self. As a general rule, he intentionally kept an arm's length with such people. But for some odd reason, when defending Ohio and the Buckeyes, he displayed a confident presentation of himself. The annoying self-satisfied manner, including the smile, just like any other Ohioan in camp.

The excitement of the game, however, came to a halt. Intelligence reports substantiated the Viet Cong is active in and around Liberty Bridge. Command Headquarters contacted Lucas to order Buchanan to Liberty Bridge to conduct Communion services for personnel repairing the bridge, including the Seabees attached to the 7th Engineering Battalion, 5th Engineering Battalion, and their own 7th Engineering Battalion. The Viet Cong shattered parts of the decking and bearings of the bridge with mortars and explosives several days earlier, and repairs on the bridge became imperative as Liberty bridge is vital to the military operations of I Corps.

The chaplain billeted to cover Liberty Bridge, Lieutenant William Tecumseh Taylor from Lancaster, Ohio, ministered to the 5th Marines. A staunch Lutheran, his father named him after the famous Union general and the brave Shawnee leader from Ohio. Taylor's absence in Da Nang came from recuperating from his wounds suffered from a Viet Cong sniper in the Arizona Territory three days ago. A series of skirmishes with the Viet Cong the past two weeks in the Arizona Territory produced extraordinary high numbers of casualties, including Taylor. Committed to ministry, he insisted on ministering to many a wounded marine in Da Nang while he himself recuperated from his own wounds. Taylor considered his billet a personal responsibility to minister to marines the Navy assigned him.

Following the Liberty Bridge Communion, the spiritual team committed themselves to a deeper combat base by jeep to an outpost a couple of miles down Route 540, deeper into the bush. Captain John Frost and Alpha Company, along with combat engineers, were isolated in the jungle bush for 9 full days rooting out Viet Cong tunnels and a grand total of 18 days devoid of contact with a Navy chaplain. The men were hungry for Communion services, Catholic and Protestant alike.

The hour and minute hands sat at 0830 hours. The spiritual team prepared for a day of ministry.

However, Buchanan found himself called to Lucas's office, informing him of the immediate request, obliged to go. With a chance of conducting services for men bereft of a chaplain for weeks excited Buchanan. To provide spiritual food necessary for spiritual growth remained most high on Buchanan's list of priorities not only as chaplain in the Navy, but as a minister and cleric to those requiring spiritual nourishment for discipleship.

Given the news, Buchanan bolted over to Jackson's hootch, informing the sergeant of the immediate request.

Exhilarated to no end with the news, Jackson's recollection of isolation in the bush for days, even weeks, in past tours conveyed many memories. Vivid reminders of depression, vulnerability, exposure to the enemy, and the elements of the jungle bush all flashed by in a matter of a split second. In past tours, his spiritual condition thrived as an unbeliever. On this tour, he knew Jesus as a believer. And he knew without a shadow of a doubt, there were Christians present in the patrol who were headed for worship, beside himself to share the Lord's presence with them through Communion.

Scheduled to conduct Communion services at 1000 hours, time was of the essence.

The time sat at 0855 hours.

Grabbing his M-16, gear, and the Communion kit, along with extra wafers as a reserve, Jackson and Buchanan set off in the jeep for Liberty Bridge. Buchanan collected his Communion kit, knowing good and well many marines and sailors were to show up for Communion.

The trip on the MSR, main supply route, filled the road with traffic, a presence Buchanan welcomed while traveling in the bush, providing a sense of security. Traveling the several miles to Liberty Bridge came swiftly.

The sight before the spiritual team's eyes were dozens of men awaiting their arrival, 59 men in all. Jackson pulled next to the supply shack near the bridge entrance. Stragglers came from all directions - marines, sailors, Seabees. Dozens of grateful marines and sailors to attend Communion services. The men welcomed the spiritual team like rock stars. At the outset, laying their eyes on the jeep, many jolted themselves from work places at the bridge area and surrounded the jeep as if John Wayne or Elvis had driven up. The men gathered around the jeep, shaking hands, and conversing with the spiritual team.

The men grew hungry to show forth their faith in God and experience His omnipresence in each believer's life through accepting the elements.

"Good morning, men."

"Hello Chaplain." "You sure are a sight for sore eyes, Padre." "Greetings Chaplain." "God is good, sir."

The men expressed the longing for intercession and proclamation in their lives through participating in Communion. Engaging in 'church' had been long overdue for the marines. The spiritual team, greeted with great enthusiasm, traveled to Liberty Bridge willing and able to minister to the men.

"Well, if it isn't Philip Jackson. Long time, no see." came from one marine, a friend of Jackson.

"Hello!" responded Jackson. He ambled his way toward the marine, a reunion of sorts, since the men have different hearts in this tour, a Jesus heart. The men now are believers. The past will always hold memories of reprobate reputations, which now God has forgiven and forgotten. Today, life is living for good, not for the adversary.

The officer in charge, Major Kyle Severson from Brooklyn, New York, directed the spiritual team to a hootch along a small hillside which served as his office.

"You and Jackson can don the service kits here in front of my office, Chaplain Buchanan. We sure are thrilled you're here, sir. I for one." said Severson.

The major, a considerate soul, confessed, "Yes, I'm a believer and Catholic. I'll tell you the truth, Padre. We've longed for some religious contact of any sort for a while now."

"We're here to serve ya, Major." replied Chaplain Buchanan in his deep southern draw.

"We've many denominations, Chaplain Buchanan. We've been attacked occasionally recently as we've worked. Hit and run attacks plenty. We need spiritual relief. Hope you know what I'm getting at?"

"Sure do, sir." commented Jackson, over hearing.

Jackson pointed toward his chest. "Third tour. First two tours with grunts. And I know what you're getting at. Ya feel - well, closer to God, better prepared if the unfortunate happens. Right, sir?"

Severson stares with intensity toward Jackson and softly says, "Yes."

Two hearts full of shared emotions between two believers in Christ, one a Protestant, one Roman Catholic. 'Cooperation without compromise' thrown into fifth gear, gaining speed. Ecumenicalism couldn't have been more alive and well.

"Well, better get things started, hadn't we? All of us are looking forward to the services." said Severson.

"Corporal! Lend a hand to Sergeant Jackson for services." ordered Severson to a young corporal.

"Yes, sir." replied the young marine, a John Petrie Coleman, 21 years of age. Coleman's duty as Severson's administrative assistant counted for more than just paper work. The men were combatants, saving each other's lives more than once.

Coleman scrounged for a fold-up table in supply, positioning the table in front of the major's hootch. With the few chairs available, Jackson and the corporal placed rows of chairs in front of the table. The chairs were first come, first serve. Remaining marines sat on their derrieres around the fold up chairs.

Jackson donned the service kit, nodding toward Buchanan. The service kit was secure and ready to go.

Severson says, "Well Chaplain Buchanan. We're ready."

Severson, confident Buchanan a resourceful man, asked, "Prior to the service starting, can I-I ask you something?"

"Sure major. What's your worry, sir?" replied Buchanan, bewildered by the problem.

"Do you have, well -." Severson appeared nervous, looking about in all directions, then stared straight into Buchanan's eyes.

Lowering his voice to conceal his dread, asked nervously, "D-Do-Do you...have nightmares?"

Buchanan, somewhat taken aback, is puzzled a bit with Severson's inquiry, and ponders for a proper answer.

A nervous Buchanan glances over to the rather large number of marines, contemplating for a few seconds the urgency of Severson's question.

Buchanan, oddly humored with Severson, thinks to himself, 'Here I am called upon, actually ordered by Lucas, to conduct Communion services to marines and sailors at Liberty Bridge, and Severson unexpectedly asks me this difficult unforeseen question.'

Buchanan, hit hard with such a casual question from out of the blue, thought the inquiry deserved more thought than just a few seconds prior to a Communion service. Buchanan presumed Severson thought he could squeeze in a quick counseling session.

Buchanan answered the major's question the best he could. "Well, sir. Yes. Yes, I do. I have them frequently. Do you really want to talk about that here and now? I mean, I can come back later. We can sit down and discuss it when we have more time."

The marines noticed the table, chairs, and service kit ready to go, making their way to the makeshift altar on their own, without Severson's calling.

"Come on, chaplain, what do you do? What do ya do to go to sleep? To avoid nightmares? Give me a suggestion. Come on, Padre. The men are ready." asked Severson, slightly smiling.

"OK. OK." said Buchanan, as the two men strolled toward the makeshift altar. "I stare at my family pictures and day dream of spending time with my children. Or I might read the Scriptures, a history book, or one of my westerns."

Pausing, Buchanan quickly pondered. "Or I might think of a favorite episode from my favorite television shows. Maybe a favorite movie, a comedy or western."

Then Buchanan put in plain words his immediate means of coping and gaining shut eye, of enduring the horrors of war. "But most recent means is Major Burns' classical music at about the time we all go to sleep. It soothes the mind, the body."

"Classical music? Yeah. *Yeah.*" Severson sensed enlightenment.

By the time Buchanan explained his sources of coping with nightmares, the men had walked into the makeshift sanctuary. Buchanan's heart burst with pride, facing the standing room only for Communion services.

Severson patted Buchanan on the shoulder, smiling. "Thank you, Padre. Thanks a lot. I'll try the music."

Buchanan turned, making his way around the table. He took his position to lead the Communion service.

Buchanan's only thought centered in on Severson's question out of the blue. Buchanan thought, 'Wow! I'm not alone. Somebody else has problems with sleep.'

As Buchanan began the service, Severson stared right at him. What Buchanan saw in the red, tired eyes of Severson was a hurt, worn, weary, and beaten marine. Standing by for consolation in active participation of Communion.

The words Jackson heard flowing from Buchanan's mouth came the most interesting, meaningful spoken expressions he had heard from the chaplain he had served the past two months. He was never more proud of the chaplain he protected with his life than this day. Emphasis for Communion touched on God's presence in the bush, protecting believers, loving Christians all the while. Adding to the devotion for Severson's sake, God is with us even when we go to sleep.

Buchanan reminded the men with his hand near his heart, "It's all about what's in here."

With the conclusion of the spoken word, Buchanan started Communion. All present, Protestant and Catholic alike, received elements of Communion or if Catholic, at least a blessing. Even a few Catholics, including Severson, received the elements from a Protestant Chaplain this day.

The spiritual team would never lead a more receptive and thankful group of military personnel in Vietnam than on this day.

Jackson and Coleman placed the table and chairs back into Severson's office, collected the service kit parts and placed them back into the service kit bags, saying their goodbyes to the men.

"Thank you very much, Chaplain Buchanan and Sergeant Jackson. You'll never know how much your presence lifted out spirits." said Severson.

"We will someday, Major." commented Jackson.

"Amen." answered Buchanan.

Severson smiles and says, "Thank you. And Amen."

The spiritual team had traveled to the isolated outpost. Buchanan conducted yet another Communion service in the bush. With hours flying by, the team spent the night with the lonely marines, driving back to Camp Love early the next morning for the 1100 hour service.

All the while, both prayed fervently nothing would prevent the two Ohioans from listening to the Ohio State football game against the Iowa Hawkeyes on the Armed Services Radio.

The Lord answered their prayers. Nothing hampered or obstructed passage to camp. Buchanan lead the 1100 hour service, enjoyed lunch with friends, then listened with other Ohioans, including Skawinski, to the game in the conference hall.

The game's broadcast ended up etched into the Ohioans' minds for a lifetime.

The competition of Iowa, as Buchanan feared, resulted in a close game, with the scoreboard displaying a final tally of 33-27. Of course, the Ohio State Buckeyes scoring the 33. The Buckeyes were annihilating the Hawkeyes with a comfortable lead, 26-6. But Iowa came roaring back, making it close. During the game, marines heard constant, boisterous roars throughout camp with an Ohio State score or grand play, causing Ohio State haters in camp to feel 'fan nausea'. A fact of consensus for college football fans denoted the Buckeyes may be the most hated team in the country. Buchanan could careless. Ohio State football represented home for Ohioans, taking the spirit of Ohio in their hearts everywhere they go. SEC country will have to get over it.

As football fervor died down in camp, Buchanan speculated on Major Severson's handling of himself back at Liberty Bridge. He placed the major on his prayer list permanently. Knowing the struggles of gaining solid shut eye, Buchanan felt his pain straining to distract his mind from the war prior to falling asleep. Buchanan made it a priority to check in on Severson from time to time. He remembered Severson through the years of his life.

Time ran fast listening to the Ohio State game, as 1745 hours came quickly. Retiring to his hootch, Buchanan set his sights on reading military history books and the Scriptures, spending a quiet Sunday evening in his own confines.

Again thinking of Severson, Buchanan thought, God does indeed protect his own. God lead him to minister to Severson, both spiritually and physically. If anything, to help Severson deal with his stress of war.

Buchanan lifted up the last two or three days of ministry to God, thanking him for the opportunity to extend a benevolent hand to spiritually thirsty marines. The future held more great days of ministry.

Regarding football, facts speak louder than words. The smirky smug smile bestowed on the faces of Ohio State Buckeyes fans before the Iowa Hawkeyes game was ever more present in camp after the game. With one game remaining on the regular schedule versus the hated rival Michigan Wolverines, Ohio State felt confident they were on course to collide with the undefeated USC Trojans and play for the national championship in the Rose Bowl.

From here on out, no one could miss Buchanan's smug smile, worn with Buckeye pride.

Skawinski, the Devil, and the Viet Cong

November 18, 1968

Killing became a norm in Vietnam. Looking forward to inflicting pain and death on the Viet Cong with indignation after the enemy took the life of a best friend or a favorite member of a platoon or company generated an intense anger and abhorrence within the hearts of many marines. Skawinski was no different. His great commitment to his faith sat as top priority in his life. The enemy and the Devil were one and the same deep in his heart and mind. No other priority in his life took precedence at this point except stopping the Devil in his tracks. By the end of the day, hating the Devil rivaled his top priority of faith.

Skawinski's combat engineering team patrolled and swept for booby traps and claymore mines practically every day of the week. Every single member of the team stood ready, willing, and able to exterminate Viet Cong rats. The young marine impressed Buchanan. His combat engineering tenacity and endurance given itself daily.

Serving the Air Force as an enlisted man and now as a Navy chaplain, Buchanan peeked from the outside in. Observing marines from a distance, he made his own conclusions that United States marines' dedication and work ethic exemplified 'esprit de corps' in every step and word of a marine, and embodied the marine slogan 'Semper Fidelis' - Always Faithful.

Buchanan's assessment of the best grunts in the Marine Corps boiled down to those marines who bellowed out the most hearty of 'Oorah's and who meant it. Those marines were combat engineers. The engineers stood tall with pride, embodying 'esprit de corps' of the marine corps, and typified 'Semper Fidelis' like no other group of marines. He credits the Marine Corps, in its illustrious history, never suffering a mutiny to its commitment and dedication of celebrated slogans of the Marine Corps.

The first combat engineers landed in Vietnam in 1965 from Alpha Company of the 7th Engineering Marine Battalion. Charlie Company served as combat support sent to Da Nang to sustain defenses for a Light Anti-Aircraft Defense Missile Battery.

Combat engineers during the war literally placed themselves between the enemy and their fellow marines and sailors. To fulfill the basic military mission in Vietnam came from the spearhead of combat engineers to construct the infrastructure imperative for the war to be won. Some historians refer to the war as the 'Engineers War.'

The MOS of a marine combat engineer in Vietnam fell into three distinct groups. The first component comprised the Division Engineer Battalions, numbering about 850 marines. Their responsibilities consisting of clearing roads of mines and booby traps using mine detectors, demolition, and accompanying infantry into the jungle bush to secure mobility of the troops. Military historians have referred to protecting infantry mobility in the bush as 'pioneer trails'.

The second group of combat engineers were the Force Troop Engineer Battalions, numbering about 850 marines, who enhanced roads, built new roads, and constructed combat bases including fire bases throughout South Vietnam. The battalions functioned to better the life of marines while serving in combat.

The third combat engineering group consisted of the Air Wing Engineers, totaling 350 marines, who improved the condition of air strips and airfields to support marine aero aircraft.

The Marine Corps assigned Skawinski to a Division Engineering Battalion billet, MOS combat engineer in Camp Love, Bravo Company, 1st Platoon. Though billeted to Bravo Company,

Skawinski's mastery of skills were used within the whole scope of operations for Camp Love.

The time struck 0500 hours.

Shuteye during the night was nothing but rock solid for Skawinski. He dreamed of going home to Ohio and his family farm. His night of pleasant dreams were genuine. So real for Skawinski, he woke up disoriented and unsettled, not knowing where he was. 'Was he in Ohio?' 'Was he at El Toro marine base?' 'Was he still in Vietnam?' When reality hit, a hard punch below the belt came for Skawinski. For he woke up in Vietnam, not in Ohio.

The young combat engineer personified a devoted Christian, a young man pursuing the demeanor of a Christian life. People coming into close contact with Skawinski daily witnessed Jesus shining through him.

However, war changed him. Hateful emotions arose in his life for the first time in his life. From birth, practically from the womb, Skawinski's parents taught him hate derived from the Adversary and the byproduct of hate comes evil intentions.

Raised with enriched Judeo-Christian ethics, Skawinski grew up with lessons teaching him hate led to behavior reflective of the Evil One and results in a destructive nature.

The enemy enraged Skawinski. He confronted an enemy whose very nature, vicious and sadistic, cared very little for human life. In a faraway land fighting a war to establish some sort of a democratic state in South Vietnam, Skawinski experienced emotions he never felt in his life. Idealistic, inspired, and hopeful, he prayed his fighting would be worth the efforts put forth in liberating the South Vietnamese from such an evil force as the Viet Cong and they too would taste the freedom and liberty he possessed as a citizen of the United States.

At this point in his third tour, the refrain from hating the VC seemed imaginary. He hated them.

Though he vehemently wanted to win the war, he agonized with frustration over the progress of the war. The outright lollygagging leadership in Washington, DC, irritated him to no end.

Regardless, he had a job to do.

His combat engineering team saddled up, eager to depart camp at 0545. Approximately 120 men departed camp to mine sweep and secure designated areas. The rather large team included a combat engineering team, three infantry platoons from Bravo Company for combat support led by Rockford, and a team of corpsmen. The contingent of troops were to mine sweep, search and destroy booby traps in and around OP-6 to string fence, and secure area around Song Thu Bon Ferry and Tu Cau Ferry. In addition, the team were to sweep and secure areas for the spreading of 360 cubic yards of rock at 7th Bulk Fuel Company. Added to the list came a sweep and to secure the bridge head walls at coordinates AT 919598 and AT 924606. The continuation of sandbagging headwalls at AT 924606, an area of heavy enemy activity for the month of November, considered a top priority for the demolition team. The Viet Cong's increase in attacks placing booby traps in the area put a damper on work in November, especially improving roads and mine sweeping. After these assignments were accomplished, the contingent would trek to Route QL-1 road, complete unfinished sweeping if the VC presence and danger were light. Regardless, the weight of the contingent of marines felt heavy countering the tenacity of Viet Cong attacks.

Despite the size of patrols departing Camp Love, Buchanan, when available, positioned himself at the camp's entrance and blessed each marine and sailor for God's armor, protection, and presence while in the bush. Knowing God's presence in the bush placed a compounded reassurance onto the marine's heart and soul for spiritual certainty. Especially if the unthinkable should woefully occur.

Brief but straightforward, Buchanan placed his hand on the marine or sailor's shoulder, lowered his head, and repeated to each service member, "God be with you, protect, and bless you. And remember, it's all about what's in here." Tapping on the marine's chest with his fingers over the young marine's heart.

If Buchanan knew a marine or sailor more personally, he referred to the marine's name in his meaningful but brief prayer.

Buchanan loved all the men. Whether or not the love he expressed resulted in reciprocation didn't concern him. If a positive response came from his ministry and the marine's life changed for the better, "Glory to God!"

No other marine in the camp did Buchanan love more than Skawinski. He, of course, kept his little secret to himself. He certainly didn't intend to hurt anyone else's feelings, especially Jackson's. Though Jackson knew the truth.

Life is funny. It brings human beings together in many situations in one's life span. The lives of Buchanan and Skawinski seemed a collision course destined to meet in the middle of the war. The friendship bonded in such a short period. The two men sensed the brief acquaintance seemed a lifetime. Though Skawinski's age produced a generation gap, he acknowledged Buchanan as a Christian friend. Buchanan's age set him exceedingly close to his biological father. The bond seemed almost a father-son relationship.

When Skawinski departed camp assigned to a patrol mission, the prayer deemed itself more personal. The prayer reflected sending out his own son amid a world out to kill him.

Skawinski. next in line, stepped up to Buchanan for departure, reciting his brief prayer, "God be with Adolphus Skawinski, protect, and bless him. And remember, it's all about what's in here." He tapped Adolphus's chest near his heart."

"See you when ya get back, Corporal Skawinski." said Buchanan.

"Thank you, sir."

With a smile and nod, Skawinski turns toward the road entrance with the assurance of God's protection, overshadowing him as he steps into the quagmire of war, the jungle bush of Vietnam.

Walking with confidence and a steady strut out of Camp Love, Skawinski walks onto the dirt road from camp. From a hundred feet from the entrance, he turns for a glimpse toward the camp, noticing the spiritual team standing self-assured of God's presence and protection for every one of the troops. The emotions of a father sending his son out into the real world for the first time, praying he will be careful of every move made, and every step taken. It became routine for Buchanan to stand at the entrance for the whole exodus of men after his blessings upon them, to watch the men completely out of sight of the camp. A superstitious move on Buchanan's part, but one of affirmation of his prayers protected the men.

Skawinski looked back one last time over his shoulder toward Camp Love, catching his eyes on the spiritual team standing, seeing the troops off to complete the mission and responsibilities as combat engineers. The camp and the spiritual team finally disappeared as the treeline came between Skawinski and the camp.

Buchanan didn't forget Skawinski's spiritual growth, slipping him a Lutheran devotional book to compliment his small print Bible he patrolled with in the bush.

To describe the fear and apprehension felt entering the bush for military personnel in Vietnam existed beyond words. Stress levels heightened for service members stepping into the bush, including Skawinski. A patrol lasting for days made matters worse due to the isolation and heightened exposure to the enemy. Sweeping patrol parties experienced a higher elevation of danger and potential casualties in the escalation of sweeping for booby traps and mines. Regardless, Buchanan's departing words and blessing reassured him of God's presence in the bush. And if any unfortunate casualties came of the patrol, at least Buchanan's prayers and presence at the entrance possibly prompted the men to think of their spiritual condition.

Two days had passed and no confrontations with the Viet Cong. Whether the heavy rain in November thwarted Viet Cong attacks or not, the patrol, head over heels no rats had come out of their holes yet, prayed the rats remained in their burrows. November suffered from over 9 inches of rain so far in the month and the muddy terrain of Vietnam created a sluggish, drawn out mission even longer.

The combat engineers completed the mine sweep, searched and destroyed booby traps at OP-6 to string fence for the area around the Song Thu Bon and Tu Cau Ferrys, which were swept and secured. In addition, a completed and secure sweep at 7th Bulk Fuel Company spread 360 cubic yards of rock. Sweeps of bridges at coordinates AT 919598 and AT 924606 were conducted and secured. The sweeping assignment to secure Route QL-1 road ended up the last assignment to complete and possibly the most dangerous because of the Viet Cong, considering roads a top priority of sabotage.

The trudge to Route QL-1 came sluggishly for Skawinski and his fellow marines. The patrol slogged through bush country to the road, a major route to Da Nang and An Hoa. The patrol cut travel time short through the slow-moving terrain rather than traveling 5 extra miles using the major road routes. The pathways through the bush cut time in half, though the danger of the Viet Cong elevated tremendously. The vitality of Route QL-1 remained a top priority to secure for military travel.

Skawinski's combat engineering team respected the leadership of Bravo Company. The patrol, accompanied by Lieutenant Rockford's 1st and 2nd Platoons of Bravo Company, swept the BT 050603 coordinate while 3rd Platoon of Bravo Company, led by Staff Sergeant Frank Smith, patrolled two and a half miles south of BT 009691 coordinate. The two separate parties would sweep Route QL-1 and meet at coordinate BT 009691, a location for a new 30' fixed span bridge on the QL-1 route. Rockford and Skawinski's platoons at Route QL-1 emerged out of the bush exactly at the midpoint of the road between Liberty Bridge and Da Nang. Rockford loathed pacing through heavy bush in the aftermath of heavy rain to get to Route QL-1, but the bush route came as the shortest, quickest route to Route QL-1.

The time sat at 1115 hours. The patrol longed to finish the last task on the tedious but vital agenda and head back to camp.

Marines in November experienced intense Viet Cong attacks. The welcomed absence of the VC on this patrol surprised Rockford and Skawinski, but welcomed nonetheless. Regardless, ears were perked and eyes were open for any VC rats scurrying out of the bush to cause havoc. Skawinski in no way trusted the Viet Cong and stood on edge the last two days of the patrol. Sweeping the coordinates of Route QL-1 for the 30' fixed span bridge was far from being the most tedious of jobs, but the men saw the light at the end of the tunnel. The quicker the better. As the marines swept the road, they pictured themselves lounging on sandbags and in their hootches drinking a beer, listening to recent popular music in camp.

Skawinski possessed a knack of sensing Viet Cong attacks and sniffing out booby traps, almost to perfection. Marines and combat engineers were thankful, yet uneasy, when the jungle fell quiet while on patrol in the bush. Skawinski's engineering team trekked west, while Rockford's command made his way toward the Da Nang Air Base. The team slugged through the jungle slowly, though meticulously, alongside the road and on top of the road's surface, searching for any sort of booby trap or mine with mine sweepers.

The long list of objectives to complete for the patrol seemed exhausting but gratifying. The marine engineers sniffed out death traps set by the Viet Cong. As Skawinski swept for explosives, he thought, 'Are the rats going to attack this patrol?' Apprehension set in. And a feeling he rarely experienced kicked in - he felt scared to death. The men felt an eerie, terrifying stillness in the air. The calmness in the air set for the perfect ambush.

The apprehension Skawinski felt flowing through his veins signaled he move in a slow, methodical pace.

As much as Skawinski loathed the Viet Cong, he knew the VC were clever, deceptive in using mines on roads. The many tricks and ploys of placing mines on the roads by the VC were set with precision. For the United States to conduct the war properly and to win it, the security and safety of the roads numbered one of the major keys for success. The North Vietnamese Army set a top priority to make use of the skills of the Viet Cong to disrupt communications and supplies of the Americans. The Viet Cong harassed Americans delaying travel and communication by planting booby traps and mines all over the infrastructure of South Vietnam, including roads. One common maneuver for the Viet Cong was digging up holes all along the road in no particular pattern, letting the Americans discover the burrowed holes they had left behind. The Americans would discover the holes, filling the holes back up. In time, the Viet Cong returned, placing a mine in the filled in hole. In the process, and enraging the Americans, the Viet Cong would place a mine in a few of the holes dug up. Additionally, scattered metal fragments were embedded into the roads to outwit the Americans. This specific tactic to delay travel served the VC well.

Another common tactic by the Viet Cong to delay road and dirt track travel was placing mines above the metal culverts. The Viet Cong, astute with explosives, placed mines above the culverts, which an unskilled American mine sweeper would overlook. The mine-sweeper detection system would pick up only the culvert. To counter this tactic, combat engineers adjusted the sensitivity of the mine-sweeper only to read or detect the culvert, then alter the mine-sweeper so the culvert would barely be recognized by the sweeper and the mines could then be detected by the combat engineer or marine.

The time quickly ran to 1230 hours.

The patrol swept a little under 2 miles worth of road when a 1st platoon member found a fifth mine in the road, halting the whole sweeping party as the combat engineers disarmed the mine. Two booby traps located alongside the road near two mines were discovered. An additional tactic of the Viet Cong placed booby traps near a mine set in the road prone to maim or kill Americans. The tactic intended to injure or kill additional Americans after the mine exploded, destroying the mine. The VC optimistically expected to kill more Americans, standing by or in a vehicle, from the booby traps set near the exploded mine. Americans eventually caught onto the tactic of placing booby traps near a mine placed by the VC in the road. When the marines learned over time of the Viet Cong's trick, the marines in the aftermath of destroying the mine would set off the booby traps off the side of the road in clearing the way of the exploded vehicle. Ingenious on their part, Skawinski hated them for it. He loathed the VC of their value of human life or the respect of innocents they may injure or kill from the booby traps they set. The mistreatment of humans pushed Skawinski even harder to defeat the North Vietnamese and the VC. Viewing protesters on television or reading of them in the newspapers back home demonstrating against the war and marching to encourage the North Vietnamese Army and the Viet Cong to win the war sickened him.

On edge, Skawinski bordered on frantic. At 1230 hours, Skawinski's stomach growled, hungry from his hard work of the past few days. With the fright, he felt surprised with his hunger. When Skawinski patrolled in the bush, his mind centered in on the vital mission. He seldom thought of food. This day he found himself anxious, sweeping a road in a wide open space and exposed to possible enemy fire.

Three members of 1st Platoon combat team were disarming a mine found in the road, as Rockford ordered Section A, 2nd Platoon of Bravo Company, in a defensive perimeter to guard the combat engineers defusing the mine.

KABOOM!

A sudden explosion.

A combat engineer made a grave error, deactivating the firing device.

"HIT THE DECK!" ordered Rockford.

Shaken, the marines hit the ground.

A few marines felt the impact of projectiles penetrating flesh.

The ferocious explosion belched out a tremendous array of shrapnel from the backside of the defensive perimeter. The impact shredded two marines, spinning them around like rag dolls.

The interruption brought about a chain reaction as the combat engineer, deactivating the mine, accidentally detonated it. The explosion threw the three marine engineers backwards with such force, the torsos of the men were shredded as if they were put through a cheese grater.

Suddenly a barrage of projectiles from 10 to 12 firearms, Soviet AK-47's and MAT-49's, from the treeline came pouring down on the patrol. Marines left and right of Skawinski fell victim, hit with projectiles from the ferocity of weapons.

In a split second, Skawinski turned his head as he hit the deck quickly, inquiring into the destination of whizzes of projectiles through the air from two grenade launchers.

Rolling into a muddy, deep ditch on his left alongside the road, Skawinski maneuvered into a prone position, ready to fire his weapon. Skawinski felt a stinging up his left arm, a pain he had never felt before. Giving himself a quick rundown, he discovered his left hand fell victim to a Viet Cong bullet, nothing life threatening, but hit nonetheless.

The skirmish escalated, as Skawinski heard distinct hideous laughter - the chuckling giggle of the Devil, reflective from a recurring dream. The laugh never forgotten, tormenting Skawinski's inner self. The constant, demonic giggle, maniacal in tone, nagging him day and night.

Within the familiar sounds of combat, the laugh turns to a cackling, dreadful glee -_*Mwahahaha! Hehehehe!*

Thinking nothing of his wound, Skawinski fires his M-16 toward enemy gunfire.

With the whistling of bullets and projectiles in the air, he swore he spotted devils in the treeline's interior, laughing and firing AK-47's toward the patrol. Alongside the devils, he caught a glimpse of the Devil laughing raucous and vigorous, in a state of glee, witnessing the good guys, the Americans, in a position to be slaughtered before his eyes.

Skawinski, frozen in shock, couldn't believe what he saw in front of him with his own two eyes - the Devil and his legions - displayed in the open, killing marines for all to see. In the past, he discussed with marines who experienced such visions, but never in his presence had he ever witnessed any physical paranormal.

Familiar voices emerged out of the chaos - screams of wounded marines. Screams Skawinski, like Buchanan, abhorred.

"Medic,!" "I'm hit! Help me!" "Mom, I'm dying!"

Screams to haunt veterans for the rest of their lives.

In all the cackling of laughter and screams of the wounded, the ever present sounds of gunfire overlapped with the hum of war.

TAT TAT TAT TAT! POP! POP! POP! POP!

The simultaneous, rapid gunfire swelling from two enemies facing one another turned into a crackling discord of boom with no pause or reprise within the continuous clamor.

The laughing from the devils, the firing of weapons, the Devil cackling, wounded marines howling blood curling screams for it all to end, and Rockford barking out orders from a prone position made Skawinski crazy.

A sudden terror struck Skawinski, a fright never experienced before.

The vulnerability of marines pinned down from an ambush is akin to cornering a lion into a corner. Sick of the Viet Cong holding on to the upper hand, the marines sent a fierce fusillade of return fire into the bush to deter the VC.

Skawinski took careful aim to eliminate the terrifying demons in the bush.

As Skawinski fired his M-16 toward the Viet Cong, he caught in the corner of his right eye 4 marines - Shaw, Kiehl, Rodriquez, and a fourth marine run into the VC's left flank, from the back of the now wiped out perimeter.

Shocked, he swore he perceived four men bestowed in a bright, glowing light, determined to eliminate all the danger follow the four marines into the bush. The glowing men possessed an air of virtue and decency written all over their faces, accompanying and protecting the four marines charging into the Viet Cong's left flank.

Once the marines charged into the bush, followed by the four men clothed in white garments, Skawinski heard the most petrifying sounds resonating from the jungle. He caught the sounds of excoriating pains and agony, and most prevalent came voices begging for mercy. Next came blood curling growls reverberating in a constant battle between good and evil. The Devil and his demons in an encounter battling the glowing angelic men. The echoes of a battle between good and evil lifted higher than those of mortal warfare. No one else in the patrol heard any of what Skawinski heard, though it was real to him.

Skawinski laid in the dirt and mud, utterly petrified!

Four minutes passed from the initial gunfire, when weapons finally ceased from the treeline. An ambush that seemed an eternity for Skawinski.

The four charging marines into the jungle opened fire and killed 6 Viet Cong, while the remaining VC fled into the jungle bush. They fired onto the fleeing VC, killing four of them.

Kiehl barked to his fellow marines, "Hold your fire! Private Benjamin Kiehl! Charlie's ran yella! Charlie's gone!"

Questions ran a thousand miles per hour across Skawinski's mind. 'What happened?' ' Was it his imagination?' 'Was it real?' 'The devils and glowing men - where did they come from?'

Rockford and Jurgensen ran toward the jungle, ordering a new perimeter to include inside the wounded and the treeline of the initial Viet Cong attack. He sent 1st Platoon, 2nd Squad to pursue the fleeting VC. Lipstone radioed in a MEDVAC for the wounded, including Skawinski. Rockford stepped from one dead VC to the next, inspecting the remains, and recognizing three of the Vietnamese from a local community, including a barber and a rice farmer, infuriating him. He stooped down to inspect the dead VC.

"This war. Who's the enemy? It can be anybody." Pausing, he vented, "Stupid Viet Cong."

Rockford glanced toward the road, noticing the many of his men weeping and grieving over lost friends. Bravo Company suffered six killed and nine wounded, and five life threatening. He now found himself in an angry mood.

Out of the blue, a marine went berserk, being held back from the dead Viet Cong, yelling and screaming obscenities, cursing them to hell.

"Ya killed my friend! Ya killed my friend!" yelled the marine.

Rockford rose quickly, stepping over to the marine to calm him down. As Rockford comforted the marine, the MEDVAC came to an ear's shot.

Skawinski all the while sat, watching Rockford and the survivors with the aftermath of the skirmish.

Bewildered of his experience, he would seek Buchanan when he returned to camp to hammer out any questions in Skawinski's mind.

The MEDVAC arrived, carrying the wounded onto the Huey helicopters and transporting the wounded to the field hospitals, including Skawinski. The remaining marines of Bravo Company finished sweeping the road and converging with Staff Sergeant Frank Smith at BT 009691 as originally planned to sweep for the 30' fixed span bridge on the QL-1 route.

Skawinski required medical attention to repair his left hand wound. His wound removed him from the 'game' for a few weeks, tops.

Time ran late as the hour and minute hands sat at 1730 hours.

The pain from the bumpy ride on the Huey helicopter to Camp Love gave way to the many questions that crossed Skawinski's mind.

The ride on the Huey amounted to an eternity for Skawinski, as he gazed out from the side of the helicopter descending toward the ground, ascending when approaching small hills.

The helicopters quickly approached Camp Love, descending upon the field beside Camp Love for the Hueys to land.

At a distance, Skawinski noticed Doc Delaney, Senior Chief Gross, Petty Officer Crowley, and a few others waiting patiently with stretchers in the field. Skawinski couldn't quite make out the entire party standing in the field waiting, but enduring the heat, ready and willing to administer their medical skills onto the wounded. The Huey came close to a complete landing with its skids parallel to the ground, when Skawinski recognized the unidentified marines standing with Doc Delaney.

One serviceman standing patiently stood Chaplain Buchanan.

Skawinski leaped out of the helicopter, trotting to Chaplain Buchanan. Standing proudly with Buchanan stood Jackson and Adkins to welcome him home.

Embracing Skawinski, the men laughed out of sheer relief. For Skawinski found himself safe and sound, back home alive and almost well.

"Adolphus, when I saw the initial list of wounded, my stomach hit the floor. We prayed it wouldn't be serious. It wasn't." shared a relieved Buchanan.

"No sir. It wasn't. It was your blessing as we shoved off - that's it." asserted Skawinski with a smile.

"Maybe, Corporal Skawinski. But the six - well, they-they didn't make it." commented a down trodden Buchanan.

Skawinski nodded.

"Don't think about that, sir." said Skawinski. "Let's just celebrate the Lord's Goodness."

Buchanan nodded in the affirmative.

Jackson bragged, "Yes, Padre. He's alive! Let's just celebrate for now, and think the other later. What do you say?"

"*Yeah*. Come on, Robert." commented Adkins, encouraging Buchanan.

Buchanan smiled from ear to ear, nodding in the affirmative.

"All right. Let's go have some fellowship together!" said a convinced Buchanan.

Skawinski's wounds were bandaged up, and he then joined his friends for some chow.

Observing the reunion from his office window, Lucas set his eyes on Skawinski, thrilled he survived the ambush. Buchanan visited Lucas' office, discussing with him how he blessed the men on their departure, though six men perished from the result of the ambush inflicted from the hands of the Viet Cong. Lucas, all the while attempting to console Buchanan, reassuring him that not all goes well in a war zone.

After his visit with the Skipper, Buchanan visited with his friends - Skawinski, Jackson, and Adkins - starting with supper. Eating dinner in the chow hall delighted Skawinski, who had his fill. After supper, the men resigned to playing Rummy before turning in for the night.

Though the evening ended up a memorable night spending it with friends, Skawinski's mental state seemed anything but healthy. He suffered from General Anxiety Disorder the whole night. Skawinski asked himself more than once - 'Why did others perish while I was spared?' Nightmares will come from it. A guilt-ridden state followed from asking such questions, longing for satisfactory answers to his questions.

Even Vivaldi's 'Spring' of the Four Seasons, a group of four concerto grossi selected from Burns for the night, failed to distract the past couple of days' events out of his mind.

As Vivaldi echoed throughout the camp, Skawinski fell asleep from exhaustion. The night filled itself with guilt-ridden dreams of maniacal laughter and the Devil. The next morning, he woke up hating the Devil evermore. He woke up hating the Viet Cong evermore.

Skawinski woke up evermore determined to conquer one goal in Vietnam serving as a marine combat engineer – exterminate as many rats as possible.

Again, Skawinski's feelings conflicted with his Faith. And again, Buchanan served as the solvent to cope with war.

Within the deepest depths of Skawinski's heart and soul, he hated the Devil. Within the depths of his inner self, he hated the Viet Cong. He hated rats. After the skirmish, his resolve toughened even stronger to settle the score for all the tortured and murdered children from the hands of the VC. Skawinski displayed in the days to come nothing but determination to wield a flame-bladed sword swinging back and forth ridding the world of the Devil and its demons.

THE MONSOON

NOVEMBER 22, 1968

The spiritual team hit the road 100 miles an hour, never slowing down in the month of Thanksgiving. Buchanan conducted countless services, accompanied jungle bush patrols, counseled and advised the men spiritually. Yesterday, November 21, he welcomed Skawinski, whose hand was healing quickly, and the sweeping party back into Camp Love. The pair chatted about his encounter in the bush way into the night the next two evenings. Buchanan's listening ear lifted the spirits of Skawinski far beyond his dreams.

The success of ministry in November to the marines ranked high in Buchanan's tour. Today, the spiritual team returned from the 1100 hours Friday Communion service administered to Delta Company while sweeping for mines on Route 1 and 540.

Besides, the month of November all across the country scheduled rival college football teams to butt heads for another year of bragging rights, including the Buckeyes of Ohio State. The Scarlet and Grey will suit up to play the Michigan Wolverines Sunday for the Big Ten championship, a trip to the Rose Bowl, and a chance to play the USC Trojans for the national championship.

The fruitful day of events scheduled the Friday night social, talking sports at the social, and spending valuable time with camp friends. The spiritual team will temporarily put the day of easy living on hold for an assignment Buchanan wished he could brush aside, dealing with KIAs.

The month of November hit the 7th Engineering Battalion with casualties quite hard - 15 KIAs and 54 WIAs. For Buchanan, it was 15 killed, 54 wounded too many. He hated men losing their life at such an early age.

Worst of all, Buchanan witnessed 18, 19, and 20-year-olds ripped apart in serious engagements with the enemy. He remembered the young men's deaths for a lifetime, never to be forgotten. Experiences few people encounter in life.

The Navy gave chaplains many responsibilities in Vietnam. One required duty Buchanan despised called him to ID the dead. The identification process required a doctor, officer, chaplain, and a couple of medics. The group would step within a metal enclosure the marines referred to as 'the cooler.' The cooler housed corpses until shipped out in a body bag. From time to time, there were bodies stacked as high as two or three on top of one another. After a marine lost his life in the bush or in station, the grunts took the remains to the cooler. The marines stripped the corpse naked except for dog tags. The corpses were identified by tying a tag on the big toe, followed by sealing the deceased dog tags in an envelope. The dog tags were then placed in the body bag with the corpse and transferred to the United States Marine mortuary in Da Nang, Vietnam. The government would then transport the deceased remains to Guam, then home to the United States.

The time sat at 1300 hours.

While eating in the chow hall, Buchanan visited with Burns. Classical music dominated the conversation. Buchanan bombarded Burns with questions linked to his selection of music the previous night, the Sonata no. 1 for violin by Bach. Buchanan enjoyed it immensely. After lunch, he set out to meet Doc Delaney to ID the casualties in the cooler. He ventured out of the chow hall, took his good ole time walking to the cooler to carry out the unthinkable, identifying the KIAs.

Buchanan despised the responsibility possibly more than any other in camp. The stench of bodies smelled putrid, tickling his nose. A smell he will never forget. With about 2 dozen corpses in the cooler to identify, it amounted to about an hour's worth of labor. Buchanan thanked the Lord the work equaled no longer than an hour. He could tolerate but only an hour of horror in the cooler. Five minutes alone in the cooler furnished enough to sicken his stomach, observing the mangled and torn bodies.

Buchanan felt the weight of the world lifted off his shoulders, signing his last John Hancock on the validation and confirmation form for the last KIA to identify. He departed the 'cooler' relieved one more day identifying KIA's has come to an end, yet left full of consternation signing his name for the last KIA. Buchanan connected with the last KIA, a jovial, bright young 19-year-old from Ripley, Mississippi. He enjoyed his company. What lied now in the cooler consisted of remains of a young kid just starting to live life. His mother, unfortunately, will soon be given the word her son will not be coming home alive and was taken from this world from the ravages of war. He will not be the last for Buchanan to witness a marine lose his life so young.

With 'cooler' duty over and done with, Buchanan paced himself promptly to the conference hall to meet Jackson for the Friday night social.

On his way to the hall, Buchanan ran into Marine Lieutenant Lawrence Jones and Marine Captain Bernard Johannsson of Charlie Company. Jones's family established themselves in the wine business and members of the Roman Catholic Church. Jones and Buchanan humored themselves with an inside joke. Jones, from Washington state, numbered few Catholic churches in the state, yet lived the faith regardless. Johannsson's family gained a reputation as prominent lawyers from New York City. As a young child, his Jewish parents escaped Europe during the rise of the National Socialist German Workers' Party. Many Johannsson family members unfortunately failed to escape Europe and perished under Nazi rule during the Holocaust. Two opposite backgrounds, but friends regardless. War brings people together who are different. People who are on opposite ends of the political, social, and religious spectrum.

"Good afternoon, gentlemen." said Buchanan, reaching out to shake hands.

"Good afternoon, Chaplain." responds a hearty Jones and Johannsson, shaking hands firmly expressing appreciation toward Buchanan.

The officers thought highly of Buchanan. Most notably, as a minister to the troops and supporter of individual religious freedom.

"I know you've been carrying out a duty you like least in camp, Padre. We saw you from a distance from the admin building." commented Johannsson.

"Yes, cooler duty is last on my priority list. Ugly in there. Ghastly." Buchanan grimaced.

The two officers nod in agreement.

"I've been in there from time to time, Chaplain. I certainly don't envy you." commented Johannsson.

Buchanan declared, "I prefer I give the 'cooler' duty to someone else. But - I know it has to be done. Part of the war, I guess. I pray it ends one day."

Again, nods of agreement.

"Besides, it's Friday night. John Wayne night." confirmed Buchanan.

"That'll brush aside any thoughts of the 'cooler'." added Buchanan. "And the game on Sunday, the Ohio State game against that 'state up north' - that'll certainly distract our attention away from the turmoil, at least temporarily."

"It's all sown up, chaplain." responded Jones. "John Wayne, the football game, they'll certainly bring pause of the war for the men. And don't worry about Ohio State, sir, Head Coach Barnes's got 'em looking good. Don't think you have to worry about them getting beat Sunday. Rushing attack might be the best in the country, but that defense of the Buckeyes - whew."

Johannsson commented, "Look for it, chaplain. Ohio State is rock solid. Besides, tonight is a John Wayne night on the agenda for movies, right chaplain?"

"Sure is. And I assure you Johannsson, *he* is." insisted Buchanan.

"Nothing better than a John Wayne to ease the tension. Right chaplain?" asked Jones.

"Amen!" responded Buchanan. "You all will be there, I hope?"

"It's a foregone conclusion, chaplain." said Johannsson.

Jones mentions, "We're headed to a briefing, so tonight will take the painful memory of the briefing away. We'll talk of Ohio State's course of action to win Sunday's game. Know you'll be thrilled with football talk, along with Skawinski." Jones chuckled. "Being required to attend one of those dreaded, gosh awful meetings sets our stomachs turning, Padre."

"Besides, Porch is leading the brief today." added Johannsson, rolling his eyes.

All laugh. Buchanan shakes his head, knowing the tedious, aggravating environment it can be when Porch directs the briefing.

"Great! We'll see you there. 1930 hours. Sharp." said Buchanan. "I'll say a brief prayer for you all as you attend the briefing."

"Thank you for the prayer, chaplain. We'll need it. See you at the social tonight. Take care, sir." said Jones.

"All right, men. Bye for now. Go Bucks!" confirmed Buchanan.

"Go Bucks!" responded the men.

Parting ways, Buchanan's thoughts centered in on Jones and Johannsson. The two men lived in such opposite worlds. One probably socially liberal, the other conservative. One wealthy, one moderately wealthy. One Christian, the other Jewish. One underlining fact held true – war will force men together opposite poles apart, clinging on to each other for dear life.

Buchanan's thoughts shifted to the recurring horrors of war.

A night of nightmares, thinking of casualties in November, and the grisly task of identifying deceased military personnel made today one desired to whip clean and start all over again.

Buchanan stepped into the conference hall and sighted Jackson, leaning on the conference hall sign, waiting patiently. He usually accompanied Buchanan in the cooler, but today he assisted Gunnery Sergeant Jurgensen in self-defense training to Bravo Company.

"Got here, huh sir?" said Jackson, with a smile of amusement written all over his face. He straightens up and adjusts his hat and uniform.

"Being late is not your style, chaplain."

"Well, Philip, I ran into Lieutenant Jones and Captain Johannsson. You know I like 'em. They were on their way to a briefing, and you know how much I enjoy their company."

"I know chaplain, I know." Jackson grins.

"The two of 'em have to listen to Mr. Wonderful today, as he enjoys listening to himself give directives and lead the briefing."

"Porch?" asked an inquisitive Jackson.

"One 'n only."

"Ugh! I can hardly look at - let alone think about the man."

"Amen to that, Philip! Amen to that!"

"Well, let's secure the hall for the social tonight." suggested Buchanan, as he motioned with his arm to Jackson to set the tables and chairs in the conference hall.

As Buchanan unfolded his first chair, he sat down immediately.

Jackson turned and asked, "You alright, chaplain?"

"Fine, Philip. Fine." Buchanan paused and stated emphatically, "No Philip, I'm not fine."

Jackson recognized the sullen mood thrown from Buchanan.

Jackson asked, "The war?"

"Yeah, the war." answered Buchanan. "ID'ing men today. You know, casualties. There's anything I hate more about this war, the exception of seeing children perish, and, well - seeing the young boys killed, I guess, is having to ID those boys. It's pathetic. They look so pitiful, so lifeless. They resemble faces of 14-year-olds to me. Lying there so stiff and rigid. I hate it. I just hate it, Philip."

At a loss for words, Jackson knew Buchanan detested casualties.

"I haven't gotten used to it yet myself, sir. War's terrible." admitted Jackson. He mulled over what words to say next. "Since I've become a believer, I now look into the eyes of one of those boys who's being taken away from us early in his life, and I wonder."

Jackson looks out into the camp from the upper screened portion of the conference hall wall and says, "I search for answers for the questions I ask. 'Who was he?' 'Where'd he come from?' 'What was his personality like?' 'Where's his spirit now?' 'Was he a believer?'

"Yeah. *Yeah*. I do the same thing, Philip." admitted Buchanan, surprised another serviceman asked the same questions concerning death. As Jackson glanced toward Buchanan, he added, "But, you know Sergeant, I ask myself something else. How's his mother going, well, going to accept the loss of her boy? The kid who's now stiff, lifeless in the cooler - the boy who was once the son of a loving mother. How's she going to suffer and grieve?"

"You're right chaplain. Might be the trickiest point to accept losing one marine because of death. A childless mother."

"Well, let's get the social set up for tonight, Philip. Maybe it'll set our minds on the better things of life and off the war."

"Let's do chaplain. I know it will. Besides, it's John Wayne night." Jackson smiles.

The team secure the conference hall in no time at all and sit to chat a bit more, as they exchange favorite John Wayne movie scenes with one another.

Jackson changed the subject. "Been listening to sports on the Armed Forces Radio on my transistor radio while you were on 'cooler' duty. Ohio State's favored to win the game, but the experts are calling for a close one. Ohio State gets a lead Sunday, you might as well call it. Ohio State is practically unbeatable when up early in a game."

Buchanan takes a seat on a chair at a back table. "Let's listen to more of the sports talk, if it's still on the radio."

"OK, sir."

Jackson joined Buchanan and located an armed services station of sports talk. The men listened to experts mulling over all the games slated for the big day of college football. Listening to the expert opinions, the 'know-it-alls', as Buchanan referred to them, all admitted the fourth quarter will be a critical moment in the game for Ohio State and Michigan.

Time now raced to 1630 hours in the late afternoon. An additional hour and a half to prepare for the social.

A stickler for starting on time for everything, Buchanan set the Friday night social to start at 1930 hours sharp.

The agenda for the Friday night social ran extensive. With promptness and precision, the spiritual team exerted teamwork and accomplished the list of errands every Friday night, crossing off each errand in sequence one by one. The agenda consisted first of food, second in arranging tables and chairs, visiting supply to retrieve the movie projector, and lastly setting the table full of food. With an extensive list, the spiritual team jumped on the tasks at hand for the evening.

Acquiring the movie came a bit more complex. Copyright and release date of the movie created issues for Buchanan from the time he arrived in Camp Love. With the full cooperation of personnel in Camp Love, including Porch, Buchanan schemed with an officer in camp referred to as 'The Scrounger' to gain access to any John Wayne movie for Buchanan. The Scrounger held all the secrets on laying his hands on such movies with the copyright and distribution of film. No one asked questions about or the disclosure of the movie's origin. The camp played dumb - 'I see nothing. I hear nothing. I know nothing'. Everyone agreed to 'don't ask, don't tell.'

A rather tedious task ended acquiring the food from the chow hall. The social comprised chips, dip when stocked, vegetables when available, peanuts, sliced canned ham and cheese with sliced bread when available, candy and chocolate. Supply provided utensils, plates, cups, napkins, and ice. The quartermaster, who went out of his way, provided candy and chocolate on Friday nights. He went an extra mile for Buchanan. It seemed the quartermaster always discovered extra candy and chocolate in the farthest corner of the shelves of food stock for his Friday night socials. Buchanan seemed clueless of the fact the quartermaster stocked a little more away for Friday nights as a favor to him, something he discovered a year later at El Toro base in southern California.

Returning to the conference hall at 1730, the spiritual team set up for the night. With teamwork, the hall came together in no time and ready to go in 45 minutes, record time.

As the last row of chairs were straightened, the spiritual team heard distant thumps and booms in the distant air. The team heard the reverberations of familiar sounds of thunder and lightning distant. What a time for it to rain, as the finishing touches for the social were being tied together. That's Vietnam weather for you. Not a cloud in the sky two hours earlier. Now - rain, and much of it. October is the last month of heavy rain and monsoons in Vietnam. And occasionally, the rain carried over into November in southeast Asia.

Rain might sway hardly anyone away from the social, but the rain might dissuade and dampen the mood.

The spiritual team stepped to the screened side window of the hall. Jackson asked, "You think the rain's going to come, chaplain?"

"I *think* so Philip. I am very sorry to say so."

Minutes later, the darkened skies unleashed rain falling from the Heavens above, saturating the earth below. Initially, a light rain from the start turned into a heavy pounding of southeastern Asian down pours giving the Great Flood a run for its money. With a hard rain in Vietnam, harsh visibility amounted to five feet in front of a serviceman. As the heavy rain eased off, a light down pour ensued, to almost a sprinkling, and then finally the rain coming to a complete halt, falling from the sky. The aftermath of a heavy rain always found an eerie silence. The rain lasted for 10 minutes, then died away and dissipated. Jackson and Buchanan then perceived to hear booming voices echo loud and clear in camp. As the men adjusted their hearing from the torrential rain, the spiritual team heard familiar marines' voices barking out orders, yelling "Get those bodies in the ditch!" "My God, the boy's exposed!" "Catch that marine, he's floating in the gully!"

Adjusting their vision, the spiritual team focused on the direction of the barking orders and discovered a horrendous sight from the window: 15 to 20 corpses from the cooler scattered in mud and ditches. The embankment slanting down from the cooler numbered at least 7 to 8 remains. The heavy rain literally picked up bodies, moving the remains outside the cooler. Bodies strung out on the ground outside the cooler deemed itself abnormal. When a deceased marine arrived in camp, the remains were immediately taken to the cooler and expected to stay put until transported to the United States Marine mortuary in Da Nang, Vietnam. But after the storm, the bodies were strung all over.

The cooler's location situated itself on top of a small, isolated man made entrenchment east of the camp. Marines raced to the cooler from all corners of Camp Love, retrieving the remains, placing them back in the cooler. The heavy rain tore open body bags. The paralyzing sight stunned the spiritual team, aghast at the sight of corpses torn and ripped to pieces lying about for all to see. Numb with the events unveiled before their very eyes, it will be a sight forever to haunt the both of them.

"Welp, there goes the Friday Night Social." confirmed Buchanan. "No one'll come now after all that! What we probably got is a depressed and dejected group of guys now. That depressed me too. Those poor boys being exposed like that. The men will just stay in their hootches for the night. I'd stay at home too, if I were them."

A downtrodden Jackson attempts to lighten the mood. "Maybe not, Padre. Hopefully, they'll realize coming to the social will do 'em good."

Jackson paused. "I will say this, though. Whoever's responsible for the KIA's gonna to be in some hot water."

"Sure are Philip. *Sure* are."

Turning from the window, the men grab a metal chair and sit melancholy with heads low.

Sitting quietly, they ponder how appalling and awful war is.

The hour was now 1900 hours. Just 30 minutes until the social.

The spiritual team thought of worrisome questions - 'Will anyone come?' 'Is the social worth it tonight?' 'Was today a washout?'

Buchanan looked at his watch, sighing heavily.

The men noted their watches. 1920 hours and no one in sight. Attendance for the socials ran high, with totals of 70 to 80 men every

Friday night. Buchanan seemed convinced the corpses, and the cooler, dampened the mood, grounds for exerting no one will show on this Friday night. Moments such as the cooler incident were depressive and put men in a melancholy state. Depressive moods pushed men to hibernate in their hootches, detaching themselves to mull things over in their individual sleeping quarters. The isolation provided a means of coping with horrific war experiences. Isolationism and seclusion served as a therapeutic means of individual therapy. The isolation served as an escape of war, an escape of the destruction at least temporarily.

Individuals deal separately with tragedy. Each and every human being is innately different. Therefore, the means of coping with war is dealt with individually.

The two sit quietly for a while, still pondering their situation at 1925 hours. By now, 30 to 40 men would have shown up for the Friday night social. Questions arose in their minds. 'Should we close up shop?' 'Secure for the evening?' Or 'Wait a little longer?'

And suddenly, in the distance, the spiritual team heard secluded voices. In the distance, they heard pleasant conversations of marines longing for an evening spent with friends and colleagues. Closer and closer to the conference hall, they came. Buchanan hopped out of his chair with enthusiasm. He viewed 10 to 15 marines headed toward the conference hall, clothed in clad, either in t-shirts or tank tops, and shorts or fatigue pants.

Nothing but smiles from ear to ear worn on the faces of the spiritual team.

Buchanan stepped quickly to the entrance and welcomed the men to the social, as he usually does. Marine after marine came through the door.

"Good Evening, marine!"

"Good Evening, Sergeant McElrath!" declared Buchanan.

"Great to see you, Corporal Jaworski." bellowed Buchanan as yet another marine entered the door.

"Good evening, chaplain."

"Glad you made it tonight, Fred Jones. Haven't seen you for a few days. Good to see my fellow Kentuckian here tonight." said Buchanan.

"Thank you chaplain. We had a notion a John Wayne movie would put us all in a better mood." stated Jones.

"Couldn't agree with you more, Jones. Come on in."

As Buchanan spoke with Jones, more and more marines stepped into the hall.

At last, Lieutenant Jones and Captain Johannsson stepped through the hall door, face to face with Chaplain Buchanan.

"Well, as promised, here's Lieutenant Jones and Captain Johannsson. Come on in, men." announced Buchanan, overwhelmed with the officer's presence. He lowered his voice. "Hope the movie tonight eases the pain from the brief." Buchanan softly chuckles.

"Thank you, chaplain." said Johannsson.

Jones encourages Buchanan, "Enjoying your company eases the pain in and of itself, Padre."

"Ohio State on Sunday, chaplain. We're excited for you. I just know the Buckeyes are going to win." remarked Johannsson.

All laugh.

"Amen! Thanks, men."

Jones and Johannsson excused themselves and headed to the food tables. The officers will have plenty of time to chat later on in the evening, talk football, and reminisce of home. The two marine officers disappeared into the mass of marines, mingling with enlisted and officers alike.

Buchanan glances toward Jackson, positioned behind the food tables, grinning from ear to ear. The air of the night changed to subdued, a change of state from the tense moments of war during the week. The men conversed - thinking of home, the talk of seeing one day their girlfriends and wives once again.

The number of marines grew with time, as Jackson took a head count, a whopping record of 119 men.

Wow! 119 men! The logical sense enabled, as Jones mentioned, the men to come and forget about the cooler incident and the war itself.

Following a time of visiting with each other in "fellowship" and eating food, Jackson started the movie. A perfect movie for the day's end, a western comedy of John Wayne's. A personal favorite of Buchanan's.

A comedy and John Wayne. The perfect combination for a depressive, horrific past week the 7th Engineering Battalion experienced. The movie, at least temporarily, delayed the reality that in just a few hours, they will confront the inevitable - face the war and the Viet Cong once again in the bush.

Thankful they choose not to close up shop and call it a night, it pleased Buchanan and Jackson the social provided a repose of comfort in the men's lives.

And for just a few hours, the men could put the war on hold. The two of them will never forget the moment for the rest of their lives. Here in Vietnam, in the war's height, two Ohioans take a break from it all to give the men a brief, but momentous event to lighten the mood of the war.

Now on to Sunday to listen to the Ohio State game together as Ohioans. Not as an officer or enlisted. Not as chaplain or chaplain assistant. But as two mutual Ohioans, both with a common interest in Ohio State winning the game. On Sunday, they listened as the Ohio State Buckeyes pulled away and won big – Ohio State 50 Michigan 14. The Buckeyes shut them out in the second half, as the two men were ecstatic with Ohio State's win over the Buckeyes' arch enemy. On now to the championship game against the despised USC Trojans.

No News is Good News

December 1, 1968

The first day of December, a Sunday. The month to celebrate Jesus' birth has finally arrived. A celebration month exalting the birth of baby Jesus, born of the Spirit and Savior of mankind.

A date on the Christian calendar uniting Christians worldwide.

The first night of Christmas music happened to be the last night of November. Burns made it loud and clear for all to hear, including the scheming, devious Viet Cong possibly hiding just inside the treeline. Once again, Christmas is to be celebrated by playing *Once in Royal David's City** from a Christmas album of the Worcester Cathedral Choir and *In the Bleak of Midwinter** from Saint Paul's Cathedral Choir, two of Skawinski's favorites. The tradition in Skawinski's home church every Christmas began with *Once in Royal David's City* played by the congregational orchestra, followed by a vocal presentation. Skawinski's Lutheran church presented a last song of *Rejoice and be Merry**, sending parishioners away with a merry message of Jesus' birth and entrance into the world.

The music created an eerie silence throughout the camp, a silence no one wanted to end. If the Viet Cong heard the composition, Burns furnished the enemy with music, filling the night air with a well-deserved calm, a message of Christ and peace through Jesus. The music expelled thunderously in the night, a result of throbbing pain in the villainous VC's ears.

Skawinski laid on his cot, staring straight up onto his ceiling, envisioning his church's performance of *Once in Royal David's City*, as he plays his baritone and singing bass in the choir following the instrumental. Oh, how Skawinski dreaded missing the Christmas season and the celebration of Christ's birth in his home church! His only consolation promised that this time next year he will be present in his home church and will take part in the celebration in his home congregation.

Burns chose *Once in Royal David's City* on many a night in December and everyone in camp knew why – his love for Skawinski.

Regardless, the spiritual team was traveling to Da Nang. They chatted of music Burns introduced for the month of December, chuckling of Skawinski's love of Christmas. The men reflected the music's magnetism onto the beauty of the topography of Vietnam as they traveled to Da Nang Division Hospital to visit recently wounded from 7th Marines, 1st Division. Buchanan possessed a built in, natural skill to boost morale with the marines, even if the men were down-hearted and discouraged from extensive war wounds.

The 6 to 7 miles to the Da Nang base shattered the monotony of isolation, contributing to a significant break from the solitude of the jungle bush. The war came to a screeching halt for the spiritual team for 9 or 10 days since the Friday night social on November 22. Camp Love experienced in November 1968 the heaviest rainfall since Buchanan set foot in Vietnam, and the rain gradually worsened as the month came to its end. The roads flooded and Camp Love's personnel found themselves stuck on base due to the heavy rain muddying out the terrain, making roads and passage ways treacherous. Accompanying patrols came frequent, but rare in November. Buchanan considered himself as "being in the way", delaying the essential work of patrols as he felt the marines gave him too much special attention to keep him safe and sound in the sluggish and soaked wet terrain due to the rain. Occasionally, the spiritual team ventured out with overnight patrols. Patrols ventured out, regardless of weather, but mechanized missions and traveling on roads were hampered because of the rain.

Friends of Buchanan, Lieutenant Daniel Fontaine Anderson, a fellow Southern Baptist from Manchester, Georgia and Lieutenant Charles Brennan, a Roman Catholic and a New Yorker, requested Buchanan undertake several hospital duties as the overwhelming numbers of wounded at the hospital in recent months weighted down medical and chaplain personnel.

Besides, Buchanan took the liberty to visit wounded from Camp Love in the hospital, affording an opportunity to kill two birds with one stone. Buchanan was happy to take on duties to encourage and motivate those incapacitated by the efforts of a no good like the Viet Cong.

Arriving at the Air Base main gate, the spiritual team presented their military IDs and drove straight to the hospital. Jackson eased the jeep into one of the two chaplains reserved spaces in front of Wing A Quonset hut of the hospital. The team stepped out of the jeep, making their way to the front entrance of the hospital, through the entrance into the reception room.

The premier hospital serviced hundreds of military personnel from all four branches of service.

The spiritual team gained familiarity with the hospital visiting wounded while stationed in Da Nang. The experience Buchanan gained visiting and counseling the marines in the hospital offered him an upper hand with the wounded. His good-humored and affable personality blended as a natural in granting a state of physical ease and, to a degree, alleviating and mitigating an individual's pain, grief, or suffering. People liked him. His presence in a room brought about joy. Human beings changed by war long for a sublime of peace and calm, and Buchanan supplied a source of inspiration of God's presence.

The small, but comfortable, waiting area at the entrance of the hospital stationed a marine receptionist at a welcoming desk. From there, visitors could locate from a list of wounded service personnel to visit.

Entering the front entrance, Buchanan, grinning, said, "Good morning, Corporal."

"Good morning, chaplain."

The spiritual team noticed immediately the young receptionist at the welcoming desk. The young marine just turned 20 years old. '*Wow!*' they thought. She looked 14 or 15 to the team. The men thought, 'This girl is so young and in a war zone at her age. The team thought she should be at home, attending college or working a civilian job.

At least stationed elsewhere in the world on a navy or marine base. Regardless, she might very well be a volunteer, loves her country and wants to serve her nation.

"Good morning, sergeant." said the corporal.

"Well, good morning." replied Jackson. He glances down at the corporal's name badge, and asks "Corporal Mayse, is it?"

"Yes, it is. I know why you're here. Chaplains Anderson and Brennan notified us you were coming today. The nurses are all looking forward to seeing you all again. They asked me to walk you down to the marine wing when you arrived. If y'all will just follow me, I'll take you to the nurses. I'll be back in a moment, private." commented Mayse to the private on duty with her.

Mayse turns, stepping through an entrance behind the desks of the front Quonset hut of the hospital, followed by Buchanan and Jackson.

As Mayse guides the spiritual team down the middle of the Quonset hut, Buchanan asked, "Are you from the south? You have an accent as if you are from the southern states."

"Yes, sir, I am. From Bartow County Georgia. It's Cartersville, Georgia, the county seat. It's off the Interstate."

"Yes, yes. It's in the mountains of Georgia. Isn't it?" asked Buchanan.

"Yes, it is. You're from the mountains somewhere yourself, aren't you, sir?" asked Mayse.

"Pike County, Kan-tuc-kee. Pikesville, across the rivers from West Virginia and Virginia. The Tri-State." informed Buchanan proudly.

"You have an accent as well, sir. And it's pretty obvious." said Jackson.

The three chuckle at the thought.

"Yes, and it's tiresome getting used to. I couldn't understand a word he said when I first met the chaplain." said Jackson.

Buchanan places his hand on Jackson's shoulder, smiles from ear to ear, as they chuckle a little harder.

Mayse led the spiritual team to the rear of Wing A Quonset hut door into a squared off patio area with a wooden roof furnished with benches for visitors to sit on. Three other Quonset huts faced the patio area, housing wounded personnel. Mayse led the spiritual team into Quonset hut, Wing B to the left, the wing Anderson and Brennan requested Buchanan to visit.

From an aerial view, the Quonset huts reflected a plus sign.

As Buchanan walks into Wing B, three Navy nurses welcome Buchanan and Jackson from the wing station.

"Welcome back, chaplain. Good to see you as well, Sergeant Jackson." said Lieutenant Commander Veronica Reagan from Provo, Utah.

"Good Morning, Ma'am." responds the team.

"Thank you, Mayse." said Reagan.

"You're welcome, Ma'am. Have a good day, sir, Sergeant." said Mayse.

"Thank you." responded the spiritual team.

Mayse smiles and steps back to her station in the reception room.

Lieutenant Nancy Burleson and Lieutenant Junior Grade Jennifer Glenn rise from their chairs and greet the spiritual team.

The nurses deemed their careers a lifelong calling. A calling to care for others wholeheartedly. The call to show concern for their fellow human beings in a holistic approach. Especially Glenn, who considered her calling to reflect her strong Roman Catholic convictions to serve others. Her efforts mirrored God's love toward others.

"Aren't you a short-timer, Lieutenant Glenn?" asked Buchanan.

"Yes. Yes, sir. I am. My last day is December 23. And I'll be in Okinawa on Christmas Day. Then, on to Hawaii on the 26th of December. And I'm *sooooooo* excited!" said Glenn. "I'm gonna order a humongous piece of beefsteak at a local steak joint I patronize when

I'm in Hawaii. Then I'm gonna go to the beach and lay out in the sun for a nice, brown Hawaiian suntan." added Glenn, with a smile as wide as the ends of the ocean.

"Amen!" confirmed Buchanan.

"I wish I was going with her." said Burleson.

"Me, too." added Reagan.

"Sounds wonderful." said Buchanan.

"Hawaii is therapeutic, to say the least." added Jackson.

"It certainly is, Jackson." responded Burleson.

All smile at the thought.

Burleson acknowledges the spiritual team's presence. "Chaplain, we're thrilled you're here. You too Jackson. The two of you have a way with the wounded like no other chaplain and chaplain assistant we know. Your six months here on the base were successful months, especially with counseling and spending time with the wounded."

Reagan said, "Our wing we're responsible for has had many wounded from skirmishes and battles of late."

The spiritual team nod in affirmation.

Glenn said, "Schedules have swamped Chaplains Anderson and Brennan with duties. Again, thanks for coming. There's one marine though. We have monitored him with his physical and mental health and it's....it's Neville Dalton. A Private. He's slept for most of the last day and a half. He's the marine in the very last bed on the right. He's from Chattanooga, Tennessee. He's not aware of his condition. He, well, he -"

"Oh. What is it Glenn?" asked Buchanan.

"Well, it-it's -" said the nurses.

"I know." hinted Jackson.

"You know what, sergeant?" asked Reagan.

Jackson said, "I know what's wrong - with Dalton. When we make our way down to him, I'll know what to do."

Buchanan glances toward Jackson, and softly asks, "Philip, what's wrong with Dalton?"

Jackson nods toward Buchanan to assure him things will work out.

Jackson respectfully took Buchanan's arm and gently pushes him to the first bed in Reagan's wing and began to visit the men.

For the visit, Buchanan supplied himself a small box of Chaplain Capodanno crucifixes to offer to each of the wounded for Chaplain Kensington's sake. Besides, Buchanan knew without a doubt the crosses resulted in providing a sense of the presence of God for the wounded in a vital time of their lives. He carted a small chair from bed to bed, conversing with the men.

A kid from Minot, North Dakota, occupied the first bed.

As always, Buchanan complemented the place of origin of the marine, to uplift the emotional and spiritual state of the young man. Reminiscing of home almost always encouraged the wounded marine.

"Minot, North Dakota? Well, that's located way up there in your state, isn't it? You receive cold weather every year." commented Buchanan.

A slight smile emerged onto the young marine's face.

"I prefer the cold over this muggy, hot, miserable heat for sure." said Buchanan.

The young marine agreed. "Yes, sir. Me, too."

"Minot is close to the Little Big Horn Battle site. It's within driving distance, isn't it?" asked Buchanan.

"Yes, sir. I've been there occasionally."

After a few moments of visitation, Buchanan requested a cross from the box of crucifixes held by Jackson. He took the cross from Jackson, extending the cross with his left hand the cross to the young marine and prayed with him.

The marine graciously thanked him, as Buchanan stepped to the next bed.

Buchanan visited nine more marines from all over the country, from Boston to San Francisco. From Chicago to Corpus Christi, Texas. Placing his hand on top of the marine's hand, Buchanan prayed with each young man. The fellowship with the military personnel became essential for Buchanan. He insisted on establishing rapport with troops, reflective of Navy chaplains during the Vietnam War.

Buchanan presented a cross to each marine, reminding each young man the cross honored Chaplain Capodanno.

Occupying the next bed laid Private Miguel Rodriquez, a member of Bravo Company of the 7th Engineering Battalion, from San Diego, California. Though he attended every service of Buchanan's, he never received communion from him, only a blessing. As a strict Roman Catholic, he took part in Communion led by a Protestant, but receiving only a blessing during the taking of the Communion elements. Though poor, he held a high IQ, dreaming of achieving his veterinarian degree one day. Prior to being drafted into the Marine Corps, he worked hard as a janitor. He suffered from a broken heart, having to come to Vietnam to fulfill his enlistment, delaying the completion of his education. As a skilled baseball player, he won a spot on a minor league baseball team, heightening his income. An admitted loner, he kept to himself.

Rodriquez caught a few shrapnel fragments in his legs from a booby trap while on patrol. A marine had stepped on a booby trap, killing him, plunging him toward Rodriquez with immeasurable speed and missed colliding with Rodriquez by two feet. A heavy impact with Rodriquez would have increased greater injury, possibly even severe broken bones. After recovery, his duties would resume in Camp Love.

Rodriquez displayed the greatest respect and appreciation for Buchanan. But as a devout and dedicated Roman Catholic, had no use for Protestantism.

"Been praying for you, Rodriquez." said Buchanan.

"Same here, private." added Jackson.

As the spiritual team conversed with Rodriquez for a moment, Buchanan presented him a cross.

"Here you go, Private Rodriquez. A cross, compliments of Chaplain Vincent Capodanno. He would've wanted you to have one." said Buchanan.

"You? Handing out Catholic Crosses, sir? I've heard of Chaplain Capodanno. Why?" asked Rodriquez.

"We're all Christians, aren't we, private?" replied Buchanan, smiling.

Rodriquez ponders the thought and returns a smile.

Buchanan prayed with Rodriquez, asking the Lord for a quick recovery for the young marine. Buchanan requested the Lord's blessings upon Rodriquez.

Following the prayer, the spiritual team gave Rodriquez their best and stepped to the next bed.

The team visited three additional marines, and finally came upon Dalton's bed, the last on his side of the Quonset hut.

Jackson leans towards Buchanan, out of earshot of Dalton, and says, "Sir, go ask the nurses to inform you of Dalton's status."

Buchanan asks softly, "Why? What's wrong?"

Jackson requests quietly, "Just go ask the nurses what you need to know, sir. I'll stay with Dalton while you're gone."

Buchanan, dumbfounded, did as his body guard asked him and turned back toward the nurses, as Jackson asked, "Well, Dalton, how's your day?"

"Great. I've been real tired though. Slept for three days straight." said Dalton.

Buchanan steps back to the nurses, and, out of earshot of Dalton, asks, "Nurses, what's the status of Dalton? What's up with this young man?"

As the nurses brief Buchanan of Dalton's status, which Dalton is unaware of, Buchanan glances down to Jackson as he visits with Dalton. With a fleeting expression towards the nurses, Buchanan unintentionally catches flies as the nurses inform Buchanan of Dalton's situation. As he listens intently to the nurses, he now stares with a hypnotic fixation into the nurse's eyes and mouths.

Jackson takes a peek toward Buchanan conversing with the nurses, and noticed an expression of confusion written all over his face, then turning white as a sheet as the nurses finished briefing him.

Buchanan turns, stepping slowly back down the other end of the Quonset hut to join Jackson and Dalton.

The journey back down to the other end of the Quonset hut will permanently be stamped on Buchanan's mind for the rest of his life. Buchanan caught in the corner of his eye every single wounded marine's eyeballs staring straight at him on his journey back down to the other end of the hut. Lying immobile in their respective beds, there wasn't one marine in the Quonset hut who envied Buchanan for what he was about to inform Dalton of regarding his personal life.

Clueness is Dalton, enjoying Jackson's company, of his physical condition. Buchanan reaches Dalton's bed, as Jackson continued to keep him company.

Buchanan softly sits back in his chair as Jackson chatted with the young marine.

"Can't wait to get back to playing football, Sergeant. I left school after my freshman year in college to volunteer for the war." said Dalton.

"I love football, too, Dalton." replied Jackson.

Hearing the last of the conversation, Buchanan felt a heavier burden, falling into a deeper distraught state.

"Private Dalton. Sorry for the delay, but the nurses briefed me on your condition." said Buchanan.

Dalton explained his situation. "Well, I stepped on a land mine and found myself thrown about something terrible, you know."

Buchanan and Jackson suddenly froze.

"I'll be up and around before you know it. Playing football. Hiking the mountains of Tennessee. Do you like the mountains, sir?" asked Dalton.

"Yes. I sure do." replied Buchanan. "Dalton. *Neville*."

Buchanan sat softly on the side of Dalton's bed and looked squarely into Dalton's eyes.

"I, well, I have something to say to you." interjected Buchanan. He never remembered such a nervous time in his life. Taking a look see towards Jackson, Buchanan glances back towards Dalton. Frozen, he lost his search for words, unnerved like no other time in his life. Times were rare for Buchanan to be in such a spot, but here he sat on the side, stupefied. He begins to sweat.

"What is it, chaplain?" asked Dalton.

Glancing at Jackson, Buchanan implores for a helping hand, asking him with his eyes, 'What do I say? How do I say it?'

Jackson knows exactly what Chaplain Buchanan needs to say and turns to Dalton, "The Chaplain has something to say to you, private. It will not be easy for you to hear it, but ya need to listen."

Gesturing toward Chaplain Buchanan, Jackson says, "Go ahead, chaplain." He nods toward Buchanan to speak. "Listen up, Neville." Jackson smiles warmheartedly.

Clearing his throat, Buchanan stretches his shoulders and wipes his brow of the sudden sweat with the sleeve of his camouflage uniform.

With all the gumption and resourcefulness Buchanan could muster, he says, "Private Dalton. I'm sorry. But you've-you've lost your legs. Your legs from your knee down."

Dalton fell in a state of shock.

The silence in the wing is deafening.

Every eyeball in the Quonset hut stared in stillness.

Then it hit Dalton. Chaplain Buchanan just informed him he's never going to play football again.

His legs were gone, ripped apart by the impact of the booby trap, and the medical personnel had no choice but to amputate his legs. With his eyes watered up, Dalton stared straight up in a trance, weeping.

In the dead silence of the room, the nurses leisurely step down to the end of the wing. Mayse made her way from the reception desk for morale support.

Buchanan said, "I'm sorry, Neville. You're going to get through this. The nurses are here. I'm here. Sergeant Jackson's here for ya."

"Why? Why me?" asked Dalton.

No one had the words to answer him.

Buchanan finally said, "I don't know why." He thought carefully and added, "They're things in this life that's unexplained. I don't have an answer. Only God knows."

By this time, everyone in the Quonset hut has let loose of their emotions.

"Will you pray with me, chaplain?" asked Dalton.

"Sure." replied Buchanan.

Chaplain Buchanan's short, but meaningful, prayer lifted Dalton up spiritually. Jackson, the three nurses, Mayse, and Buchanan all surrounded the bed.

The sudden shock which hit Dalton threw him into a deep depression. He will lay flat on his back for a day and a half chock full of medication, and sleeping out of sheer exhaustion of the injuries suffered.

Before departing, Buchanan presented Dalton a cross, grasping the crucifix hard and firm.

"Let this cross give you a sense of presence of Jesus." prayed Buchanan. "And look to him for strength. He loves ya."

With a long stretch of silence, Dalton said, "Thank you, chaplain."

Buchanan smiled. "You're welcome, son."

Jackson places his hand on Dalton's shoulder, reassuring Dalton the team will check in on him prior to being shipped out for the Okinawa hospital in the next few weeks.

Burleson and Mayse sat with Dalton consoling the heart broken young marine for an hour.

The spiritual team visited the rest of the marines on the left side of the wing, handing out crosses, praying with the wounded, and visiting those desperately in need of God's presence in their lives.

The team visited every single bed. After visiting all the wounded marines, the team walked back down to Dalton, still in shock. Buchanan felt the moving of the spirit to pray one last prayer with the young marine.

Mayse, who dreamed of attending nursing school, spent the next few weeks with Dalton.

The spiritual team said their goodbyes and departed the hospital. As the team stepped into the jeep, the two friends, one an officer, one enlisted, sat in their seats, stunned. Slowly taking a peek at one another, the two men sat speechless and teary-eyed.

Grimacing, Buchanan broke the silence, "I certainly hope I never have to do that again."

"Me too, chaplain. Me too." said Jackson.

Pausing in thought just as he was about to turn the ignition of the jeep, Jackson displayed an expression of pride on his face, peering over toward Buchanan.

"You did good, sir - with Dalton."

Buchanan gawks toward the floorboard of the jeep and says, "Yeah."

Fighting back the emotion, Jackson pats Buchanan's shoulder to express support. The men already experienced too much war in Vietnam. The strong support for one another within the chaplain's office and the extensive time spent together built a strong bond between the two men.

The men ate supper in the base chow hall, then traveled home the 6 to 7 miles to Camp Love.

Buchanan loathed the necessity of delivering unfortunate news to marines who lost one or both legs. Dalton certainly wasn't the last marine Buchanan delivered unfortunate news to during his tour in Vietnam. As a chaplain, he dreaded conveying such horrific news of losing a limp. A depressive, yet necessary, responsibility of a Navy Chaplain in Vietnam.

The Navy Officer

December 4, 1968

Lieutenant Colonel Lucas couldn't remember waking up in a better mood than this morning. Sergeant Vickers, sitting at his desk, welcomed the Skipper as he stepped into headquarters to start the day.

Lucas loved the Christmas season. The month of December in the Lucas household celebrated the birth of Christ Jesus.

Last night, Burns played 'Christmas Oratorio' by J. S. Bach. Lucas, a lover of classical music, thoroughly enjoyed the piece of music chosen by the proud West Virginian music teacher. Burns chose unique pieces of music each night throughout the Christmas season, generating a seasonal spirit for the marines. In Ohio, Lucas, a season ticket holder, attended the Cleveland Symphony often. Watching and listening to *The Nut Cracker* ended up one of his favorite evenings of the Christmas season.

Lucas sat back in his chair, thinking of the freezing wind off Lake Erie, as he loved winter. He envisioned entering Cleveland Ohio's symphony hall, walking to his seat with his wife to listen to a winter themed concerto or symphony.

As Lucas reminisced, Hans abruptly jumped onto Lucas' desk from the bookshelves for attention, with his tail straight up in the air, purring as loud as a roaring lion. Though his fond memories of Ohio came interrupted by Hans, he didn't care.

His two loves in life thrived within classical music and cats! Hans leaped down in front of Lucas, demanding attention. Lucas groomed and petted Hans, enjoying every minute spent with his feline friend. He once read that cats are the greatest pieces of art. His sister in Ohio maintains two things exist to make life good - books and cats. Lucas is humored by the thought. He certainly doesn't believe in reincarnation. But if it existed, he wished the cat haters will come back in the next life as mice!

As he enjoys the company of Hans, he noticed the time sat at 0800 hours.

Lucas looked forward to a day of little to no interruptions. Recently, the war slowed down a bit, quieting down

with relatively less combat. An environment complementing a suitable ambiance to relax more during the day.

His mood for this morning called him to sit back, read a book or two for pleasure off his bookshelves, and spend

quality time with his Siamese cats. There might even be time to write some personal letters. He even scheduled

time in the day to dictate letters to Sergeant Vickers, and then call it a day.

The day called for little fanfare.

No such luck! Nothing could interrupt the sublime but an annoying pain in the neck.

Even classical Christmas music failed to lighten the day's confrontation about to ensue in Lucas's office.

Lucas heard the front entrance screen door swing wide open, quickly slamming shut. Next thing he heard came a voice ingraining on his nerves like no other voice. A whinny, squeaky voice - Major Michael Porch.

"I'm going to speak to the camp commander." barked Porch.

Hearing Porch's voice, Hans perked up, with his back arched and his hair standing on end, jumped back up onto the bookshelves, growling all the while. Hans knew Porch's voice, and a feline's active and long-term retention memory holds strong.

Lucas softly states to Hans, "I wish I could jump on the bookshelves and hide from Porch with you, Hans."

Unfortunately for Lucas, the relaxation of the day ends with a forced confrontation with Porch.

Taking one look at Porch standing in front of him, Vickers knew Porch intended to be a thorn in Lucas's side so early in the morning. Lucas began the day happy as a clam, and abruptly, Hades just walked through the door.

Vickers despised Porch. Wary and circumspect of Porch, Vickers thought of him as nothing but a 100% grade-A jackass. Despite his feelings toward the ring knocker, Vickers respected the uniform but not the person wearing it.

Turning towards Lucas' door with his back towards Porch, Vickers pacified the major. "Yes sir. I'll let the Skipper know you're here."

"He knows I'm here." insisted a sharp, sarcastic Porch, pushing Vickers aside with his hand.

All the energy and molecules in Vickers body prevented him from punching Porch smack dab in the mouth.

Porch marched firmly and confidently into Lucas' office, with a folder in one hand and a Bible in the other, and stands directly in front of Lucas' desk while Lucas sat back in his swivel chair.

"I want to file a complaint." said an adamant Porch sharply.

"Wait a minute. Wait a minute, now." urged a resigned Lucas. "Not a 'Good Morning' or 'How is your day, sir?'" asked a contemptuous Lucas.

"No! I have no time for formalities this morning, sir. I spend my time wisely, with prudence. Again, I want to file a complaint."

"Oh? Against who? And why?" asked Lucas curiously. He knew exactly the identity of the accused.

Buchanan and Porch despised each other. Lucas was well aware of the rivalry.

"Chaplain Buchanan." declared Porch.

"Chaplain Buchanan? The *chaplain*?" asked Lucas with contempt. He glared eye to eye with Porch. He asked, "For what? What'd he do?"

Porch stands stoic, staring out the screened window straight into the jungle bush, vain and self assured.

Sarcastically Lucas asked, "Help the villagers get clean drinking water in the An Ngai Tay Hamlet? Or, what about, I know - supplying clothes and shoes for the kids at the Catholic school Chaplain Kensington ministers to?"

Porch methodically glances down at Lucas, with rage smeared in the pores of his skin.

Listening to Lucas, Vickers fights back the laughter boiling up inside of him.

Porch expressed disdain, glancing toward the camp entrance.

The cats on the bookshelves glared at Porch, growling toward the callous, pompous ass.

Lucas insisted once again, "Filing a complaint - for *what*?"

Porch states meticulously, "On the grounds of proselytizing the troops."

"Proselytizing *the troops*? For crying out loud, Porch. What'd he do?" pleaded Lucas.

Lucas gawks up at Porch, grimacing at a natural nudnik.

A frustrated Lucas conveyed, "Please - you are a thorn in my-my flesh. Why do you have to be such a nosey-parker?"

"W-What, sir? What?" asked Porch.

"Never mind!" bemoaned Lucas. "Sergeant Vickers, get Chaplain Buchanan over here. Send Corporal Kowslowski next door, who's in admin today to fetch Buchanan."

"Yes, sir." answered Vickers, slipping out of the office. He steps over to administration, ordering Kowslowski to Buchanan's hootch.

Lucas stepped over to his window, gazing out into the camp. In jest, he thought silently, 'Lord, why is Porch in my life? Did you send him to strengthen my resolve or what? Well, it worked Lord, you can send him away!'

Lucas chuckles softly.

"What is it, sir? What's so funny? It better not be me, sir. I'm just doing my duty." said Porch with conviction.

Lucas turns to his side, glancing towards Porch. "Oh no, Porch. I'm sorry, *Major* Porch, it wasn't you. I was thinking of the Cleveland Symphony - back home."

Lucas's silence spoke volumes. Obviously, he dared not say another word. His hesitancy to speak came the fear he would let loose on Porch a barrage of profanity prompting him to feel obligated to bring charges against Lucas, charging him with disrespect and Article 133 of the UCMJ*, conduct unbecoming of an officer. The cussing he would throw at Porch would certainly provide a vent most satisfying to the commanding officer.

Ten minutes passed since Vickers ordered Kowslowski to fetch Buchanan. The time spent seemed an eternity to Lucas. Kowslowski finally walked through the door with the chaplain, and Buchanan immediately sensed something amuck in the air.

"Good morning, chaplain." Vickers politely acknowledged Buchanan, attempting to lighten the mood.

Vickers pointed his finger toward the office door and mouthed words Buchanan failed to read coming from his mouth. Buchanan failed in life at reading lips.

"Good morning, Sergeant." responds Buchanan with a bit of bewilderment, shrugging his shoulders.

Buchanan stepped into the office. He now perceived without a doubt the problem which emerged out of nowhere from the man standing in front of Lucas' desk, a man who wears an incredulous expression regularly and one Buchanan recognizes daily – Major Porch.

Porch steps and turns, glancing towards Buchanan, stepping once again forward with his back facing Buchanan.

The chaplain rolls his eyes, sighing heavily, "Whew!"

Stepping forward at attention, Buchanan belches, "Sir. Reporting as ordered, sir."

Lucas froze, staring out the screened window, turns slowly to face Buchanan with a slight smile. "Good morning, chaplain. Hope you enjoyed the music last night, as I did."

Porch interrupted, "We're not here to talk classical mus -" Lucas raised his hand scrupulously to Porch for silence.

Frowning, Lucas stares with anger at Porch. "As I was saying Chaplain - were you as engrossed with the music as I was last night?"

"Thoroughly, sir." replied Buchanan with a grin.

Lucas admitted, "I appreciate your promptness so early this morning, chaplain. I heard you had a friendly visit to the hospital the other day. I know Robert James Buchanan is uplifting for all the wounded men."

Smiling, Buchanan shrugs his shoulders, somewhat embarrassed, and says, "Sir, you make it sound easier said than done."

"No, chaplain. No. The men love ya." insisted Lucas.

"Well, sir. I just want the men to know that," Porch interrupts Buchanan and blurts out, "Listen, we're not here to have a pep rally for Mr. Wonderful here!"

Gesturing toward Buchanan, Porch insists, "We're here to inform Chaplain Buchanan of formal charges pressed against him. Can we please get on with it?"

"Charges? *What* charges? For what?" inquired Buchanan.

Buchanan, bewildered, glances towards Lieutenant Colonel Lucas with astonishment and confusion.

"Major Porch here wants to bring a charge against you, a formal charge mind you, of proselytizing the troops." said Lucas.

Stunned by such a charge, Buchanan asserts, "That's ridiculous sir."

Lucas shrugs his shoulders and falls into his swivel chair.

"No, it's not!" implored Porch. He pulled out from his upper left pocket of his dungarees a small notebook containing written notes throughout and flipped to a page bound with notes jotted down all about Buchanan dating back to October.

Porch rattled off a rampage. "I heard you the other day encouraging the men to become Christians." He pauses. "*Don't* deny it." Porch flew his index finger and hand toward Buchanan's face, practically pointing his finger at Buchanan's nose.

The agitated chaplain grimaces towards Porch. He continued his tirade. "You said, and I *quote* – 'Jesus transforms a person into an improved human being. And *nooothing* else can make you a better person than Jesus.....nothing.'"

A bewildered Buchanan rolls his eyes.

Frowning, Lucas sighs heavily. He despised Porch to no end. He exerted the utmost of energy, on par of an Olympian running the 100 yard dash, to show even the slightest sliver of Christian benevolence toward Porch. And even after all the labor of Lucas, he still faces an aggressive Iago. The only connection the two men shared came from their common membership of faith in the Roman Catholic Church.

"I also charge this chaplain of unbecoming of a Naval officer. The regulations state, *clearly*, that there is to be a gap between enlisted and officer. You're too close to the men." added Porch.

"What do you say to that, chaplain?" asked Lucas.

Buchanan again rolled his eyes, paused and pondered the ludicrous charges by this nincompoop of an officer.

"It's ridiculous. It ain't worth the time or effort. And I said ain't. I have to, well - I think I'm doing what I've been called to do. Called to minister to the men. That's it." declared Buchanan in his heavy mountain accent.

"You're responsible for protecting the religious freedom of the marines and make sure that each man's faith is provided for, and proselytizing the men is *not* one of them." responded Porch.

"Look, Porch - I'd like to," Buchanan, rudely interrupted by Porch, fought the anger which plagued him prior to becoming a Christian. Porch said, "That's *Major* to you chaplain. You need to start acting like a Navy offic-" Buchanan interrupted Porch, "Don't interrupt me, *Major* Porch. I am a Naval officer and a chaplain of the United States Navy."

Listening to Porch, Buchanan remembered Scriptures instructing believers not to bother themselves to argue with idiots, such as Proverbs 9. Buchanan remained silent, at least temporarily.

Porch stepped closer to Buchanan, close to his face. "As I was saying before I was *rudely* interrupted. You need to start acting like a Navy officer and displaying more military discipline. I know Navy regulations and you're not conducting yourself as a Navy officer. You're nothing but a country bumpkin preacher who is scrounging off the government with the salary you're making. If you were in civilian life, you'd be nothing. You fraternize too much with the men."

Buchanan had had enough. Whether Porch was an idiot or not, he rattled off a tirade himself. "The men are making progress with their spiritual life. And for your information, *Major*, I know the gap between officers and the men. I entered the enlisted Air Force years ago, as you're well aware of. Many chaplains I came into contact with were distinguished men. But, though spiritual men, I wish now that those chaplains would have showed a little more concern for me and the men I worked with to come and visit me in my workspace. Some of them rarely came by unless it was bad news to relay to one of the enlisted personnel. Some acted as if we were the plague or something. Some chaplains just sat in their office all day and read magazines or a murder mystery novel. So *I* am going to get to know the men, know their wants and needs. And I'm going to visit the men regularly whether *you* like it or not. You want to bring charges against me, then go for it!"

Porch, beat red in the face, started in on Buchanan once again. He complained the socials on Friday Night added up to too much fraternization between the ranks. Next came a tirade arguing the chaplain's office spent too much time with the CAP in An Ngai Tay Hamlet and the close relationship Buchanan developed with the men bordered on unprofessionalism.

Regardless of Scriptures warning believers against arguing with idiots, Buchanan again ripped into Porch. He defended himself. Getting kicked around by some irrational trouble maker had come to an end.

The men ripped into each other back and forth, ready to wring each other's necks.

Suddenly, silence loomed. Lucas belched out, "OK, that's it! I've had it!"

The marines and sailors knew an upset Lucas existed in camp when hearing his voice bounce off the surfaces of camp in all directions. Lucas had let the two officers go at it, but he had had enough.

Lowering his voice, Lucas said, "You listen to me, Porch. If you bring charges against one of the most popular chaplains I've ever met while in the Marine Corps, then you might never get back home.

Ya might go back home, but you'll be in a black body bag or in a pinewood box. You get my drift, Porch?"

"What if I go over your head? I can ya know...*sir*." said Porch with resolve in his voice.

Lucas said, "You really want to do that, *Major* Porch? The only reason you're doing this is you're not as popular as Chaplain Buchanan here and that just annoys the hell out of you, doesn't it? Maybe if you displayed a little more Jesus demeanor as Chaplain Buchanan does, the men might respect you as they do Buchanan here. So what if the chaplain here is Baptist? He cares for nothing but good things to happen to the people in An Ngai Tay Hamlet, regardless of their faith."

Buchanan stands and listens.

Porch now looked as if he would pop his blood vessels in his neck. He knew everything Lucas said paralleled the truth.

Hearing the cats growling, Porch knew his welcome had run out.

Lucas continued to lecture Porch, "And besides, Chaplain Buchanan is popular. And if you go over my head, you should know that your complaint will be read by several high-ranking chaplains, including the Divisional Chaplain, Divisional Commander, Brigade Chaplain, and yours truly. All of whom are Roman Catholic and proud of their faith. All of whom like Buchanan very much, who happens to be Southern Baptist. What I'm telling you, Porch, is this: no one wants to listen to your complaint. It has no basis or foundation. Stop using your faith and your rank to pick on someone you despise."

Lucas' words sunk deep into Porch's inner being. The ultimatum resounded loud and clear.

The Skipper went a step further and said, "That's an order. And if you disobey this order, I promise you. I'll bring charges against *you*."

Silently, Porch nodded in the affirmative. With an about face, he peered incredulously toward Buchanan out of the corner of his eye, and walked out of the office.

As Porch passed Vickers, the sergeant addressed him, "Have a good day, sir."

Furious, Porch knew better to say a word. He paused at the entrance of the office. With a forceful push of the screen door, he jolted through the entrance and marched himself to his hootch, sulking with his crony friends. Dejected and angry, he thought, "That chaplain will not get the best of me. He will not get away with embarrassing me. I'll see his day come one day."

Lucas had had it. He lit a cigar and took a good puff of one of his enjoyments of life. He sat back in his swivel chair and called his cats off the bookshelves onto his desk.

"Here Hans."

"Here Brahms."

"Jump Ludwig. Jump, boy."

The cats dived onto the desk to comfort their master, as Lucas pets his feline friends, purring to High Heaven with the attention given.

Brahms jumped off the desk onto the floor, rubbing himself against Buchanan's legs, purring as loud as the Heavens. The feline sensed Buchanan needed a friend. Buchanan reached down, took hold of Brahms in his arms, grooming him.

"Brahms thinks Porch is the back side of a donkey as well chaplain." joked Lucas.

The men chuckle.

Buchanan petted Brahms. "Thanks Brahms. Thanks for being my friend." He placed Brahms back onto the desk with the other two cats, asking permission to be dismissed. Lucas stood up out of his swivel chair, granting Buchanan's request.

Lucas encouraged Buchanan. "Listen chaplain, you're a fantastic chaplain. I've never seen a chaplain used greater by the Lord than you. Keep up the good work. And if he -" Lucas points his thumb toward Porch's hootch, "gives you any more trouble, you can come straight to me. You know that."

"I know that, sir. Have a great day, sir."

"You do the same, chaplain." said Lucas.

Buchanan turns to depart, as Lucas throws in a last word. "You know what gnaws at me the most, chaplain?"

"What's that, sir?"

Grinning, Lucas comments, "He's of my faith. He's Roman Catholic like myself. I think he needs to go to confession or something. What do ya think?"

Buchanan smiled. "I'd say so, sir. I'd say so."

Turning, Buchanan says his goodbyes to Vickers, venturing out into camp to visit the wounded in medical and marines in their respective hootches.

Lucas sits back in his swivel chair, petting his cats. He knows deep down inside he's not heard the last of Porch.

Visiting the Innocents

December 9, 1968

The Season of giving is the month of December. It's the time of year to express Christian benevolence and compassion upon those in need.

The spiritual team set out to meet Doc Delaney and several medics in An Ngai Tay Hamlet to deliver Christmas gifts and food. The chief of the hamlet, a staunch Roman Catholic, thrived in a Christmas mood as the month of celebration of Jesus' birth came upon them.

An Ngai Tay Hamlet, pro-American and longing to experience American freedoms, served as a bullseye target for VC harassment and intimidation. The villagers loathed the Communists. The hate for the VC hit an all-time high. The citizens of the hamlet longed to live with freedoms long lived by Americans, especially the Freedom of Religion.

Populated with Roman Catholics, the hamlet comprised of villagers who fled North Vietnam in the last ten years because of religious persecution. The CAP in An Ngai Tay earned wholehearted support from Camp Love with enthusiasm. The desire to live freely filled every heart in the hamlet.

Nurses Reagan, Glenn, and Burleson, accompanied by a few other nurses from the Da Nang base, were scheduled to arrive to lend a hand wearing Santa Elves nightcaps to distribute gifts to the children, along with delivering food.

Arriving at An Ngai Tay at 1000 hours, the spiritual team noticed the extra concertina barbed wire and abatis around the perimeter due to the rise of VC activity in the area. The spiritual team also noticed double armed guards and security around the perimeter. Regardless, the Christmas season shifted into high gear just one week into December. Love for those innocent in the war filled the air.

Buchanan hit the road running 100 miles an hour as he stepped into the hamlet, visiting members with Jackson, including Bi'hn. The elderly lady sold canned American pops and drinks, along with a crocheted sweater spelling USA, to Jackson. "I'll wear it with pride." said Jackson. He never could visit An Ngai Tay without purchasing a pop or something home made from Bi'hn. Deep down inside his heart, Jackson found it impossible to say no to Bi'hn. Feelings deep within himself obliged him to patronize her like many other military personnel in the Christmas party. The warm fuzzy gratifying sense within one's self of swelling the livelihood of another human being by forking over money to purchase a pop or a clothing article from her seemed to be worth every penny spent.

Capitalism fascinated Bi'hn and loved the idea of entrepreneurship, procuring a monetary profit. Besides, no one ever accused her of passing on to others tainted goods or pulling a fast one. The marines loved her and thought of her merchandise of good quality and authentic from Vietnam.

The pacification program of President Johnson propelled military personnel with a strategy of protecting villages and hamlets such as An Ngai Tay, and individual citizens such as Bi'hn.

The efforts to protect An Ngai Tay came with additional barriers of protection to the hamlet.

The VC and NVA increased terrorist activities during cultural, political, and religious seasons, including specific holiday dates. The American forces and their allies were on high alert during the war, especially during holiday seasons such as Christmas and specific days such as the 4th of July. Christmas 1968 was no different. The additional barbed wire and abatis spikes were understandable, considering the devious workings of the VC during seasons of special days.

Cultivating positive, long-lasting relationships with the Vietnamese accounted as an essential part of the pacification program implemented by President Johnson to win over the hearts and minds of the South Vietnamese, supporting a democratic form of government in South Vietnam. Buchanan, Jackson, and members of Bravo Company, present more or less for a security patrol, spent time with the hamlet members until the nurses and Doc Delaney's contingent arrived at An Ngai Tay.

The Doc and medics arrived with section 2 of Alpha Company in two trucks, full of gifts and food at 1020 hours.

Just as soon as the nurses arrived from Da Nang on choppers, the hamlet children ran in mass to meet them at the gate. The children in mass marched the nurses every step of the way to the community pavilion, the center of the hamlet.

The metal roofed pavilion stood swollen with pride on its eight columns, with wrapped footers reinforced with stone sidings. The pride of the Seabees spoke through a metal plaque which read:

AN NGAI TAY HAMLET PAVILION

Built by Naval Military Construction Battalion 9 and Marine Engineers on November 27, 1967

Hamlet Chief
Giang Phem

Hamlet Elders
Hung Tran
Minh Huynh
Huy Do
Sinh Pham
Sang Ngo
Thanh Bui
Chi Duong
Hien Ly

May the An Ngai Tay pavilion provide community cohesion, cooperation, and participation to promote freedom and respect of individual beliefs to support common and shared interests and life goals.

Promoted and supported by Medical Civic Action Program (MedCAP), 7th Engineering Marine Battalion, Field Hospital and Chaplain Office

The pavilion served as the heart of community activity for the hamlet centering around civic participation and carrying out democratic principles such as debating and voting on hamlet matters. The nurses were frequent visitors, cultivating deep, meaningful relationships with the children.

The nurses, part of many MedCAPs within 10 to 12 miles of Da Nang Air Base, participated when free from duties at the hospital. The An Ngai Tay Hamlet served as a special interest for the nurses. On one hand, the hamlet proclaimed itself pro-American. On the other hand, the nurses, young and vibrant, fell in love with the children of the hamlet. The nurses were motherly and loving individuals with a deep care and concern for the children, both mentally and physically.

Prior to the nurses' arrival, preparations were set for chow. After chow, the nurses would distribute their gifts. Bravo Company set a perimeter for the MedCAPs, while Section 2 of Alpha Company set the food under the community pavilion.

Evidence of hunger showed with the consumption of every morsel of food eaten by the Americans and the Vietnamese. Everyone ate to their heart's content, with no crumbs left. The lunch consisted of a mix of traditional Vietnamese food, along with American food. Especially the hamburgers and hot dogs, a treat for rural Vietnamese.

With raised eyebrows, Buchanan stepped toward the trucks to discover Lipstone, Dobbs, and Kowslowski 'gun ho' assisting the nurses, wearing Elves nightcaps, and assisting in the distribution of gifts to the children of the hamlet. Doc Delaney posed as Santa for the day, all decked out with a white beard and red suit.

Buchanan motioned Jackson, talking to Rockford, toward him in eyeshot of the 'gun ho' marines distributing gifts to the children at the trucks.

Nudging Jackson's shoulder, Buchanan said, "Some men brushed aside in October as unreceptive to our side are coming around a bit, aren't they?"

"Sure are, sir."

The Christmas gifts, donated from Roman Catholic Churches all over Asia along with churches in the United States, numbered in the thousands and designated for several hundreds of villages and hamlets in Vietnam. Each gift given a label of 'boy' or 'girl'.

Laughing and giggling, the children were all eager to be given a gift, a treasure for the rest of their lives.

With presents marked as 'boy' or 'girl', a nurse doled out gifts and received with a gleaming smile from each child.

As the children unwrapped presents, the Americans noticed the glee of adults within the hamlet as children received such joy from the gifts.

Particularly fond of a young girl named Chinh, nurse Glenn cherished the young girl's innocent disposition and the display of a typical eight-year-old perception of the world. The Viet Cong murdered Chinh's parents before her very own eyes for practicing Roman Catholicism and voicing a pro-American stance. Chinh possessed a good-natured, tender, kind-hearted personality, typical of most children in Vietnam. Children caught in the middle of a war, innocent and vulnerable. Children losing parents and their own lives because of friendly and enemy fire.

Burleson gained a newfound friend with Tuan, a young boy she took a liking to. The 7-year-old and orphan raised by an aunt in An Ngai Tay hamlet. He, too, possessed a kind and tender heart. Tuan's disposition called for a life to live as a boy. He longed to live the charming personality the Lord granted him without someone or something threatening him daily.

The jubilation of the children pleased the adults, especially the adult elders and the hamlet chief. The gifts given instilled some hope and love within their hearts.

The nurses interacting with the children presented the picture perfect image of mother figures bonding with a child and the innate nurture of a mother. Though many of the children in An Ngai Tay were orphans, the nurses held a special place in the hearts of the children. The nurses' tender loving care for the hamlet children reflected the love of a biological mother for her child. Many children witnessed their parents murdered by the VC or the Viet Minh in the 1950s for practicing their Catholic faith. Presenting a gift during the Christmas season lifted the spirits of the children beyond measure.

No one in the hamlet, American or Vietnamese, longed for the moment to end.

Though the joy of Christmas, the gifts, the children's joy, and the fun for adults in this brief snapshot in time, almost dream like, there still remained the fact the war remained real. And unfortunately the war will return soon for all parties concerned. The war, however, will fail to take the joyful memory of this day away from anybody's indelible, permanent memory who witnessed it.

A war existed about and a threat to life, but the hope and joy of Christ rang loud and clear this day in the middle of Vietnam and all the turmoil within it.

Thankful he had a part of the merriment, Buchanan carried out the words of The Beatitudes of peace, love, and hope bringing Christmas alive to those who long for the meaning of Christmas to be bestowed in their world.

Stuck in the Mud

December 15, 1968

Exhaustion hit Buchanan hard, as dead on one's feet. Following the weekly Sunday Communion services, the spiritual team visited An Ngai Tay, delivering shoes and socks donated by marines in Camp Love to the hamlet children. With an additional Christmas gift to An Ngai Tay, the spiritual team desired to reassure the citizens of the hamlet the sincerity of benevolence of the MedCAP.

Jackson drove next to Chaplain Kensington's school, resulting in, as always, a pleasant visit. The cheerful children at the school and orphanage inevitably placed the spiritual team in a pleasant, agreeable mood. The team delivered shoes and socks, along with school supplies, such as writing journals, pencils, paper, crayons, colored pencils, and office supplies. The marines donated the supplies from the 1st Marine Division, 5th and 7th Marines. Along with the school supplies, the team delivered Christmas themed coloring books.

The day began an hour earlier for the team, hitting the road racing a 100 miles an hour, non-stop all day.

Fatigue hit Buchanan hard, as the hands of time fell at 1830 hours.

Chaplain Kensington accompanied the spiritual team to their jeep to depart for Camp Love. Just as soon as the team sat in the jeep, exhaustion set in.

Buchanan yearned for sleep. His energy level dropped close to empty.

Jackson drove, traveling on Route 1 toward camp. The anticipation of gaining some shut eye became unbearable. In no time, the spiritual team drove but two miles away from camp. The team drew near an eroded hole in the road, nothing unusual in Vietnam during the war. Eroded holes in the road resulted from the inconceivable amounts of rain the country received in a year. The many trucks, jeeps, and tanks traveling constantly on the surface of the road led to the muddy, messy, mucky and waterlogged holes. The team faced an eroded hole which reached a whooping 100 feet from one end to the other.

Driving upon the hole, Jackson displayed nothing but worry and doubt all over his face. He knew the hole was impassable. Jackson approached the hole almost to a stop, finally bringing the jeep to a standstill just 20 feet from the hole.

"That's definitely going to be - well, a problem, isn't it, Philip?" asked Buchanan.

"Don't know yet, chaplain! That's definitely a hole in the ground, though, for sure. I certainly don't want to get stuck in the mud." Jackson showed nothing but fret in his eye.

Glancing toward Buchanan, Jackson pointed toward the hole with his head. He stressed the situation. "I mean, look at it, sir. Look at it."

Buchanan centered in on the hole with intensity. Squinting his eyes, he caught himself catching flies with the widest of open mouths.

"Deep, ain't it. And muddy. Doesn't look good." Jackson doubted their chances getting through the hole without experiencing problems. Buchanan fixed his eyes on Jackson with reservation.

Buchanan turns his eyes once again upon the hole and mulls over the predicament the spiritual team found themselves in.

Buchanan says innocently, "It's muddy alright."

At a snail's pace, Jackson turns his head towards Buchanan, and, with a half grimace, half smile, says, "Yes, Padre. It's muddy alright."

"And deep." added Buchanan as a after thought.

Jackson grins, shaking his head. "Yes, sir. And deep."

Buchanan had yet to witness in Vietnam a hole eroded in the road from heavy rain and traffic. Until today.

The hole with all the mud stretched at least 100 feet long.

Buchanan said innocently, "'I think we can get her through the mud, Philip."

Jackson glanced toward Buchanan with consternation. He asserts, "Are you kidding, sir? It's risky. I just don't know, sir. If you think we can, then we'll go for it." Jackson pauses. "OK, sir. We'll try. I've seen it done only a time or two, but we'll try."

Buchanan reminds Jackson, "Besides, I'm tired. I want some shuteye."

"Me too, sir. OK. Let's just go for it."

"Amen!" said Buchanan with the utmost confidence.

The men smile, feeling the presence of the Lord.

Jackson pressed the accelerator, approaching the hole with trepidation.

As Jackson approached the edge of the hole, the speed of the jeep picked up, drawing nearer the edge and over, descending down the core of mud and sludge of the hole. As Jackson pressed down farther onto the accelerator, the jeep picked up speed. All the while, Buchanan prayed as the jeep drove to the base of the hole. The momentum of speed exerted the jeep up, crossing the halfway point of the eroded muddy hole.

As the jeep reached the base of the sluggish muddy hole, it ascended back up the opposite incline of the hole for 10 feet as the entire set of tires spun, losing traction, and throwing mud in every direction. Jackson desperately pressed on the accelerator, attempting to impel the jeep to heave solely out of the opening, a gap in the wide open road - but to no avail.

Taking a crack at pushing forward, Jackson pressed down onto the accelerator, digging into the solid earth a few more inches. Now in panic mode, the sergeant, intelligent and bright, failed in his better judgment, jamming the gears of the jeep in reverse at a desperate stab of hauling themselves out of the hole. Pushing backwards resulted to nil. Backing out came futile, worsening the team's situation.

The proposition of rocking the jeep forward from Buchanan went in one ear and out the other for Jackson, prompting a stare of dismay from Jackson. The sergeant succumbed to the fact the jeep was going nowhere.

Numb with the fact the jeep sat immobile, the spiritual team stared straight ahead. Isolated in the jungle bush and threatened by the Viet Cong, possibly a few hundred feet away, threw the team in shock and disarray.

Buchanan broke the silence, asking nervously, "What do we do now, Philip?"

Jackson answered hesitantly, "I don't know. Give me a minute to think, sir."

Initially, driving around the eroded hole exiting the man made dirt thoroughfare onto rain soaked, saturated natural terrain stood dead in the water, and the team knew it. The jeep's weight simply made it too heavy to drive in the rain soaked soil. Top soil saturated from rain fall came frequently in Vietnam. The rain had poured down for hours the previous two days.

The jeep sat dormant, smack dab in the center of the base of the hole.

Taking on a panoramic view of the situation, the spiritual team discovered the top edges of the hole flanked the jeep just a tad above the hood of the jeep. Giving a guarded peek over the edge of the hole, the team viewed nothing but marshy fields soaked from rains earlier in the day. Eyesight of the surroundings came scarce. Glancing over the edge of the hole, the team viewed nothing but isolation, delivering a strike of horror down their back.

Heavy danger filled the air. No one in Vietnam sought to find themselves isolated in the jungle. Military personnel avoided isolation like the plague. Shaken, the spiritual team considered their perilous situation.

Sensing danger in the air, Buchanan asked, "You think somebody will get a clue and come for us?"

Alarmed, Jackson answered, "Odds are marines have called it a day. Any venturing out at this hour is not an option. As far as the grunts are concerned, everything is secure and they're ready for some R&R."

Buchanan's stomach turns into knots.

Jackson reassures Buchanan. "But they'd be here ASAP, if they knew our predicament."

Grinning, Buchanan turns toward Jackson.

Time turned to 1900 hours sharp. Marines on Sunday nights kicked back and relaxed. Possibly to read or play 500 Rummy. Possibly visiting friends. Sitting in the middle of the jungle bush stuck in the mud isolated with Viet Cong running about is the last place the spiritual team wanted to be.

Jackson knew the dangers of isolation in the bush. The danger felt within Jackson sparked a frenzy state of mind. As a bodyguard for the chaplain, Jackson's inclination narrowed down to two alternatives. The two choices boiled down to either running to Camp Love to seek help from the Seabees, or escort Chaplain Buchanan two miles back to Camp Love. If Buchanan accompanied Jackson back to camp, it required him to expose the jeep to theft from the Viet Cong, and Buchanan, on foot alongside Jackson, certainly placed the pair at a sluggish pace. The pair trekking back to Camp Love in the jungle consumed time, a danger in and of itself. Jackson's first alternative required him to run by himself to Camp Love for assistance. His athleticism enabled him to hurry back to camp. To preserve Buchanan's life set the adrenaline flowing within Jackson. He longed to deliver Buchanan safe and sound before sundown. If darkness overcame the jungle bush, the danger of isolation heightened. He chooses the former as his choice of action.

"Chaplain, I'm going to Camp Love by myself."

Anxiously, Buchanan asked, "What? You're serious?"

"Yes. You're fine, Padre. I'm leaving my M-16 with you."

Pointing with his thumb toward the back seat of the jeep, Jackson says, "Two .45's in the back, in the chest. I'll take one, you keep the other for yourself. Magazines are in the chest on the back floorboard. I've seen you fire weapons, sir. Ya know what you're doing."

He reassures Buchanan. "Back in a jiffy."

Buchanan asked tentatively, "I can't go with you? Why can't I go along?"

"Listen, sir. I can run the two miles in nothing flat. I can run it in 12 minutes, maybe less, if I push myself. Just hold tight." said Jackson, patting Buchanan's knee.

Jackson tilted his forehead toward Buchanan. "Back before you know it. 30 minutes tops. Promise!"

As a child, a young Buchanan experienced frightening incidents. As a 9-year-old on Greasy Creek, Kentucky, he woke up in the middle of the night facing a rattlesnake asleep in the corner of his bedroom, terrorizing him and his cousins. As a young teenager, his father's brakes went kablooey on a hilly rural road in southeastern Ohio, terrifying him and his brothers to death. Other daunting, memorable events came racing across his mind. Never in his life did Buchanan feel more frightened than at this moment. He felt scared to death.

In training, instructors beat a dead horse into the ground, reminding chaplains never to find themselves isolated in the bush. A captured chaplain solicited free rein for the Viet Cong to entertain themselves courtesy of the captured chaplain. Facing horrific torture and death at the hands of the Viet Cong terrified Buchanan, an event he would avoid at all costs, even fighting the enemy to prevent such an experience.

Jackson placed his M-16 along with ammunition into Buchanan's hands, setting extra ammunition in the driver's seat. The extra shells, within arm's length, were ready at a second's notice in case he confronted the enemy.

"I'll be back." said a confident Jackson.

"Hurry back, Sergeant." pleaded Buchanan.

Jackson nods, smiling toward the chaplain he committed to protect.

The nearly two-mile trek for Jackson began at 1912 hours. Buchanan, glancing at his watch, gaged the time spent running to and from Camp Love.

Jackson's run began at a steady pace, increasing speed at more of a brisk pace toward the end of his journey. Top priority for Jackson amounted to conserving his energy by running under the scorching, blazing sun. From dawn to dusk, Vietnam's temperature equaled nothing but hot and humid. The spiritual team loathed the weather in southeastern Asia.

From the start, a fight against time ensued, forcing Jackson to make the best use of every ounce of energy in his body to fight off the heat of the sun. Seconds ticked away fast, as the day called for dusk to come. The incredible will within himself to return before dusk with the Seabees and machinery to pull the jeep out of the mud pushed him to limits he wasn't even aware of. The sun's heat intensified as he ran further and further away from Buchanan and their valued transportation for minister. Jackson knew full well the longer he was absent from Buchanan, the severity of danger enhanced immensely. His pace toward Camp Love increased.

All the while, Jackson remembered reading the account in ancient Greek history of Pheidippides, running 25 miles to the gates of Athens to deliver the news of the great Athenian victory over the Persians and Datis at the Battle of Marathon. Pheidippides ran 25 miles to the gates of Athens. When Pheidippides arrived, he yelled at the top of his lungs - "Nike!" The young Athenian runner collapsed and died. Jackson thought his entire run - 'I must give my all as Pheidippides. I must make it to Camp Love for Chaplain Buchanan's sake.'

The young marine certainly wanted to end his run, declaring "Victory!" He prayed his run will result with a shower and shave, instead of the ultimate price.

A Viet Cong capture of Buchanan will result in death. The notion pushed Jackson to the limit.

Buchanan whispered, "Hurry back." He declared to the Heavens "Bring him back safe!" But a yell would have attracted the most unwelcome of creatures, including the Viet Cong.

Buchanan observed Jackson from the start. The race against time grew with every step of Jackson's feet on the ground. He noted every step Jackson put forth, ever-increasing the distance between the two spiritual leaders. Buchanan desired to roar out, "Come back. Don't leave me alone, Philip!" But thought twice committing such a foolhardy move, as screaming will welcome a death sentence. The scheming Viet Cong roamed every nook and cranny of the jungle bush. Buchanan hooked his eyeballs on Jackson like a fish takes to bait. He engrossed himself on Jackson, step by step. He glued his eyesight on his bodyguard as isolation increased with every step taken in Jackson's run. With every step, isolation held a tighter grip upon Buchanan, deep in the bush.

As Buchanan watched Jackson, he felt more and more distant, more isolated. As long as Buchanan caught sight of Jackson, he sensed a degree of security.

Jackson's distance reached 1000 feet away, barely visible.

Jackson momentarily disappeared from Buchanan as he ran down an incline. Only to re-emerge as he ran on an upward slope.

Squinting at a speck, Buchanan adjusted his eyes to view Jackson. Buchanan again lost sight of Jackson as he ran once again down a small incline. He once again caught Jackson's torso at a squint, as he appeared to near nothing as Jackson re-emerged in view, running back up an elevated slope. After a feverish search for binoculars in the glove compartment, he positioned them to view Jackson, frantically locating Jackson just one last time through the prism and lens of the binoculars, only to see him momentarily from the torso up as he ran out of view over the last hilltop.

Buchanan's stomach hit the floor with the last glance of Jackson descending out of sight. Isolation now set in. Now secluded in the jungle with nothing but wild animals, the weapons left behind to defend himself if the need arose served as his security blanket.

Buchanan found the dead silence deafening. He prayed he had grit enough to battle the fear of isolation. A burdensome, terrifying silence. A sensation unbeknownst to Buchanan till now.

Numbness and fear overwhelmed him. Buchanan stooped farther down into the jeep, securing himself from the vision of the Viet Cong. Measuring the depth of the eroded hole with the top of the jeep, he recognized the depth of the hole concealed the view of the jeep to any outsiders. The thought eased the tension within him, providing a better sense of security. Reaching into his upper left pocket of his field jacket, Buchanan drew out his tobacco pouch, placing a pinch of chewing tobacco into his mouth. The chewing tobacco eased the tension and calmed his nerves, distracting him from his predicament.

As Buchanan discharged a mass of tobacco juice into the sea of mud below, the dead silence cracked, interrupted by the echoes and rustling of the jungle bush.

The calls of animals from the thick bush filled the air. Buchanan recognized the monkey chatter and howls. Then heard the snort of a mongoose calling out. Then a wild cat hiss and growl. Next came the grunts, snorts, and squeals of a wild boar. Buchanan heard next a zebu bellow. Whether imagination or not, wild animals were present in Vietnam, making his experience a bit more nerve-racking.

The calls of birds now added to the racket. The mumbled cuck or tuk of a robin or the trill or chatter of a sparrow ran dominant throughout the jungle. The reverberations reflected a million birds calling out to Buchanan's ears.

Most eerie to Buchanan was the present swish and rustling heard within the foliage of the jungle bush. He found himself baffled by the origin of the rustling within the foliage of the jungle. Questions emerged in his mind. 'What was the swishing of the foliage in the wind?' 'Was it caused by animals?' Or 'Was it the Viet Cong moving about?'

He lifted a quick prayer. "Lord, let it be animals, not the VC."

Most bothersome came from the wind blowing. Buchanan frowned, bordering on a state of paranoia and panic, a state he avoided with all costs.

To calm his nerves, Buchanan began to softly quote Psalms 46 - "God is my refuge and strength, a very present help in trouble. Therefore, we will not fear...."

As he quoted the Scripture, a constant reminder lifted his spirits: 'Jackson will return. Jackson will return.'

Glancing at his watch, he noticed 12 minutes exactly passed since Jackson's departure, 12 minutes of horror. The anticipation of Jackson's return heightened as time passed by.

Jackson insisted his athleticism gave him an advantage over time. Convinced he could run the two-mile trek in 12 minutes or less, he felt confident the Lord's presence ran along with him. If true, Jackson had arrived in Camp Love. By now, he has collected help from the marines and the Seabees. And soon, a return trip back to the jeep. If not, Jackson has hit a snag of some sort, causing a delay.

Regardless, Buchanan adjusted a bit more with his isolation. Spitting an additional gob of tobacco juice into the mound of sticky, slippery soil on the base of the hole, he discovered himself chewing faster and spitting more frequently.

To Buchanan's horror, he next heard human voices. The chatting of people conversing and reflecting Vietnamese males. His first inclination asked - 'Were the voices bona fide?' 'Is the enemy on the other side of the treeline?'

Buchanan sustained his sanity by softly quoting more of Psalms 46 - '.....though the earth should change, though the mountains shake in the heart of the sea;'

Slowly rising out of his seat, Buchanan peeked over the edge of the eroded hole. With his eyes level with the edge, he continued quoting Psalms 46 - '....though its waters roar and foam, though the mountains tremble with its tumult. There is a river whose streams make glad the city of God, the holy habitation of the Most High.'

As Buchanan quoted Psalms 46, he turned a complete 180 in his seat, inquiring of any VC in eyeshot. The treeline of the jungle bush measured approximately 150 feet from the eroded hole.

Without a presence of Viet Cong along the treeline reassured Buchanan at least for a while longer he remained safe. Buchanan stooped secure back down into his seat, holding on to Jackson's M-16 for dear life, continuing to quote Psalms 46 to assure the Lord's presence in his state of isolation. '...God is in the midst of her, she shall not be moved; God will help her right early. The nations rage, the kingdoms totter; he utters his voice, the earth melts.'

Curious of time, Buchanan glanced once again at his watch as 5 more minutes of time passed by. He reasoned Jackson had departed Camp Love, about to finish his return trip back to the jeep. He lifted a prayer for it to be so.

Abundant mental prayers saturated Buchanan's mind, as he continued to quote softly Psalms 46: '...The Lord of hosts is with us; the God of Jacob is our refuge. Come, behold the works of the

Lord, how he has wrought desolations in the earth. He makes wars cease to the end of the earth; he breaks the bow, and shatters the spear, he burns the chariots with fire!'

Quoting Scripture calmed his nerves to a degree, as Buchanan glanced once again towards his watch, estimating 10 minutes tops for Jackson to return.

Spitting additional tobacco juice into the mud, Buchanan noticed a darkened mound of sludge mixed with saliva and tobacco juice. Humored with the sight, he passed time by spelling words with the juice, starting with 'ball'. Spelling words helped ease the tension, but worry prevailed.

"Please hurry." pleaded Buchanan.

To pass more time, he silently listened to music, humming the notes. Though his love of music aided him in coping with war in normal situations, humming the music proved to worsen his situation. The calls of the jungle bush and whirling of the wind presented an intimidating grouping of reverberations overwhelming his mental symphony.

He spelled the second 'l' in the word ball with his next wad of tobacco juice. He spit more juice out of his mouth, placing yet more tobacco in his mouth. The chewing seemed to calm his nerves.

He again rose out of his seat to peer over the edge, assuring himself the Viet Cong were nowhere in the jungle or in the fields surrounding the jeep.

Turning a complete 180, he aimed the M-16 toward the voices. And totally overwhelmed with fear, Buchanan started to shake and felt lightheaded.

Tons of questions arose in his mind. 'Where are the Viet Cong?' 'Are the VC attacking me?' 'Will he ever see his wife again?' 'Will he see his children again?' 'Will he see his siblings again?'

Nonetheless, he sat poised, ready and willing to fight if need be.

When Buchanan arrived in the jungle bush, he swore he would never to be taken captive providing the Viet Cong a prize prisoner. He pledged never to grant the Viet Cong the pleasure of torturing him to death, as long as he could defend himself.

Buchanan prayed softly, "Lord, protect me with your armor. Protect me and deliver me from the evil ones."

5 minutes passed and still no Jackson in sight.

Buchanan had started a new word with the tobacco juice - the word faith. The letter 'i' came next, as he spit sufficient juice to dot the 'i'.

Buchanan, even more fidgety and jumpy, reacted even more abruptly with every little noise he recognized in the jungle. Crawling to the back seat of the jeep, Buchanan sensed a more secure position as he set himself in a kneeling stance with the M-16. Every noise startled him, aiming his weapon erratically in every direction a noise emerged from the jungle.

He found himself haphazardly and clumsily aiming the M-16 and searching for the source of voices and threatening noises.

Anticipation heightened as Buchanan reached for the binoculars in the driver's seat to search for Jackson. Lifting the field glasses up to seek him out, Buchanan's disappointment at spotting him resulted in a punch below the belt. A sickened feeling fell upon him.

Buchanan set free his right hand down to his knee, holding the field glasses. The extension of time isolated for a chaplain in the bush during the Vietnam War boosted the threat of either capture or certain death. His nerves set on edge, he bordered on panic mode.

Thinking the worse, Buchanan heard in the distance bumps and clanks, obviously man made mechanized contraptions, overwhelming the ongoing echoes and booms of the jungle bush. Nervously, Buchanan aimed the weapon toward the banging and clanks of the clamor, evidently actual noises. The sharpshooter aim Buchanan displayed of the M-16 in his hands revealed determination to defend himself as he pointed the weapon toward the clamor, coming from the direction of Camp Love. As Buchanan focused on the sight of the weapon, reality hit him. The face of a human being he longed to see came crystal clear in the sights emerging over a small hill. It was no ordinary human being. The man at the end of the M-16 sight thrilled Buchanan's soul, smiling from ear to ear.

What a sight to see! Covered with sweat, Jackson's skin layered black with filth and dirt. Red faced from the scorching heat of the sun. Buchanan never set his eyes on such a beautiful sight in his life.

As Buchanan lowered his weapon, resting the M-16 onto the floorboard, he finished quoting Psalms 46. "Be still...and know that I am God. I am exalted...among the nations, I am exalted...in the earth! The Lord of hosts is with us; the God of Jacob....is....our...refuge."

Now safe and sound, Buchanan clutched the binoculars, focusing in on Jackson, laying his eyes on his courageous, steadfast body guard. In flesh and blood, Jackson ran toward the jeep. What a blessed sight!

Buchanan was never so happy in his life to ever see a human being in the flesh!

In the distance, Buchanan identified the Seabees with a tracker to haul the jeep out of the mud.

Buchanan let loose the binoculars, crawling out of the hole, with a confident sprint toward Jackson. The spiritual team met, hugging as if long-lost brothers. Falling to the ground in exhaustion, the team gave in to the mental tiredness, laughing and wholeheartedly consuming every second of the experience of being stuck in the mud. The fact the Lord looked over the men through their moment of isolation and danger encouraged the men to push forward with the war.

Panting, Jackson said, "S-Sir, I'm-I'm promising you...you something right...right here - and now. I'll never...leave you alone ever - again. You can count on it."

"What's done is done, Philip. I'm so happy you're back. You saved my life. I'll never forget it."

Buchanan has never been so grateful in his life.

Standing up, the men stepped back toward the jeep. The team stood at the edge of the eroded hole waiting for the Seabees and the tracker to haul their transportation out of the mud. They thanked God for protecting them in the jungle bush.

As the Seabees yanked the jeep from the eroded crater in the earth, Buchanan clued Jackson in on his experience of isolation, and his commitment of fighting to the death to avoid capture of the Viet

Cong. Patiently, Jackson listened, consoling the chaplain, knowing full well the chaplain's life was indeed in danger.

Slide photos of Buchanan sitting in the jeep, the eroded hole, and the Seabees hauling the jeep out of the hole snapped one after the other. The snapping off of slide pictures of the experience seemed more than 'having fun'. The two men, their relationship slowly turning into a lifelong friendship, craved for loads of pictures for Buchanan's pictorial chronology of the dangerous event.

Driving to camp for a good night's rest, Burns' choice of music raised the roof. Beethoven's piano concerto number 5 in e-flat major, op. 73 ended up the selection chosen for the marines. A perfect piece of music to listen to prior to pulling off some shut eye. The emotional music moved the men. The piece of music possessed a series of virtuosic pronouncements with intervals of mammoth chords. Considered intense, the third movement consisted of a short candenza and vigorous orchestral responses, becoming a favorite for Buchanan of classical music. The selection of music was perfect for easing the tension of the day.

The day strengthened the spiritual team's resolve. They will never forget this day.

Only God knows if the evil Viet Cong roamed the jungle 200 feet away in the bush, eager to flush the life out of Buchanan. Regardless, the Lord protected him. If the VC were present in the bush, the Lord blinded them of the obvious. What mattered most revolved around the fact the spiritual team was alive and well. The spiritual team lied down on their cots listening to Beethoven, staring straight up into their hootch ceiling, thinking of the day and what transpired throughout it all.

Buchanan's thoughts ran in all directions, including the role the Lord played in the day's events.

The Omniscience of God reigned supreme. No one but the Lord knew if the VC roamed the treeline of the bush ready to devour the spiritual team. His presence alone pushed the team forward in the days ahead.

For God protected them.

A Conflict of Theology

December 19, 1968

The early morning sunrise gleamed with golden rays of the sun beaming brightly upon the hills and valleys of My Son. The beautiful morning set the day for an uplifting temperament in camp. The only threats to break the welcomed good mood might come from the enemy or any other given pest. One thorn in many a marine's side came down to the one and only Major Michael Porch. His presence alone made for a depressive state for any sane human being. Porch determined to ruin the beautiful morning temper by making his presence known in An Ngai Tay and he had set out to mend any damage Chaplain Buchanan might have done in his estimation in the few months of ministry with the CAP. The major packed with him dozens of Catholic doctrinal booklets and small booklets outlining the history of the Roman Catholic Church.

He sought to discover any wrongdoing, at least in his estimation, by the spiritual team, serious enough to take straight to the divisional chaplain. His attempts with any beefs presented in the past to Lucas have fallen completely on its face. Porch's visit to the hamlet searched for attempts by Buchanan to proselytize the villagers to Protestantism, the perfect grievance. Porch felt convinced the Chaplain Chain of Command would surely frown upon a Protestant Navy chaplain attempting to convert a Catholic hamlet to the Baptist faith.

Porch arrived in An Ngai Tay at 0800 hours, along with a select number of friends from Camp Love and an interpreter. He and his friends, who likewise despised Buchanan, distributed equally the doctrinal booklets to individual members in the hamlet. They distributed the booklets to the heads of the family and then shared with the rest of the family members.

Knocking Buchanan down a size or two and sending this country bumpkin preacher, at least in his estimation, packing for home would make the beautiful, sunny day even brighter for Porch. According to him, Buchanan accounted for nothing more than a hillbilly in a Navy uniform. To take in consideration Buchanan's educational background or his history of ministry mattered little to Porch. He, on the other hand, exalted himself. He thought he knew better than Buchanan what a chaplain ought to be and how a chaplain ought to conduct himself. What gnawed at him most was Buchanan's popularity.

Porch and his friends distributed the booklets throughout the hamlet as if Jesuit missionaries set out to share the literature of Jesus to human beings who have never heard of Christ. Smiling and shaking hands, the scene snow balled into a pitiful sight. Porch took the liberty to realign the religious convictions of the An Ngai Tay hamlet. He set himself as a self-appointed protector of the Faith. Most of his friends lending a hand from camp were not even Roman Catholics. When given the opportunity to show up Buchanan, Porch's friends were more than willing.

Porch attained very little Vietnamese to communicate, as he spoke to the An Ngai Tay citizens through the interpreter. The search for substantial proof of proselytizing against Buchanan, Porch asked questions such as "When the Navy Baptist chaplain, Buchanan, comes to visit, does he ask you questions such as 'Do you know Jesus Christ as your personal Savior?' or 'Do you want to become a Baptist?' or even 'Do you want to be immersed in baptism?'" He also asked if Buchanan ever implied Roman Catholicism seemed phony or non-Biblical.

All Porch accomplished in his quest for a complaint had been utter confusion. The villagers in An Ngai Tay posed a curious question. 'Why is this man in the hamlet asking questions inquiring of Chaplain Buchanan?' A significant number of villagers, dumbfounded, never set eyes on Porch, a stranger in their own home, without an invitation.

Buchanan bestowed nothing but benevolence in An Ngai Tay, never once attempting to proselytize. With assistance of his Catholic chaplain friends, Buchanan fulfilled commitments of the CAP in the hamlet providing clothes, shoes, food, and other charitable contributions. Besides, the spiritual team insisted on cooperation with Catholic Chaplains, including Kensington and Marino, favorites of the hamlet.

Frustrated in getting nowhere, Porch attempted to coax the populace to divulge anything incriminating to exploit against Buchanan. The effort fell short, futile.

The hands of time came to 0900 hours. Still nothing substantial to bring against Buchanan. A whole hour spent, amounting to nothing. Porch flaunted oodles of Achilles' heels in his DNA, but quitting was not one of them. A never-ending determination pressed Porch forward on his quest to rid the popular Buchanan out of Camp Love.

The witch hunt proceeded to no avail.

As Porch and his friends rallied near the hamlet pavilion, they caught sight of, in the distance on Route 1, several jeeps coming their way. Porch caught sight of the front passengers in the first jeep, none other than Buchanan and Jackson, the spiritual team. The chauffeur of the second jeep, Private Rodriquez, the Vet, a dedicated and loving Roman Catholic, drove with pride toward the hamlet loaded down with Catholic chaplains as passengers. As distance closed between the hamlet and the first jeep, he recognized two chaplains accompanying the spiritual team. Driving to the hamlet entrance, the jeeps parked bumper to bumper, followed by a mass of passengers confidently stepping out of the vehicles with purpose in their footsteps.

The visitors surveyed the robust fortifications to guard against the Viet Cong. The physical barrier between the evil surrounding the hamlet and the safe haven within An Ngai Tay pleased the cohort of religious leaders.

Buchanan stepped up to Porch toe to toe, face to face with the major, shaking his hand.

Porch posed nothing but surprise and agitation.

"Good Morning Major Porch. What a beautiful day, isn't it?" declared a beaming Buchanan in his sturdy mountain drawl.

"Good Morning - Chaplain Buchanan. How - How are you?" asked an embarrassed Porch.

"Great. Just Great." Buchanan smiled.

"Sergeant Jackson." added an uneasy Porch. Jackson nods, saying, "Sir."

Jackson noticed the booklets in Porch's hand.

"Hmmm. What's in your hand, sir? I see the elders in An Ngai Tay holding one too. Are those the nutrition booklets we distributed last week?" asked Jackson, pointing his ear toward Porch.

Hesitantly, Porch informed the group of religious leaders what the booklets were. "Uh, um… no, Jackson. They're not. They're, uh - well. Booklets, yes, booklets outlining the, well - the theology of the Roman Catholic church a-and Catholic Church history."

An inquisitive Rodriquez asked Porch, "Are those the booklets you gave me, sir?"

"I, yes Private Rodriquez, uh, the booklets are those I presented to you a few weeks back. I thought it would be a good thing for the villagers to, well - have a refresher on the, well, you know, vitality and nature of the Church as well." Porch chuckles in a state of trepidation.

Pausing, he attempts to explain himself further when a voice suddenly spoke, "Well, I love it. I absolutely love it. Good for faithful Catholics to be familiar with the history of the Church. Besides, a solid refresher history lesson is always good for the soul." The voice matched none other than Chaplain Lieutenant Commander Jacob Marino, a courageous and accomplished priest. He accompanied Buchanan to inspect and observe for himself the impressive news of An Ngai Tay and its desire to achieve religious freedom. Buchanan enjoyed immensely the company of Marino, whose roots derived from Chicago and whose family for five generations made their living in the book business.

"Well, I thought since I'm Catholic and, well, I could reinforce their faith by distributing these booklets." explained Porch.

Marino thanked Porch graciously. "Well, yes. If there's one feature in life I love - it's books. My family back home owns a chain of bookstores in Chicago. Good. Good to see, major. Good to see fellow Catholics educating the lay people. Thank you, Porch. Thank you."

"See there, Major Porch, y'all are both from Illinois, *and* Roman Catholic." grinned Buchanan.

All laugh, including Marino, unaware of Porch's intent in An Ngai Tay.

Clueless of the conflict between Buchanan and Porch, all Marino understood was a lay Catholic leader facilitated spiritual guidance and education to his fellow Catholics.

"Yes, Major. *Chaplain* Marino knows your concern for your fellow Catholics is top priority." commented Buchanan, smiling with a bit of smug. "And Lieutenant Michael McMillan, Roman Catholic priest from San Francisco." He grins straight at an abashed Porch, speechless and powerless to acknowledge his actual intent in the hamlet. The spiritual team had been well aware of his motives.

Nervous, Porch shakes McMillan's hand, shielding his sheer embarrassment the best he can, acknowledging the chaplain, "Padre."

Turning to Buchanan, Porch asks, "Um, and your purpose here today, chaplain?"

"Why I've come to support my Catholic chaplain friends lead in the Eucharist. They frequent the hamlet often, leading in the Eucharist, especially after the absence of local priests in the area. You didn't know they came on a weekly basis from 1st Division to conduct services? Did you?" asked a surprised Buchanan.

Porch answered cautiously, "N-No. No, I didn't."

"Well, you know now, don't you, sir?" added Jackson with indignation.

Porch thought in silence, 'How can I head to divisional headquarters and throw a complaint toward Buchanan of proselytizing the hamlet of An Ngai Tay when he's inviting Catholic Navy chaplains to conduct services?'

"Hey, I've got a great idea, Porch. Why don't you stay longer, attend the services, you'll be supporting Catholic ministry here in the hamlet? That'd be nice." suggested McMillan.

"Well chaplain, I - well, I need to head back to camp. I'm sure there's plenty of work back in camp." Porch, knowing his aim in An Ngai Tay the whole while, set himself to hightail it out of the hamlet.

Porch, embarrassed, felt out of place, in the wrong place at the wrong time. McMillan and Marino were clueless of Porch's intent, but he knew, and the 'guilt ridden' marine major fled the premises.

With the weight of an unbearable state of embarrassment, Porch could no longer last as he and his party hopped in their jeeps, headed for home. Porch left defeated, failing to nail a blotch against Buchanan.

The interruption at An Ngai Tay emboldened Porch to push forward with even more ardor and fervor.

As Porch and his friends departed in their jeeps, he glanced over his shoulder, sighting the Catholic chaplains preparing for the Eucharist. In eyesight, he caught a glimpse of an enthusiastic Private Rodriquez assisting Jackson in the preparation for the Communion kits, lending a hand to his fellow Catholics.

Dismay overcame Porch with the fact a Protestant Buchanan supplicated Catholic chaplains in An Ngai Tay.

The fiery, intense clash between Buchanan and Porch only heightened with the obvious defeat suffered in An Ngai Tay for the major.

Buchanan won the day's battle, but the war was far from over.

Murdering the Innocent

December 20, 1968

The ecstatic ambiance in Buchanan's hootch reflected one of great satisfaction knowing the Kingdom of God grew with numbers and in Spirit with the ministry in An Ngai Tay. McMillan and Marino laid forth before God Almighty a commitment and devotion to fellow Catholics sharing the love of Jesus, the Savior of mankind. The grand desire of Americans for citizens in the hamlet to attain and practice religious freedom without threats from any adversaries, especially from the Viet Cong, to violate that freedom became a top priority for American spiritual leaders.

After a hearty breakfast, the spiritual team prepared for a day of ministry on a spiritual high, gun ho for a follow-up visit to An Ngai Tay.

The Viet Cong increased their tactics of intimidation and terror in northern and central Vietnam in the past 6 months, much of its nocturnal activities in hamlets and villages. The nocturnal visits to Catholic villages and hamlets ended up as intentional, murderous, and unfortunately effective.

Today's visit in the hamlet came forth as an effort to reinforce support for the American cause. The spiritual team sought to reassure villagers they had a solid protection from the United States to protect their religious freedom, and to fight any Communist who abhors and detests the freedom of religion.

The spiritual team set off for the hamlet. The departure from Camp Love, their comfort zone, always struck the spiritual team with a sudden dose of anxiety. Jackson never shed the queasy feeling in his stomach departing a base or a camp, either by foot or by vehicle. He glanced over his shoulder one last time toward Camp Love. The superstition of glancing back one last time seemed to ease the pain entering the jungle bush for him. The odds of his name on a KIA list heightened with every departure of Camp Love, a fact permanently in the back of his mind.

The team drove the dirt roads in the wide open space of Vietnam till Jackson reached Route 540, turning left onto Route 1 toward An Ngai Tay.

Jackson mentioned, "An Ngai Tay is coming along quite well. Isn't it, sir?"

"Yes. Yes, it is."

"Have you noticed those in the hamlet who welcomes you most are children?" Jackson pauses. "We humor them, don't we, sir?" He smiles.

"Yeah. They're thinking, 'those Americans sure are nutty, aren't they?' I can hear them now, 'If these Americans are anything like these marines, it sure is a nutty country.'" shared Buchanan, grinning.

They chuckle at the thought.

"I sure butcher their language when spoken, though. Don't I? They sure find it humorous when I mispronounce something." The men laugh.

"You do struggle with the Vietnamese language, don't ya, sir?" asked Jackson.

"Well, I can't help it. I can't seem to shed my mountain accent. Their letters, the words - similar to pictures and....well, symbols. It's confusing."

"You enjoy studying the Hebrew though. Don't ya sir? And you've always said it resembles pictures and symbols. What's the difference?"

"Well, the Hebrew's closer to -" Buchanan pauses, and searches his mind for an answer for Jackson. "Well - to, the western world languages." Buchanan glances over at Jackson, expressing confidence.

Peeking over toward Buchanan, he shakes his head, grinning, knowing Chaplain Buchanan was full of it! Turning back toward the road to drive, Jackson thinks of the phenomenal job the Lord put forth forming and molding Chaplain Buchanan together, creating the eccentric personality he has come to know.

Jackson smiles at the thought.

Buchanan wonders what might be festering in Jackson's mind and smirks. "Ms. Bi'hn's my favorite in the hamlet. Loves capitalism - doesn't she Sergeant?"

"Sure does, sir. She sure does."

The team pauses from conversation, admiring the beauty of rural Vietnam.

Breaking the silence, Buchanan comments, "Sure is beautiful, isn't it, Philip?"

"Sure is, chaplain. Sure is."

The spiritual team is now two miles away from An Ngai Tay.

Jackson asks, "What do you think is going to happen to the people in An Ngai Tay hamlet, chaplain?"

"What? Asking a thing like that? I don't know."

Pondering the thought, Buchanan confidently asserts, "Well, we're going to win this war and they're going to live in peace and possess religious freedom that we affirm. That's what."

Jackson deliberately turns his head toward Buchanan, expressing pensiveness and disgust.

Buchanan, second guessing himself, understands the absurdity of his answer to the question.

"We better change our overall strategy right now, chaplain. We might win all the battles, sir. But we're unfortunately losing the war."

Buchanan grimaces. "I know, I know. I just want those villagers to know what it is to truly be free. Know what I mean?"

"Yes, sir. Yeah. I know."

The spiritual team continues to admire the majestic topography of Vietnam in silence, but now thinking of what sort of hand the South Vietnamese will be dealt.

An Ngai Tay hamlet measured now a half a mile in plain sight. The spiritual team flew high with confidence as lofty as a kite, cultivating a stronger relationship with the people of An Ngai Tay.

As distance closed about 200 feet between the jeep and the hamlet, the spiritual team noticed two companies of Bravo Company inside and out of the fortified perimeter of An Ngai Tay, led by Lieutenant Rockford, along with two platoons of Delta Company.

The spiritual team, now just 100 feet away from the main gate, noticed nurses from Da Nang hospital, including Reagan, Glenn, and Burleson, standing on the edge of the treeline parallel to the defensive perimeter with Bravo Company.

Jackson noticed 2nd Platoon of Company D positioned in a defensive position all around the hamlet's perimeter and 1st Platoon of Company D patrolling northwest of the hamlet. Rockford and Bravo Company stood positioned along the treeline, securing the edge between the jungle bush and the village perimeter. The nurses, visibly upset, stood with 2nd and 3rd platoons of Bravo Company at the treeline, while 1st platoon secured the road and pathways south of the hamlet.

With the obvious discontent and consternation expressed in villagers, marines, and nurses alike, Buchanan noticed the nurses were in complete shock. The bewilderment upon the natural, soft, and compassionate chisel boned structured oval faces of the nurses puzzled the spiritual team. Tears profusely poured down onto the cheeks of the devastated nurses. The team obviously now knew something discovered inside the treeline caused a traumatic and unsettling environment.

Stunned by the sight in front of them, the spiritual team sat in the jeep, shocked, numb with the apparent doom and gloom.

Buchanan spotted a familiar marine major under the pavilion - none other than Major Michael Porch! Buchanan discovered a persona he never perceived in Porch. He obviously displayed a troubled and emotionally distressed man. CPO Dingus stood aside Porch comforting the marine.

Tight-lipped, the spiritual team seethed with anger.

"What's happening here, Sergeant? What happened?" asked Buchanan.

"I don't know yet, chaplain? But let's go find out."

The two quickly stepped through the gate on their way to Porch, totally dismayed by the situation at hand.

When they reached Porch, Buchanan asked, "Micheal? Is there anything I can do for ya?"

"Why chaplain, why?" asked a shocked Porch.

Buchanan turns to Dingus, shaking his head bewildered, beyond words.

Obviously, Porch stood shaken by the events of the previous night. Porch, as white as a sheet, stood a nervous wreck, at a loss for words. Buchanan set his eyes on a Porch he had never seen before. Porch, a man of pride, initiated daily efforts to display demeanor exhibiting confidence and self assurance. Today, standing in front of Buchanan, a man of unhinged emotions - and for good reason, as Buchanan will soon discover.

Buchanan patted Porch on the shoulder.

"The treeline, Sergeant." ordered Buchanan.

"Yes, sir."

The spiritual team left Porch with Dingus to console him the best he could.

As the spiritual team turned, stepping toward the hamlet gate, the team examined the shock and bewilderment of the citizens of An Ngai Tay. Expressions of disbelief and incredulity. Citizens obviously wary and deflated of emotion with the events of the previous night.

Most notable of the citizens were the dispirited frowns. Grimaces replaced the usual bright-eyed expressions of familiar pleasant smiles.

Passing through the gate, the spiritual team turned left toward the treeline, strolling around the edge reaching the nurses and Bravo Company. The team held their tongue. The spiritual presence alone spoke for itself, supporting friends in emotional pain and agony.

"Why chaplain? What possesses human beings to commit such atrocities against other human beings?" asked Glenn, the short-timer. Just three more days in Vietnam and her tour will end. Glenn had it set within the heart and soul to visit the precious children of An Ngai Tay one last time. The fact she had spent so much time and investment in the health and wellbeing of the children and nursing those in need, she had to visit the hamlet one last time. After today, she wished she had never come close to the village following the discovery of the marines inside the treeline.

Rockford, barking out orders to secure the hamlet 100 feet from the perimeter, caught in the corner of his eye the spiritual team.

Stepping from the perimeter toward the treeline, the obvious truth hit Buchanan like a ton of bricks. While in the perimeter's inside of the hamlet, he noticed the absence of the chief and the elders of the hamlet, several women, and the children of the An Ngai Tay. 'Where are they?' he asked himself.

The nurses, sitting on tree stumps and a dirt mound from the clearing for the perimeter, were crying and speechless. They attempted to recompose themselves.

Rockford and 2nd platoon, including Dobbs and Rodriquez, struggled to console the nurses. Rockford approached the spiritual team.

"In here, chaplain." Rockford motioned to the spiritual team to cross the treeline into the jungle with him.

Buchanan stepped toward the treeline when Rockford gently placed the backside of his hand onto Buchanan's chest. "Chaplain, I want you to know, well, it's not pretty. The VC definitely sought to show the evil in their wicked hearts for what they did here last night."

Buchanan cocks his head, bewildered by Rockford's statement.

"Jackson, chaplain." Rockford finally led the spiritual team into the jungle bush.

Rockford, followed by Jurgensen, a corporal from 2nd platoon, a few other marines including Dobbs and Rodriquez, and finally the spiritual team bringing up the rear. Dread filled every molecule within Buchanan, entering the treeline, as only God knows what lies ahead.

Just a few feet within the treeline, horror hit Buchanan as he laid his eyes on the hamlet chief.

"Oh Jesus. Father, God in Heaven." blurted Buchanan from shock.

Tied to a tree, the chief endured horrendous torture, suffered from the hands of the Viet Cong. Gagged with a handkerchief, the VC carved him up with a machete, his tongue cut out, and burned with a hot iron rod in his armpits and torso. Finally done in with a slit to his stomach, followed by his intestines falling onto the ground in front of him.

A sign nailed above the chief's head read in English, 'No more Freedom of Religion.' Rockford read the sign out loud. Buchanan's blood boiled.

Dobbs fought back tears. Noticing the young man, Buchanan discovered a soft heart within the non-believer, after all.

Shaken, Rodriquez expressed anger. "Murderers. What'd he ever do to you to deserve this? You'll get yours."

The VC began their murderous rampage with the chief followed by the repeated rape and torture of his wife and young daughters, ages 11 and 14, right in front of him, tied to the tree. The chief's wife and young daughters forced further into the jungle, raped for the last time, but in ears shot for the chief to hear screams and pleading for their lives.

Rockford and Jurgensen guided the spiritual team back some 20 feet further into the jungle, showing the team the naked bodies of the wife and daughters mutilated and tortured. Buchanan falls deeper into shock at the severity of violence. "Jesus. Blessed Jesus in Heaven."

Jackson, tight-lipped and red in tooth and claw, placed his hand on Buchanan's shoulder, breathing hard and panting from shock. No eye remained dry in the party of marines. The sorrow all felt from the loss of their Vietnamese friends and allies saddened them to no end. The presence of Jackson's hand on his chaplain's shoulder at least comforted him.

Never would Buchanan shed this memory of this day for the rest of his life. The first experience a serviceman or woman in Vietnam witnessing a horrific and cruel act against a human being by the diabolical hands of the Viet Cong resulted in a permanent, lifelong memory.

Dobbs, incensed, asked softly, "Chaplain, why? What'd they do to deserve this?"

Buchanan paused and said, "Nothing."

Buchanan thinks to himself, 'What does an unbeliever like Dobbs think of atrocities committed by such evil individuals against innocent human beings?'

The growth of a healthy relationship between Dobbs and a few children at Chaplain Kensington's orphanage created a soft spirit within the unbeliever. He now has seen how evil the dark side really is.

The slaughter of An Ngai Tay extended past the chief and his family.

"There's more Chaplain." said an angered Rockford.

"What? Who? What else could there be?" asked Buchanan.

Rockford motioned the party to walk an additional 15 feet into the bush to 14 children of the hamlet, raped and mutilated by the Viet Cong. Chinh, the sweet and innocent eight-year-old Glenn became so fond of, laid upon the ground a victim of VC evildoing. Tuan, the 7-year-old orphan nurse Burleson found a liking to, laid murdered on the ground from the wicked hands of the VC. 14 Vietnamese children murdered. Children murdered to intimidate the villagers to support the Communist cause.

Flabbergasted beyond words, Buchanan sunk in a deep state of disbelief. His denial of what laid in front of him led to an even a greater disdain for the Viet Cong. Blood boiled in every marine, vowing for revenge.

Rockford glanced slowly toward Buchanan. "I'm sorry chaplain, but - there's more."

Rockford mentioned to Jackson, "Sergeant, the VC are straight out of hell. The Devil's work wasn't finished here. Come with me."

The spiritual team followed Rockford. The men pivoted 15 degrees east, 10 feet of the murdered children. Rockford pushed back foliage for an open space for the spiritual team to step through into the think jungle. The unspeakable, revolting sight before the spiritual team added to the urgency of revenge for the atrocities of the day. Hanging from a tree in a fetal position, a woman's body, mutilated from head to toe, bared the horrifying cuts of severe, repeated knife wounds.

The woman tied to the tree was Bi'hn.

Tortured to death and suffering, the pain of her tongue cut out, the VC nailed the tongue to the tree she hung from. A sign nailed onto the tree above her head read in Vietnamese – 'Capitalist whore'.

Following the reading of the sign to Buchanan, Jackson declared, "I hope we find the damned to hell evil murderers and punish them hard. I hope we give to them what they deserve."

Confidently, Rockford agreed. "Me too, Jackson. Me too."

Jackson noticed nothing but vengeance in the contour of the Americans. Never in his life had Buchanan been so angry. Angry enough to kill. Buchanan finally witnessed with his own two eyes what sorts of punishments the VC dishes out to those unwilling to cooperate with Communists or to south Vietnamese innocents who cooperate with the Americans.

Rockford's party, along with the spiritual team, made their way back through the jungle, out into the bright sun and sweltering heat of Vietnam. Rockford stopped just outside of the treeline, receiving reports from platoons sent out for reconnaissance to seek the guilty Viet Cong who committed the various atrocities. The gathered reports showed no VC were in the vicinity. Rockford asked permission to venture out to patrol the next day.

The spiritual team stepped toward the jeep, noticing an absence of the nurses. The nurses had had enough, fed up with the tragedy, and had set out for home, Da Nang Air Base. Climbing into the truck, every nurse regretted making the trip to the hamlet this morning, including Glenn, who will remember this day for the rest of her life. Three days left in Vietnam and she witnessed the most atrocious act of inhumanity in all her days in Vietnam.

The marines eventually caught five young Vietnamese men, tied to one another in a line outside the hamlet and transported to 1st Marine Headquarters, to be questioned by South Vietnamese Army investigators and United States interrogators.

The spiritual team conversed with hamlet elders through interpreters informing them if any wants or needs arose to contact them. When Buchanan arrived back at Camp Love, he immediately contacted Chaplain Marino, informing him of the murders in An Ngai

Tay and to send Catholic priests, if all possible, to the hamlet to minister. Stunned from the terror of events last night, the people of the hamlet sat traumatized, dazed from the Devil's work.

The day began jubilant for the spiritual team departing Camp Love and ended with hatred toward the murderous Viet Cong.

The spiritual team stepped into their jeep for a depressive, down trodden trip back to Camp Love. Tight-lipped in the jeep, thoughts ran wild in their minds, attempting to put into perspective the sequence of events of the last 24 hours.

When the day started, the spiritual team loathed the Viet Cong. By the end of the day, prayers lifted to God asked the Lord to swipe His hand down from Heaven onto Vietnam and rip to pieces the North Vietnamese Communists and the VC, every last one of them, dumping them into the hottest part of Hell.

Not a word came from the spiritual team's lips on the trek back to camp. Little emotion came from either of them. Though the spiritual team sat in the jeep speechless, on the inside - a passionate fury burned within.

Buchanan asked for daily reports from Rockford about the progress in reaping revenge on the Viet Cong for the senseless murders at An Ngai Tay.

With the Christmas season upon the spiritual team, the Christmas Spirit came to null to void this day for the pair.

Camp Love gave no room for forgiveness and understanding. The spiritual team expected nothing but a substantial and weighted punishment for the murderers.

Nothing else would remedy the situation but a quick and ferocious retribution for murdering the innocents.

Bad News From Home

December 21, 1968

Though Buchanan's Christmas mood seemed abysmal, Christmas day neared just around the corner. And An Ngai Tay came first and foremost on Buchanan's mind. He handled the shock of depression of the An Ngai Tay atrocities by staying in his hootch most of the day. He isolated himself praying for comfort and, most important, understanding. He prayed for deserved blessings in the lives of the South Vietnamese people. He prayed for a victorious end of the war.

The day began late morning, as the spiritual team spent most of the day in Buchanan's hootch, consoling and counseling one another.

American casualties were light for the month of December, sparing the 7th Engineering Battalion the usual pain of death and agony. Regarding civilian casualties, not even the supplementary fortifications of An Ngai Tay spared the hamlet the pain of war.

Grief gripped Buchanan. Last night, forced to endure hours of darkness full of nightmares of the Devil, he experienced a night falling asleep thinking of nothing but An Ngai Tay hamlet.

In the years to come, Buchanan experienced a recurring dream, one of many last nights, that left a permanent memory within his mind. Repetition of the dream night after night left lasting imprints of war memories and entailed a marine officer.

The dream sequence followed a general chain of events. The first sequence of the dream consists of a marine officer sitting in a chair at the front gate of Camp Love, playing the role of gatekeeper. He sits, waiting patiently for visitors to enter the camp. Overtime, scores of visitors gradually emerge out of the jungle bush, sneaking up on the gate. The visitors disclose themselves as Viet Cong insurgents. The intruders expressed the thirst and want for blood smeared all over their faces. Instead of defending the gate entrance, the marine officer opens the gate, granting permission to the VC to penetrate the camp. One insurgent after the other given permission to enter camp. Following the infiltration of the camp, the VC crept into hootch after hootch, slitting the throats of each marine. Nothing but pure evil running throughout the camp. The pure pleasure of killing and murdering marines ran through the blood veins of the VC, scampering through the confines of the camp, slitting the throats of a hated enemy. All the while, the marine officer, evil and conniving, secures the gate, giggling maliciously as he methodically converges to the center of camp. As the very last marine is slaughtered in Camp Love, the VC merges with the marine officer to the heart of camp. The VC save Buchanan last to kill, as the marine officer will take all the pleasure of killing him. The anticipation of killing Buchanan expressed in the glee of the marine officer's eye and an exuberant smile on his face. The officer steps onto the highest elevated point in camp triumphant, with all the pomp and circumstance of a king! Congregating around the marine officer, the VC yell as if he had just led them in a great military victory! With risen knives and swords splattered with blood, a spontaneous metamorphosis process takes place as the VC gradually changes into red eyed murderous demons and nymphs of the Devil! Cackling and giggling with evil intent, the VC chant, "Kill Chaplain Buchanan! Kill Chaplain Buchanan!" As demons and nymphs chant, the marine officer begins a slow process of metamorphosis himself, with his eyes changing slowly to red and his body transforming into the Devil. The demons and nymphs continue to chant, "Kill Chaplain Buchanan" "Kill the man of peace!" With time, as chants resound louder, the mass of demons and nymphs turn a frenzy, twirling their swords and waving their knives. The mass of demons and the Devil move in unison towards Buchanan's hootch. In a mass movement towards Buchanan's hootch, the Devil positions himself in the assemblage's heart, as demons howl and repeat even louder, "Kill Chaplain Buchanan! Kill Chaplain Buchanan!" The masses surround Buchanan's hootch and now chant "Kill" "Kill" "Kill" repeatedly! The mass of demons and nymphs form a hole for the Devil to step his way to Buchanan's hootch entrance. The Devil strides methodically up Buchanan's steps of his hootch, leisurely pulling his knife out of its sheath, pacing up the steps reaching the top, and instead of an amble step into the hootch, a metamorphosis occurs and the Devil turns into a slithering massive boa constrictor. Sliding over ever so slowly to Buchanan's cot, he curls himself round and around and under his cot. Once curled completely around Buchanan's cot, he places his head perfectly above Buchanan's with an inch from his nose. Smiling wide, two arms emerge from the boa constrictor under belly. With one hand grasping his knife, the other pulling Buchanan's head back, stretching his neck long and wide for the Devil to slit the throat ever so clean. The Devil, with knife in hand, sharpens it back and forth on Buchanan's neck, smiling broad, waiting to cut the skin. Licking the edge of his knife, he measures up Buchanan's neck with the knife. As the Devil's patience runs out, he has had enough playing and toying with Buchanan, and places his knife just under the Adam's Apple to cut his throat. The evil satisfaction of the Devil killing his menace and ridding himself of a man spreading peace in war will now come to an end. But just as the Devil puts pressure on the skin to slice his neck, Buchanan wakes up from his dream.

Frightened, sweaty, and exhausted, Buchanan leaps from his cot, rushing over to his sink. He splashes water on his face, grabbing a paper cup to drink some water. The water never tasted so good. Buchanan hated the heat. The utter scorn within his heart of scorching, seething hot weather was never hated more than this night. His recurring dream did nothing but make matters worse as his body temperature rose, drenching his clothes with sweat. His hot and sweaty body resulting from the mental attack of his dream.

The dream saturated the energy out of him. Nausea set in.

From paranoia, he stepped to his hootch door, cracking it just a smidge, reassuring himself Camp Love remained secure. Scanning the camp from one end to the other, Buchanan set his eyes on a safe camp. He sighs heavily. "Whew. It's just a dream."

Now assured the camp remained secure took nothing from the fact Buchanan despised and reviled Porch's behavior. In his estimation, the marine officer reflected his confrontations with Porch. The dream reminded him of the fact that Porch is a jackass. Buchanan did not like him. Rarely, if hardly at all, did Buchanan display hostile manners towards others as he did for Porch. The major emerged as an exception. The hostility towards Porch did not equal hate, but did border on the cusp of down right despisement. Usually, Buchanan brushed aside smug people in life, giving them little attention. The chaplain turned people possessed of smug over to God. He often pointed out, "The Lord will put them in their place in time."

Buchanan thought of Porch as different. Facing Porch daily, he held back his days of living life as an unbeliever. He defiantly rejected the temptation of the little demon on his left shoulder, urging him to step smack dab into Porch's face and punching him in the nose. In the end, he gave in to the angel standing on his right shoulder, encouraging him to turn the other cheek.

In the years to come, the Devil in the dream never starts taking the life of Buchanan. He's always roused from sleep before the Devil gets the chance of taking his life in such a violent manner. The fact his life is never taken, he felt Porch, who Buchanan estimates is the Devil in his dream, will never get the upper hand in real life either.

Time rang at 0300 hours in the morning.

Now wide awake, Buchanan feared falling asleep, risking the chance of experiencing the recurring dream once again. The fear enticed him to stay up. Besides, this dream he considered the nastiest recurring dream he encountered dealing with the war.

To shift his thoughts, he read a history book, then the Scriptures. He then prayed for blessings for Sunday. He scanned the newspapers Dorothy sent him. Reading the newspapers, he opened the sports page on an article reviewing the big matchup between Ohio State and Southern California. The article did the trick, deflecting his mind off the dream. Buchanan's adrenal glands perked up, reading an article about the big matchup on January 1, 1969.

Buchanan prepared himself to shower and shave, an everyday occurrence unless out in the bush. As he was about to administer shaving cream to his face, a knock came from the door.

A knock on the door? At 0400 hours in the morning?

Buchanan received visitors at all hours of the day, especially marines in desperate need of the chaplain. But suffering through such a horrifying dream, Buchanan woke up in no mood for a visitor. Still paranoid, he readied himself to pounce on the Devil and his demons as he opened the door of the hootch. The dream affected Buchanan so real; he stood at his door a bit flustered.

A soft voice broke the early morning silence of the camp, "Chaplain."

Waiting patiently for a response, the marine heard nothing but a short, anticipated pause of silence.

With a bit more urgency in his voice, the marine once again softly called for the chaplain, "Padre."

With a second impelling plea from the marine, Buchanan replied, "Yes."

"It's me, Corporal Jaworski, from Bravo Company. From communications."

"What is? Who?" asked Buchanan quietly.

"Corporal Jaworski, sir. Sir, I need your help. Right now, sir."

"What is it, corporal?"

"Well, it's not me, sir. And I hate disturbing you at this hour, but I need your help right now." Buchanan recognized a tone of panic in Jaworski's voice.

Buchanan quickly unlocks the door, delighted with no end to see Jaworski standing there instead of the Devil.

"Whew! Not the Devil." blurted Buchanan. Looking up to Heaven, he says, "Thank you, Jesus."

"Sir?" asked a befuddled Jaworski.

Waving his hand in the open says quickly, "Never mind, corporal. Nothing. It's nothing corporal. Come in. Come in."

"Thank you, sir."

Buchanan inquires more of Jaworski's problem. "Now what's this about? Tell me. Is it serious, corporal?"

"Is it ever, sir. It's, well - it's Sergeant Michael McMillan. You know, the kid from Kentucky you favor. The kid you've helped in counseling, guiding him to be a better person."

"McMillan? The Paducah native?" inquired Buchanan.

"One and only, sir. From Paducah. Come quickly, sir."

Buchanan grabbed and donned his dungaree cap, and stepped out of the hootch with Jaworski.

Quietly, the men double timed to Jaworski and McMillan's hootch. Jaworski, in a soft voice, informs Buchanan rapidly, but precisely, McMillan's problem.

"Well, it started yesterday, sir. It's like this. McMillan received word from home his mother, well, is dying from leukemia, a short time to live. When I received the communique, I quickly passed it along and conveyed it to Michael. Well, he has but just four more days of his tour, and you know it's his third tour in a row, sir. Well, I don't have to inform you, sir, he's a champion demolition expert in the Corps. It's why he's here, one of the best at what he does. He works in automotive, but the higher ups use his skills as a demolition expert daily. He's ready to go home, sir. Now. Well, to make a long story short, guess who's to sign papers for him to go home four days early?"

"The jackass." answered Buchanan, with disdain.

"Who, sir?" asks Jaworski with interest.

"Uh, well....I mean - is it, well, Porch?" answered Buchanan.

Grinning, Jaworski answers, "You got it, sir. Michael marched himself over to Porch, and he emphatically denied signing his papers. He went back to Porch with Sergeant Burnside, his superior in automotive. Again, Porch denied the early leave papers to go home. The pair even went to Major Carroll, jumping chain of command, who has to sign for early leave as well, and informed them Porch would have to OK it first before he signed anything."

The two men are now 10 feet from the hootch, stopping to finish the conversation out of earshot of McMillan and whispered. Jaworski finishes the low down on McMillan. "And as you know well, both of them are sticklers for military chain of command."

Jaworski prepares Buchanan for the topper. "Well, listen to this, Padre. Porch boldly informed Michael he had a job to do, and his job ended on his departure date, and no sooner. Sergeant Burnside intervened on Michael's behalf – and you know what Porch said to Burnside, sir?"

Buchanan, by now catching flies, shook his head, answering, "No."

Staring straight into Buchanan's eyes, Jaworski disclosed, "Go to hell. Yes, sir. He said, 'Go to hell.'"

Surprised, Buchanan stood with raised eyebrows and a widened mouth evermore in total shock.

"That's what he told him, sir. Can you believe it? Told him 'To go to hell.' Well, the both of them shot out of the office as fast as your cat up a tree chased by the neighbors' German Shepard. One more second in the office, the two of 'em would have gone off on Porch, and you know Porch, he'd have drawn up some dumb charge against them. Later on, Michael assured me it took every molecule in Burnside's body to stop him from beating up a superior officer to a bloody pulp. He didn't want to ruin a long career because of an ass who deserves a beating."

Jaworski leans towards Buchanan in a serious stance. "Padre, Michael's been up all night considering what to do. Well, 15 minutes ago he goes nuts, pulls his .45 out of his holster, says he's going to kill Porch and Carroll. I think he means it, sir. I really do. I told him to stay put, not to leave, that I'd be back with help. He's all crumbled up in a fetal position in the hootch's corner, sir, with his .45 caliber."

"Whew." expressed Buchanan. He paused, looking out into the still darkness of the jungle bush, pondering what to do or what to say. Nearly three months in the Vietnam jungle and nothing such as this has ever stuck its ugly head for all to see in Camp Love. Buchanan carried out his duties as a chaplain in camp with little life threatening fanfare - until now. "Let me talk to him."

"Be careful, sir. He's not happy with the situation."

"I will, corporal."

Stepping in the hootch slowly, with caution and trepidation, Buchanan searches in the darkness for McMillan from the dim light streaming between the nooks and crannies of the wood structure of the hootch. Catching a glimpse of McMillan in the hootch's corner in a fetal position, Buchanan searched for words to say to the irate sergeant.

The broken silence in the hootch came from a soft voice. "I'm going home."

Darkness concealed McMillan, but Buchanan recognized his heavy Kentuckian accent. Out of the darkness came a lonely voice, startling Buchanan. He sensed an eerie air in the hootch.

Experiencing one of the worst nights he had had in Vietnam, he endured one nightmare after another, haunting him. And now this. On top of it all, Porch played a role with practically every integral part of the entire night.

Careful in the words he said to McMillan, Buchanan had yet to say anything, fearful his words will set him off.

"Chaplain?" inquired McMillan.

"Yes, Sergeant."

Buchanan felt relieved beyond measure as McMillan broke the ice speaking up first, minimizing the tension.

"Porch won't let me go home." The short, uncomfortable pause ahead of McMillan speaking up once again, rattled Buchanan to no end.

"I'm going to kill him, Porch. Carroll too." insisted McMillan.

Buchanan cocked his head toward the entrance, in shock at the situation.

Again, Buchanan's loss of words to calm McMillan's nerves shook him to no end.

"I - like you, want you to' see your mother Michael. You go off and do something like shooting holes into Porch and Carroll, you'll – you'll never see her again." Buchanan, in his sturdy Kentuckian accent, shared the consequences for McMillan if he killed the marines officers. He swallowed hard, worried he chose the wrong words.

Hearing McMillan sighing deep with frustration, he added in his own strong Kentuckian accent, "I want to see my mother."

McMillan paused, sighing heavily. "I'm tired, sir. I certainly don't want to be in this God forsaken place when she passes on. I've seen many get it in their last few days in Vietnam."

Buchanan ponders of what he should say proper. "Listen, Michael. Let me talk to the Skipper. Lucas is a reasonable man. I'll talk to him first thing this morning. Promise."

A soft voice uttered, "No."

Buchanan pleaded with him. "Michael, you have so much leave days and you have such an impressive record serving the Corps. L-Let me just talk to Lucas. Just - just secure your weapon and let me go to the Skipper right now."

Nothing but silence filled the air in the hootch.

Buchanan thought - 'Uh oh! What's McMillan thinking?' 'What is he about to do?'

"Michael, I want nothing but good for you. You know that. Why don't you, well, secure your weapon and just let me talk to Lucas right now? Please. I have clout, ya know."

Waiting for a response seemed an eternity for Buchanan. Just as he was about to express a second thought, he heard the safety latch of the .45 flipped and watched McMillan rise out of the corner. He slowly stepped with measure to a coat stand, placing the .45 caliber back in the holster hanging on a hook.

Taking a quick peek at McMillan from the streaks of moonlight shining through the cracks of wood of the hootch, Buchanan spotted expressions of determination and buoyancy in his face. He wore the eyes of a proud marine.

"Alright, Chaplain Buchanan. I'll give you a shot."

The time quickly ran to 0545 hours. Stepping out from the hootch, Buchanan literally bumped into Jaworski, who had sat patiently outside the hootch, listening to every word. He had prayed the whole while for a favorable outcome.

Jaworski, done in out of sheer exhaustion, stands up to deliver a firm handshake with the chaplain, expressing a great appreciation for a job well done.

Buchanan immediately bolted over to Lieutenant Colonel Lucas's hootch, interrupting his morning routine. He explained the situation to the commanding officer, intentionally leaving out the fact McMillan, hell-bent to fill Porch and Carroll full of holes, armed himself to the hilt. Buchanan willfully left the commanding officer's hootch failing to inform him McMillan stood at the ready to send Porch and Carroll an early ticket back home in a body bag.

Buchanan marched his way back to his own hootch to shower and shave. He made ready to start the day off on working to see McMillan off to Kentucky.

Eating their usual breakfast together, the spiritual team headed off in camp to carry out the usual Saturday schedule, except for solving McMillan's situation.

The day passed with little fanfare.

At 1930 hours in the day, one last helicopter came into sight of Camp Love to pick up a package from Porch. The package, scheduled for delivery in Da Nang, would travel back on the helicopter, while two Navy officers stepped off the helicopter to report to Camp Love. One officer assigned to the Seabees to construct bridges, while the other will work in Porch's office for the next two weeks.

"OK, Lieutenant, that's it. You're ready for departure back to base, Da Nang." yelled Porch over the helicopter noise.

"No, sir. There's a passenger to go back." The helicopter pilot looked at his schedule sheet. "A Sergeant, uh, let's see - a Michael McMillan. He has leave to go home to Kentucky, my home state."

"Wrong! He's staying here for another 4 days. His tour is up on that day and no sooner. *Good day*, Lieutenant." Porch stood determined.

"But, sir." pleaded the pilot.

"I said *good* day Lieutenant."

Glancing over Porch's shoulder, the pilot pointed with his index finger. "Look, sir!"

Turning, Porch spots Sergeant Vickers running as fast as he can straight at him with McMillan running step by step behind Lucas' administrative clerk. He notices leave papers in Vickers right hand attached to a clipboard.

Furious, Porch discovered even further in the distance a poised spiritual team standing behind a gun emplacement bunker.

A cocky Buchanan, with his foot confidently placed on an empty ammunition box, spit tobacco juice his way. Jackson, smirking, stood with his hands on his hips in disgust.

Porch glanced to his left, over Buchanan's right shoulder. In the distance stood Lucas peering out his window, holding on to one of his cats, Hans, hissing toward Porch.

Lucas, looking down onto the landing field, waited for Porch to sign the leave papers.

Vickers and McMillan finally arrived at the helicopter. He shouts over the helicopter noise. "I got something here for you to sign, sir."

McMillan, staring cold and hard into Porch's eyes, is completely ignored out of sheer anger and embarrassment from the major.

"No! No way! And I mean no! He will not go over my head, and that's that!" yelled Porch.

"Who, sir?" asked Vickers.

"Him!" Porch swung his arm out over toward Buchanan, pointing his index finger right at him. "I'll go over his head, and he knows I can."

"Well, sir! The chaplain can and he went over your head. You see *him*?" Vickers swung around and pointed his index finger up to Lucas.

"Yeah. So what?" answered Porch defiantly.

"Well, sir. It's, well - it's like this. The Skipper said if you go over *his* head, you would look like, and let me make myself perfectly clear, sir, and I quote him, *sir*, 'look like a bona fide 100%, grade-A jackass.'" Vickers contemplated his next words and spoke clearly, pointing his finger back up towards the Skipper. "He said anyone with just an ounce of compassion would permit this battle hardened marine to go home. He's served three years here and his mother could die any day. You'd look foolish, like an *ass* if you were an obstacle to it. So here, sir."

Vickers shoved the clip board towards Porch for him to sign his John Hancock. "Can you please sign on the dotted line, sir? You know where to sign, sir." Vickers smirks.

Knowing Buchanan exercised his liberty as chaplain to break the chain of command and go over his head, Porch swiftly grabbed the clipboard from Vickers and signed the leave papers. Porch glanced toward McMillan, boarding the helicopter with his gear. The mutual disdain the sturdy, stout marine and Porch had for one another stood for decades.

Porch, Vickers, and the visiting officers stepped safely away as the helicopter lifted and flew away.

Looking back towards Lucas' office window, Porch discovered Lucas stepped out of sight. Glaring at the spiritual team with repugnance, Porch suffered a defeat, a giant blow delivered by Buchanan. He loathed Buchanan even more, marching himself to his hootch, seething with anger. His pompous officer friends consoled him.

Buchanan did his duty. Rarely did he use his autonomy as chaplain to break the chain of command. But when appropriate, he would take the liberty to go the commanding officer concerning a problem. Regardless, his confidence knowing he had made the correct decision spoke loud and clear in his heart. Yes, he broke the chain of command, but knew the necessity of McMillan going home.

Porch nearly won in his dream. He came an inch closer to crossing the goal line in real life. But Buchanan knew right remained on his side, while Porch stood as an obstacle of what towered as right and just.

With God's help, he persisted in doing His work.

Christmas Eve

December 24, 1968

Christmas Eve. One of the most anticipated days of the Christian calendar. All over the world, Christians will celebrate the birth of Jesus with anticipation. A celebration of Hope, Peace, and Good Tidings to all through Jesus Christ.

In a war zone, hope and peace is a universe or two away from planet earth.

Christmas 1968 in Camp Love celebrated Christmas Eve with children from An Ngai Dong school and orphanage. If any children deserved a fun Christmas, Chaplain Kensington's kids certainly did. Buchanan will forever remember the day with fondness. The precious children lived as victims of the war. Eyewitnesses of their parents tortured and executed by the Viet Cong. The children will grow up into adulthood with memories of war. The children on this day will live a memory of celebrating Christmas Eve with marines. Men who visit the orphanage from time to time under the leadership of Buchanan.

Jackson, along with Adkins, Skawinski, Jones, Rockford, Kowslowski, marines representing all four companies, and even Dobbs ate dinner with the children in the chow hall. The dinner supplemented the Father-A-Day Program, which a marine selects a child to mentor, crafting a father figure relationship with the child.

The scheduled dinner came slotted at 1700 hours with the children arriving at 1630 hours. The spiritual team greeted the children at the gate.

The scheduled dinner, led by Buchanan and Kensington, provided the children a bit of semblance of the Christmas season. After dinner, the camp distributed presents to the children from Santa, a role played by Burns, and his Elves, played by chaplains and marines. The marines playing the role of elves accompanied the spiritual team periodically to the school as part of the CAP. Many of the marines grew to love the children. The torture Communists would inflict upon the children if the United States failed to maintain a presence in Vietnam pushed the marines to defeat the Viet Cong ten fold.

The dinner surpassed expectations as children ate to their heart's content. The dinner comprised beef, vegetables, a salad, fruit, and desserts of cookies and various cakes. Christmas Joy filled the chow hall.

The marines presented Christ's love by simply spending time with the children, granting them a deserved amount of attention. They shared laughs and jokes forever remembered. Besides, the marines were proud fathers of their own children back home. Some men functioned as mentors to younger siblings growing up. The marines shared a common trait as fathers, brothers, and uncles. Fulfilling their role this day, the men provided Christmas joy to the children.

Buchanan after dinner made his rounds within the crowd as usual, making conversation with marine and child alike. The marines bestowed many complements to the children, throwing a joke or two at the marines. Expressing to each child how beautiful each and everyone of them were in God's sight, he made it loud and clear to the children God loves them. Besides, God created them. He preached human beings have a destiny and a purpose in life, including the An Ngai Dong children.

Following dinner, Santa Claus will enter at 1800 hours, followed by the presentation of gifts to the children.

Time finally came sitting at 1800 hours sharp. Buchanan announced, "OK, everybody. Time now for what everyone has anticipated for – Santa Claus!"

A loud "Hurrah!" from the chow hall echoed throughout the camp.

Burns waited patiently outside the front door of the chow hall. Dressed as Santa, he carried over his shoulder duffle bags loaded with wrapped toys for the children. Chaplains Brennan, Kingslerly, Marino, and Wynn all played elf roles, along with enlisted marines, aiding in the distribution of the gifts.

Burns, stepping into the chow hall, roared a joyful and confident, "HO! HO! HO! Merry Christmas! HO! HO! HO! Merry Christmas!"

Again, a bellowing "Hurrah!" from the chow hall echoed throughout the camp.

Following dinner, the marines lined along the wall of the chow hall sitting with their Father-A-Day Program child.

Starting on his right, Burns dispatched gifts to the children. At his disposal came two gigantic bags full of gifts, a jam-packed blue bag of gifts for boys and a pink bag bursting at the seams full of gifts for girls. Gifts of stuffed animals, trucks, marbles, Lincoln logs, coloring books of all sorts with crayons, with a various array of other male toys filled the blue bag. Doll babies, Barbie dolls, play tea sets, coloring books of all sorts with crayons, and other gifts for girls from the pink bag distributed by Burns to the girls. Burns found playing Santa a blast.

Greeting the children individually and a quarter of the way around the chow hall, Burns acknowledged a specific child. "Well, little girl. What's your name?"

The little girl smiled from ear to ear, sitting on Private First Class Pokorny's lap.

"This is Kieu." said PFC Pokorny.

Kieu, an orphan, lost her whole family at the hands of the Viet Cong. She suffers from the memories of that fateful day every day of her life. At least this night will be a joyful, permanent memory stored in her memory bank. This day will be an encouraging mental image of human beings coming together, showing love to fellow believers in Christ.

"Oh, Kieu is your name. It's beautiful. Do you know what your name means? It means 'to be pretty.'" Burns, who knew a little Vietnamese, brought a smile to Kieu's face, saying, "Bạn thật xinh đẹp."

Burns complimented her beauty in Vietnamese.

Kieu blushed.

"She sure is pretty. Just like my young daughter back home in California." Pokorny loved Kieu. She reminded him of his own flesh and blood.

Buchanan expected marines from Bravo and Charlie Companies to take up a friendship with children at the orphanage. Pokorny favored Kieu from the start. She displayed a most pleasant, beautiful smile, precious in God's sight. Pokorny yearned for his own young daughter. He intentionally singled out a young girl to become friends with.

As Kieu opened her gift, Burns continued to distribute gifts as he made his way around the room. The most joyful smile, glowing with the joy of Christmas, emerged from a young girl from receiving a pink elephant. Her face glowed, filling filled the room with the Spirit of Christmas.

Skawinski and Da o, a young child whose parents the Viet Cong killed during the Tet Offensive in the city of Hue, unwrapped her gift with a roaring voice. "Một con búp bê!" which in English means, 'a doll.'

Corporal Kowslowski, a devout Roman Catholic, became exceedingly dedicated to the CAP at Kensington's Catholic orphanage sat with Tuan, his young friend. Tuan, older than most of the children from the orphanage, stood beside the corporal with a bit of trepidation. Still distrustful of Americans, his trust for marines come about over time.

"Well, who do we have here, Corporal Kowslowski?" asked Burns.

"This here's Tuan, Major. I mean Santa." Kowslowski laughs for his slip of the tongue.

Laughter roared from Kowslowski's Freudian Slip.

"HO! HO! HO! Merry Christmas Tuan." Burns, leaning down toward Tuan, informed the young child. "I came tonight all the way from the North Pole for a gift for you as well."

Handing the gift to Tuan, who graciously, but with a bit of suspicion, accepted the gift from Burns' hands.

Burns and Tuan mutually smiled with a gleam of satisfaction as the major continued to make his way around the chow hall.

He delivered gifts to Lipstone and Bi'nh, Remington and Die^p, Kiehl and Lanh, Petty Officer Dingus and An, Jurgensen and Hie^'n, Rodriquez and Hanh, and Sigmanson and Duc. The remaining marines with their Father-A-Day child in the chow hall received a gift to open with all the joy and fun that comes with Christmas gifts.

Burns came to the tail end of the children and their American friends when he faced Buchanan and Thuy. He hollered out another "HO! HO! HO! Merry Christmas!"

Burns squatted down to speak to Thuy. "I know you already? Don't I, little girl? Giáng sinh vui vẻ!" meaning Merry Christmas in Vietnamese.

Reaching into his pink bag for a gift, Burns pulled out a present wrapped in Mrs. Clause paper. Thuy pointed to the paper and exclaimed, "vợ ông già Noel của!" meaning 'Santa Claus's wife.'

Thuy laughed as she opened her gift. Raising up the gift to Buchanan, she motioned for a lending hand to open the package. Buchanan assisted Thuy, discovering inside the package a Vietnamese doll!

Buchanan sat Thuy on his lap, as she admired and mothered the doll. The gift provided a means of normalcy for her.

Thuy, the last child for Burns to visit in the room as Santa Claus, sensed his role called for an exit.

"HO! HO! HO! Merry Christmas!" bellowed Burns. "I have to be on my way now, children. I have presents to deliver. Tomorrow's Christmas. God Bless you and may Peace come, allowing you to be children as God intended you to be. HO! HO! HO! Merry Christmas!"

Burns exits from the chow hall with a boisterous roar from all the children and the marines. "Yay!"

The children failed to comprehend half of what came forth from Burns' mouth. His words mattered least. What mattered most to the children came with the presence of Santa Claus. What Santa Claus says in any language is enough for any child in this world. Santa represents the good of all people. And the children desired peace and good tidings in their own lives.

The children who survived the rest of the war remembered this day for the rest of their lives. They will remember the day as a day of peace. A day of affection lasting forever.

The Christmas dinner ranked as a grand success.

Kensington thanked Buchanan, along with the other chaplains visiting from 1st Division, and Lieutenant Colonel Lucas for the dinner. Most thankful for Kensington comprised the gifts and the party following supper. The innocent children longed for love in their lives. Gathering up the children, Kensington departed back for the orphanage with the nuns and priests who accompanied the children.

Camp Love personnel cleaned up the chow hall for breakfast the next morning.

Jackson accompanied Buchanan to his hootch to prepare for the next day, Christmas Day. A day spent in Da Nang for a special Christmas service. A gathering scheduled with internationally known Reverend Billy Graham, the greatest evangelist in modern times.

A Day of Peace

December 25, 1968

This Christmas day will be like no other for the marines and sailors in Camp Love.

Buchanan and his friends were absent from their families, away from their hometowns. The men in Camp Love were absent from home, opening up gifts around the decorated tree on Christmas morning with loved ones. They were absent from home, celebrating the birth of Christ at the dining room table to eat Christmas dinner. Nevertheless, the men were going to celebrate the birth of Jesus.

Buchanan and his friends were amid a war unlike any other the United States had committed to. A war all in the entourage to hear Billy Graham preach looked forward to end, and soon.

Buchanan, Jackson, Adkins, Skawinski, members of Bravo and Charlie Companies, segments of Alpha and Delta Companies, Lucas, and Burns arrived in Da Nang in trucks and jeeps to attend the Reverend Billy Graham service.

The convoy of vehicles secure with an escort of three jeeps full of guards at the point of the entourage, followed behind with Lucas in a jeep. Buchanan and other officers followed in jeeps behind Lucas, with several trucks of enlisted committed to attend the Billy Graham service. The men promised to attend the service and hear the delivery of Graham's sermon. Scuttlebutt spread quickly in camp that Jurgensen strongly armed the most reluctant to attend, who made a last second effort to back out the last minute.

Humored with the notion Jurgensen probably came close to ordering some of the most reluctant to attend, the spiritual team didn't care. The troops will hear the Gospel on Christmas day by the most energetic evangelist in the modern era.

The caravan of vehicles from Camp Love entered through the main gate at Da Nang Air Base at 1100 hours. Ecstatic with the high representation from camp, the spiritual team remained humored. Jurgensen pressured the second guessers, who at the last minute did not want to attend. He insisted the men keep their promises. The Gunny insisted they show some integrity. The team proceeded into the base as if spiritual conquerors returning triumphantly from defeating evil in the world.

Buchanan considered the trip progress by presenting the joyful existence of life as a believer in Jesus. Many who will hear the Gospel today are searching for answers to questions in life. The message of Graham, sharing peace and compassion with a suffering and violent world, will deliver a message in the right place at the right time. War is a beat down, a depressant. War hammers away devastating blows day after day onto the mental sanity of marines and sailors. Billy Graham was the perfect shot in the arm to push back on the stupor and lethargy of war.

The convoy traveled to the drop off point for troops attending the service. The 58 marines attended an enlisted Christmas party and dinner in a supply warehouse. Two separate dinners occurred simultaneously for staff and line officers, while a second dinner came reserved for Navy chaplains. The chaplains luncheon slotted several special attendees, including Billy Graham, Rear Admiral Lower Half John White, Chief of Chaplains of the Navy, and General John Sands, Commanding Officer of 1st Marine Division.

The scheduled service was in the evening.

The spiritual team parked near the transport trucks. As the team stepped out of the jeep, Buchanan insisted Jackson accompany him to the chaplains luncheon, a representation of many denominations. Buchanan practically had to talk Jackson into attending the luncheon. He felt he would stick out too much like a sore thumb with all the brass.

Many denominations attended the luncheon. Presbyterians. Methodist. Lutherans. Roman Catholics. Baptists. Episcopalians. Greek Orthodox. The multifaceted group even included a substantial number of Jewish chaplains. The luncheon reflected thoroughly the Navy's chaplains motto in Vietnam, "Cooperation Without Compromise."

While walking to the hangar holding the Christmas luncheon with Billy Graham, Buchanan bumped into his chaplain friend, Lieutenant Commander Dwight Maher, between the drop off point and the hanger.

"Well, Chaplain Maher. Good to see you!" greeted Buchanan. "You remember Sergeant Jackson?"

"Why yes. Yes. Good to see you, Sergeant." Maher extending his hand for a handshake, greeting the spiritual team.

"Yes, sir. A day of peace and celebration, sir. Hearing the great Billy Graham will be a well-deserved break for all of us." commented Jackson.

"I agree. I agree, sergeant." added an excited Maher.

Turning to Chaplain Buchanan, Maher confirmed, "He will certainly preach The Gospel today, you can count on it. To many a marine and sailor who needs to hear it."

"Amen!" acknowledged Buchanan.

The three stepped toward the hanger for the luncheon, discussing the pleasant day. The men agreed Billy Graham's visit will plant a seed in many of the men and women attending the service.

Once Maher walked out of eyeshot of the spiritual team, the team smiled, motioning with their hands Maher's two six shooters, which were missing on this Christmas Day. The pair felt moved to let loose the most boisterous of laughter when laying their eyes on Maher. He humored the team. The two men possessed the greatest of discipline, holding in their emotions. The emptiness of the six shooters holstered around his waist cleared the team's mental picture of Maher as a frontier circuit preacher.

The men shortly arrived to the hangar as Chaplain Maher's chaplain assistant stood patiently waiting for him to enter the hangar for the luncheon.

The high attendance for the luncheon included Lieutenant Junior Grade Brian Kensington, Lieutenant Charles Brennan, Lieutenant Daniel Fontaine Anderson, Lieutenant William Tecumseh Taylor, Ensign John Campbell, Lieutenant Leon Kingslerly, Lieutenant Scott Lumberton, Lieutenant Commander Jacob Marino, and Lieutenant Melvin Abrams. As a Navy Jewish chaplain, Abrams preserved the Navy motto "Cooperation without Compromise", supporting his chaplain friends by attending the Graham service. Besides, Billy Graham showed the utmost supportive of Jewish efforts all over the world. Abrams returned the reciprocal support to Graham.

The Protestant chaplains attending the luncheon fell into a metaphysical bliss of joy. The aura within the hangar felt a heavy presence of God. The chaplains felt confident the delivery of Billy Graham's sermon will preach and spread the Gospel to the troops.

Though the Spirit felt strong amongst the chaplains, the spiritual team received the most glossy of stares entering the hangar. Buchanan and other chaplains accompanied by their assistants spoke volumes from staunch and stiff-necked chaplain officers expressing their discontent with enlisted personnel attending a chaplain's luncheon with Billy Graham.

Buchanan thought to himself, 'Get a grip. Lighten up.' Besides, Jackson played a significant role with the 'ministry team.' He served as a spiritual mentor to the marines alongside Buchanan. He just rolled his eyes at the hard-nosed chaplains.

Besides, no memorandum ran across Buchanan's desk informing chaplains the luncheon was officer only. Buchanan held high chaplain assistants serving side by side with a Navy chaplain. Many chaplains present lacked combat experience in the bush. None experienced firsthand how vital the chaplain assistant served in combat situations.

The luncheon in the hanger presented itself as vast. The 30 round tables seated 8 individuals, each with no assigned seats. The chaplains seated themselves first come, first served. Buchanan and his friends took a claim of a table in the back corner, avoiding turtleneck, stiff-necked type chaplains. He didn't want to rock the boat too rough in the presence of high-ranking officers.

The extensive and extravagant menu listed many favorites amongst the religious leaders. The entrée, along with the entire meal, unveiled a considerable upgrade from the C rations in the field. And what a meal to enjoy. Steak, seafood including lobster, potatoes, green beans, squash casserole, salad, rolls, and several desserts including pumpkin pie, red cake, and carrot cake – three of Buchanan's favorites.

Buchanan took a panoramic view of the flavorsome and scrumptious meal before him. He enjoyed his pleasurable food in this rare moment of peace in the middle of a war in Vietnam.

The luncheon came about buffet style as Navy cooks served both sides of the tables to speed up the process.

Chaplains filled their stomachs close to popping. Many officers and enlisted alike stepped up to the buffet for seconds, even thirds.

Leaning over to Chaplain Buchanan, Jackson softly says, "Look at 'em, sir. Chaplains partaking of seconds and thirds. I bet they're bush chaplains soon to return to C rations."

Smiling, Buchanan nods.

After the meal, Billy Graham and Rear Admiral Lower Half John White spoke to the chaplains. Admiral White spoke first with words of encouragement and rejuvenation. Words to uplift the morale of those sent forth to minister to marines and sailors in the field.

"Men. Chaplains. Reverend Billy Graham, General John Sands. Thank you for inviting me today. As Chief of Chaplains to the Navy, and chaplains serving here in Vietnam, I want to say I have heard nothing but exemplary reports of the outstanding performance you've carried out here in Vietnam. The spiritual and emotional wellbeing of the troops has been top-notch. Why? It is because of the performance you have carried out in the field. Thank you and I know, without a shadow of doubt, families back home of men and women you have ministered to here in Vietnam appreciate the efforts to protect their religious freedom and to meet spiritual and *all* needs of the troops."

As White continued to speak, he interrupted himself and said,

"And let me mention the chaplain assistants, both Marine Corps and Navy. These men have shown nothing but an impeccable performance. You've carried yourselves well. I haven't read better reports that's crossed my desk concerning enlisted personnel ever in my career. I see some assistants are present today. Thank you for your service men. You're doing a phenomenal job!"

The nods of affirmation, including Jackson, thrown toward Admiral White was genuine. White clapped his hands, spurring chaplains to show their appreciation for the assistants. Embarrassed, Jackson and the other assistants simply sat in their seats, waiting patiently for the attention to be turned back onto the chaplains and their work.

The smug chaplains shifted in their chairs, looking in every direction out of embarrassment.

Jackson leans toward Buchanan. "Wish they would stop clapping, just doing our jobs."

Buchanan smiles. "You've been my guardian for four months. You've been an inspiration to the men just as much as I have, if not more. I owe a lot to ya, Philip. I *really* do."

Jackson stares at the podium, smiling.

"Maybe we can have a joint luncheon next time." White laughs at his own jest, as enlisted chuckled at the notion.

Buchanan says a soft, "Amen!"

White finished up thanking everyone, encouraging the religious military personnel to continue the mission of the chaplain corps, and turned his attention toward Billy Graham.

After introducing Graham to the religious leaders, Graham confidently rose out of his chair next to White's. Stepping up to the podium with purpose, he spoke to the chaplains. Short in addressing the audience, Graham desired to make one point perfectly clear – God's omnipresence is in every camp, in every base, and with every patrol stepping into the jungle. God will never leave them.

After his acknowledgments and thanking the chaplains, he addressed the men.

"Chaplains, I know you're called to secure freedom of religion for the troops and to minister to the spiritual, emotional, physical, and the mental stamina of troops here in Vietnam. Your role of the mission to secure peace in southeast Asia and bring a peaceful end to the war is vital and will not be forgotten. You, as an individual, have a place in this world and are important to God. Your service is important to Him. You're ministering to those in need to experience the Gospel. Scriptures remind us never to be afraid of stepping out into the midst of dangers only few know and have experienced in a lifetime."

He quoted two passages of scripture. The first came from the book of Joshua.

Joshua 1:9 "Have I not commanded you? Be strong and courageous. Do not be afraid; do not be discouraged, for the Lord your God will be with you wherever you go."

and

Psalms 56:3-4 "When I am afraid, I put my trust in you. In God, whose word I praise — in God I trust and am not afraid. What can mere mortals do to me?"

Graham praised the religious leaders. "I lift you up and pray for God's armor to be bestowed upon you as you carry out God's calling in your life."

Graham quoted an additional piece of Scripture, Ephesians 6:10-18 "Finally, be strong in the Lord and in his mighty power. Put on the full armor of God, so that you can take your stand against the devil's schemes. For our struggle is not against flesh and blood, but against the rulers, against the authorities, against the powers of this dark world and against the spiritual forces of evil in the heavenly realms. Therefore, put on the full armor of God, so that when the day of evil comes, you may be able to stand your ground, and after you have done everything, to stand. Stand firm then, with the belt of truth buckled around your waist, with the breastplate of righteousness in place, and with your feet fitted with the readiness that comes from the gospel of peace. Besides all this, take up the shield of faith, with which you can extinguish all the flaming arrows of the evil one. Take the helmet of salvation and the sword of the Spirit, which is the word of God. And pray in the Spirit on all occasions with all kinds of prayers and requests. With this in mind, be alert and always keep on praying for all the Lord's people."

The chaplains clapped in appreciation of Graham's words. An uplift for Buchanan he so desperately longed for after the war experiences of the past few weeks.

Graham again quoted Scripture as a motivator, reciting Matthew 28:19-20, the Great Commission, sending the chaplains, mostly Protestant, out to fulfill the mission of the Chaplain Corps. Thanking all who were present, he ended by praying for the chaplains and their ministries.

Four hours later, Buchanan received a second dose of inspiration from Graham at the service. Listening to the Gospel preached to Navy and marine corps personnel thrilled Buchanan's soul. If Jesus can change his down trodden life into one for good, He can change anybody's life, including the marines and sailors attending the Graham service today. A few thousand adhered Protestants attended, though Catholic and Jewish personnel were also present. Peppered throughout the thousands were Army and Air Force personnel, though the majority came from Navy and Marine Corps branches.

The sermon hit dead center of the bullseye. An evangelistic message delivered from Graham with subliminal messages throughout inspiring the marines that God's presence was real in their lives and present in the effort to bring democracy and freedom to the people of South Vietnam.

With the conclusion of the service, the men departed for their respective duty stations all over the I Corps sector.

Buchanan wanted a, what Baptist would call an invitation, offered at the end of the service. He felt the venue seemed ripe, especially if a marine appeared ready to commit a life for Jesus. But evangelical chaplains feared an evangelistic invitation invited criticism from adverse elements of an attempt to proselytize marines of other faiths and denominations at the service. Evangelistic chaplains, including

Buchanan, longed to avoid trouble at all costs with the chain of command and asses like Porch.

Though evangelicals wanted an invitation, one accomplishment for them this Christmas day came with the many seeds planted within the hearts and souls of many marines and sailors. A seed of Jesus knocking on each heart's door for him to enter and change their lives for good. For those who needed to hear the Gospel on Christmas day, Graham delivered on December 25, 1968.

For Buchanan, that alone deserved a hearty "Amen!"

God Protecting the Unprotected

December 28, 1968

Buchanan received the best Christmas gift of the season: news of retribution for An Ngai Tay.

Waking up on Saturday morning, Buchanan discovered a hot and muggy day. Nothing but a cruel, seething heat from the sun beating down on the camp. The good news of An Ngai Tay balanced out the physical beat down from the weather.

At 0515 hours in the morning on a sweltering, humid day, Jackson rushed up to Buchanan's hootch, entered without knocking. With no cordial greetings, he abruptly asked, "Chaplain. Guess what?"

Taken aback sitting in his chair, Buchanan responded, "What?" Jackson interrupts quickly, "The five young men suspected being VC the day of the murders at An Ngai Tay were questioned, and guess what?"

Buchanan cocks his head, asking with his hands pushed forward in front of Jackson, 'What?'

"All five men - Viet Cong insurgents." answered Jackson. "Can you imagine, chaplain? Five of their very own members of the hamlet aided and abetted the Viet Cong in murdering their own chief and family."

The astonishment and disgust of betraying family and friends to the Communists overwhelmed the insides of Buchanan.

"I talked to Rockford in the middle of the night, sir. He stressed that the Viet Cong scared the citizens of An Ngai Tay to death and the murders hurt them. The VC deflated them. Almost to the point of giving up."

"Did Rockford mention a visit to the hamlet might help?" asked Buchanan.

"Well, sir, he mentioned a presence of Catholic priests would at least boast spiritual well being."

"Well then, we'll get on the horn today, contact Chaplain Marino, and see what he can do."

"Yeah. That'll help matters, sir."

Jackson sighs heavily. "There's the news of the suspects. Rockford filled me in the marines tracked down the murderers and killed them for the atrocities committed - some 14 of them in all. The murderers fought to the death, refusing to be taken prisoner. Bravo and Charlie Companies pursued, attacked, and captured or killed 79 Viet Cong in or around the vicinity of An Ngai Tay."

Buchanan shook his head excitedly with the combat success.

Jackson added, "Four Viet Cong tunnels were located and destroyed by United States marine combat engineers, including our very own Skawinski. Quite a few casualties for the enemy, don't you think?"

Buchanan agreed. "*Yeah*. But, Sergeant, don't you ask questions about what we have experienced? How can a human being commit such obscene, cruel, and evil crimes on another human being?"

Sitting in front of the desk, Jackson paused. "Yes, chaplain - frequently. It's pure evil. Just pure evil."

Buchanan grimaces. "After seeing Bi'hn, the children and the rest. You're right, Sergeant - pure evil."

Sitting in silence, the men prayed for peace in South Vietnam. A knock on the door broke the silence.

A visitor! At this hour? At 0530 hours in the morning?

"Yes?" asked Buchanan.

"It's me, chaplain."

Smiling, Jackson whispered to Buchanan, "That could be anybody."

Pausing, Jackson says, "Just as long as it's not Porch."

"Come in." Buchanan grins.

As the marine steps into the hootch, the spiritual team's jaws hit the floor. Stepping through the door came none other than Gunnery Sergeant John McElrath.

At a loss for words, Jackson asked, "Well, what a surprise. What brings you here, John?"

"Well - I just want-wanted to, uh, take a.....break from paper work. Thought I'd hang out with y'all for a bit." McElrath sighs heavily.

"Good." said Jackson.

Leaning back in their chairs, the spiritual team smile from ear to ear.

"Listen, we're off for some breakfast. Want to come along with us?" asked Buchanan.

McElrath ponders the thought. "OK. I will."

Grasping their covers off the desk, the men briskly make their way to the chow hall to eat a hearty breakfast.

Since October, Buchanan found out early morning breakfasts consumed in Camp Love did nothing but slow the pace while accompanying patrols in the bush. Fortune came to Buchanan this day as there were no Communion services scheduled in the bush. The heat made the bush unbearable, making Communion services a struggle to conduct without distraction.

After breakfast, the spiritual team and friend set out to visit the medical aid station.

McElrath had never stepped foot into medical for any reason. As he put it, the aid station gave him 'the creeps.'

As the men arrive, the spiritual team immediately greets eight wounded marines, inspiring the injured. The men received minor wounds, but needed medical attention.

Following the quick visit, the party entered Doc Delaney's small, miniscule office.

"Good morning, Doc." said Buchanan in his robust Kentuckian accent, shaking Delaney's hand.

Delaney greeting McElrath and Jackson, shaking hands.

"Good morning, sir." answered the enlisted men.

"How's the wounded Doc?" asked Buchanan.

"Physically good. Mentally, a bit shaken, Padre. Really shaken."

"Oh? They came close to getting it worse, did they?"

"Just a foot or two to the left or the right, and many of 'em would be a statistic on the KIA list. Fortunately, none were in the direct fire of the enemy."

Delaney paused. "They're in the ward, Padre."

The party of three tagged along behind Delaney, back into the ward connected to his small office.

Entering the 18 bed recovery room, Buchanan and his friends observed Petty Officer 3rd Class Lawrence Sigmanson, a preacher's kid from Miami, Florida and non-denominational working in the medical aid station. On duty along with Sigmanson worked Senior Chief Petty Officer Carlson Gross, career Navy, and whose parents were career corpsmen. The dedicated pair meticulously joined forces to care for the courageous wounded marines who fell victim from the hands of the devil's legions.

"Good morning Petty Officer Sigmanson. Good morning Senior Chief. Good morning men." said Buchanan, stepping toward the beds to visit the wounded.

While visiting the wounded either in the camp's medical aid station or in the Da Nang hospital's recovery wing, Buchanan set as a top priority to visit every single marine in every single bed. Exceptions came from special requests to visit specific individuals in the hospital for a specific purpose. Today was no different. Eight wounded marines required attention from the enemy attacks the previous night.

"Hello Smith." Buchanan didn't know the young man well resting in the first bed, but he attended communion services and was two months shy of turning 19. The cuts and scratches caused by shrapnel were visible from head to toe all over his body. Delaney considered

Smith lucky the shrapnel failed to cut deep into his flesh, causing deep lacerations.

"You're from Florida, right son?" asked Buchanan.

Smiling, Smith nodded.

"I remember your home state while the Air Force stationed me in Florida long ago enlisted in the Air Force. You and I have commented on your home state's weather. This heat, you mentioned you can't even tolerate this Vietnam heat and you're from Florida." said Buchanan, grinning.

"Yes, sir. That's right." Smith smiles wider.

"Wish the Lord threw us a little of your winter weather, Padre. It would serve as a good reliever from this heat."

"Amen to that. Yes, Smith, it would."

"Thanks for the encouraging words at communion services, Padre. You might not know, sir, but I'm Catholic. I appreciate your uplifting words. Though I've not met too many Protestant ministers in my life. You're OK."

Pointing with his finger toward his heart, Buchanan smiles. "Thank you Smith. Just remember – it's all about what's in here. Jesus wants us to look at how we live inside and out. He wants us to reflect Him in our lives."

Smith nods. "Yes, sir. Difficult in a war zone. Isn't it, sir?"

Buchanan ponders the thought. "No Corporal. It's not. Sometimes, I myself get up in the morning and want to arm myself and fight the VC."

"Yes, sir."

"Do you have a Chaplain Capodanno crucifix cross? It's the cross Chaplain Kensington distributes to the marines?" asked Buchanan.

"Yes, sir. I do." Smith lifts his cross out from under his white t-shirt with his right hand, displaying his cross for all to see.

It thrilled Buchanan, seeing the testimony of Smith. "Amen. Good. Good! Chaplain Kensington's a great Navy chaplain, he wants especially Catholic marines to live the faith while in Vietnam. The cross is a spiritual reminder Jesus is protector of us all."

"Yes, sir." Smith, smiles from ear to ear, uplifted with the spiritual team's visit.

"Corporal, you're in good hands. We've got other visits, so I've got to go. I'll be back later to check in with y'all. Doc Delaney and his corpsmen - top notch in the Navy – so you're in excellent hands. I'll pray for you." Buchanan delivers a prayer.

When finished, Buchanan says, "Good day, Smith."

"Good day, Padre."

As Buchanan turns to the next bed, Smith says, "Sir. Padre?"

"Yes, Corporal?"

"I'll be rooting for Ohio State. I know you're excited about the Rose Bowl."

"Thanks, Smith. I'm excited too. Go Bucks!" said Buchanan, grinning. He turns to the second bed to visit. The spiritual team visited the next marine from Albany, New York. Again, the marine laying wounded appreciated a Navy chaplain.

When finished visiting the New Yorker, the spiritual team, along with McElrath, visited in sequence seven of eight beds. The three visitors converged onto the last wounded marine lying in some pain. They discovered the young marine in a state of melancholy, with fright written all over his face. When laying their eyes on the marine, their jaws hit the floor, with a loss of words to say. No one knew what to do or the ministry approach to take with the marine.

The young man ended up as none other than Private First Class Michael Dobbs.

Buchanan thought - 'Great. How do you visit an atheist?' Baffled how to start a conversation with an unbeliever, the men just smile at Dobbs.

The moment hit Buchanan like a ton of bricks. He had never visited an atheist yet in Vietnam.

McElrath found himself at the foot of the Dobbs' bed, while Jackson stood on the left. Buchanan sat in a small chair he grabbed at the end of the small aid station used by the corpsmen.

The other seven wounded marines smiled from ear to ear, knowing very well how vehement Dobbs presented himself in his denial of the existence of God.

Putting it mildly, McElrath felt nervous and out of place, shifting his feet, inconspicuously glancing left and right. The spiritual team found themselves fidgety, clearing their throats to signal the other to start a conversation.

The short list of moments in Buchanan's life when he found himself at a loss for words were few. Buchanan added Dobbs to the list.

None forced a launch of conversation.

Dobbs bailed them out, breaking the ice. He admitted, "Boy, was I scared last night. *Reeeeally* scared."

There came nothing but double takes from the spiritual team toward Dobbs.

"I thought life was all over, man. I mean - sir."

The visiting party smile.

"I thought I'd never see my uncle again who raised me."

"What happened?" asked Jackson, with curiosity in his voice.

With a bit of trepidation in his voice, Dobbs explained, "Well, we're on patrol. Pokorny's the point, and Corporal Kowslowski took the slack position. Pokorny signaled the Lieutenant something stunk high Heaven."

Dobbs paused. "Sergeant, you've been there. You know, that gut feeling there's something in the air."

Jackson and McElrath nod their heads.

"Well, to make a long story short, Lieutenant Rockford slowly, in a crotched position, stepped up to Pokorny, briefed Rockford on the situation. I-I was maybe sixth or seventh back from the point, and just as Rockford was about to turn toward us - I figure to signal to us – all Hell broke loose. We're caught in an L shaped ambush. We - We straddled right into it."

McElrath and Jackson sighed, exhaled out of disgust. Marines never aspired to be caught in an L shaped ambush, a frightening situation no patrol wished to fight out of.

"The enemy took us all by surprise." Dobbs continued his account of the firefight with as much energy as he could muster. "Enemy fire came in from all sides. AK-47's, grenades, you name it. It seemed the enemy threw everything at us. We attempted to fire back as best we could. As I hit the ground as fast as I could, I returned fire in the direction of the muzzle blasts. Pokorny and Rockford are fortunate men. They-They came out unscathed, but the two - maybe three marines behind them, well - they were torn apart, killed."

Dobbs paused. He thought of the men who 'bought it' in front of him. "The enemy's marksmanship sucks."

The visitors smile with Dobbs' contempt of the enemy.

"They're clumsy marksmen or God Almighty was, well - with Pokorny and Rockford."

Dobbs noticed with humor in his heart the apparent eyebrows raised on all three visitors. Dobbs credited God for nothing in this life. To hear Dobbs lift God up and recognize His Omnipresence in life pleased Buchanan to no end. In his estimation, the ambush has really shaken Dobbs.

"What'd you do next?" asked Buchanan.

"Well, sir. I don't know. I sure felt the pain all over. It seemed I just fired my weapon toward the enemy. Over time, the VC ended up killed or ran off. After Charlie hightailed it out of there, I discovered I was pretty scratched up from head to toe by the explosions near me. My body found the receiving end of nicks and scratches all over." Dobbs laid shaken.

"Was it NVA or just VC?" asked McElrath.

"Just VC we figured. Accounts for the poor marksmanship. Though some VC can be pretty accurate with weaponry."

With a pause, Dobbs asked, "You know something, chaplain?"

"What? What Private Dobbs?"

"I did something I've never done before, sir. You want to know what I did?"

Contemplating the thought, Buchanan asked, "What'd you do, son?" Though he had a notion of Dobbs' secret.

"I asked God to save me, guide me out of the firefight without getting killed. I asked God to protect me."

With emotion written all over his face, he longed for answers to tons of questions. Dobbs asked, "Chaplain? You have one of those crosses you pass out? You know, one of those crosses to remind everyone you're protected by God?"

"Why yes, Dobbs. I have plenty of 'em." Buchanan reached into his side dungaree pants pocket, pulling out a cross for Dobbs. "Here you go, PFC Dobbs. This cross represents the power and presence of God as you carry out your duties and service."

"Thanks Chaplain."

Buchanan encouraged Dobbs. "Listen, I've got to go. You can be rest assured we'll all be praying for you. Prayers for a quick recovery. Then, in the future, prayers for your safety as you patrol in the bush from here on out."

Jackson turns toward McElrath with a bit of wit on his face, raising one side of his mouth, grinned. Knowing McElrath claimed not to be religious, Jackson ate up every minute, watching McElrath turning slowly to a life living for Jesus.

"Is Sergeant McElrath going to pray for me too, sir?" asked Dobbs.

"Yep. Sure is. I'll see to it." Jackson abruptly assured Dobbs, leaning leisurely toward McElrath with the most smug grin.

"Yes. *Yes*, Dobbs. Even Sergeant McElrath will pray for ya." added Buchanan.

Dobbs nods in the affirmative.

"You need anything else, Corporal, you know I have an open door policy. Remember, it's all about what's in here." Buchanan points towards his heart.

"Yes, sir." replied Dobbs.

"Have a good day, Corporal. Have a good day, men." Buchanan encouraged the wounded as the spiritual team set to depart the aid station.

"Good day, Padre." responded the men.

"Good day men." said Jackson and McElrath.

Conversation on the way back to Buchanan's hootch lasted as one for the ages.

"Are you gents crazy? Telling the wounded back there I'll be praying for'em. Those men know me, they're all laughing their heads off back there, saying right now lying in their beds, "Please! McElrath praying for us? That's like asking the Devil's Nymphs to pray for us."

Grinning, the spiritual team softly chuckles.

"What are you talking about, John?" Jackson plays dumb regarding God's hand in using his friend to encourage the marines.

"Me praying?" McElrath scoffs.

"Well, regardless. The Lord definitely used you today." Grinning, Buchanan knew the Lord had used him this day.

An embarrassed McElrath, looking away, expressed a timorous countenance at the thought.

"Let's get back to the hootch and relax." said Buchanan. The spiritual team smile thinking of McElrath's new role in the camp – 'spiritual mentor to the wounded.'

Buchanan seemed pleased. McElrath witnessed how God works good out of something evil. Besides, McElrath's jocular and witty personality creates a warm and comfortable setting wherever he goes.

Arriving back at the hootch, the men yearned to relax amid a hot, sunny Saturday in southeastern Asia.

Lady Luck accompanied Dobbs into the bush. The Luck of the Irish, so to speak, tagged along with Rockford, Pokorny, and Kowslowski.

Death stared Dobbs down square in the eyes. Unawares to the young man, the unbeliever, the Protector shielded the unprotected.

A Little Closer To Home

December 28, 1968

The time struck 1000 hours sharp.

Nothing felt more desired for the men but to relax. Arriving at Buchanan's hootch, the men situated themselves in a seat, sighing heavily. The men knew enemy firefights will heighten next week all over South Vietnam.

Sitting on his cot, Buchanan caught the peace and calm of the day without interruption. Taking a glance toward Jackson and McElrath sitting on his small couch, admired the two leaders. He considered himself fortunate to have such reliable marines surrounding him during his tour. The pair of enlisted were mentors to the troops.

The entire month of December is the Christmas season. Burns felt determined to play seasonal music up to the very last day of the month.

Over time, Buchanan came to favor Vivaldi's works through the influence of Burns. His music spoke volumes of an extraordinary musician as Buchanan became more familiar with classical composers. Vivaldi turned out to be one of Buchanan's favorites.

Burns' selection last night? Vivaldi's Winter, along with three other Christmas selections. Burns considered the Winter movement a monumental piece of classical music. Besides, the piece moved Burns emotionally.

Last night added to the evenings, five for the month, Burns elected to play Vivaldi's Winter to end the day with music.

'Really? Again?' thought Buchanan.

Buchanan figured five nights of Vivaldi's Winter equaled five nights of preparing meatloaf, five evenings in a row for supper.

Yet, still a newcomer to classical music, Buchanan gained an ear for the genre. He quickly appreciated the quality of pieces of music and learned rapidly to decipher composers who were predominant and foremost in the world of classical music.

Regardless of the number of nights played, Buchanan discovered the Winter movement awe-inspiring and enlightening as he laid back onto his cot last night, listening and enjoying Vivaldi's Winter for the fifth time in the month. The longer he listened, the stronger of a sensation within his heart grew with the beauty of Vivaldi's Winter just as much as it did for Burns.

Yet still, Buchanan yearned for a bit of variety for the night.

As Buchanan and his enlisted friends sat soaking in all the harmony and stillness, Buchanan broke the silence. "Why don't we listen to some music? How about something different?"

"Like, *what* chaplain?" McElrath thought Buchanan's idea of something different came with a genre such as 'the Greatest Hymns' album of George Beverly Shea. A strike of fear shot down the center of McElrath's back, knowing positively Buchanan sought to push him to be a 'believer' tonight. And who else better as a topper for the day than George Beverly Shea, serving as the last contributing factor to convert him? If so, the excuse to depart for his hootch would be a sudden stomach ache or some other lame excuse.

Jackson suggested, "Pick something good, Padre. Something with some pep. You know, some beat to it. Something moving and grooving." Jackson felt excited in listening to some music. "Let's listen to a new album Burns sent over to ya. You know, something - as you always say - 'you can dance to.'" expressed Jackson, with a bit of energy in his voice.

"Well, see here McElrath." Buchanan motioned with his hand. "Burns sent this phonograph record player over to me to play the classical albums he gave me to introduce to me such composers as 'Vivaldi and his Four Seasons', a 'Greatest Symphonies' album, and 'Beethoven's Nine Symphonies.'"

Grinning, McElrath swallowed hard. "Uh...that's nice, sir."

"*But* I got some new albums in just the last few days. Let's listen to one of them." said Buchanan.

'Oh no!' thought McElrath. 'Here it comes. George Beverly Shea's greatest hymns album.'

Buchanan, reaching into a vinyl record storage case filled with many record albums attained from 'The Scrounger,' Captain Case, withdraws two albums.

"Heeeere we go." said Buchanan.

McElrath tightens up, readies himself for the inevitable.

"How about these famous country singers greatest hits or Sam Gorton and His Famous Horn Players?" said Buchanan.

Smiling, McElrath sighs heavily in relief.

Buchanan comments, "Sounds great to me. How 'bout the two of you?"

"I know Sergeant McElrath is pleased." Jackson smiles, knowing a pleased McElrath did not have to listen to George Beverly Shea.

Glancing toward Jackson, McElrath grins, knowing full well Jackson is aware he had no desire listening to a Christian hymn album, though Buchanan possessed a few in his record collection.

Clueless and unaware of McElrath's apprehensions, Buchanan set himself to listening to music setting a room full of normalcy. But Jackson sensed McElrath's apprehension, thinking Buchanan set for himself a goal today to convert him as a believer.

Jesus changed Buchanan's life to live a Christ like. The thrill in his soul burst with joy the minute a person, void of Christ, receives Jesus as the change agent to live for good. Buchanan desired individuals to become Christians. He will never let up witnessing to others. In his estimation, it seemed useless to force individuals into Salvation, which seemed to strengthen their resolve tenfold to resist no matter what you wish for them to accept.

Buchanan asserted the effort of pounding the Bible on top of the heads of individuals, force-feeding Jesus down the throats of free individuals who possess a freewill, amounted to nothing but counter-productive. In his experience, this approach usually ended up hardening hearts even harder.

"Let's listen to Sam Gorton and His Famous Horn Players. It's a fun group of musicians. I've already purchased a couple of albums in California of Sam Gorton and his horn players. They sure are talented, aren't they?." Buchanan burst with pride his album of one of his favorite groups.

"Sure are, Chaplain." said a relieved McElrath.

Grasping the album, Buchanan pulled the record from the slit of the album cover, gently placing the album on side A on the turntable, placing the needle carefully on the edge of the vinyl record at the beginning of the album.

Buchanan selected the album *Now and Forever*, one of his favorite albums.

The first piece of music played, '*Now and Forever*', the album title song.

Buchanan and his enlisted friends enjoyed the music. Bouncing their heads, clicking fingers to the beat, and tapping their feet to the beat of the music. The song held strong to a consistent, melodic beat with a pleasant variation repeat of notes that is gratifying to the musical ear.

'*Now and Forever*' ended and the second track begun, '*The Redhead*.'

'*The Redhead*' again initiated the heads and fingers to move with the beat of the music, along with the feet tapping. The track possessed a pleasant variation of note repetition with a wider range in the music to further enhance the inner enjoyment of the music.

Close to the end of the track, Buchanan noted, "Song sure reminds me of my wife. She has red hair."

His enlisted friends slowly turn towards Buchanan, attempting to read Buchanan's thoughts.

Laying on his cot, Buchanan stared straight up toward the ceiling of the hootch, thinking of home and his family. He thought of playing with his boys with their new firetrucks and Hot Wheels. Or playing capture the flag, a family favorite, in the public park with the whole family.

McElrath thought of his sister. "*Yeah*. This song reminds me of my sister. She has red hair too. They go perfect with her green eyes. She's beautiful."

The friends paused, thinking of home, while listening to the music. The men froze mentally, preoccupied by what awaits them with their return home.

As Sam Gorton continues to play, homesickness sinks deeper within their hearts and minds, thinking about life back home.

McElrath, the Texan, misses his vast home state and the cattle ranch life. He misses his red-haired, green-eyed sister who handles the business so well. The Texan longs to consume a 12 ounce steak some day with his parents on the back patio of the family ranch home.

Jackson, the Cincinnatian, reminisces of his family and the four seasons Ohio offers to Midwesterners. It reminded him of the aspiration of enjoying the snow in the winter and gardening edible vegetables in the summer. The Jackson and Buchanan clans mutually enjoyed the four season weather cycle immensely. The Cincinnatian longed for home to renovate an old car to a new mint condition automobile with his father, one of the better auto body repairman in the Tri-State area of Cincinnati.

"Doesn't she run your ranch, John? Your sister?" asked Jackson.

"*Yeah*." McElrath answered with pride. "She does such a great job. Dad pretty much lets her run the place."

As side A of Sam Gorton finished up, the reminiscing of home threw out an aura of melancholy.

The time was now 1145 hours.

The men departed for lunch in the chow hall. On returning to the hootch, Buchanan seized from his metal chest recent newspapers sent from his brothers in Ohio and a recent audio tape of his children sent from Dorothy, with voices heard celebrating the eldest of the children's birthday.

Leafing through the newspapers generated much talk between the men on every topic and subject, from politics to sports, which initiated two and a half hours of dialogue exchanged by three men longing to go home.

Though McElrath and Jackson never met Buchanan's family, hearing the voices of children celebrating his eldest Robert James II's birthday created an internal sense of separation from home none were willing to show.

Time quickly flew by as the hands of Buchanan's wall clock showed 1515 hours.

The men longed for nothing but to jump on the next plane destined for Los Angeles.

The talk of home dominated time and space facing the men this night.

Time ticks away quick, but a military tour of duty seems an eternity. Spending time with McElrath and Jackson inspired Buchanan to feel closer to home.

As the day came to a close, McElrath put it best. "This was a good day. A day felt a little closer to home."

The 'Super Sophomores'

January 2, 1969

Smug and resolute. The only two words to describe Ohioans in Camp Love in the early hours of January 2, 1969.

Ohioans in Camp Love stood atop a gridiron mountain peak, conquering the football world on an all-time high. No Ohioan, Kentuckian or West Virginian in camp who possessed Ohio ties, believed Ohio State will play to a losing end in the Rose Bowl today. The new year had begun in the United States. The one game Big Ten football fans looked forward to every year on New Year's Day belonged to the Rose Bowl played in Pasadena, California.

The Ohio State Buckeyes vs the USC Trojans.

Two teams destined to collide. College football will crown the winner national champions in college football.

The 1969 Rose Bowl proved to be one of the most anticipated games ever played in college football history.

Undefeated Ohio State Buckeyes vs. The Undefeated USC Trojans.

The game itself presented many clashes for the Rose Bowl. No. 1 Ohio State vs. No. 2 USC Trojans. A Heisman Trophy winner vs. Ohio State's tough, rugged defense. The Ohio State's famous running game vs. USC's high rated defense. A famous Ohio State head coach in Jack Barnes vs. USC's famous head coach, James Reynolds. The Ohio State's "Super Sophomores" vs. a USC Tradition of winning.

The winner of the game 'goes home with all the marbles.'

The Ohioans in Camp Love, along with the Kentuckians and West Virginians with Ohio ties, were all congregating in the chow hall to listen to the game on Armed Forces Services Radio. All who gathered were to root the Buckeyes on to victory.

Unfortunately for USC fans and Californians, Lucas forced them to congregate and listen to the game in supply. Though spacious enough for the large numbers of USC fans to gather, the many Californians in camp considered it a snub being forced to listen to the game in supply. The number of native Californians outnumbered Ohioans in camp 2 to 1. Supply turned out to be earshot of the chow hall. The anticipation of Buchanan and fellow Ohioans to hear the moans and groans of USC fans as the Trojans slowly lost the game heightened as the game neared. As Buchanan had put it prior to the game, "the Buckeyes will cut them down to size."

Knowing the fact he lived life as a born again sinner, Buchanan showed a solitary, genuine disgust and hate with one aspect in his life - college football. He hated Michigan. He hated USC. He hated Notre Dame. Ohio State played USC on January 1, 1955, once in the Rose Bowl and the Buckeyes won the game with a final score of 20-7. Overall, Ohio State tallied a record of 7-5-1 against the Trojans and the Buckeyes craved to add another win in the winning column. Buchanan became convinced in his heart this college football rivalry reached a new height with this historical game, empowering fans with strong bragging rights for generations to come. His sentiments for USC spelled one word: hate. His step-mother vehemently taught him growing up the word 'hate' itself embodied evil. Using the word hate, and even the messages and images related to the idea of hate, leads a person to travel down dark and uncharted roads leading to a destructive life. She taught him to accumulate a vocabulary of comparable words in the place of 'hate.' Words such as 'disgust' or 'dislike' or 'disdain.' As an avid Ohio State fan, he just could not help it. He 'hated' Ohio State rivals.

Sitting in his hootch, the hour came to 0200 hours in the early morning of January 2, 1969. Buchanan rose out of his cot at 1159 hours, alert and 'gun ho' for the game. Sleep was scarce with the anticipation of the upcoming game.

The game aired on Armed Services Radio at 0400 hours January 2, 1969 in Vietnam and 'every one and their uncle' in Camp Love looked forward to the championship game.

Buchanan woke up, showered and shaved. The Ohioan waited for patiently for his fellow Ohioan, Jackson, to arrive to accompany him to the chow hall for breakfast. The two Ohioans looked forward to listening to the game on the radio as Ohioans. Not as an officer and enlisted men, but as proud Ohioans.

Skawinski and Adkins would later join their fellow Ohioan friends in the chow hall.

Those who cared listened to the game all night long. Late night hours brought little sleep for a heavy laden schedule of January 2, 1969. The schedule comprised Communion services in the bush for Alpha and Delta companies, to visit the wounded in the aid station, and to visit individual departments in the camp.

Buchanan waited with great anticipation for Jackson to arrive at 0345 hours. The spiritual team looked forward to eating breakfast, then listen to the game.

Buchanan faced an hour or two to waste, pumped up for the game, along with all his fellow Ohioans in camp. The Ohioan contingent in camp woke up, ready, and set for a football game. To pass time until 0345 hours, Buchanan reached for and pulled off the shelf David G. Chandler's *Napoleon's Campaigns** and A. G. MacDonell's *Napoleon and his Marshalls**. His love of study for the Napoleonic Era expressed itself in his library back home, stocked with dozens of Napoleonic volumes. Chandler, a recent newcomer of authors of Napoleonic history, became an immediate favorite for Buchanan. He knew with conviction in his heart English westerners interpreted Napoleon with a Francophobia slant, disregarding the fact Napoleon himself hated the French. All Buchanan picked up from spoken English westerners mouths were slanted, ill-informed members of a society who considered Napoleon nothing but a war monger - nothing more, nothing less. Buchanan in his lifetime constantly uttered, "If they'd pick up a history book and read, maybe they would cease being so 'ignorant' and 'stupid.'" Buchanan longed for an ignorant populace in the west to crack open a history book, permit the light bulb to go off and discover the fact Napoleon catapulted France into the modern era. A book just might Enlighten them to the social, economic, political, and religious achievements of Napoleon while the Emperor of France. Achievements such as a universal education program for the French, an infrastructure to strengthen the country, a prosperous banking system, and universal religious freedom for all Frenchmen, including Jews and Protestants.

Avoiding his blood pressure elevating off the scale to the point of shooting a hole through the hootch roof, he brushed aside the 'ignorant', promising himself not to fret over the 'ill-informed' masses of westerners impressions of Napoleon, and simply enjoy his reading.

Engrossed in reading Chandlers's volume, Buchanan came across a passage politicians in the United States should take note of. Chandler stressed the Emperor Napoleon wasted no time in negotiating with an enemy till he annihilated his enemy, winning the war. Buchanan, in jest, considered sending copies of Chandler's passage to President-elect Nixon and elected congressional representatives in Washington, DC, throwing a hint of advice in their direction on conducting a war.

Reading military history ended as he recognized familiar footsteps, either Jackson or Skawinski's. Then came a knock on the door.

"Yes, Jackson. Or is it Ski? Come in. Come in."

"It's Ski, Chaplain, not Jackson."

"Adolphus Skawinski! Great to hear your voice. Come in! Come in!"

Skawinski, pulling the hootch door open, stepped in with hands hidden behind his back as if hiding a surprise. "Thought I'd come early. Surprise you Chaplain."

"Well, I'm sure glad ya did, Ski."

"Stay where you are, sir. Don't get up." Skawinski, pushing with one arm extended toward Buchanan, placed his hand back behind him. "It's a day to win a football game. And I brought you a little surprise for this special day. A deal here, a deal there, some might insist shifty deals, including The Scrounger. I acquired something for us to enjoy the game more today. I've been saving it for weeks."

Slowly exposing his hands out from behind him, he clutched an object Buchanan at first failed to identify and with a quick jolt of his right hand, Skawinski shoves his hand smack dab in front of Buchanan, presenting an Ohio State baseball cap - identical to Jack Barnes's hat he wears during football games with a red "O" and black base.

Popping up out of his chair toward Skawinski, Buchanan yells, "Amen!"

The jolt of Buchanan from his swivel chair to Skawinski came as a blur as the proud young marine handed the hat to his chaplain. Buchanan hastened to his mirror over the sink, smiling from ear to ear, gazing at his reflection in the mirror showing off the Ohio State baseball cap. The cap filled Buchanan up with a full sense of Ohioan pride.

"Beautiful. Just Beautiful." Buchanan, fixated on the reflection of home on the top of his head, beamed with Buckeye pride smugly.

Glancing toward Skawinski, he points his right index finger up towards his head. "Whayathink?"

"As you said, chaplain, beautiful." Grinning, Skawinski stared at a 37-year-old man who acted as a 12-year-old who received his gift he wished for from Santa on Christmas morning.

The enlisted Ohioan draws out from the back of his civilian shorts his own hat. Donning his hat with pride, he asks Buchanan, "Whayathink, chaplain?"

Buchanan grins slightly. "Beautiful. Just beautiful."

Caught up in total Ohio euphoria, the Buckeye pride felt in the air set the tone for the two Ohioans to listen to Ohio State dole out a bloody nose to the Trojans. They prayed for USC to knuckle under.

Amid all the Ohio elation, the Ohioans failed to perceive how smug Big Ten and Ohio State fans portray themselves in public, a fact SEC football fans are well aware of. Regardless, the Ohioans proudly wore smug smiles displaying Ohio pride in their new Ohio State hats.

"These hats were easy to get, sir." Skawinski admitted. "I did some swindling to get'em, but I got'em."

The men chuckle. Buchanan commented, "I'm sure it was all on the up and up. I'm just thrilled to flaunt Ohio a bit and let everybody know how special Ohio State football is to us, especially the USC fans and the southerners."

The euphoria slowed a bit with a knock on the door.

"Hello?" The men quickly recognize the voice. "It's me. Sergeant Jackson."

"Yes, come in. Come in, Sergeant." said Buchanan with energy.

Jackson immediately steps in as Skawinski, without delay, hands him an Ohio State hat.

"Wow! Thanks Ski. I really appreciate it."

"No problem, Sergeant. I thought the hats might add to the thrill of the day." commented Skawinski.

"You're spot on, Ski." Jackson felt good about Ohio State's chances of winning the game. "Ohioans have woken up this morning expecting to be number one when they hit the sack to get some shuteye at day's end."

The men grin with confidence.

"I just pray Ohio State wins by 50, not a last-second field goal win." said Buchanan with a tone of divine intervention in his voice.

"Amen to that, sir." said Skawinski.

"Well, let's go men. The game starts soon. We'll want to eat our breakfast before the game starts." Buchanan wanted to get an early seat.

The small party of Ohioans arrived at the chow hall and ate breakfast. The men sat patiently at their table, ready set to listen to the pregame alongside their fellow Ohioans.

The chow hall served chow all night due to the game start.

Ohioans in camp were fortunate to eat breakfast and sit in the chow hall to listen to the broadcast. Lucas' Ohio hand as commanding officer reserved the chow hall for the Ohioans, compelling him to order the Californians to listen to the game in supply. Snubbing the Californians access of the chow hall during the broadcast seemed beyond Buchanan's encouraging words of 'forgive and forget' in his Communion services. The Californians will never forget the snub.

The numbers of Californian personnel in Camp Love doubled the Ohioan numbers, a fact accentuating the snub. Besides, as a native Ohioan, Lucas took advantage of the perks as commanding officer. For 200 years of Navy history, the Navy gave commanding officers the liberty to act accordingly. And in this case, Lucas just happened to be from Ohio.

Californians arriving in the chow hall to eat breakfast delivered to the Ohioans a few good grimaces while consuming their food. The convenience of listening to the broadcast in the chow hall frothed the Californians.

Regardless, January 2 in Vietnam is the day two groups of marines will listen to one of the greatest games ever played in college football, as Southern California fell 14 hours behind Vietnam's time zone.

Lucas and Chaplain William Tecumseh Taylor, from Lancaster, Ohio and friend of Buchanan, finished eating breakfast at a corner table. Skawinski stepped up to the officers, offering an Ohio State hat to his fellow Ohioans. The officers appreciated the gesture.

The officers displayed nothing but pride sporting off their new Ohio State hats.

The game started at approximately 0414 in the morning. Camp Love bared the semblance of two camps. The Ohioan pitched their tents in one corner of camp. The Californians pitched their tents in another corner. All in part with the anticipation of their respective team to hoist the championship trophy up for all to see.

Following introducing the starting lineups and the playing of the National Anthem from the Ohio State marching band, the much expected toss of the coin begun.

The USC Trojans won the toss and elected to receive the ball first. The championship game began for the 1969 Rose Bowl as the Buckeyes kicked off to Southern California.

The game's start did not bode well in the first quarter for either team, as neither team scored. Ohio State punted twice, and the offense produced a meager, sluggish 72 yards. A perturbed mood, to put it mildly, filled the air in the chow hall. The Ohioans wanted an early lead and received nothing but mediocrity. Within themselves,

Ohioans fumed. Every Ohioan heart in the chow hall knew the most perturbed for the poor 1st quarter performance came from Coach Jack Barnes. Fans privileged to attend a game in the Horse Shoe witnessed first hand Barnes's demeanor during the game as he directed and motivated his players from one end of the sideline to the other. Though the men lacked the convenience of a television set, Buchanan and his fellow Ohioans all knew Barnes carried himself on the sideline with animation between the first and second quarters. Barnes appeared fired up in between quarters, encouraging his team to play with purpose for the rest of the game.

Time begun in the second quarter, with Ohio State failing to score on the first play with a missed field goal for the Buckeyes.

"Yippee!" "Hurrah!" "Yoo-hoo!" filled the camp's air heard from USC fans in supply. The thunderous, booming cheer heard loud and clear in the chow hall. More than likely heard by the Viet Cong hiding just inside the treeline, if there were any at all this night prowling about.

The USC Trojans marched down the field in their first possession of the second quarter, gaining 74 yards. The Trojan Heisman Trophy winner accounted for 65 yards of the drive, both rushing and receiving. Fortunately for Ohio State, the Trojans had to settle for an 11 yard field goal.

"Yaaaaaay!" "Woo hoo!" "Take that Ohio State!" The cheers of celebrations came from USC fans once again, but louder, more boisterous the second time around.

Fortune fell upon the Buckeyes, as USC scored only a field goal. USC drove the ball down to Ohio State's 3 yard line. The Buckeyes defense stiffened up, averting a touchdown on three straight plays, resulting in a loss of 1 yard following the 74 yard drive.

Black clouds emerged on the horizon as the Ohio contingent in the camp faced worry and doubt following the USC field goal. As the football gurus and analysts deemed, USC ranked as one of the greatest teams to take the field in college football in decades. USC lifted up their Heisman Trophy winner as the template for running backs for years to come. The Ohio contingent in camp dreaded the possibility of facing the Californians following an Ohio State loss. USC flaunted a potent, unstoppable offense in the last USC drive. The last thing Ohio State wished to comfort in the ball game would be a two score deficit. A difficult hole to climb out of for Ohio State if forced to face such a complete football team such as the USC Trojans.

In life, one misfortune comes up on the neck of another. In sports, when it rains, it pours. Ohio State's next possession in the second quarter resulted in a punt, giving the football back to USC. The Trojans gained self-confidence in the previous offensive drive, moving the ball downfield. Though down, the Buckeyes felt a smidge of poise after the drive gaining 18 yards, including one first down, throwing a boost of confidence the Ohioans way.

Anyone of the Ohioans could have heard a pin drop in the chow hall. A quarter and a half of football played and Ohio State has yet to show the country any evidence the Buckeyes deserved a number one ranking. The Ohioans thought of little to cheer about. The mood for Ohioans denoted a considerable quiet and lugubrious chow hall.

Breaking the downhearted mood, a smiling Clevelander uttered, "I still think we're going to beat these guys."

Every Ohioan in the room thought, 'leave it to a Clevelander to say something out of place.'

Skawinski attempts to reinforce the positives vibes from the Clevelander. "*Yeah*. It's just 0-3. Just three points. And it's just the second quarter." He patted the Clevelander on the shoulder.

Buchanan added his two cents. "*Yeah*. This has been a great group for Coach Barnes this year. He won't let these boys just give up." Buchanan turns towards Lucas, grimacing.

After Ohio State punted, USC's first play called for a designed pitch out from the Trojans quarterback to their Heisman Trophy winner. The play will be one college football fans will remember for decades.

The marines and sailors in both football camps heard the radio broadcaster call the play -

"USC starts this drive from their own 20 yard line. USC's quarterback is under center, calling the play. He takes the snap, turns left from center, he pitches the ball to their top player. He takes the pitch, there's nothing but Buckeyes in front of him running to his left, he cuts back against the grain, there's a missed tackle, and yet another missed tackle. Three or four Buckeyes run into each other, he runs past 'em! Uh oh! He's in the clear at the fifty! He's running now in open field! He runs the 100 in 9-5! He has a wall of Trojans behind him! He's at the 30! The 20! The 15! 10! 5! Touchdown USC! What a run by the Heisman Trophy Winner! Listen to these USC fans. They know their team is up. Now leading by two scores."

Nothing but a deafening silence in all four corners of the chow hall.

Dead silence reflected nothing but trouble brewing in the air for Ohioans following the top USC player's run.

No words. No reaction. No cursing. Nothing but silence trailing the shock of the electrifying run.

The thrilling run felt the coup de grâce, with the game at the mere halfway point in the second quarter.

Buchanan broke the haunting silence in his mountain accent. "Come on now. It's just the second quarter. Coach Barnes will get 'em fired up for the rest of the game. You'll see."

A hundred or so eyeballs stared sharply at Chaplain Buchanan with faces baring half crooked smiles, emulating expressions of waving a white flag.

Buchanan attempted to lighten the mood. "Now - Now. We're Ohioans. We're Buckeyes. We're not going to give up just yet, are we? Come on, let's have a little hope in this Jack Barnes coached team."

After a long pause in the chow hall, marines lightened up a bit, especially after the Buckeyes received the kickoff.

"OK, Chaplain. I'm with you, sir." commented a marine from Canton, Ohio, pacifying Buchanan with a little support.

"Me, too, sir." agreed a Groveport, Ohio native showing more spirit.

The Buckeyes received the Trojan kickoff at the 13 yard line and returned the kick 18 yards to the 31 yard line of Ohio State.

With a deficit score of 0-10 against USC, the Trojans owned one of the best players in college football history. It seemed all USC had to do to win the game was simply to hand the ball off to their Heisman Trophy winner, and watch the yards pile up and time tick away. Watching him run on TV or in person, he immeasurably impressed fans with his skills, thinking he came from another world. He resembled a football specimen built in the intergalactic space of the universe molded from the hands of football gods in another galaxy.

Thus far in the game, not much moved in Ohio State's direction. The scoreboard tilted in the Trojans' favor. The Trojans possessed the best player on the field in their Heisman Trophy winner. The Buckeyes are now forced to overcome a two score deficit. Not much of the game resulted in favor of Ohio State. Another touchdown score for USC and Ohio State's odds of victory diminished with it. Many college football fans in the country have already assumed Ohio State has lost the game.

In college football, teams, players and coaches occasionally give up in a game down by two scores against a team such as the 1968 USC squad. But the Trojans confronted an Ohio State football team of 1968, which reflected the demeanor of an incredible self will and determination unlike any other football team of the past. The 1968 Ohio State team was not just your average football team. Jack Barnes was coach of the 'Super Sophomores.' and Ohio State's defense was one of the best in the country.

The game, far from over, still had two and a half quarters to play.

Ohio State started at their own 31 yard line and marched 69 yards down the field and scored a touchdown. The Buckeyes gained five first downs during the drive. OSU gained 24 of the 69 yards from Ohio State's fullback, a 6'0" 208 pound junior. In the drive, a converted 3 down and 13 yards to go at the USC's 21 yard line proved an essential conversion for the touchdown score and, if not successful, might have been a determining factor in the final results of the game.

Ohio State drove the ball to USC's 3 yard line for a goal to go. On first down and goal to go, Ohio State's fullback took a handoff and ran behind the right guard, gaining 2 yards. The next play, on a second down and goal to go, called for the Ohio State fullback to run right behind the right guard for a touchdown. He chose to dive into the end zone rather than running the ball in for the touchdown.

The roar of Ohioans in the chow hall grew louder than the Californians' cheer for the exhilarating USC running play. Camp Love knows well that Ohio State scored, including the USC fans in supply. The hush in supply was quiet as a mouse.

Buchanan, Skawinski, Jackson, Lucas, Chaplain Taylor, and the Ohioans cheered at the top of their lungs.

"Yippee!" cheered an Ohioan from Orrville.

"Yaaaaay!" blurted Skawinski.

"We're back in it!" shouted Jackson. "You're right, chaplain. The Buckeyes marched right down the field and scored."

The demeanor of the proud Ohioans in the chow hall took a 180* turn. The Buckeyes in camp again assumed a win for Ohio State is again forthcoming.

The Trojans took the kickoff from the Ohio State Buckeyes. The Trojan receiver caught the kickoff at the USC 16, running for 15 yards to the 31 yard line. The first play from scrimmage called for a handoff from their quarterback to the Heisman Trophy Winner for four yards behind the left guard and tackle of USC's talented offensive line.

A gain of 4 yards on the first play of the drive resulted in a roar from supply, loud and undeviating. The intent of the cheer came loud and clear.

The Californians' uplifting, exhilarating cheer smacked of smug. The Ohioans understood the intentional jab toward the Buckeyes. The Ohioans hoped and prayed for a win. The thought of having to face USC fans if Ohio State lost gnawed at their gut.

"Why don't you say a prayer, chaplain?" asked a Racine Ohio native.

"No - No. If I do, the Lord just might let USC win to humble us all." said Buchanan, with a chuckle.

"Yes. Yes. You're right, Padre!" agreed the Racine native.

The Ohio contingent laugh.

Inside, though, Buchanan prayed a silent prayer, 'Lord, please let the Buckeyes win.'

The next two plays for USC failed to reflect the first scoring drive of the game for the Trojans. The second down play resulted in Ohio State sacking the USC quarterback for a loss of 13 yards. The roar of the Ohioans again made a loud and clear statement to the Californians, sending a sure message the Ohio State football team has not folded. Ohio State has played their way back into the game.

The 3rd down and 19 yards to go play snapped at the USC 22 yard line resulted in a pass thrown out of bounds. Ohio State forced a USC punt, awarding the ball back to the Buckeyes. Again, the camp heard a resounding shout of approval from the chow hall.

Receiving the punt, the Ohio State player fair catches the ball and fumbles, but fortunately recovered the ball at the Ohio State 40 yard line. A piercing 'ohhhh' from the Ohioans reverberated throughout camp as the receiver fumbled the football, followed by a reassuring 'sigh' from every Ohioan in the chow hall as he recovered the ball.

After receiving the ball, the Buckeyes drove down the field uncharacteristic of Ohio State football. The first play resulted in a big gain for Ohio State, a 17 yard pass from Ohio State's quarterback to his receiver. Five plays later, Ohio State snapped from center from the USC 4 yard line and kicked a field goal at the 14:57 mark on a 3rd down to play with seconds left in the first half.

The last three seconds ticked off the clock as halftime finally arrived. The USC sideline ran off the field in shock, looking up at the scoreboard with a halftime score of 10-10. Ohio State forced the Trojans to swallow quite a bit of pride, seeing a 10-0 lead vanish against a team USC felt had no business stepping onto the football field to compete against them, the reigning national champions. The fans in the Rose Bowl sitting in the stands knew another score from USC in the second quarter which would have extended their lead to a 17-0 deficit would have been too much of a hole for Ohio State to overcome.

Foremost for the marines were to stand and stretch at the half, gaining a mental break from a nerve-racking half of football. The time stood at 0535 hours in the morning in Vietnam. Listening to the game forfeited a full night's sleep. The fact sleep and rest accrued fuel for the crucial mission for engineers in Camp Love came pigeonholed for the time being. The excitement of the game thwarted exhaustion or fatigue.

January 2, 1969, did not differ from any other day. Camp Love still considered its responsibilities of sweeping for mines, fulfilling road repairs, guarding the Seabees on construction assignments, and other duties more important than football. But the game provided for a well-deserved pause from the war.

Losing sleep over the game turned out to be well worth it. The men put their feet up and enjoyed the game as if in the family TV room back home.

The university bands played their halftime shows, bringing fans in the Rose Bowl stadium to their feet. The musicians performed with pride for their respective universities as members of two of the best marching bands in the country.

"There's no doubt the Ohio State band is best." commented Skawinski, followed by cheers from his fellow Ohioans.

Celebrities attending the game added to the fanfare for the day. Icon Bob Hope and newly elected President Richard Nixon, whose wife Pat, a USC graduate, attended the game. Governor Ronald Reagan and his wife Nancy enjoyed the game representing the great state of California. The Rose Bowl promised an electrifying game. And there has been nothing but electricity in the air. Buchanan and his fellow Ohioans in Camp Love prayed for more electricity from Ohio State.

As the football teams re-emerged from locker rooms to kickoff the second half, players threw smug grins toward one another. As the first play in the third quarter begun, energy filled the air from fans and players alike. Optimism displayed body language and a glowing confidence from players from both teams, as if they were the winning football team walking to their sideline.

Ohio State received the opening second half kickoff, returning the ball to the 14 yard line. Ohio State fans were ready, looking forward to the Buckeyes marching down field and scoring in the opening moments of the second half. But to no avail. A three and out resulted from three straight plays from the Buckeyes with their first possession of the second half. In the possession, Ohio State handed the ball to the fullback for two plays for a grand total of seven yards gained, while the 3rd down and three resulted in an incomplete pass dropped by the receiver, which would have awarded the Buckeyes a first down and ten.

Ohio State punted the ball to USC, handing the Trojans an attempt to drive the ball down the field. The Trojans moved the ball with marginal success, gaining yardage for two first downs and converted one 3rd down conversion. In the drive, the Trojans faced a 2nd down and nine yards to go at the Ohio State 42 yard line. The Trojan quarterback pitched the ball out to their top running back who fumbled the ball. One of Ohio State's top talented defensive backs recovered the ball.

"Yaaaaaaaay!" roared the Ohioans.

"Way to go, Buckeyes!" Everyone heard the Buckeyes from the chow hall all over camp. If there were any Viet Cong if the jungle bush, they heard the Americans jubilation, sickening their Commie stomachs to no end.

"Yes, we've got possession!" yelled Skawinski.

Back and forth went the opposing football teams, mirroring a game of attrition. The last thing Ohioans in the chow hall desired in the third quarter came was a stalemate. Ohio State and USC hammered away at each other, grinding out one play after another for the rest of the quarter.

The third quarter amounted to five possessions total from both offensive squads resulting with a mere field goal from Ohio State in their third possession. In the third quarter, very little racket came from the direction of supply.

The third quarter ended with the Ohio State quarterback under center taking the snap, dropping back to pass on a 2nd and 7. Discovering no open receivers, he scrambled, rushing for 14 yards and a first down and ten to the USC 4 yard line. Ending the third quarter with such an exciting play handed Ohio State a start of the fourth quarter with a favorable line of scrimmage and a 1st and goal at USC's four yard line.

Entering the fourth quarter, a score of 13-10 favored Ohio State. The last 15 minutes gave the Buckeyes the greatest of opportunities to increase the lead with a touchdown.

The first two plays from scrimmage in the fourth quarter Ohio State called two rushing plays. The first play gained a mere 2 yards by the fullback, followed by a play for the Ohio State quarterback to rush for a loss of 2 yards. The 3rd and goal play called for a pass, resulting in a touchdown pass to an open receiver, followed with the extra point. The Buckeyes were now up 20-10.

The roar of cheers from the Ohioans shook even Marble Mountain miles away. The Californians, sitting on supply crates, boxes, and the few chairs provided, reacted deflated as quick as a tire slit from a Viet Cong machete. Panic spread quick throughout the USC contingent with the Ohio State touchdown. The Ohio State defense proved all year long it deserved respect. And since the explosive 80-yard run in the second quarter, USC's Heisman Trophy Winner had been kept in check by the hard as nails Ohio State defense.

After Ohio State's touchdown to extend the lead to 20-10, the offensives carried out one possession each with no score. USC possessed the ball for a second possession in the fourth quarter starting at the Trojan 21 resulting in one play for the drive, a pass to Heisman Trophy Winner who fumbled the ball and a loss of five yards, recovered by Ohio State at USC's 16 yard line.

"Yaaaaaaay!" "Yippie" "Yes! Yes! Yes!" shouted the Ohioans.

Buchanan made a point. "The Buckeyes can *reeeealy* put pressure on those Californians now! And their Heisman Trophy Winner will walk away from this game today, certainly humbled. I heard on the radio and read in the papers how over confident he is. He's not so special now, is he? He thinks pretty high of himself, doesn't he Skawinski?"

"Yeeaaaaah!" bellowed the Ohioans. The fans, coaches, alumni, band members, and even casual fans of Ohio State now knew a victory and a national championship neared just 10 minutes and 5 seconds away.

The Buckeyes were pleased. Ohio State ran one play resulting in a touchdown. And all to the thanks of one fumble from USC's best player.

Now the score tallied a 27-10 lead.

Not a peep out of supply. Not even the modest echoes from the Californians.

At this point in the game, many Californians departed from supply for their own hootches. The bleachers clear out of stadiums when the final outcome is evident. And the Californians now know a devastating defeat is forthcoming, as time will run out for the USC Trojans.

Every Ohioan present - Skawinski, Buchanan, Jackson, Lucas, Chaplain Taylor, and their fellow state citizens displayed nothing but exuberance with the scoring touchdown. A proud, self-evident smug smile slowly emerges on each and every face, officer and enlisted alike.

The Ohioans nowhere saw smug smiles on the faces of Californians. No smug smiles. No sarcastic remarks. Just frowns.

Four possessions mounted between the two football squads in the fourth quarter as USC scored a single touchdown and a failed two point conversion attempt, making the score 27-16 with only 45 seconds left in the game.

Even with the touchdown, USC had lost the game. The score came too little, too late!

Ohio State players, coaches, and fans now knew the Buckeyes were destined to win the game.

Ohio State called three plays from the sideline, as the Buckeyes ran out the last 45 seconds of the game, winning the game with a final score of 27-16.

The time stood at 0638 hours in the morning. A sleepless night - but worth it, especially for Buckeye fans.

One fact spoke for itself. Whether marine or Navy personnel, or on the winning or losing side of things, the game mentally distracted the minds of the Americans from the horrible war of attrition, all caught in the middle of depleting them of mental and physical wellbeing.

For just a mere few hours, the men felt a normalcy, as if at home with family and friends back in the United States watching the game on television, and no war to worry about. The moment exhilarated the love of college football and the normalcy of home. Unfortunately, the intrinsic, temporary short time of normalcy and the congenial, confined mood came to a close as the game ended.

With the conclusion of the game, the men longed for the game to go on and on. All numb from the war, the men felt themselves in a space-time continuum all wished turned into eternity. The game at least put the war on hold, though impermanent.

Following the post game show, the marines and sailors departed to their respective hootches in an attempt for an hour of shut eye, if all possible.

The shut eye itself served as a halftime of sorts, a buffer from the game and the war, about to start up once again in just an hour or two for the marines and sailors in Camp Love.

A bout of homesickness struck the men in camp like no other following the broadcast of the game.

The desire for normalcy of life overcame the camp and the normalcy of the football game never ceased mentally for the men, even for USC fans.

HUNTING FOR GAME

JANUARY 2, 1969

With time at 0645 hours in camp, those who listened to the game attempted a quick snooze, which gained nothing but a waste of time.

No sleep. No snoozing. Zilch. Nothing but thinking of the game and home.

Exhilaration ran high within the Ohio State contingent in camp. For USC fans, nothing but agony coming from such a crushing loss delivered upon the Trojans from the Ohio State football team. Adrenaline hit an all-time high for Ohio State Buckeyes fans.

Regardless of fan base, all wanted to go home and enjoy the moment.

At 0700 hours, the marines and sailors were up and at 'em. Gun ho to go to work.

Buchanan faced a soft schedule for the day. He visited the wounded and followed up with sessions with counselees. He then took time in the day to catch up on his paperwork. A top priority for the day followed with visits to individual departments.

If Buchanan was in camp and not accompanying a patrol, he stationed himself at the front entrance of the camp. He positioned himself to lay hands on the marines, praying a prompt prayer for God's presence with the men as they depart camp and enter the bush to patrol. Buchanan graciously offered a Capodanno cross to any marine, wishing one to hang around his neck for a Divine presence and protection while facing the enemy. The positioning of himself at the front entrance allowed him to greet men returning from the bush and to pray over the KIAs at the rear of the patrol. Though in his heart he desired to fall on his knees and weep openly from the sheer waste of young lives taken so early. Buchanan thought better of it and prayed over the remains, giving his last respects. He would later grieve in the privacy of his own hootch over the loss of such young men.

Bravo Company and Rockford, along with two rifle squads from Company C, were scheduled to depart camp to patrol. They were to patrol with a combat engineering team ordered to continue daily sweeps of Route QL-1 at coordinates AT 999707 to BT 090555. Added to the tasks were Route 8 and Route 540, from AT 949707 to 926606, two main routes. The roads were vital for tactical and communication movements for United States military goals in Quang Nam Province and Military Region I.

When possible, Buchanan every morning blessed a special marine who departed Camp Love, praying for God's presence to be bestowed upon him venturing out into the bush. Sergeant Carl Remington loved to hunt. Buchanan felt a heavy bond with his fellow Kentuckian, whose family also chain migrated into Ohio in the 1930s and 40s looking for work when coal mines shut down.

At dusk every morning, Remington made his way out beyond the treeline, deep into the depths of the jungle to hunt game with bow and arrow, along with a .45 caliber holstered on his hip. The game came plenty with wild hog, voles, gaur, tapir, deer, and wild bird such as pheasant. His personality reflected a reserved, soft-spoken young man. Buchanan's revered admiration for the young marine widened as Buchanan took great pleasure from Remington's sense of humor.

"Good morning Padre! And what a beautiful day it is." Remington, in his genuine deep Kentuckian accent, greeted Buchanan with the most gentle smile.

"Good morning Corporal Remington." responded Buchanan with his mutual Kentuckian accent.

Remington received a quick once-over from Buchanan, as rapid thought patterns ran past in his mind. 'Wow! How can this courteous, reticent, self-contained young man be such a ferocious and searing killing machine in combat when facing the VC or NVA?'

As a part of Skawinski's combat engineering team, Remington's MOS as combat engineer placed him in an 'expert' role in a demolition team.

Skawinski ran out of fingers to count the innumerous tight spots Remington bailed out his team in the bush. The young men shared an intense struggle deep within their very souls in taking the life of other human beings. Combat experiences forced many unwanted personality traits to emerge during war.

Remington struggled with his combat duties versus Christian commitment to follow the teachings of Jesus. He experienced countless combat situations taking the life of the enemy, either by his bare hands or with a combat weapon. The necessity to seek comfort and console with his struggle laid at Buchanan's feet. Although he held a reputation as a killing machine in combat, his devotion to his Christian commitment came challenged daily in a war zone.

"Will you pray for me, sir?" asked Remington.

"Sure thing, Sergeant." answered Buchanan.

Placing his hands on Remington's shoulders, Buchanan prayed. "Lord, protect Carl as he enters the jungle to enjoy his most treasured pastime in his life. Amen."

"Thank ya, sir."

"You're welcome, Sergeant." replied Buchanan. "So long."

"So long, sir." Remington turned, making his way toward the jungle treeline.

As Buchanan kept an eye on Remington hiking down the dirt road through the camp perimeter, the young marine exited the perimeter, turning right toward the jungle treeline. Buchanan once again prayed to the Lord, "Father, please bring the boy back to us."

The logic behind Remington to leave the perimeter in isolation baffled Buchanan. He thought to himself, 'Well, it *is* the 1960s. Rules don't count anymore.' He rolls his eyes, shaking his head.

Buchanan gazed at Remington till he faded from sight into the jungle.

Remington meandered no farther than a mile radius of camp, rarely venturing beyond that point. Without exception, Buchanan set his eyes on Remington vanish into the bush out of sheer superstition, worried 'tooth and toenail' he might one day never re-emerge out of the jungle. In Buchanan's odd and eccentric mind, he rationalized that if he watched Remington step into the jungle, his return trip out of the bush would come without question.

Time set at 0730 hours. Though Buchanan ate just a mere few hours ago, he felt his stomach growl. He ambled over to Jackson's hootch to pick him up for breakfast. Following a hearty breakfast, the spiritual team set out for a full day of ministry. The agenda to begin the day scheduled a trip by jeep to provide Communion Services for Alpha Company out in the bush at 1030 hours, followed by visiting the wounded in the aid station. The day ended by visiting the separate departments in the camp.

A top priority set for Buchanan came to bring a normalcy of life to the men by visiting the marines in the separate departments of camp and individual hootches. Buchanan's genuine personality eased the tension of others around him and people naturally benefited from his presence. His company aided marines whether troubled with personal or military dilemmas and usually came with a response of geniality and openness from the men.

Buchanan talked of home, chatting with the marines of their families and civilian life, such as work. The telling of jokes with an amusing punchline from time to time came naturally for Buchanan, an ingrained part of Buchanan's personality. He learned in a war zone humor and jokes stood out as audacious, out of place of sorts and reserved only for the right time and place.

Relaying to other's humorous stories and expressing amusement flowed within Buchanan's blood veins. And the men loved him for it. The marines grew to appreciate him, discovering he genuinely cared for the marines as men.

The team drove to Alpha Company 4 miles away, west of camp to conduct Communion services.

Father Time passes fast as the communion service fleeted by in nothing flat.

Jackson snapped a few slide pictures during the communion service in the bush to add to Buchanan's pictorial record of his ministry in Vietnam, taking two group shots of Alpha Company after the service.

The spiritual team made ready for their return trip back to camp to continue the day of ministry.

Hopping into the jeep, Jackson asked, "The men in Alpha Company sure are going to be weak, weary, and worn in the slide pictures taken, won't they?"

Buchanan asked, "What?"

"The pictures. The men. They sure looked like they had the w's."

Buchanan paused, glancing out toward the fields of rice patties alongside the road. He calmly says with discontent, "*Yeah*. They sure did."

"They sure sprouted up though, when you arrived today. You were a sight for sore eyes. You were definitely an inspiration to the men. One look at you and it was all smiles. They loved ya chaplain." said Jackson.

Buchanan, fidgety in his passenger seat, turned red faced from embarrassment. Glancing toward Jackson, he smiled. "Well, just want the men to believe in the good things. Let'em know Jesus loves 'em too."

Jackson bared a grin of adoration. "I know Chaplain. Well, you'll…never know."

"What?" Buchanan seemed puzzled.

"The men. You've helped them beyond all measure. They might not say it to your face, but you've been a God sent."

Buchanan loathed public adoration. He detested those in public life who conducted themselves as if their sole purpose in life called for a pursuit of public adoration and public awards. In Buchanan's estimation, those who behaved in such a manner lived simply to show the world how much more brilliant and amazing they were over others. Buchanan figured attention getters found their inspiration from the Devil himself. Buchanan focused on fulfilling God's will in his life, and receiving attention from others for selfish means played no part in that focus.

As the spiritual team made their way back to camp, the team stumbled upon a Buddhist funeral. Fascinated with the procession of the funeral, Jackson halted the jeep as Buchanan quickly stepped out of the jeep, snapping rapid slide pictures for the pictorial record of his tour. Buddhist priests served as pallbearers, carrying the remains in the casket on their shoulders. Several other priests clutched poles with Buddha quotes written on the side of the poles with all the pomp and circumstance of a Buddhist ceremony. The most fascinating facet of the funeral processional for the spiritual team were the professional mourners at the tail end of the ceremonial entourage. Later on, Buddhist friends in An Ngai Tay informed Buchanan the mourners' tears were natural. And when the time came to turn on the spigot, the mourners were willing and able to let the tears flow.

After the picture taking and absorbing in all the Asian culture from witnessing an event the team found extremely profound, the men stepped back into the jeep to continue the journey back to Camp Love.

The spiritual team arrived back at camp at 1300 hours. Jackson parked in front of Buchanan's hootch as Corporal Jones rushed up to the spiritual team. In his strong mountain accent, Jones informed the spiritual team. "Sergeant Remington hasn't returned from his hunt. All in the camp are worried and ready to send out search parties. Do y'all want to come?"

"You know it. Corporal Jones." said Jackson.

"Count me in too." added Buchanan.

Jackson darted to his hootch, snatched his reconnaissance bag and his extra .45 caliber, while Corporal Jones briefed Buchanan of the situation, walking to the main camp entrance to rally with elements of Delta Company forming a search party for his Kentuckian friend. Present in the search party stood Skawinski, a longtime friend of Remington's.

Buchanan walks up to Skawinski's left, who is in an intense conversation with Delta Company's Gunnery Sergeant. Turning toward Buchanan, Skawinski updated his chaplain on Remington's situation. "He's usually back every morning by 1000 or 1030 hours, Chaplain. We're worried."

"*Yeah*. Me too." said Buchanan.

Jackson steps up and asks, "Well, Ski, where is he? He's back by 1000 or 1030 hours every day."

Skawinski is worried. "We know."

"Just saying." said Jackson.

As Buchanan pondered the whereabouts of Remington, all looked toward the treeline of jungle foliage. The greenery of the bush moved ever so slightly. And low and behold, walking out of the bush carrying a wild boar over his shoulder, walked Remington.

"Hurrah! Hurrah!" roared the marines.

The sight of Remington followed with cheers of excitement as loud as roars for a home team winning in the bottom of the ninth inning of a baseball game.

The search party caught every step of Remington making his way back to camp. Waiting at the camp entrance for Remington stood patiently the search party, staring with an intense glare upon a marine doused with sweat, dirt, and smelled of high Heaven. The hunter could have cared less. A hunter never gives up. And Remington tracked with caution a wild boar for hours, appraising the whereabouts of the Viet Cong the whole while. He remained resolute in pursuit of his game, refusing to let the boar slip away.

Remington's closest friends, Skawinski, Jackson, Buchanan, and Jones dashed to greet him at the camp entrance from the treeline. His friends examined his stride around the perimeter, then through the dirt road up to the entrance to Camp Love.

The men met the hunter at the entrance thrilled beyond measure Remington arrived safe and sound. His friends hugged him. The group ambled their way farther into camp. Jackson, along with others, delivered a good tongue lashing to him for appearing two and a half hours late from hunting.

Adkins and Rockford stepped up to the group. Rockford, in a firm tone, admonished the young hunter. "Sergeant Remington. You're a worry. You know that."

All smiled, including Remington.

"The Lord was with Carl." Buchanan reassured Remington of the Lord's presence with him in the bush.

"Yes sir. Amen to that, sir." Remington felt sure the Lord's presence walked every step of the way with him in the bush. He described his experience. "I discovered fresh tracks, evidence of rooting and wallowing of a wild boar. I lost my bearings in the jungle, but bumped into tracks of the wild boar 100 feet within the edge of the treeline and extended for a mile or two away from the treeline."

Remington explained his moves in the jungle, tracking the boar. He then confessed, "I'm hungry."

Buchanan suggested eating lunch with his friends. "Let's celebrate his return by eating lunch together. You can tell us the rest while eating."

The group of close knit friends made their way to the galley, relieved Remington come through safe and sound. The men filled their bellies with hamburgers, chips, and soup. Remington informed his friends the rest of his adventure.

"I tracked and tracked that blasted boar till I cornered him into a gully. I came pretty close to a VC patrol or two. The VC - they're out there, even in the daytime. They're like the rats. They always show up everywhere you go. It's scary. I didn't really come up on Charlie till I was over a mile away from camp. If anymore VC showed up, I was going to have to call it quits. But they never showed, and I was grateful."

Buchanan nodded, pleased with his safe return.

The young marine paused as he glanced toward each one of his friends. Grinning from ear to ear, each friend listened to every word Remington spoke in his strong Kentuckian draw, retelling his story of trapping the wild boar. "Anyhow, when all was clear and secure from Charlie, I continued to track the boar and do him in with my machete. I never have felt so accomplished in my life as a hunter. I dodged the danger and succeeded - regardless of the situation."

Remington, glancing downward toward his plate, pondered a profound thought. "But I don't think I'll ever do that again."

He took a glimpse toward Rockford, with fret written all over his face.

Rockford enlightened Remington. "Hope you learned your lesson, Sergeant. You went out farther than the authorized mile radius you may go."

"Sure did, sir. I won't do it again. I can assure ya of that." Remington promises his friends never to go out of his allowed radius again.

Grinning, Rockford nods.

Buchanan reassures Remington. "Well, the Lord sure was looking out for you. As the Lieutenant said, you need to stay within the mile radius."

The fellowship strengthened the men's excellent relationship. Buchanan sensed a tightening of friendship, a strengthening of a bond between men lasting for a lifetime.

Sergeant Vickers interrupted the fellowship, making his way into the chow hall, stepping up to Remington. "Sergeant, the skipper wants to see you. On the double." Vickers turned and hustled back to Lucas' office quickly.

Remington, a little shaken, turned as white as the recent snowfall in southern Ohio. His friends, staring at him, sat at a loss for words.

"You want me to come with ya?" asked Buchanan with concern.

"Uh - No. No, sir." Remington, full of confidence, sought to face the commanding officer as a man.

Then Rockford offered his presence for support. "Do you want me to come with you?"

"No. No, sir." Remington, with even more confidence, felt self-assured to face Lucas alone.

"I'll vouch for you, Carl." assured Jackson.

"No. I'll take responsibility for my own actions. I was in the wrong. I'll face the Skipper on my own. I'm a man, I can take it."

Remington knew Lucas, as commanding officer, sought the appropriate punishment for the young hunter for taking the liberty to track game outside the one-mile radius for him to hunt.

"OK." said Jackson, with half a grin.

After chow, the men returned to their respective hootches meditating on the tragedy Remington dodged in the jungle bush, reflecting on what could have been.

Buchanan simply thanked the Lord He had protected his fellow Kentuckian.

Later in the night, Remington visited Chaplain Buchanan, informing him Lieutenant Colonel Lucas blasted him with a good tongue lashing. The Skipper informed him one more incident venturing out more than a mile - and there will be no more hunting privileges in the morning.

Venturing out by one's self during the Vietnam war came with extreme dangers. However dangerous hunting in the bush might have been, Remington never considered being isolated in the jungle a deterrent for him to cease in engaging in his most desired, most fulfilling venture in his life – hunting for game. He again will face another morning of hunting, adding close calls and more danger. The hunting in the days ahead will only add more game to track in the bush.

The war failed as a deterrent to stop Remington from living his life to hunt freely.

Remington dreamed one day of hunting once again in the mountains and hills of his beloved Bluegrass state of Kentucky.

Buchanan, out of sheer worry, will lift up extra prayers in the days to come sending Remington into the bush for his mornings of hunting. Buchanan is well aware of the Devil's legions running rampant in the jungle. The evil which runs ever present in the unknown depths of the jungle bush searches and preys for victims to devour.

Kentucky

January 8, 1969

Nothing is as warm and uplifting for a military service member as receiving a letter from home.

Buchanan's most recent 'shot in the arm' of encouragement came from kinfolk in Kentucky.

He finished his daily devotion and history book at 0800 hours in the morning. He then re-read his letter from home he received yesterday.

For the spiritual team, the calendar month had been hectic, along with frequent and many casualties. Combat engineers worked non-stop, twenty-four seven in January, 1969. The engineers responded to an increased series of Viet Cong nocturnal activities due to the religious holidays scheduled on the western calendar, Christian and Jewish. On one hand, Viet Cong attacks on important days such as the 4th of July appeared offensive. On the other hand, attempting to kill intentionally on religious days infuriated Buchanan to no end.

Today, Buchanan visited the An Ngai Dong orphanage and school, followed by a visit with Doc Delaney and the MedCAP in the An Ngai Tay hamlet.

The letter came from one of his favorite aunt's back in the mountains of Kentucky.

Sitting at his desk, he peeked out his window, thinking of his family back home.

Buchanan's favorite family members were his aunts, the matriarchs of the Buchanan's, who he dearly loved. Much of his family lived on

John's Creek and Greasy Creek in the deep hallows of Pike County, Kentucky. The matriarch of the family in the mountains of Kentucky and the grandmother of his aunts rested in the personality of 'Big Mama.' As Buchanan's great-grandmother, she influenced him from a distance, as she preferred to remain in Kentucky with Buchanan's great-grandfather. However, Buchanan's grandfather's family moved to Ohio, preceded by Buchanan's father, after the coal mines shut down early in the century, infuriating the mountain folks. The railroads kept a significant portion of the family in Kentucky with employment. Appalachian populations distrusted 'government men'. After the shutdown of the coal mines, government officials marched themselves into the Tri-State area of Pikeville, Kentucky, promising the essentials of life from jobs to medical care and a general 'better life.' Kentuckians in the general area noticed loads of 'promises' from the government, promises broken after the coal mines shut down. Employment for eligible workers in the Tri-State came from the few remaining coal mines left open and the railroads. Later on in Tri-State history, transportation and gas employers provided livelihoods for households. Most of Buchanan's aunts stayed in Kentucky or in Williamson, West Virginia, across the Tug Fork River, which runs into the Big Sandy River.

Buchanan read the short and sweet piece of correspondence from his aunt out loud.

"December 22, 1968

Dear Robert,

Greetings! What service you have given to our marines. Dorothy and I spoke on the phone, and informs me you're doing God's Will with the troops. Keep it up! Everyone loves you and knows you care for the marines. God is with you and will protect you. Remember that!

Things here at home are basically the same. The economic situation is slightly better. People are still suffering through these years since coal mining took a dive. Some business has come to the area, but it's still difficult. Pikeville College has grown a bit and has helped with job opportunities in the area. The financial situation has improved on campus with the slightest of growth. Though you went to Georgetown College, Pikeville College has always held a special place in your heart. Maybe the fact you were partly raised a Presbyterian! HA! HA!

The family is doing OK! Pop is doing well with his farm in Ohio. I know you love your grandfather. He helped raise you and he did a great job! Your father in Albany, Ohio, received a promotion at work. He is so proud!

Enclosed in the letter is a picture of your cousin, John, who works in the coal mines across the river in West Virginia. He is about as filthy as a coal miner can get. But he has much pride being a third generation coal miner family. He sends his love!

Must go. The family prays for you every day. Keep up the great work for the Lord! The CAP's Dorothy informed me of I think are great! The Lord will use your influence on the people of Vietnam in ways you will never see, but God knows.

We love you!

Your Aunt,
Melinda Adkins"

Buchanan, in a state of euphoria, sat in his swivel chair in a mental state of complete bliss, thinking of the Tri-State Ohio River Valley.

The high spirits ended with an abrupt appearance through the hootch door.

"Chaplain. Chaplain!" blurted Jackson, quickening himself to the desk.

"Yes, Yes, Sergeant. What is it?" asked a bewildered Buchanan. Jackson stood firm in front of Buchanan, smiling from ear to ear.

"Well, are you going to tell me? Or just stand there with that silly grin on your face." Buchanan paused. "Well, Philip? What is it!?!" Buchanan rose out of his swivel chair.

"Guess."

"I can't guess."

"Guess!" Jackson insisted.

"Just spit it out."

"No. Come on, sir, guess."

"All right. Well - the North Vietnamese are -" Jackson quickly interrupted Buchanan, who says, "The Jewish chaplain you were looking for to conduct a late Hanukkah ceremony? Well, you found one - Chaplain Lieutenant Melvin Abrams."

Out of great satisfaction with the news, Buchanan jolts his head upward, smiling from ear to ear. Buchanan celebrated, "Amen!"

"Ole' Melvin." said Buchanan, with a bit of admiration in his voice. "Ollllle' Melv'. I sure do like him. He's a good one. Great chaplain!"

"He said he'd come, sir. In fact, he radioed in, said he'd be here today."

"Great! He can, what? Uh-oh. What? Today?" Buchanan, surprised by the arrival time of Abrams, is taken aback with the news.

"He informed us in his message today is the only day he could come. Is there a problem, sir?"

"Yes, Sergeant. There's a problem. A few Jewish marines are part of that lengthy patrol in and around the Tvy Loan River. Others are on the lengthy missions on the other side of Monkey Mountain, including Private Varnes who requested, no....*insisted*, a Jewish priest come and conduct the service." Buchanan paused, thinking to himself. He says with consternation, "Some of those missions are two, three - even four-day patrol missions. Varnes' group, Company A, won't be back till Friday, two days from now. Captain Johannsson, our good friend, is accompanying Ski on a combat engineering patrol till tomorrow."

Jackson concurred. "Well, I remember Varnes putting up a stink insisting a Jewish chaplain conduct the service. Having a Protestant chaplain present as Jewish personnel went through each step just wasn't going to happen for him, was it?"

"Nope." commented Buchanan.

"It just isn't good enough for us to help them conduct a small service while they participate. And again, I think they have a point, sir." Jackson admired his fellow Jewish marines' strict adherence to their faith. Buchanan nods in the affirmative.

"Well, what are we going to do, sir?"

"I'm thinking. I'm thinking, Sergeant." After careful thought, Buchanan reckoned a solvent for their problem. "We'll keep him here for two or three days. A deal here, a deal there."

"Uh-oh. I see that look in your eye, sir. That sneaky, conniving, I'm thinking up a deal with Case look." Jackson perked up.

"I got it." said Buchanan.

"What, sir?"

"Well, this is how we're going to do it." Buchanan attempts to talk Jackson into a series of negotiating deals. "We'll start at the top - with Lucas. He gets the oak bookcase. You remember, the antique bookcase we saw in Da Nang in that colonel's office, the one he doesn't care to own anymore, and Lucas does. We'll talk Lucas into signing that two-day pass for Major Harley Stewart, in order for him to fly to Okinawa to visit his wounded brother. Major Sanborn's going to get his agriculture supplies to continue his training with the Vietnamese in An Ngai Tay hamlet and surrounding areas, which Stewart has to sign the authorization for."

Jackson stares in amazement.

Buchanan continues. "Major Sanborn will requisition the prime steak for Sergeant McElrath he longs for from Texas and the explosives he desires. And last, McElrath is going to provide an extra M-16, shotgun, a .45 caliber, and, and this is going to be the most difficult, the newest state-of-the-art bow and arrows for Sergeant Remington who works in communications from time to time."

Jackson asked, "How does Captain Case fit in?"

Buchanan explains, "Well, Case, the Scrounger, is just going to encourage Remington to ask headquarters to receive permission to keep Abrams here for another two days."

Catching flies, Jackson stares intently at Buchanan.

"Case does work in communications." Buchanan makes a vital point, with the broadest smile ear to ear.

Out of curiosity, Jackson asks, "In other words, the air traffic is going to have a traffic jam, right?

Buchanan receives nothing but more stares of amazement from Jackson. "How are we going to do all this in the next two days? He can only be here today. And besides, your list of deals is *waaaaay* too complicated to set in place in so short of time."

"Have some faith, baby. Just a little faith." Buchanan lost control of himself. He heard himself talking as if he were a hippie back in southern California. He startled him.

Buchanan insisted on fulfilling his promises. "Listen, Philip. I promised Johannsson and Varnes a Jewish priest, and I'm going to follow through with that commitment. Our Jewish marines have been isolated out here, and we're going to provide for their spiritual wellbeing."

Jackson smiles, nodding in agreement. He pacified Buchanan with a bit of uncertainty in his voice. "Well, I suppose we can try."

"Try? Try Philip?" Buchanan paused in thought. "No, no, no, Philip. It's faith. The Lord will provide." Buchanan sounded off with the utmost of confidence.

"You know something, sir. I think I'm inclined to believe ya."

Buchanan makes a point. "Well, you know what Ralph Waldo Emerson once said, 'Once you make a decision, the universe conspires to make it happen.'"*

Jackson smiles. "Well, let's get moving, sir. I'll start with Stewart and you start with Lucas said Jackson."

"Sounds good to me, Sergeant."

As the spiritual team departed the hootch, the camp noted the too familiar of a pounding bang obvious to everyone in the camp.

The team heard a familiar ping on the roof of the hootch. Then another. And another.

And out of nowhere, out of the blue, a sudden rain came pouring down hard and heavy.

Buchanan thought, 'Really? In January, a hard rain?'

The spiritual team stood on the inside of Buchanan's hootch screen door, watching the downpour, praying for a frog strangler. The roads muddied from torrential rains in Vietnam foiled transportation for days on end. Consecutive down pours drenched the landscape.

In Vietnam, rain reflected a fury, especially during the Monsoon season. Buchanan equated the noise resulting from the smashing of rain onto the ground in Vietnam with a thousand drums thumping nonmetrical beats, adding a 1000 locomotives amid tons of tennis ball size hail hitting the ground and rooftops of the hootches in camp simultaneously. The clatter numbed the nerves of marines and sailors. Down pours tested the resolve of military personnel. Rain fall came randomly at the start of the monsoon season. As the season began, the sporadic rain fall came hesitant and cautious, with dreary clouds in the sky. As the season kicked in full throttle, the rains came with a vengeance. In the bush, rain fall soaked every inch of foliage in the bush. Anything at all barren turned out drenched in a matter of seconds. Millions of rain drops pouring down on the surface of the earth bursting onto the ground generating a red sea of muddy, soggy conditions. Droplets of rain pounding upon the ground resulted in mini bomb explosions, relentless sheets of rain resembling a regiment of a drum core reverberating the power and the sheer destruction of man-made constructions such as plumbing and bridges erected by marine engineers and Navy Seabees.

Spiritual men in the bush huddled in their hootches till the down pour ended, praying to God to bestow mercy onto the camp, to protect it from the destructive damage the rains inflicted upon man and man made. Not only did the rain come suddenly, the lifting of the rain came abrupt as well. Marines leisurely emerged from their hootches after the rain, as several marines, drenched from head to toe from the heavy rains, inspected the damage done from the sky above. The pound of force from raindrops onto the earth's surface threw mud onto hootches and metal roof top buildings in the camp. Mud thrown up on the lower half of the constructed buildings splattered an evenly waistline of smeared muck around the buildings. Every nook and cranny of camp possessed a pool of water, with a covering of smog above the ground's surface from the smoldering heat of Southeast Asia.

Buchanan abhorred monsoon rains. The destruction which ensued after a hard downpour threw Buchanan into a melancholy mood. For once, he welcomed the unexpected rain. The beast of nature above served a purpose in delaying Abrams, requiring him an extended stay in Camp Love to perform his duties as a Jewish chaplain, preserving Buchanan's perfect record of oversight to protect the men's religious freedom.

Buchanan set as a top priority the preservation of a marine's individual freedom of religion, regardless of denomination or faith.

As initial rains poured down, Chaplain Abrams, assigned to the 1st Battalion, 5th Marines An Hoa, rode into Camp Love in a truck from Da Nang. In his second tour in a row, he had visited the Da Nang Air Base hospital to visit recently wounded from the 9th Marines. Just a mere six miles away from Camp Love riding shut gun, he expected a ride shut gun back to Da Nang, climb onto a helicopter, or climb up into a truck scheduled for transport to the vicinity of An Hoa.

"Yes! Rain!" yelled Jackson.

"Amen!" Buchanan affirmed the Lord's preferential will. "Thank You Lord! Let the rain pour down from the Heavens!"

"Rain will keep him here, sir!" said Jackson with a tone of assurance.

Unbeknownst to the spiritual team, Abrams, already in camp, stood ready, willing, and able to fulfill his duties as Navy chaplain in the dentist's office. He and the truck driver scampered into the dentist's hootch, just two hootches from Buchanan's. Abrams fled the drenching downpour of millions of monsoon raindrops descending onto human flesh as mini iron pellets seeking to penetrate the vulnerable five layers of skin.

As the rains came down, the spiritual team reassessed the situation.

"Well, Sergeant. I think because of the rain, we're home free." Buchanan commented with a smug smile.

"Yes, sir. I believe I can agree with that assessment. Scratch plan A?"

"Yes, Plan A is history, with each and every trade off, including The Scrounger's."

"Amen to that, sir."

"Yes, Amen!" agreed Buchanan.

Lasting for over five minutes, the rain came to a screeching halt. Buchanan constantly came taken by surprise with the abrupt start of monsoon rains, and came just as surprised with the sudden and swift end of a torrential monsoon rainfall. The storms appeared and vanished in a blink of an eye.

The spiritual team stepped out of the hootch, perused a sea of red mud resulted from the drowning of rainfall covering the perimeter and the treeline. The hard rain left the hootch tops and buildings muddy. The rain fall left slippery surfaces, causing unwanted falls resulting in a possible broken bone. The top of the earth's surface delivered a maroon shade of mud coated onto the ground, which deemed an appearance of a chocolate bar.

The dentist, followed by Abrams, and the driver, stepped out from his hootch. The threesome stood on wooden stilts protecting military personnel from water and reptiles. Abrams stepped down onto the muddy surface, noticing the spiritual team. The team unawares of Abrams' presence.

Taking a panoramic view of the camp, the spiritual team assessed the aftermath of the rain. The team thought, 'I wonder if Abrams turned and attempted to hightail it out of here, back to Da Nang.'

Simultaneously, the team asked each other, "You don't suppose he went back due to the -"

"Chaplain Buchanan!" interrupted Abrams.

Turning their heads swiftly, the spiritual team caught sight of Abrams standing right in front of them. The unbelievable sight displayed before the team came beyond description.

Abrams experienced seven straight days out in the bush of horrific, savage war. In the past week, the 5th Marines of I Corps engaged the enemy in harsh and ferocious combat. He made his way from An Hoa assisted by the 1st Battalion 5th Marines to Da Nang to visit recent wounded from major confrontations with the Viet Cong in the vicinity. Abrams exhibited a depiction of a spiritual warrior entrusted with achieving the chaplain corps slogan, 'cooperation without compromise'.

The spiritual team observed a worn out chaplain underneath a muddied, dirty, grim soaked uniform, even blood stains on his dungaree top and trousers. His hands blackened, brown from hardships in the bush covered with grim. Abrams' eyebrows and gruff hairs on his face from the neglect of shaving for several days were jam-packed with dirt. A casing of dirt and grim attached to his facial skin from the bush exposed the white of his blue eyes standing bright and shiny, rendering a glassy stare. Portraying a human being drained of energy, Abrams amplified without choice the three w's – weak, weary, and worn. His uniform presented as torn, mangled, sagging from moisture and exposure of the elements. His green camouflaged helmet covered brown, black, and maroon from the horrors of war. He stunk high Heaven from the stench of sweat, blood, dirt, death, and war. The sight screamed of exhaustion and sleep deprivation.

"Good to see you, Chaplain Buchanan." Abrams extended his right hand to his spiritual friend, shaking hands with confirmation.

"Nice seeing you, Chaplain Abrams."

Abrams proclaimed, "Heard great things about you. You're doing a great job."

"Thanks, Melvin. I've heard the same from you. I can certainly see you have been working hard."

The men chuckle.

Abrams shakes Jackson's hand. "Sergeant. It's been a while. Good to see you. Different times. Different person in front of me, I see."

"Uh. Yes. Yes, sir. Different person for sure, sir."

Grinning, Buchanan raises eyebrows.

Jackson fidgets as he explains, "Sir. We've some Jewish personnel that insisted a Jewish chaplain be present to conduct a Hanukkah service. Sir, we've been isolated for months out here in the bush and our Jewish personnel haven't seen a Jewish chaplain for probably, oh, say, four months or so."

Buchanan expounds, "That's right, Melv. There's one enlisted and an officer exclusively requesting a Jewish chaplain to lead in a

Hanukkah service. We've offered our services to assist as the Jewish personnel would lead and take part in the ceremony. But they, well, honestly, insisted on having a Jewish priest present. It's two, three weeks late now for Hanukkah. It's not even the Season now."

"Well, taking in the situation at hand, better late than never. That's what my mother always used to say." Abrams grins, followed by smiles from the spiritual team.

Buchanan remarked, "When I put the word out for the need for a Jewish priest, well, thought I'd have waited even longer than we did today. I'll tell ya, I'm thrilled it's you who's responded."

"Well, from the looks of the road there -" said Abrams, glancing toward the road, "I ain't, and I say, *ain't* going anywhere."

The spiritual team chuckle knowing the rains saved the day.

"Skies still dark and the clouds are gray, Melvin." mentioned Buchanan.

The spiritual leaders discuss the Jewish personnel's absence in camp because of patrols. The duration of the absences will expand two to three days tops, and the interim of time for a return from patrol duty and heavy rains made possible a justified delay for Abram's departure.

Frustrated with the news and annoyed, Abrams points out the obvious. "Not good, Robert. I'm to return to the 5th marines today, tonight. Not three days from now. The good news for the 5th Marines, there's a lag in fighting the last day and a half, and the marines needed the coffee break, so to speak."

Buchanan says, "The ARVN and South Vietnamese marines, fighting alongside the 5th, needed a break as well. They're dog-tired."

The men nod in the affirmation.

With all sincerity, Jackson makes a point. "Sorry, sir. But we have some devout, committed and faithful Jewish personnel here in camp. Our concern is to fulfill the responsibility to protect marines' religious freedom. That's all."

"That's right, Melv. Uh...listen Melvin. If you can't stay, we understand. We'll-We'll get you back as soon as we can." commented Buchanan.

As Abrams was about to respond, a faint flow of raindrops felt from the sky above reached the surface of the earth. The men gazed upward into the gray clouds, when suddenly heavy volleys of rain begun. The sheets of rain hammered down a severe bloody nose onto the camp, dealing a sombering ambiance in Camp Love. A second go a round of weighty sheets of torrential rain delivered the coup de gras onto the marines, forcing the camp onto its knees waving a white flag.

The scamper to Buchanan's hootch came about as comical, displaying body language of desperation to reach dry space to escape the dense pellets from the sky above. If bystander marines viewed the men's attempt to reach Buchanan's hootch door as the rain started, the bystanders beheld three intelligent men slip, skit, fall to the left and right, and comically attempt to lend a hand to hold one another up from the slippery surface. The whole while, the three men humored one another with their efforts to hold one another up from falling onto the muddy surface.

The velocity of rain increased and the density of rain thickened, falling by potency and weight with the second wave. Buchanan understood the monsoon rains prior to arriving in Vietnam. The season sped into a full swing in January. The monsoon rains today prevent the normalcy of life and thwart vision five feet in front of you.

Buchanan's hootch stood on wooden stilts to protect the inhabitants from the dangers of rural Vietnam, including monsoon rains.

The men continued to step toward the hootch as the rain poured down. Visibility became null to void, as the men searched for the wooden steps of Buchanan's hootch, which were slippery. The elements made the perfect combination for an uphill battle to step into a dry floored hootch.

The men finally reach dry ground, entering the hootch, humored and shocked by the sudden rainfall.

"Well, Melv. Another one such as this rain, you'd be here for a week, not a day or two." said Buchanan.

"For sure, Robert. For sure."

"You want to shower and shave?" asks Buchanan naively.

"No! Absolutely not!" came an abrupt answer from Abrams.

Taken aback by Abram's hasty response, the spiritual team sensed some pride in his tone of voice.

"Sorry, Robert. No. I don't care to clean myself up just yet." Abrams apologizes.

"Ok. OK, Melvin. That's fine." Buchanan didn't push the matter.

"Would you like something to eat, sir?"

"No Jackson. I'll just sit for a moment." Abrams caught sight of Buchanan's cot, brushing aside his chairs, sitting on his backside on the foot end of the cot falling back, exhaling a heavy but soothing sigh.

"Uhhhhhhhhh! That feels awesome!"

"Sure you don't want any chow, sir?"

With his eyes closed shut and a slight grin on his face, Abrams thought of home he longed for. "Sure, Sergeant. If you insist on getting some chow for me, go ahead. I'll be here."

The spiritual team turns toward one another, smiling ear to ear. Buchanan motions with his hands to go to the chow hall for some food, and moves his lips, 'Get something good.' He rubs his stomach and throws a thumbs up.

As Jackson exits the hootch, Buchanan sat in a chair quietly, retrieving a military history book. He took advantage of the quiet moment.

Thinking Abrams fell asleep, Buchanan read his history book. Following several minutes, Abrams asks, "Tell me of your ministry here in Camp Love, Robert. I'm interested."

Taken aback, Abrams surprised Buchanan, thinking he had fallen asleep.

Buchanan explained his position in camp. "Well, it's a general ministry to the men. There are the regular visits, venturing out on patrols for the usual services. Then there's the CAP's, the An Ngai Tay Hamlet and An Ngai Don hamlet and orphanage, which might be my favorite elements of our ministry. The two orphanages..." He continued a few minutes or so, speaking of the CAPs until he finished.

"And then there's the ministry to marines out in the field, my other favorite part of ministry. Let me tell you about my experiences in the field. I love that portion of the job description - so to speak." Buchanan chuckles.

Glancing toward Abrams, motionless and still, Buchanan leans towards him. He asks, "Chaplain Abrams? Melvin? You awake?"

Slowly grinning, it hits Buchanan Abrams is zonked. Gone! Hit the hay. Abrams waved the white flag. Surrendering to exhaustion.

Leaning back in his chair, Buchanan gives Abrams a good, intense stare. Laying before him, zonked out on his cot, stretched his grimy, grubby, friend in a soiled uniform who had given his all days on end for the Lord.

Seven rough, violent days of combat in the bush, placing himself in the line of fire to pray over the dead and dying, and the wounded. Seven days of overseeing the spiritual needs of men fighting for freedom and to preserve the freedoms of fellow combatants, the ARVN.

Buchanan prayed Abrams experienced pleasant dreams avoiding nightmares, knowing Abrams gained little sleep in the past week.

Buchanan spoke a soft prayer, "Lord, please permit Melvin, a dear friend, to experience pleasant dreams of home and family. Amen."

Watching Abrams sleep and examining his uniform reminded him of the picture of his cousin, John. Dirty, filthy, hardly recognizable, and dog-tired from working in the coal mines. Showing signs of suffering from the three w's in the photograph resulted from long shifts, tedious hours in the mountains, the darkness of the caves, and constant fear of cave-ins. Employment requiring the utmost respect from others.

Cousin John lived a dangerous, high stakes position of employment.

Regardless of the risky dangers of his cousin's employment, Cousin John's dangers paled in comparison to Abrams dangerous, high stakes position of Navy chaplain in the bush of Vietnam. Abrams position faced a much steeper gamble with the threat of his life being taken away from him.

Jackson finally returned with a tin plate and cover with meal in hand, along with a tin bread holder full of bread.

As Jackson entered the hootch quietly, Buchanan motioned with his index finger up to his mouth the 'shush' sign.

Jackson noticed Abrams tuckered out in a deep sleep.

The time stood still at 1100 hours sharp.

The spiritual team left Abrams alone, as the men sat reading history books. Abrams laid in such a deep state of sleep, the team even excused themselves to eat in the chow hall.

Returning from chow, the men dove back into their seats to read more history by the side of the exhausted chaplain, with an occasional question from Buchanan asking Jackson a military question.

"You suppose he wears his bullet-proof vest in the bush? I know it's heavy and all, but can it really save a person's life?"

"Well, sir. The vest is optional for chaplains, as you well know. Seeing him lying there, he might be wearing it."

Jackson smiles.

The two men continue to read.

Abrams slept for eight solid hours, waking up at 1830 hours.

"What? Where am I?" Abrams shifts his head as he woke up.

"Chaplain Abrams. It's me, Chaplain Buchanan."

"What? What time is it?" asked Abrams as he slowly recognizes his surroundings.

"You're in Camp Love. Remember?" said Jackson.

Buchanan updates Abrams on the time. "It's 1830 hours. You've slept for eight solid hours, Melvin."

"What!?!" Abrams excitedly jumps up, unbeknownst to the time. "I can't stay here. I got to get out of here!"

"Wait. Wait, a second Melvin!" said Buchanan.

Jackson informed Abrams of the situation. "Roads are closed down, sir. There won't be a vehicle for at least two days, chaplain. And practically all the helicopters have been reassigned 15 miles northwest of Da Nang to give a hand to evacuate many South Vietnamese soldiers who are in a quagmire of firefights between the US XXIV Corps and ARVN forces against the NVA 368th B Regiment and elements of VC forces."

Buchanan furthered the point, "Besides, the enemy has seemed to have shifted their fighting north of Da Nang. The 5th has reported that the enemy is withdrawing from all the sectors they have been fighting in. They are going to be given a break, the 5th."

Abrams listened to every word from Buchanan, sitting back down on the cot, sighing very hard.

"You have pleasant dreams, Melvin?" asked Buchanan.

"As a matter of fact, I did."

"Amen!"

Abrams described his dreams. "I dreamed my family drove up to New Jersey for a beach picnic. My grandparents were there, though they're dead and gone. My brothers and I wasted all our money on games in the Arcade. Of course, we tested the waters, getting our feet wet. We've never really been beach people, though. How 'bout your family, Robert?"

"No Melvin, not really. Beach life seems dirty to me. It seems like you're constantly picking sand off yourself, though we enjoy walking the beach in the evening. Now that's beautiful, walking on the beach at night. *Yeah*, that's fun."

"Yeah, you're right. Dusk is beautiful. It really reflects the beauty of God's creation, doesn't it, Robert?"

Buchanan stares out in space with the slightest grin. "*Yeah*. It sure does."

"It's beautiful, isn't Sergeant?" Abrams asked Jackson.

"Sure is, Chaplain Abrams. Sure is."

Smiling, Abrams said, "Along with the picnic, you know, in the dream, my father brought a few sets of checkers, and we had a mini checkers tournament. My sister, who's intelligent, won the tournament. She won in real life too. She's always been intuitive."

"Checkers player is she, sir?" asked Jackson.

"Yep. Chess too."

Buchanan commented, "Well, she'd blow me away both in chess and checkers. I'm not much of a player, you know. I can play, but not much of a player. Sergeant Jackson there might give her a game. He's not bad."

Jackson, nodding, shrugs his shoulders. He admits, 'I'm not a terrible player.'

Abrams said, "Maybe we'll play one day when we have more time."

"Yeah, that'd be nice, sir."

After a bit more fellowship, Abrams eventually showered and shaved, clueless he now was here to stay. He accompanied Buchanan for two days as the chaplains ministered to the men.

The rapport Buchanan had established with the men impressed Abrams.

When the entire component of Jewish personnel returned on Thursday January 13, 1969, Abrams led the Hanukkah service. Varnes, Johannsson, and 12 additional Jewish personnel finally took part in the traditional service, including Chaplain Abrams. Varnes could have cared less about the lateness of the service. He, along with his fellow Jewish friends of faith, came off pleased Jewish marines could finally celebrate the season.

Foremost for chaplains in Vietnam required them to exert patience and versatility. Overcoming religious and social barriers during a war pleased religious leaders. Religious ceremonies, from time to time, required modification to provide military personnel the ministry Navy chaplains were called to fulfill. The troops adapted to intricate situations in the war without losing the intrinsic elements of spiritual needs.

Abrams eventually trekked back to the 5th Marines via a truck to Da Nang Air Base, followed by a Huey helicopter to the bush to minister to the 5th Marines, 1st Marine Division. Seven months remained in Abrams' tour.

Not a day passed which the spiritual team did not lift up prayers to God for Abrams in the field providing ministry to the marines.

Buchanan's prayer list expanded exponentially but thought nothing of it.

Buchanan loved Melvin Abrams. Buchanan prayed every day his friend took comfort in God's protective armor to shield and guard him from enemy threat and peril.

Without a doubt, the spiritual team woke up everyday confident God's protective shield will protect Abrams for his remaining seven months of duty till he boards a plane to go home.

To board a plane for home and picnic in New Jersey with his family.

A Full Day of War

January 14, 1969

Buchanan experienced indelible hectic days of ministry in January. The 14th day resulted in many chaotic incidents, one after the other. Whatever Buchanan dreamed of making a day miserable, it happened. The day consisted of counseling marine after marine due to receiving a dear John letter from home - not his favorite face-to-face counseling session. Part of the day embraced stressful counseling sessions, coping with the mental strain of war and coming to grips with the death and pain of war. The spiritual team conducted services in the chapel, visited the wounded, visited the departments in camp, and the worst situation of the day involving a marine who struck his superior officer across the jaw. The young marine connected a fist upon the officer's chin out of frustration with his life taking a downward slope, feeling deep inside all the roads in his future seemed to paint a gloomy end of life. The marine received a dear John letter, his parents were getting a divorce, and several infractions were thrown his way, including insubordination. The bombardment of disappointments came from all directions, throwing him into a tizzy, losing all control of himself. Distant from home and the incapability of solving his problems from Vietnam weighed too much for him. He lost his scruples, attacking his superior officer.

Exhaustion hit Buchanan like a ton of bricks, numb from the spirited day. Drained of energy, he succumbed to his fatigue, pure and simple. As dusk drew near, he desired nothing but shut eye, longing to offer his worn body a deserved rejuvenation.

For the past two and a half months on Tuesday nights, Buchanan and his friends, enlisted and officer, gathered to play 500 Rummy. The usual bunch to play cards were Buchanan, Doc Delaney, Senior Chief Gross, Vickers, Jurgensen, Remington, Jackson, Sergeant Burnside, Burns, Adkins, Frost, Skawinski, Rockford, Rodriquez, and sometimes Lucas and Sigmanson. Occasionally, the group invited a visitor to play with the close-knit group. Of course, the group of friends, officer and enlisted vetted special guests thoroughly prior to dealing any cards to the individual. The card players considered the group's integrity impeccable, guarding against cheaters infiltrating the field of play. Most attended the night to gamble, or at least a night to relax. Besides, one lucky marine or sailor will walk away with all the winnings after giving it a crack at making some dough.

The men played a penny for every point lost in a game played. So if a player had 250 points at the end of the game, he would lose $2.50. Sometimes, when playing for higher stakes, it would be two pennies for every point lost. The group awarded half the money won to non-profit causes such as Kensington's orphanage, the An Ngai Tay Village, the Catholic fund, or another such nonprofit organization. The remaining fifty percent given to the winner for the night. Occasionally, the men agreed the winner would receive the whole jackpot for keeps. Tonight was one of those nights.

Buchanan desired to stay home and rest. His day had been taxing. The temptation to hibernate in his hootch to relax ran high, skipping the night of playing cards to either read history or write a letter to Dorothy. But tonight came a scheduled winner take all, and winning a roll of dough tempted him more than hibernating for the night. So he played. Besides, the addiction to competitive board and card games in the Buchanan household ran through their blood veins, especially 500 Rummy. Changing into his shorts and t-shirt for the night, a rarity for him, he departed his hootch dressed in unusual, informal attire. But the usual humid temperatures reached scorching levels throughout southeastern Asia this day. Buchanan cared little about his informal appearance. He hated the heat, refusing to suffer through the evening.

Buchanan walked briskly to Burns' supply office, the usual spot to 'deal the cards.' Supply provided the office space to play cards with plenty of room for fold out tables and chairs. Buchanan walked an obvious confidence to supply, certain lady luck accompanied him tonight, making him the big winner. He glowed with self-assurance. He looked forward to "rake" in the money, to 'win all the marbles' as he liked to put it.

Most of the group arrived for the night to start the 'gambling,' as Adkins referred to the card playing. He and Burns were on their way to supply, as Burns prepared the music selected for the night. When not playing cards, Petty Officer Sigmanson volunteered on Tuesday nights to begin the music at 2130 hours. Adkins had had a long day on a construction assignment with the Seabees and had a long day.

Tuesday nights undeniably placed Buchanan in a setting of congeniality and a sense of being home with family.

Adkins and Burns still had yet to arrive, as an antsy Buchanan felt eager for the first hand of 'gambling' to begin. He wanted to hear 'They're off' with the first hand dealt, knowing without a doubt the presence of 'lady luck' stood on the side of the chaplain this night. Frost and Jackson set up the tables and chairs with help from Skawinski and Remington. The remaining card players chatted about the recent Viet Cong attacks in the vicinity, eating finger food contributed by group members.

The mind set of Buchanan focused on nothing but winning some dough.

"You ready to lose some money tonight, *Padre*? A night for keeps, ya know." said Jurgensen.

"Listen here Sergeant, the Lord knows I've been eyeing a new camera in the commissary at the base. It's mine. You're toast tonight, Sergeant. Besides, the Lord's on my side!" responded Buchanan with a broad grin.

"Ha!" responded Jurgensen.

"Wrong, chaplain. The Lord's going to humble you tonight. That's the truth. I'm gonna humble you when you lose all your money tonight, sir. Besides, I've been eyeing something myself. Additional train cars for my boys back home. Those train cars are mine." added Jurgensen with a sneer smile.

The chaplain and the Gunny eye one another with winning confidence.

Adkins finally arrived, entering the office. His friends thought he presented himself with a bit too much of a strut of confidence, especially for Buchanan's liking.

"Please John, you're not going to win tonight and that's that. So don't come strutting in here as if you're going to own us tonight. You're only an amateur in comparison to the rest of us." Buchanan, with a slight smile and a bit of sarcasm, gave his friend the business in his little speech.

Adkins said not a word. He sat down in a chair opposite of Buchanan in the room, smiling. Adkins pointed to his chest, motioning with his mouth, "I'm going to win."

Buchanan shrugged him off with a smug grin, turned and sat at a different table.

"OK gentlemen, you're in for a blistering tonight. Lady Luck's on the side of the Master, me." insisted Skawinski.

"Pleeeease!" responded Skawinski's friends.

"Look, Ski, you think you're the Master. Lady Luck is on the side of officers tonight, and you're no officer." Frost pauses, chuckling. "Besides, look at Adkins there. He thinks he's going to win the big stash tonight. HA!" Frost glances with certainty toward Adkins.

The combat hardened Seabee throws a simple half grin at Frost with indignation.

"Let's just get going. I'm hungry tonight for some dough. I'm Bret Maverick* and nobody can touch me tonight." commented Burns.

All laugh.

"Seriously, James? Bret Maverick can't match Bat Masterson*, and I'm he." said Rockford, laughing.

The entire group again laughs at the ridiculous showboating by practically everyone in the room. They were ready to play. Prior to the first card dealt, all were reminded once again of the rules from Burns.

Burns took a moment to re-brief the players of the rules of card playing for the night.

The rules for Tuesday nights were simple. The night of card playing comprised a tournament style format, eliminating the bottom two players from each table after each round of play. The night would start with 3 or 4 men at each table for the first round. The top two winners from each table in each round advanced to the second round, which would have four players each at two tables. The third and final round consisted of one table and again four players. The top player won the night's winnings, keeping the money. The players, when arriving at Burns' office on Tuesday nights, chose freely to sit at any table that suited their fancy. The players practiced first come, first served. Each table played with 6 jokers in the deck of cards worth 50 points each, enabling most hands to be played quickly, resulting in high scores with each hand. The group automatically eliminated a player with no wins entering the last game of competition. Each table played six games per round. Advancement required winning the most games, not total points.

One Draconian measure adhered to by all in the group and enforced if caught was cheating. The person caught cheating found himself banned from the 500 Rummy group, prevented from attending the Tuesday nights of normalcy. Needless to say, no marine or sailor risked losing a night of normalcy simply by getting caught cheating at cards. And the marines were men of integrity, so they ever caught anyone cheating.

Adkins intentionally sat opposite from Buchanan at another table in order to play him the final round. The friendly rivalry between Adkins and Buchanan on the card nights resulted in evenings of friendly competition. Though they were friends, the men possessed a competitive spirit.

When players arrived for the night, they sat randomly, usually positioning themselves opposite of each by rank. The intentional mix of enlisted and officer at each table generated a competitive aura in the room. The rivalry between the ranks emerged naturally to Buchanan.

A tie of games at the end of a round would be broken by totaling the combined points scored from the six games from each of the players who tied with total wins. Each winner advanced to the next round with winnings won. The first dealer for the night came chosen by each player drawing a card out of the first deck of cards played and the highest card in value determined the first dealer. This night, Buchanan drew a King of Hearts, the highest value of cards drawn at his table, so he dealt first.

Twelve men arrived for the night of card playing, requiring three players per table. The top two winners advanced to the next round. The night started with Burnside, Jurgensen, and Frost at one table. The second table slotted Rockford, Jackson, and Skawinski to battle each other. The third table positioned Buchanan, Burns, and Vickers against one another. The last table to butt heads were Adkins, Remington, and Gross, clashing in the first round of competition.

Buchanan dealt the first hand and, as custom, whether he dealt or not, he let all of his cards fall face down on the table. After the cards were dealt, he would pick up one card at a time, inspecting each one separately to determine how to play the card in his hand. He placed his cards accordingly in his hand with possible spreads on how he could score points. For some odd reason, Buchanan seemed to possess superstitious genes in his DNA. He lifted each card in this manner with every hand ever since his poker days while enlisted in the Air Force.

The elation of the value of cards he dealt himself filled him with joy as he lifted his cards to view one by one. His first card valued an Ace of Diamonds. The second card dealt valued an Ace of Hearts. The third card picked up amounted to a joker, while the fourth card turned revealed a Ten of hearts. The fifth and sixth cards were two more tens, the spade and clubs. Buchanan lifted the corner of the last card slow and methodical, taking a quick glance at the value - and thrilled to no end for the last card disclosed a joker. Two jokers, two aces, and three tens. Wow! What a hand to start the night!

With his combination spreads, Buchanan went out on his first turn of play, placing his opponents in an enormous hole. It was a great start for Chaplain Buchanan and a sizable lead.

However, the moment of jubilation ended just as quickly as Buchanan never saw another lead in points or monies the rest of the evening.

Lady Luck showed no favoritism toward Buchanan this night. She brushed him aside, showing no mercy on him. The camera with his name on it in the Da Nang commissary will sit on the shelf a bit longer. After the first hand, he rarely won another, losing every penny from his lock box he stored his Rummy money in.

The first round passed in a blink of an eye, following high scores and fast hands. Adkins and Skawinski landed a seat in the second round. Buchanan, as usual, hung around to the very end on Tuesday nights, curious to know which friend will win the night's winnings.

One of a few superb players in the group, to everyone's surprise, proved to be Adkins. The Navy Seabee displayed himself as a stiff-necked military officer. A conservative Baptist null and void of religious toleration. But as the men in camp became accustomed to Adkins, he exhibited traits of a man who deep down inside possessed consideration, holding the love and forgiveness of Jesus. Adkins had played his cards well, winning more money for the night.

Buchanan watched his friends play the final round. Six games played in the second round were quick with high scores as Adkins and Skawinski played themselves into the final round. Buchanan set his sights in the beginning of the night on purchasing his camera, but the camera would have to be put on hold.

Advancing with Adkins and Skawinski to the final round were Burns and Jurgensen.

The final round started fast for Adkins, winning the first two games with ease. Scoring 605 points the first game, one of the highest scores for the night, and 570 points for the second game. Burns totaled 495 points in both games, lacking a last turn of play, preventing the music lover from positioning him in a commanding lead.

Adkins was in a brilliant spot to win the night's play of Rummy. A win following the third game would set him with a three games to nothing lead, basically eliminating each player in turn as they would lose the fourth and fifth games, given Adkins avoided losing himself.

Lady Luck smiled on anybody but Adkins thereafter, especially Burns.

The third and fourth games found Jurgensen and Skawinski in the winner's circle. Jurgensen, a fine card player himself, won the vital fifth game, positioning himself in a first-place tie with Adkins. In shock, the Seabee sat in disbelief. The fact Adkins held a two to nothing game lead on his opponents and failing to win a third and crucial game felt the air let out of the balloon. A complete collapse on Adkins part.

Avoiding a tie breaker, Adkins faced a do or die situation, forced to win the last game. There was plenty of Rummy to be played and Adkins still sat in the driver's seat. However, the fact Rummy consisted of fifty percent luck and fifty percent skill, Adkins worried his 50% of luck had run out.

The card playing friends had eliminated Burns from play falling short of winning a single game, while the three remaining players set themselves for the sixth game. The standings for the sixth game slated Adkins winning the first two games, Jurgensen securing two, and Skawinski respectively winning the fourth game, and Burns tallying a miserable zero.

Adkins shot out of the gate, winning big. The first hand Adkins scored a whopping 235 points, giving him a sizable head start entering the second hand. Again, Adkins won the second hand, combining multiple jokers with spreads, posting a score of 220 points. Jurgensen scored 275 while Skawinski gained 260 points following two hands.

Wow! 455 points combining two hands of play as Buchanan noted the smug smile splattered all over Adkins' face only he could possess. Now cocky, he felt destined to win. Buchanan glanced toward Adkins, expressing in body language, 'don't count your chickens before they hatch'. Adkins merely smirks. The fact he wore a smug grin smeared all over his face, just about every marine and sailor in the room longed for nothing but for Adkins to lose.

Lady Luck paid a visit to Jurgensen and Skawinski in the third and fourth hands, as the two marines respectively scored 150 and 145 in the two hands. Adkins scored a measly 25 points combined for the third and fourth hands, with now a score of 480. Jurgensen's score tallied 425 points while Skawinski's score totaled 405 through four hands. Jokers enabled Adkins to establish a large lead, but the power of jokers empowered Jurgensen and Skawinski to make a run at Adkins in the third and fourth hands.

Skawinski laid out two spreads his second turn in the fifth hand placing Adkins and Jurgensen in the hole. The sixth hand spotted Jurgensen going out on his third turn, placing Adkins and Skawinski in the hole. In just two hands of Rummy, Adkins' score fell from 480 to 310 points. Twice in the night, he placed himself on the verge of winning the pot for the evening. Again, he seemed flabbergasted how close he was to winning, but failed. In the seventh hand, Adkins finally ended the hand as he laid out two spreads in his third turn going out, positioning himself back in the game with 405 points while Jurgensen placed first with a score of 425 while Skawinski followed suit in third place with 385 points. The final round turned into a night of attrition, with a sense Lady Luck sat along with the winning player willing to slug it out to the end.

The eliminated Rummy players looked on with excitement, generating encouragement for friend, while discouraging and jabbing slights toward foes.

The eighth hand finally determined the winner, as frustration kicked in towards the end of the night, as each player was on the cusp of winning the night's pot of money. As the players rotated with three turns each in the eighth hand, every player laid down on the table one or two spreads. Neither Jurgensen, Skawinski, or Adkins risked holding any spreads this late in the game. In the three turns, Jurgensen played 70 points worth, Adkins 55 points, and Skawinski with 35 points. Finally, in the seventh turn, Jurgensen went out drawing a joker from the deck and played the 50 point card with 2 aces he had been holding, along with a 8 of diamonds he discarded to play out his hand. Lady Luck shined on Jurgensen this night.

"Woo hoo!" yelled Jurgensen.

"I won. I won! My boys are getting new cars for their trains back home." bragged Jurgensen. He won the night with $69.35.

"Congratulations sir." Skawinski shook Jurgensen's hand.

The group congratulated him.

"Well done, Gunny. You played like the Vegas player you are." commented Adkins, smiling with less smug.

Buchanan sensed disappointment from Adkins. His intention of winning dollars settled sending the money home to his son to purchase a new bicycle. A stranger stole his old bike right under his family's nose from the basement directly below the kitchen while his family ate lunch.

"Well, Adkins, you came smug, but you're leaving with your tail between your legs." quipped Frost.

Adkins felt as if Frost deserved a fist across his chin. The Seabee officer could hold his own. He was no slouch himself. As a former enlisted marine, he could account for himself if backed into a corner.

"No kidding Frost. You figured that out all by yourself, huh?" replied Adkins with sarcasm.

"You gave a heck of a fight, though. I have a feeling you're not going to be easy to beat from here on out." stated Frost. He threw a brash glance toward Adkins as if to say, 'I told you so.'

"No, no I'm not. Expect a 'maniac' type of player from here on out." commented Adkins.

The group knew Adkins' conservative approach to life, humoring them.

With nothing but sportsmanship and friendship in mind, group members eliminated from playing cards remained to support fellow friends, supporting one another in the night of normalcy. Tonight was no different. Every Tuesday night provided a means of coping with the war.

"Oh well, John." Buchanan consoled his friend. "There's always next time."

Adkins half grins, accepting the hard loss with his head high.

"It is what it is. The Gunny's sons are younger than mine and they'll enjoy the new train cars." conceded Adkins. "Besides, a new one come May will be a great birthday gift. Money left over, I was going to purchase some new Napoleonic military history books by the recent newcomer, David G. Chandler. They're expensive, you know. Besides, the bike and the books are wants, not needs, as you know well."

"That's the time." encouraged Buchanan.

"Hey, it's time for music." Burns with anticipation looked at his watch. "It's 2130 hours. Petty Officer Sigmanson is to start tonight's piece - Kunstlerleben op. 316 by Johann Strauss, a waltz. Gents, enjoy, for this is a favorite piece of music and believe me, you're going to love it."

Sitting back in their chairs, the men soaked in all the music, which soothed the heart and mind. Every marine and sailor in the group suffered a strenuous day. Frost lost a marine killed and four wounded in an ambush, Jurgensen dealt with discipline problems, and Gross woke up in the morning bombarded by wounded in the medical aid station. Problems for Buchanan mounted hour by hour during the day. The music, at least momentarily, placed daily problems aside, at least for a moment in time and space. Buchanan heard a waltz or two in his life, but this waltz in particular by Strauss pleased his heart, therapeutic for his war-torn heart and soul. The inspiration for writing the waltz followed the defeat of the Austrians from the hands of the mighty Prussian military machine in 1866 at the battle of Koniggratz. The waltz, written in A minor, began with a brass solo followed by a soft string passage. The waltz consisted of high-spirited tunes, dramatic chords, and melancholic tunes. The piece of music complemented with a strong percussion foundation throughout the waltz.

As the music played, the group detected a whistle in the air from the outside of supply.

Immediately, Frost recognized the whistling as projectiles! "Hit the deck!" yelled Frost.

BANG! BANG! BANG!

KABOOM! BANG!

POP! POP! POP! POP!

The familiar sounds of combat echoed within the camp.

The music, rudely interrupted by weaponry and mortar fire, continued to play as a battle begun inside the perimeter of Camp Love.

The VC sneaked into camp under the darkness of dusk through the east perimeter of Camp Love. A dozen or more VC entered the camp through the main entrance. The camp received enemy fire from all directions of the perimeter. A most terrorizing threat came from mortar fire raining down onto the camp from the west end of the perimeter.

Marines who had been lounging in their hootches near the main entrance quickly secured the main gate.

38 Viet Cong infiltrated the camp from the east perimeter and through the main entrance.

Frost and Jurgensen crawled to the corner of Burns' office to retrieve their M-16's.

Burns popped up, turning off the lights.

"Get down, James." barked Frost with authority.

"I don't want them to see us, Frost." responded Burns.

Frost rolls his eyes, chuckling out of disbelief.

Burns scampered to join the others in the back of the office.

Adkins, Skawinski, and Rockford had luckily holstered their .45s, drawing their weapons, ready to defend the group to the death.

All four corners of the camp came under fire. The card players by now heard Vietnamese voices in all the commotion of gunfire, in and out of the camp.

Listening to the battle and unaware of the whereabouts of the enemy made the situation even more horrific for Buchanan and his friends. All the nerves turned wrecked in supply.

"40 to 50 VC from the sound of gunfire." asserted Frost with confidence.

Marine officers and sergeants could now be heard barking out commands.

"Charlie - main entrance! Fire! Fire!" "Muzzle blasts east perimeter! Fire! Fire!" and "VC at supply!"

Supply measured a mere two buildings from Buchanan's office.

Burns fetched three extra .45s he stored in his upper right-hand drawer of his desk, along with his own .45, distributing them to Remington, Jackson, and Burnside.

The men in supply braced for an enemy attack in Burns' office.

VC voices again were heard near the supply door or on the other side of the north bulkhead, in between the rapid fire of weapons.

RATATATATATA!

POP! POP! POP! POP!

The fighting continued for another minute, as the men stayed put until given notice it was safe to leave Burns' office. Frost and Jurgensen possessed a fighting blood which flowed within their veins and refused to sit back and do nothing, as friends and colleagues fought the enemy to protect the camp.

Frost and Jurgensen leaped out the front door, positioning themselves behind the barrier of sandbags protecting Burns' office. They spotted four VC charging toward supply. Taking aim, the marines aimed and killed two of the VC. The remaining two VC returned fire, nearly hitting Frost. Jurgensen took aim, firing his M-16 toward the muzzle blasts, killing the two charging infiltrators.

Those handling .45s ran out of supply, joining Frost and Jurgensen behind the sandbags, ready to defend their fellow friends. Jackson stayed behind to protect Chaplain Buchanan.

"Just what the hell do y'all think you're doing?" yelled Jurgensen. "Burnside, you and Burns have little bush combat experience!"

"Well, there's always a first time!" shouted Burns. Jurgensen rolls his eyes toward the green marine.

The attack began at dusk, bringing about an intense havoc snow balling into a dangerous position beyond measure. The fright of the men, unaware of the location of the enemy lurking within the camp, experienced an event no civilian back home would comprehend.

Frost and Jurgensen searched for enemy combatants to confront. In the distance, gunfire continued to ring out in all four isolated corners of the camp as the attack died down. The marines thoroughly secured the camp building by building, sector by sector.

"Someone or somebody assisted in this attack - an insurgent." said Frost.

"Yes sir. I swear on my mother's Bible a VC insurgent or insurgents lent a hand in this infiltration. Scary. But who?" asked Jurgensen.

After five minutes of a brisk firefight, the attack quietened down. The long hours of training paid off as the marines sprang into swift action, sending the Viet Cong to an early meeting with their Creator. The marines annihilated the Viet Cong mortar fire from the jungle with rocket and mortar fire of their own, killing the Viet Cong mortar men.

The Viet Cong paid a heavy price for the infiltration of Camp Love, 41 killed and 4 captured. The VC afflicted Camp Love with 3 KIAs and 29 wounded. Light compared to the VC killed and captured. Nonetheless, the numbers don't lie - 3 killed and 29 wounded were too many for Buchanan.

The 500 Rummy friends departed for the night, retiring to their separate hootches and bunkers. The men patted each other on the shoulders in Christian unity and thanked God for his presence during the attack.

The next morning, January 15, Lucas toured the camp, and the damage inflicted by the VC infiltrators with Major Don Boling Stewart, one of the security officers. Lucas frowned upon the easy infiltration of the enemy into camp.

Stewart briefed Lucas the root cause of the infiltration came from a marine falling asleep on guard duty on the east perimeter. The VC slit his throat, killing him.

The card playing group of friends gathered the next morning to tour the camp themselves, led by Frost and Jurgensen. The self-guided tour began at Burn's office, ending at Chaplain Buchanan's hootch. The tour made a complete circle of camp, encompassing all the damage done. The intent of the VC to hit and run, killing as many marines as possible, then hightail it out of camp, failed miserably. For the Viet Cong suffered a 4 to 1 ratio killed in the attack.

The group paused at the duty station where the marine fell asleep on guard duty.

Jurgensen stepped to Buchanan's side, put his hand on his shoulder. "See chaplain, this is why sleeping on guard duty is taken so seriously. One idiot can get us all killed."

"Yes, Sergeant. You're right. It isn't a game, is it?"

"No, sir - it isn't. My sons train cars seem trivial now, don't they, Padre?"

"Well Gunny, fighting to provide freedom for the South Vietnamese, to prevent the evils of Communism coming down on 'em is worth something, isn't it?" asked Buchanan.

Jurgensen nodded in the affirmative.

Buchanan asserted, "And besides, fighting for your boy's freedom and their way of life is all important. Look how these Communists treat people in society. They murder 'em. They intimidate 'em. They're pure evil."

"Yes, sir." said Jurgensen with confidence.

The group made their way from the point of attack on the east perimeter toward Buchanan's hootch, which suffered damage and shot all to pieces. When the group reached his hootch, they examined the damage done. The consensus for the group conceded if Chaplain Buchanan occupied his hootch during the attack, more than likely he would have been killed or at least seriously wounded.

Skawinski agreed. "Chaplain, you're fortunate you were playing cards last night. You would've been killed if you were here. I, for one, am thankful for your presence in our lives right now. I don't know what we'd do if the Lord would've taken you from us last night."

Embarrassed by the lofty accolades Skawinski placed upon him, he said modestly, "Thank you, Ski."

"Corporal's right, Chaplain." acknowledged Frost. "They would have killed you for sure."

Jackson pointed out the obvious to Buchanan as he stepped up to one of the small trees in front of his hootch.

"See here, sir." Jackson pointed to holes in the tree. "Projectiles came from heavy pieces of weaponry such as a .60 caliber machine gun or an AK-47."

"Well, I slept here last night and these bullet holes give me the creeps." said Buchanan, grinning simply out of shock.

The interior of Buchanan's hootch revealed more damage. The hootch received multiple hits, shot all to pieces. Peeking inside the hootch, the group viewed evidence of 20 to 30 projectiles hitting the interior of the hootch. The men noticed the sink blown to pieces, the mirror atop the sink blown off the wall, bullet holes in and around his desk, and his cot torn up a bit. Buchanan felt a sigh of relief, knowing his books survived unscathed by the rapid gunfire from the night before. The group recognized the Lord's presence as a Protectorate of Buchanan in the attack.

In his heart, Buchanan knew the Lord looked after him. He believed vehemently in God's Will. Every day of the rest of his life, he earnestly believed that God moved him to join the others to play cards instead of turning in early for the night.

The group departed to their respective assigned duty stations for the day. All knew anyone of them could have been killed last night, especially if Chaplain Buchanan stayed in his hootch instead of playing cards.

Buchanan lifted a hand up toward Heaven, praying with his devoted friends, thanking the Lord for another day of life. He thanked the Lord for bestowing His safety upon them last night. All the while, no one in the group of Tuesday night card players knew what the future held for every one of them.

The full day of war reinforced a permanent, single truth which stands on its own - war brings about a depressive state in a human being's heart and soul. Buchanan and his friends came to grips long ago that war brings about unwanted changes into individual lives. Regardless of what the future held in the days to come, all asked for God's presence in their lives.

Prayers in this early morning were for a prosperous, peaceful day. A day void of a full day of war.

Close Call in the Bush

January 16, 1969

Time passes rapidly in life. The eight days spent since Chaplain Abrams arrived in camp to conduct the Hanukkah service. Eight days ago, 48 total military personnel attended the service, including Chaplain Abrams, along with 12 Jewish personnel.

Three days ago, Chaplain Abrams climbed up into a truck at 0730 hours destined for Da Nang Air Base, followed by stepping up into a Huey helicopter in Da Nang to transfer him back into the bush to serve the 5th Marines.

Three days ago, the spiritual team accompanied Abrams to the truck to see him off. Jackson stood beside the passenger door with the utmost respect and adulation for the battle hardened chaplain, eager to return to his ministry.

The apparent admiration for one another appeared obvious, as the chaplains held a hand on one another's shoulder. Emotion took the best of them. Incapable of holding back the emotion, the two men wondered if they would ever see each other again in this life.

"Go get'em." said Buchanan.

"You bet." responded Abrams. He climbed up into the truck donning clean jungle combat fatigues, grasping his military gear, and sat in the passenger seat. As he looked down at his friends with a gleam in his eye, the spiritual team expressed pride and gratitude.

"Oh, the crosses! Sergeant, you brought 'em?" asked Buchanan.

"Oh, yes sir. Here you go!" answered Jackson with enthusiasm.

Jackson hands Chaplain Buchanan a small ditty bag of crosses, who relays the crosses to Chaplain Abrams.

Buchanan with elation exclaimed, "Crosses to pass out to your Catholic men and whoever else wants one to cling onto the Lord. They're from Chaplain Kensington. They're crosses Chaplain Capodanno distributed to his men."

"We'll do." said Abrams. "And remember, men. As I've heard you mention Robert in the last several days, it's all about what's in here." Abrams gently gestured toward his chest over his heart. The spiritual team, in return, gently gestured with their fingers over their hearts.

"Amen!" declared Buchanan.

"Oorah!" said a smiling Abrams.

"Oorah!" responded the spiritual team.

With that, Abrams set off to Da Nang Air Base.

Jackson caught Buchanan in his ear, softly pray, "Please Lord. Watch over my friend. Keep your ever most powerful shield upon Melvin. Amen."

Buchanan glances back toward Camp Love and says, "Well, it's back to the old grind. Rains are gone, and it's Thursday."

"Yes, sir." answered Jackson.

Today, January 16, the spiritual team jumped to an early start in the day, eating chow at 0700 hours to reserve time in their respective hootches to prepare for the plan of the day.

The spiritual team faced an uphill battle with a strained schedule. The standing schedule set Thursday for communion services at 1300 hours, followed with a devotion at 1900 hours in the camp conference hall. To add to the grinding schedule, a bush service for Bravo and Delta Companies accompanying combat engineers came scheduled at 1600 hours, followed by another communion service at 1700 hours. Through the chain of command, Lucas added a doozy of an appointment. He ordered a mandatory counseling session at 1100 hours in Buchanan's hootch with a marine to solve some personal problems. The piling on of complicating dilemmas in the young marine's life pushed him to the limit, latching out at others from frustration, including his superiors. Buchanan loathed the counseling sessions with troublesome marines. He thought of undisciplined young marines - 'For crying out loud! Just do as you're told, and life will treat you a lot better.'

Jackson sat on his cot reading updated military memos from command. He contemplated the last few days of ministry and felt lucky serving with such a great chaplain so conscientious of men's wants and needs.

Buchanan impressed Jackson by searching diligently for a Jewish chaplain to conduct a Hanukkah service for a mere 11 Jewish personnel. He thanked the Lord he served with such a conscientious and devoted chaplain. He knew in his heart the Lord placed him in a position to assist such a faithful servant of God in ministry.

Jackson pondered 'what in tarnation would bring two men, one Christian, one Jewish, with such a chasm of theology so close together as human beings?' His only conclusion turned out to be their deep love and care for one another, throwing aside their discrepancies for the betterment of mankind and to bring forth some sort of good out of a war politicians back home do not care to win, regardless of how winnable the war is.

The morning hours struck 1045 hours.

Jackson rose out of his cot, securing his gear and weapons. He hurried to Chaplain Buchanan's hootch to secure and replenish the service kit.

The two enjoyed chit chat, waiting patiently for the appointment to arrive.

With a knock on the door at 1055 hours, Jackson stepped to the entrance. "Come in, marine."

The young marine half smiled, standing defiantly in front of the spiritual team next to the entrance.

Upon leaving, Jackson glanced at the marine, recognizing him as a troublesome kid.

Jackson departed for some chow, elated he will find himself absent from the counseling session. He lacked patience for marines who failed to obey orders, especially after his spiritual conversion experience.

The young 20-year-old marine, with a baby face of a 16 or 17-year-old, faced an Office Hours, or NJP, Non-Judicial Punishment. The Skipper restricted his MOS duties as a marine combat engineer assigned with the Seabees. Skawinski, Adkins, and others in leadership roles considered him a danger as combat engineer - a Private Schmuckatelli. His neck of the woods rooted deep in the Indianapolis, Indiana suburbs. Lucas restricted him from leaving the camp, assigned to laundry and sanitation duty to the Indiana native all day long. Buchanan considered the odd punishment humorous, smirking with the thought of working with poop all morning, then washing dirty uniforms in laundry in the afternoons.

The hour of counseling brought nothing but utter torment, a mental strain of pain and agony for Buchanan. He sat in his chair, annoyed, thinking, 'Is there anything this kid doesn't complain about?'

The hour passed sluggishly. Finally, the hour long misery ended. Buchanan, thrilled the irksome young marine left his office, considered the young kid nothing but a punk. He came close to wishing the kid a good butt kicking to teach him a lesson.

"Whew!" sighed Buchanan.

Jackson intentionally made his way back to Buchanan's hootch to just miss the young marine going out the door. He knocked on the hootch door, asking, "May I come in?"

"It's OK, Sergeant. He's gone."

Jackson stepped in and asked, "Well, how'd it go?"

The austere expression on Buchanan's face said it all. "I hope that kid gets a potent *shot* in the arm of Jesus, because that's what it's going to take for that kid to turn around. He complains about *everything.* The duty hours, everything. He *hates* it here. He *doesn't* care for his officers. He *doesn't* care for his noncommissioned officers. He is determined no one cares about him and his problems. He *hates* the food, and he *doesn't* think he's being treated fairly by anybody because he fell asleep on guard duty. But here's the topper - he *doesn't* think the Skipper should've ordered him on laundry *and* sanitation duty at the same time. I've had enough of that kid."

"He feel asleep on guard duty?" asked Jackson with a frown on his face.

"Yep." answered Buchanan. "*Yeah*, there's plenty of things here in this war zone that depresses me as well, Sergeant, but you can't let 'em control you or they'll destroy you. That kid has a lot to learn about life. A captain in Company D informed me he chewed a gunnery sergeant out over at laundry. The captain informed me it took eight men to hold the gunnery sergeant back from killing that kid." He paused. "Ya know who he reminds me of, Philip?"

"No, sir."

A frustrated Buchanan answers his own question. "Those silly and naïve kids back home protesting the war. A war they know nothing about and a war attempting to prevent a murderous, oppressive ideology from controlling the people in South Vietnam. Kids who have no inkling of rules and discipline in life. This attitude of 'I'm making up my own rules as life goes along.'"

"Psssstttt." added Buchanan as an afterthought. He continued his tirade. "What are they going to do when their own kids, their own flesh and blood, flip them off and disobey the rules set in their own home as parents?"

"Well, sir, I think -" Buchanan interrupts Jackson and says, "What we need to do is to send him back to those protesters. At least he would be good for something. I don't know what it is, but -" Jackson interjects and says, "Sir. *Sir*, calm down. I've never seen ya this hyped up." Jackson paused. "Remember, sir, it's all about what's in here." Jackson touches his chest above his heart.

Sighing heavily, he falls back onto his small couch, staring down at the floor. He inaudibly mumbles something to Jackson, who says, "It's Jesus he needs, sir."

"Well, let's go. Maybe some chow will put me in a better mood before chapel services." said Buchanan, grinning from the embarrassment of letting a scrawny little punk get the best of him.

After some grub, the spiritual team conducted the scheduled services, including the bush service, arriving back at Camp Love at

1840 hours to conduct the devotion in the camp hall. On their way to the hall, a corporal ran up and handed a message to Buchanan.

The message read: 'Chaplain Buchanan is requested to report to Seabees Command, Liberty Bridge for communion service on the morning of 17 January 1969, Lieutenant Commander John Adkins.'

"Well, John must need us. His people probably haven't seen a chaplain in weeks. We'll have the devotion. Replenish the service kit and go." commented Buchanan.

Jackson said, with a bit of hesitation in his voice, "We're going to catch the three w's before it's over with, sir. Weak, weary, and worn is going to get the best of us."

"*Yeah*, but it's all for the Lord, Philip. All for Him. Getting there is going to be a problem, however. How are we getting there?"

Jackson answered Buchanan's question, "Well, Rockford should be along Route QL-1 at bridge locations at coordinates AT 928517 or AT 939688 in a safer location with increased numbers of friendly troops. We can travel out with Charlie Company tonight, who's due to join up with Rockford to relieve his companies. We can come back with Rockford in the morning, who's due to return tomorrow in time for the Friday social. Rockford should pass by the bridge in order for us to have the service."

"Sounds good to me. Let's go."

After the devotion, supplies were replenished and the spiritual team waited patiently in Buchanan's hootch until departure hour - 2030 hours. The team will venture out with Charlie Company to Rockford's encampment. The encampment location, coordinate AT 928517, sat near the Seabees command at Liberty Bridge.

Once they arrived, the three w's weighed them down. Exhausted, but dared not to show it.

The time sat at 2115 hours.

"Good evening, Chaplain." said Rockford.

"Good evening to you, Lieutenant Rockford." answered Buchanan.

Everyone and their uncle greeted the spiritual team. Kowslowski. Lipstone. Remington. Shaw. Rodriquez. Kiehl. Jurgensen. And, of course, Adkins. The men greeted the spiritual team, "Good Evening, sir. Good Evening, Sergeant."

"Good evening, men." said Buchanan.

Dobbs, who kept to himself, nodded toward Buchanan. A good sign for the spiritual team, for at least Dobbs acknowledged the team.

Buchanan took a good survey of Adkins' condition of his uniform. He asked, "Lieutenant Commander

Adkins, is that you? John, you look - well, as if...well - as if you were...*working.*"

The friends chuckle.

Adkins' condition appeared far from Chaplain Abrams. But he stood in front of Buchanan as one who had gotten his hands dirty, for he had not had a bath for days on end. He appeared as if immersed in mud and grim. He had been in the bush working for three days straight.

"Good to see ya." said Adkins.

"Good to see you, John." Buchanan replied with jubilation.

Adkins looked down at his watch. "We better get in as much talking as we can. Rockford's probably going to give the order here soon to cease any talking and to hit the sack."

Adkins, Buchanan, and Jackson chit chat of the last three weeks of ministry and construction projects of the Seabees and marines. And of course, the Ohioans talk Buckeyes football and their victory over USC.

Adkins confidently declared if it had been Nebraska playing, the Cornhuskers would have cleaned house with either Ohio State or USC. The Ohioans roll their eyes and just grin. Adkins, the proud Nebraskan, loved Nebraska football.

Conversation ended, as the three wished one another a 'good night' and immersed into their respective spots within the perimeter of camp. The encampment's position looked down off a slope with machine gunners on top of the hill, with guards overlooking the companies.

As always, the chaplain situated himself in the center of the perimeter. The spiritual team secured their air mattresses for the night. Buchanan, pooped from exhaustion, felt his body ready for some shuteye.

Buchanan bedded down with his t-shirt on the top side, leaving his combat trousers and boots on for the night. He hated snakes, and leaving his boots on eased his mind. His boots served as a protection against snakes and dog size rats looking for a midnight snack on a toe or foot.

Nobody slept with their boots off in the bush anyhow.

Jackson muttered toward Buchanan softly, "Uh-um."

"What?" asked Buchanan, playing dumb, as if puzzled by Jackson's utterance.

Jackson handed Buchanan a shovel with poise. Buchanan took the shovel out of Jackson's hand with obvious annoyance. Buchanan scoffs softly, "I'd not forgotten. I just put it off as far as I could. I'm tired. I'm just not in the mood to dig a hole in the ground."

Rockford overheard, smiling. He thought of the superb job Jackson has done protecting Buchanan. After briefing his officers and platoon squad leaders, he gave orders to secure for the night.

The time ticked to 2230 hours.

The squad leaders stepped to their platoons, giving the order for lights out and to cease conversation.

Jackson finished his hole in no time, 22 minutes tops. Possibly a personal record for digging a hole for the night in the bush.

Buchanan certainly did not match Jackson's physical shape or his age. His body had simply run out of gas, plum tuckered out. Buchanan, far from completing his hole, discovered a helping hand from Jackson to finish Buchanan's individual pit.

Buchanan whispered in Jackson's ear, "Thank you Philip."

"Chaplain." Buchanan heard a slight voice coming from Rockford.

Buchanan and his enlisted friend thought, 'Uh-oh! Rockford's going to chew us out for uttering a word after lights out in the morning.'

Smiling, the men nodded in acknowledgment to avoid Rockford in the morning, mouthing 'Good night.'

Buchanan crawled down into his hole with his air mattress in hand serving as a cushion from the cold ground surface. Jackson likewise followed suit. Buchanan stored no fond memories in his memory bank sleeping on the ground in the bush. But he understood hardships come when ministering to those who are in the evil one's pathway.

Besides, his two favorite scriptures assuring him of God's presence in the bush were Joshua 1:9 - 'Be strong and courageous; do not be frightened or dismayed, for the Lord your God is with you wherever you go.' And John 1:5 'The light shines in the darkness, and the darkness has not overcome it'.

Repeating the Scriptures in his mind, he contemplated the power within the verses providing the highest of assurances for the night.

The time is at 2350 hours. Wake up will come quick at 0500 hours. Over five hours' sleep and beauty sleep, it is not.

Laying back onto his air mattress, Buchanan stared into the sky. His state of mind centered on the vulnerability and threats of what he referred to as the devil's legions, the Viet Cong. On these particular nights, he searched the world over in his mind to clear his thoughts. A cloudless night spoke volumes of God's creation and His awesome handiwork of the universe. The far-reaching space of every star stared back down at him, laying out God's exceptional creation. The many patrols into the bush in his tour were basically the same: generic. But tonight, the brightest of stars spoke of the magnitude of God's presence in the universe. Every star, every fixed radiant point millions of miles away distant from the earth's surface streaming light down upon the globe to guide and direct human beings throughout. A light to shine in the bush's darkness and what lies within it.

The stars reminded Buchanan of God's power. The reinforcement of Scriptures of God's presence in the world gave Buchanan certainty God's presence flourished in the bush for yet another night.

The Scripture passages solidified the reassurance of God's protective arm as his thoughts ran rapid, pondering the power and majestic presence of God.

He thought of his wife and kids, his cousin working in the coal mines, President Nixon's approach to managing the war, the great young Cincinnati Reds catcher, sports, and eating in his favorite steak joint. As Buchanan's brain continued to play with his feelings, he discovered himself drowsy, with slow eye movements, then body temperature decreasing and the heart rate slowing down. Reaching the REM stage, the dreams came heavy and often.

The many dreams which crossed his mind this night would come and go, with no nightmares. However, one dream stood out he would never forget.

In his dream, his Kentuckian family, along with Ohio kin, were celebrating the 4th of July at night along Raccoon Creek in Rio Grande, Ohio. The traditional food, hamburgers and all, laid out on picnic tables with a traditional checkered top tablecloth. The numbers of tables seemed infinite, with family numbering in the hundreds. After the meal, the family played horseshoes, croquet, volleyball, and canoed along the Raccoon Creek. Buchanan enjoyed the canoeing. He competed and won in all the activities. The family celebrated the victories. When the night moved in on the afternoon activities, county officials set off fireworks. The clear dark sky Buchanan looked up to in his dream reflected the same sky he fell asleep to as he stared up into the darkness of Vietnam's skyline. The fireworks lighted up the southern hills of Ohio, filling every nook and cranny of darkness in the deep crevasses of the hills of Ohio. The illuminations shined bright, with a glow of every color imaginable. The beaming bursts of sparkling and glinting silver showers of stars highlighted plant life, oak and cedar trees, spider formations, and flower-like ornamentations.

The finality of fireworks started when Buchanan heard faint voices, "Chaplain. Chaplain! It's 0500 hours. Time to get up. Sunrise is about 45 minutes from now." said Jackson curiously. "You must've been dreaming, sir."

Buchanan stood up out of his makeshift bedding for the night opposite of Jackson standing on the other side of the hole.

"I was - I was dreaming!" responded Buchanan, with adrenalin following high with anticipation.

"My family was celebrating the 4th of July. There were fireworks. We were having fun." Buchanan grinned.

Jackson smiled as he pulled Buchanan's air mattress out from his hole. "Well, it seems to have held its own last night, sir. Look here, not much air leaked out last night."

Jackson stood, shaking his air mattress up and down, laughing.

Buchanan stood, nodding in agreement. "Well, it's better than lying on solid, compacted doggone ground only to give you back problems."

Jackson grins, saying, "Yes, sir. Good thing you don't have a bayonet attached to ya?"

Buchanan, with all the condescension could give in an expression, looks back toward Jackson with disdain.

Jackson chuckles, looking down into Buchanan's hole. With an abundance of shock and bewilderment, he stares down into his hole and says with a tone of thankfulness and fright, "Holy Mother of Jesus." He added with surety, "Your Protection is always near, Sweet Jesus."

With trepidation, Jackson points down towards Buchanan's hole. "Look, sir."

Buchanan examines his foxhole thoroughly and, in the minimum amount of light for the morning hour, he spots three hated, loathed reptiles curled up with one another - bamboo vipers.

Standing limp and catching flies, Buchanan murmurs something inaudible to Jackson.

As the spiritual team hover over the snakes in amazement, other marines join the team staring down into Buchanan's foxhole, who shriek at the menacing creatures curled up with venom at the ready to strike its next victim a death sentence with a quick piercing strike of its fangs into human flesh.

One of the deadliest snakes in the world, the binomial name of a bamboo viper was Trimeresurus stejnegeri. The venomous reptile grew to a maximum length of 30 inches. The powerful hemotoxin of the bamboo viper caused excruciating pain once bitten, as if burned by a heated stove top burner. The pain lasted for hours on end, possibly over 24 hours. The initial pain occurs with flesh surrounding the bite turning black and purple, emphasizing the penetrated wounds. The wound swells as the skin and flesh turn black because of necrosis.

Buchanan hated the vipers. The snake's skin, however, manifested beautiful shades of the dark green vegetation of Vietnam, though various bamboo vipers in other parts of the world varied with color. Though the obvious beauty of the reptile's skin bared an impressive array of color, the venom within the bamboo viper held deadly consequences for those receiving its poison, resulting in a death sentence.

At a methodical, slow pace, the marines turn their heads toward Buchanan, with every eyeball transfixed on the startled chaplain. As a few marines glare at him catching flies, others smile from ear to ear.

The humor fell short of a jeer or a jab at Buchanan, but an instinct which kicked in for all the marines, as the men failed to hold back their laughter. The marines knew full well God granted His full armor to Buchanan during the night. Others thought of it as just plain luck.

Buchanan stood motionless. Speechless, saying nothing.

Half grinning, he presented himself dumb and befuddled.

Adkins stood with sheer amazement written all over his face. He asked, "Robert, you say a special prayer last night? Ya must have. You're still standing."

Buchanan just shrugged at the thought.

"Wow." blurted Dobbs. "Huh. I guess God really protects ya."

Buchanan glanced toward Dobbs. He thought to himself, 'Yes, I am very fortunate. And, yes, I believe in miracles.'

"You must be -" Kowslowski interrupts himself as he chuckles, "warm and cozy at night, Padre. Those vipers thought so."

A few marines grin in response.

"The reptiles knew. They knew not to bother you, sir." said Rodriquez with a smile.

"Thanks Rodriquez." said Buchanan.

Adkins smiles at the thought.

All the skeptics in the group gathered around, snickering, saying to Rodriquez, "Please, Vet."

"What do they know, huh, Rodriquez?" asked Buchanan.

Rodriquez grins and nods in the affirmative.

One by one, the marines stepped back to their own dwelling of last night to eat breakfast, then securing their gear to saddle up.

A circle of men - Buchanan, Jackson, Adkins, and Rockford - departed the hole after looking down into the pit and thanked God for the sparing of Buchanan's life. It indeed proved a miracle Buchanan survived through the night without being bitten by the murderous venom.

"That's the closest you've come in the bush with snakes, chaplain. That was a close call out here in the bush." said Rockford with a bit of assurance in his voice.

Rockford gently pulled his KA BAR knife out of his sheath as he leisurely walked over to Chaplain Buchanan. He gives Buchanan a choice, "Well, Chaplain. Are you going to do it? Or do you want one of us to do it?"

Rockford grinned. He flips the KA BAR knife in his hand with the handle pointed toward Buchanan.

"Do what? You mean - cut the heads off them varmints?" asked Buchanan.

"Well, I'm not. They slept under you, not me." insisted Rockford with a smirk.

"That's right, Robert. Under your air mattress, in your hole." added Adkins with a slight grin.

Buchanan glanced at Jackson with trepidation. He looked Rockford straight in the eyes, and with the slowest of grins surfacing on Buchanan's lips, says, "Gimme that blasted knife."

Taking the KA BAR knife from Rockford's hand, there appeared to be a gleam in his eye, a gritting of his teeth, with rage written all over his face, exposing his deep belligerence toward the bamboo viper. Belligerence none had seen from Buchanan in the past.

"I've been wanting to do this for a long time. I hate those things. I really do!" insisted Buchanan.

"Kowslowski! Kiehl! Get over here with those flight gloves." ordered Rockford.

"Yes, sir." responded the men.

Kowslowski and Kiehl pulled out of a utility bag two sets of specialty gloves in handling snakes and walked over to Buchanan's hole.

The snakes by now detected danger, moving about in the hole's bottom, sensing the end was near. Rodriquez and Lipstone made their way over to Rockford and Jackson to help corral the snakes to prevent a snake from scurrying off into the jungle.

Kowslowski and Kiehl with precision clapped down onto two snakes with a prod around the neck of the reptiles, holding the snake in place with gloves in order to provide Buchanan plenty of room to cut their heads off. Jackson and others corralled the third snake.

"OK, chaplain. They're ready for the guillotine. HAHAHAHAHA." declared Kiehl with a fiendish laugh.

Buchanan stepped up as Kiehl held the snake up off the ground, squirming. The snake curled itself up into a ball, as Kiehl detained the snake in his hands.

With Buchanan's friends watching, he took the knife, placed it under the snake's head about an inch and slit the head completely off, as the snake instantly went limp, hanging from Kiehl's hand.

Bystanders who knew Buchanan best noticed the pleasure and glee in his face when cutting off the head of the first serpent. The event for Adkins and Jackson proved memorable.

Buchanan slit the second snake's head off Kowslowski held.

Contented and elated, Buchanan satisfied his scorn of ridding himself of a nagging menace even more so by eliminating the second snake.

Buchanan felt the satisfying sensation of an overwhelming victory over an arch enemy, eradicating a nemesis of evil. He did his part in annihilating the devil's legions.

Buchanan's emotions ran high. He absolutely hated the snakes. He went to sleep every day and night for the last four months in Vietnam with the fear of snakes overwhelming him. In one brief episode in Vietnam, he evened up the score. Buchanan reaped his revenge upon the snakes for the restless nights given to him at night. He eventually, over time, equated snakes with the evil one.

Marines gathered around for the third kill. They were just as eager to do away with the third companion of the devil.

Buchanan stepped toward Kiehl, holding the third snake. He delivered one quick swipe, cutting off the head with a "Ugh!", grunting from the uttermost depths of his gut and with weight.

Lifted from the men came a load roar of approval for their chaplain, claiming a victory over one of his most loathed pests in Vietnam. He reported later on in his hootch to Arthur and Churchill, his allies and guardsmen of his personal domain, his claimed victory over the vipers with pride.

In one earth-shattering moment, the marines felt Buchanan had become one of them. He now had gotten dirty and rough in the bush. He knew now even more so the fears and worries marines faced in the bush.

"This'll be one you'll be able to tell to your kids, sir." mentioned Jurgensen.

"Yes, Gunny. And with glee!" replied Buchanan.

"Three fewer horrors of the night to deal with, huh, Chaplain." commented Shaw in a congratulatory tone.

"Amen!"

"Feels good taking the heads off those damned to hell, as you say, varmints. Doesn't it, sir?" asked Jorgensen.

"Amen to that, Gunny." replied Buchanan.

"I've seen the taking off of snakes' heads since I've arrived here in this snake invested Vietnam. And I'd always wished to do that." added Buchanan.

"Well, your wish has come true today, sir." answered Jurgensen.

"Sure has. It sure has." said Buchanan with contentment in his voice.

Time stood at 0615 hours. Everyone finished chow and Bravo and Charlie Companies made their way toward Liberty Bridge, absent of a visit from a chaplain for three weeks.

Bamboo vipers slithered in all directions in Vietnam. They made their presence known every five feet in front of a point man, in personal hootches, in every nook and cranny, and under every rock in Vietnam. The vipers added to the overall strain and worry of the war. But for a few brief moments in this stressful and burdensome war, it seemed to Buchanan the bamboo vipers in Southeast Asia disappeared from planet earth.

Unfortunately, bamboo vipers would again emerge from the depths of the devil's abyss and endanger Buchanan and his friends all over again.

The night had been a close call in the bush for Buchanan. A close call he will never forget.

The Orphanage

January 18, 1969

Sunday. The Lord's Day. A day to worship and serve the Lord. Buchanan took this day just as serious as any other Navy chaplain called by God, regardless of denomination. As usual, he led in the 0900 and 1100 hours services for the marines and sailors on Sundays. And as usual, the services were standing room only, especially the 1100 hours service. The 1100 hours' service usually ran high in attendance due to combat patrols arriving from the bush and men relieved of duty stations in Camp Love.

Buchanan visited the An Ngai Don school and orphanage every other Sunday. Today was the Sunday for a visit.

Following the two services and an informal roll call on Sundays, which amounted to reporting to your platoon sergeant, Buchanan loaded up the volunteers to visit An Ngai Don. The marines crammed into two jeeps, two trucks, with a third jeep as a point leading the convoy. Jackson proudly drove the chaplain's jeep following the point jeep, as Buchanan set out to fulfill God's Will.

Scheduled trips to An Ngai Don had been short and sweet, but the men left with a great sense of fulfilling the Great Commission.

With innate Christian hospitality, Chaplain Kensington and two nuns greeted Buchanan's procession of vehicles delivering the charity and benevolence of Jesus. Kensington and Buchanan were friends. Regardless of the theological differences and diverse geographical traits of their upbringing back home in the states. The least they could do for one another was to support one another's ministries in Vietnam.

The visitation of schools and orphanages such as An Ngai Don became a common practice for Navy chaplains in Vietnam. The visits were not results coming from directives from the Chief of Chaplains desk, but from a genuine concern and obligation to carry out the Great Commission. The men simply desired to bring Jesus to those who needed His everlasting love. Chaplains placed a top priority on carrying out the Great Commission and meet the wants and needs of the South Vietnamese through the CAPs. The orphan children of An Ngai Don, victims of a horrible war, had a special place in Buchanan's heart. In reckoned years later, the children were special because his own mother left him at age nine, leaving him with the emotions an orphan might feel.

As infuriating as Buchanan might feel, the demise of the children existed beyond his power to change their status in life. Buchanan had children of his own and was certainly willing to fight tooth and toenail to protect them from experiencing the heartache and pains the children in the orphanage experienced. His heart weighed heavily with sadness and compassion for the children.

Buchanan asked for volunteers to visit the orphanage on Sundays. And all he had to do to find volunteers for any chaplain's office project would be to open up his mouth and the volunteers would come to him from all directions. If he asked for volunteers for anything, half the camp showed up. The marines simply supported him.

The convey of marines pulled up in front of the headmaster's building of the orphanage's school.

Buchanan, Rockford, Skawinski, Jackson, and others leaped out of the vehicle's gun ho to show forth Christian charity toward the children. Disappointing to Adkins, he had orders to fulfill a construction assignment at Liberty Bridge and could not attend the visit. The visit every two weeks had become two days out of the month for Adkins to show forth the love of Jesus, instead of living 28 days of the month attempting to take another human being's life in a war.

Stacked up in the jeeps and trucks in vacant spaces, the Americans transported boxes, crates, and duffel bags full of socks, shoes, baseball caps with the school name on the bill, collared shirts, and t-shirts both plain and with emblems such as sports teams or businesses. Hygiene products such as toothbrushes, toothpaste, cotton swabs, cotton balls, diapers for babies, Q-Tips, deodorant for the older children, and much more arrived with the marines and delivered to Kensington and the Catholic leadership of An Ngai Don.

What caught the eye of the children most were the boxes and bags of chocolate, gum, and candy. When in eyeshot of the sugared treats, the children ran in mass toward the chocolate and candies.

Several marines handed the clothing, sugared products, and hygiene supplies down from the truck and jeeps and into the supply building in no time, using the fire bucket method.

When all said and done, Kensington thanked the marines. "Thank you, men. Your charity is appreciated and your efforts will enhance the Kingdom of God. Thank you, men."

"You're welcome. Sir." responded the men.

The Catholic priest said in English, "Thank you United States marines. I will ever remember your benevolence in our hearts and the Lord will reward and bless you for it. Thank you, again."

"You're welcome, Father. You're welcome, Padre." responded the marines.

The many Catholics in the cohort – Kowslowski, Rodriquez, Jaworski, PoKorny, and Porch - were full of pride partaking in the CAP. With the violence and mayhem almost daily, the trip to An Ngai Don was worth more than silver and gold.

The last delivery to An Ngai Don handed down from the trucks came from the chow hall. The cooks prepared food for lunch, but financed by the chaplains allocated funds. To provide food to the marines and sailors always came first and foremost. To feed the orphanage school, an outsider supplemented funds for a meal of this magnitude.

The donated money came from a mysterious person, anonymous. It took great care to finance a meal of such magnitude without being noticed. The person showed good reason to keep anonymity in financing such a meal. But who funded the meal and why, became questions the spiritual team searched high and low for an answer.

The spiritual team's greatest desire came in wanting to thank him, or her, for the show of benevolence toward the school children.

The men organized the meal buffet style in two lines to quicken the service for the children. The meal comprised hamburgers, hot dogs, all the trimmings - pickles, relish, ketchup, mustard, a little cheese for the hamburgers, tatter tots, French fries, chips, vegetable trays, and packaged brownies for desserts. A fortune spent in some circles. Whoever financed the meal projected a genuine interest for the children.

Children and marines consumed the feast as if there was no tomorrow. All ate till their little heart's content.

After the meal, the marines visited the children as usual. The men befriended specific children in the school over the past few months. The spiritual team reserved Sundays to show love and attention to children suffering in a malevolent world which had only shown them cruelty and destruction.

Two Sundays out of the month, the spiritual team observed marines sitting down with precious innocent children and peacefully and graciously showing the love and compassion of Jesus, Our Lord. The same marines who in battle take the lives of many human beings in fits of rage, exhibiting the antithetical traits of Jesus, while the enemy took the lives of marines in grotesque and savage actions. The moments brought the spiritual team close to tears and were beyond words to describe.

Skawinski, Lipstone, PoKorny, Rodriquez, Kiehl, Jackson, Remington, and even Porch spent time with an orphan, parentless and homeless, a double whammy in the child's life. Porch's demeanor took a radical one hundred eighty degrees turn surrounded by the children of the orphanage. The children brought out of Porch a sense of Jesus' behavior and compassion Buchanan rarely observed.

Buchanan considered the visit to the orphanage twice a month as a morale booster for the marines.

Even Dobbs and McElrath attended the monthly visit. The spiritual team guessed the visit came as a next step in the pair's eventual change for the good.

This visit came no different than any other to the orphanage. The men attempted to bring forth the love and compassion of Jesus into the lives of the children.

A child Buchanan himself befriended, a two and a half year old orphan girl named Thuy, became his favorite child in the orphanage. Her mother and father were violated and killed literally before her very own eyes in the center of her home village. Left in the middle of the village sitting all alone, on the ground and isolated, to fend for herself, crying and bewildered by the violence toward her parents. Rescued by South Vietnamese marines 20 feet from the center of the village an hour later, the marines delivered Thuy in the An Ngai Don orphanage. She found her new home with loving Catholic nuns and a chance to be surrounded by moral and humane caretakers. Her state of mind for a two and a half year old amounted to confusion, disorientation, and lost in an abnormal world.

When Buchanan heard of Thuy's story in October 1968, her story moved him, touching his heart. Affected by her situation in life, he insisted in adopting Thuy into his own family.

Every request to adopt her into Buchanan's own family came with a reverberating no from the Catholic nuns. They refused, handing over a Catholic child to a Baptist minister, without a guarantee she would be raised a Roman Catholic. Buchanan, with a sincere heart, could not grant such a guarantee to the nuns.

He spent time with her as if she possessed his very own flesh and blood. She loved Buchanan. On Sundays, Thuy would hand him her doll baby to play with or her mini chalk board to draw pictures, her only toys she possessed. Buchanan sat with her on his lap on benches provided for the children in a makeshift pavilion in the middle of the school, drawing her pictures with chalk. The marines jabbed at Buchanan, who could not draw worth spit, but drew pictures for Thuy anyhow in a childlike manner only Thuy could understand, though probably confusing and distorted to adults.

The marines never let Buchanan live it down his elementary pictures drawn.

"What's that, Padre? An elephant?" Jaworski would ask with chuckles.

"*No*, private. That *happens* to be a horse." answered Buchanan with sarcasm.

"A horse? Sure is fat." said Jaworski with a smirk.

"Let me see, sir?" asked McElrath with curiosity.

Buchanan turned the mini chalk board toward McElrath and he says, "See there, Gunner. A horse."

McElrath looks away, smirking. "That's the most elephant looking horse I've ever seen, sir."

The marines laugh, along with Buchanan.

"Never was much of an artist." commented Buchanan, with a tone of regret.

"Neither was I, sir. Neither was I." responded McElrath.

Jaworski and others nod in agreement.

"Besides, Thuy doesn't know any different anyhow." added Buchanan.

McElrath, with his head downward, says, "You really think so, sir?"

"Yeah." responded Buchanan with assurance.

McElrath shakes his head, and continues to visit with his young Vietnamese friend, a young six-year-old whose parents were killed by North Vietnamese artillery.

Buchanan showed the picture of the horse to Thuy and would ask in English, "Do ya like the horse drawing, Thuy?"

Thuy takes one look at the picture and laughs.

Buchanan attempts to use the little Vietnamese he has learned to converse with Thuy.

"Con ngu'a." said Buchanan pointing to his picture of a horse, attempted to pronounce horse in Vietnamese with his strong Kentuckian accent. No telling what she might have heard.

Thuy again looked at Buchanan's drawing, then giggles.

The young orphan thought, 'He said horse, but it looks like a pig.'

The reciprocal bond of love between the chaplain and the young Vietnamese girl grew strong. The attachment between the other children and marines grew as the adult mentors shared compassion onto the young children.

The bond between Americans and the Vietnamese children mattered least to the Catholic nuns. On every occasion, even on the very last day of his Vietnam service, October 7, 1969, the nuns presented Buchanan an uncompromising 'no' in adopting Thuy and taking her to the United States to be part of his family.

Buchanan reluctantly accepted an answer of no adopting Thuy. But still loved her as a fellow human being and as a father figure as long as he served in Vietnam.

Saddest of all for Buchanan is the fact the North Vietnamese and the Viet Cong invaded and militarily overwhelmed South Vietnam five and six years later. The South Vietnamese will feel the sting of Communist aggression upon those allied with the Americans during the war. The NVA and the VC will slaughter hundreds of thousands, fighting for a democratic way of life and seeking freedom. Slain in 1974 and 1975 would be Vietnamese, such as the priests and nuns at the orphanage, along with Thuy.

After the war, the newspapers and the media gave word to Buchanan and military personnel who served in Camp Love many in northern and central South Vietnam suffered horrendous atrocities from the brunt of murderous invaders from the North years later. Buchanan and his friends prayed Thuy and the children escaped South Vietnam on the scores of boats after the Communists invaded the south. Buchanan prayed to the Lord he would spare the precious children of An Ngai Don from the horrors of brutality from the hands of the Devil's legions.

THE KILLING MACHINE

JANUARY 27, 1969

Eleven days had passed since the An Ngai Don Sunday visit. Memories of the visit set Buchanan's mind, at least temporarily, at ease. Memories of peace. A time of solemn and charitable benevolence toward the innocent children in a war zone. Buchanan set a mutual, confirmed tone of concern for the children's overall wellbeing with the marine visits.

Vietnam, however, passed far from being peaceful and solemn. For the past six days, Camp Love operated under a high alert. News from high command down to individual squads and platoons reported Charlie prowling about in the jungle, increasing nocturnal terror activities to curb United States support of South Vietnam. Attacks heightened from NVA troops supported by Viet Cong battalions onto villages in the past ten days. The presence of enemy movements in villages and hamlets in a 15-mile radius of Camp Love felt the terror and intimidation of the NVA and VC. The Viet Cong conducted thug like tactics to amass a forced tax collection at night, confiscating rice, spreading lies, and scattering false propaganda about democracy to the South Vietnamese. Skawinski's combat engineering squad and all four marine infantry rifle companies in the camp received orders on high alert when on patrol. When going into friendly villages, the marines checked villagers for South Vietnamese identification cards. If caught without possessing a card, a South Vietnamese citizen could be accused of participating in VC nocturnal activities. Skawinski disarmed more booby traps, tree trunk studded bamboo spikes, M18 claymore mines, and land mines in the past ten days than all the days of December.

Buchanan will receive a taste of what his friend, Chaplain Abrams, experienced weeks ago in the bush. He will accompany a mission with Lieutenant Jones of Charlie Company 1st Squad 2nd Platoon and Rockford's Bravo Company, who accompanied Skawinski's combat engineering company to knock out a torrent of booby traps set by the Viet Cong. The nocturnal activities of the VC to intimidate the South Vietnamese heightened to slow the pace of American and South Vietnamese successes in gaining more villages and hamlets to support the advances toward democracy. The long, tedious mission set out to protect the hamlets and villages, including An Ngai Tay, resulted in a high rate of achievement. The NVA and VC hammered the villages day and night by artillery attacks, and suffered day and night from booby traps set by the VC to hit American and friendly civilians alike.

Rockford and Lieutenant Jones led their respective companies as part of Operation Linn River, along with 2nd Battalion 26th Marines and 1st Battalion 7th Marines. The men carried out the operation approximately twelve miles south of Da Nang and north of Route 4 with an aim of encircling and sweep a seven square mile area to support the Accelerated Pacification Program. The 5th marines simultaneously conducted Operation Taylor Common, a similar operation of the 7th marines.

Between January 27 - February 7, 1969, American marines carried out a joint operation to establish a cordon to keep Viet Cong guerrillas out of a 50-mile radius, including Camp Love. The chain of command deemed the operation a success as the marines created the cordon. The marines confronted VC and NVA troops in minor battles and skirmishes during the operation. Confrontations with the enemy amounted to pursuing and chasing the VC and NVA out of the cordon. Though the United States killed only fifty-three in the operation, victories came in repositioning nearly a thousand friendly Vietnamese to government resettlement villages and annihilating enemy bunker tunnels and fortifications.

All four grunt companies – Alpha, Bravo, Charlie, and Delta – accompanied combat engineers to sweep for mines, booby traps, VC bunkers, and VC insurgents in hamlets and villages.

On the first day of the operation, the rather large detachment from Camp Love set out to accomplish the objectives of Operation Linn River. On the first night of the operation, Rockford, along with Lieutenant Jones of Charlie Company, bivouacked for the night at coordinates AT 965766 and AT 972753. Rockford radioed squads and platoons of Companies B and C, as well as combat engineers to report by radio for a roll call, then bivouac for the evening at whatever coordinates the squad or platoon were presently in.

The men were dog-tired, looking forward to shut eye and some rest.

The size of the marine patrol to bivouac in the bush in so many locations simultaneously rarely occurred at night. The marines looked forward to sleeping in their own hootches for the night in Camp Love. Not out in the middle of the jungle along with 'critters', as Buchanan would refer to the creatures of the night. Mine sweeping and the search for booby traps kicked into overtime and the pitch darkness will come quick. The overall fear of Rockford is the isolation of a squad or platoon dangerously exposed to enemy nocturnal movements. If an isolated squad or company came under attack, the entire contingent of men risked total annihilation from heavily threatening numbers of Viet Cong and even possibly regiments of the NVA. The situation became dire as companies and squads spread far and wide. Rockford and Jones' hands were tied in securing a most dangerous of circumstances.

Buchanan felt safe for the night. He found himself surrounded by two squads of Bravo Company, one platoon from the ranks of Charlie Company, and his competent bodyguard in the center of the perimeter.

Mostly, the perimeter lacked a thick dense foliage. On high ground, the perimeter laid with patches of vegetation peppered with small trees, and mostly with an open setting to secure a perimeter.

Unbeknownst to Rockford or Jones, and though no intelligence reports officially confirmed any enemy movements or concentration of enemy in the area, the North Vietnamese Army and the Viet Cong had amassed just west of coordinates AT 965766 and AT 972753. Nearly a thousand of the enemy gathered west of Route 4 to attack Americans isolated in separate squads and platoons during the night. The situation forced Rockford and Jones to bivouac in the open jungle, as the terrain literally exposed marine encampments to attack in vulnerable territory. The VC assumed the isolated squads and platoons welcomed passivity. The enemy considered the Americans invited an attack, opening the door to rout the Americans piecemeal, one squad and platoon at a time. The overwhelming numbers of collective VC and NVA in the area conveyed a false sense of superiority to the enemy.

The fact one American marine equaled the equivalent of 4 VC or 3 NVA revealed itself obvious from casualty numbers in many battles and in every single month's reports of the war.

Rockford ordered to set the perimeter and bed down for the night. The scuttlebutt Rockford and others received of enemy movements and covert massing of enemy troops fell short of official confirmation, but his gut reaction with the rumor mill proved accurate, creating a nervous anxiety, convincing him to decide with great caution and conviction. He looked at his field watch, noticing the time struck 2100 hours.

When the order came to bed down, Buchanan, as usual, dug his hole next to Jackson. With practically four months in the bush under his belt, Buchanan became an expert at digging his foxhole. In fact, Jackson felt impressed with Buchanan's speedy efficiency in digging his foxhole. His developed skills over the past four months exemplified a chaplain who doesn't want to be caught in the middle of a firefight with a bullseye on his chest, simply from the neglect of digging a foxhole for a night's rest. In the past two weeks, Jackson rarely lent a hand to finish up digging the chaplain's hole.

It took approximately 30 minutes for the spiritual team to dig their holes for the night. Buchanan felt weak, weary, and worn. The ground seemed hard, as the spiritual team caught a dose of the 'w''s with the long days in the bush and the ministry duties administered to the men.

Time came to 2130 hours sharp.

The Americans sought some shut eye.

The spiritual team ran through a ministry gauntlet in the past few days, ministering to the troops. The team faced a bombardment of ministry responsibilities, including three KIA memorial services for eight men who had perished at the hands of the devil's legions. Leading in the memorial services, especially those in the bush, were not one of Buchanan's favorite duties as a Navy chaplain. The memorial services were depressive to conduct. Buchanan, knowing the last breath breathed in this life for a marine came in the bush, isolated and alone, terrified his inner soul. The marine, knowing his last moments in this life are coming to an abrupt end, will stand face to face with his Creator in split seconds with no preparation granted placed the young man in a horrifying situation.

Along with the KIA memorial services, Bravo and Charlie Companies engaged in a share of firefights. The bonding between Chaplain Buchanan and Company B seemed inseparable. The rapport he established had become set in stone.

And rightly so. His first congregates to receive Communion from him in October 1968 were members of Company B. The men in the company frequently insisted Buchanan accompany them on patrol to pray and deliver the last rites with a marine going into eternity in case the unfortunate marine received severe wounds. Company B accompanied Skawinski's combat engineering team frequently to sweep for mines and detonate or defuse booby traps.

Company B exemplified volunteer work like no other company or unit in Camp Love and answered the call when summoned upon. The hearts of those in the company reflected the heart of the Lord, and this naturally attracted Buchanan to the men.

The scripture reflective of Company B came from Romans 13:4 - 'for he is God's servant for your good. But if you do wrong, be afraid, for he does not bear the sword in vain; he is the servant of God to execute his wrath on the wrongdoer.'

Either in camp or in the orphanage, Company B exemplified and embodied the traits of the 'Fruit of the Spirit'. The men carried out the commands of Jesus as best they could, 'Treat others as you would want to be treated'. Christian traits in the Beatitudes, such as peace maker and forgiving others for wrongdoing, showed forth from individual men in Bravo Company.

Of course, all men fall into sin and disappoint the Lord from time to time. The men of Company B were no different. They, too, sinned and would have to make amends. Many a night in Vietnam, Buchanan sat in his hootch and simply listened, hammering out the problem a marine felt forced to deal with.

Still, Buchanan sensed God worked for good in Company B. The potential to further the Kingdom of God on earth flowed evident in the hearts of the men. There were many members of Companies A, C, and D who exemplified Jesus Christ's traits. Buchanan developed a special bond with Bravo Company.

But the persona of Bravo Company could not be anymore different than in combat.

Buchanan witnessed Bravo Company confront the enemy in many skirmishes and battles. The efficiency and accuracy of eliminating and destroying the enemy presented itself quite impressive.

Company B served notice to the North Vietnamese and the Viet Cong when patrolling the jungles of Vietnam.

The enemy heard loud and clear from Company B - 'Watch out Viet Cong!' 'Watch out NVA!' 'Watch out devil's - you have met God's wrath upon you!'

When in combat, the enemy knew better to stand in the way of Bravo Company.

The company served as a primary source, an eyewitness account of the cruelties and brutality of terrorism perpetrated by the hands of the Viet Cong in nocturnal assaults to intimidate the citizenry of South Vietnam. Mostly, the treatment of children and the elderly infuriated westerners and people of democratic zeal. The intimidation of the VC enraged the westerners to no end. Company B thought of themselves as 'The Reaper' to deliver God's wrath upon the apathetic guerrilla fighters.

Every member in Bravo Company set out to fulfill their mission in Vietnam - to defeat the North Vietnamese Army and Viet Cong, democratize South Vietnam, and come home.

Buchanan felt safe with Company B like no other unit or company billeted in Camp Love.

Gunnery Sergeant Richard Neville Warwick Jurgensen, attached to Lieutenant Rockford, and Staff Sergeant Frank Smith, assigned to 1st squad 2nd platoon, epitomized the combat potency of Bravo Company. Smith from time to time led a platoon in Charlie Company when short handed. In civilian life, the two sergeants portrayed anything but a marine with the endurance of a ferocious lion strengthened with courage. Jurgensen came from a strict Roman Catholic background, one of a conservative foundation for his faith. The paternal side of the family tree came filled with educators. His father held an honorable and illustrious career in the faculty at USC in the history department, known as a renowned ancient world archaeologist. The Gunny himself held a position of college professor and a member of the 7th Engineering Marine Battalion Reserve Unit in Los Angeles. He volunteered for duty in Vietnam. His reputation grew as a fierce fighter in Camp Love. Jurgensen reminded Buchanan of a comic book World War II character he collected back home. The sergeant in the comic mirrored a rugged, determined, ferocious marine sergeant in battle. Jurgensen presented himself as no slouch, standing at 6'1", and 220 pounds of pure muscle.

Staff Sergeant Frank Smith came from a long, rich tradition of an aristocratic family in Williamsburg, Virginia. His family income thrived from a distribution business. Secondary income for his family came from two large, profitable farms in Thomas Jefferson's beloved state of Virginia. He exhibited a man of strength, standing tall at 6'0". Just as intimidating as Jurgensen, his religious convictions were of an Episcopalian background and appreciated Chaplain Buchanan for his ecumenical tendencies.

Impressed with the men, Buchanan loved the level of intellect of the two sergeants. His impressions of the men heightened even more with the innate DNA of ferocious warriors within each of them. The combination of the two extremes humored Buchanan. In the years to come, Buchanan mentioned to friends in jest that if you ever found yourself in a bar-room brawl with Jurgensen and Smith, you better pray you're swinging your fists alongside with them. If not, and you're facing the two sergeants, you'll find yourself not only limping out of the bar, but crawling out after receiving some heavy blows from the hands of two of the most fiercest fighting warriors Buchanan had ever seen.

Jackson snapped a slide photograph of the two sergeants with Buchanan in the evening just prior to sundown.

The two men shared a double life. They lived a mild-mannered civilian life, but a wild, ferocious 'killing machine' in combat. Buchanan witnessed both personalities from the talented combat sergeants.

Buchanan referred to them as 'The Killing Machine.'

On the early morning of January 28, 1969, at 0457 hours, Buchanan witnessed Jurgensen and Smith flaunt that roaring 'killing machine', a well-oiled mechanism turning its cylinders full speed, cutting through the enemy at full throttle ripping them to pieces. The machine reflected a well-oiled, fine-tuned race car at the racetrack or a high-speed piece of machinery in a factory.

The night settled calm enough for a perfect evening of rest. The weather called for a partly cloudy night, cooler than usual. The marines expected an uneventful night with no interruptions. The men slept, mostly on snooze. A calm night.

Suddenly, the calmness of deadly silence erupted into a melee of savagery, with no-quarter taken. An outright brutal hand-to-hand combat from both sides.

A marine from Charlie Company west of the perimeter, with a mere three minutes left for guard duty, nodded off with only moments left on his call. In the distance, elements of the 577th NVA Battalion, the 20th Viet Cong Infantry Battalion, the VC 89th

Sapper Battalion, and the 25th VC Infantry Battalion were at the ready to swoop down onto Rockford's contingent of marines. A team of Viet Cong reconnaissance noticed the young, foolish marine doze off. An ambitious, young NVA captain turned to a young Viet Cong insurgent, smiled, and tilted his head to sneak forward to carry out the evil deed of slitting the young marine's throat. The young VC set out toward the marine in a crouched position close to the ground, till he came 25 feet of the marine, falling flat on the ground crawling toward his victim as a demon creeping up onto his prey. Once upon his quarry, he snuck up behind the marine and slit his throat.

The marine made one of the most deadly mistakes committed in Vietnam - going to sleep on guard duty.

With the sentry killed and eliminated, the floodgates opened as the enemy flowed onto the edge of the western perimeter with no resistance. The young Viet Cong insurgent stooped down behind a fallen log to conceal himself, while the VC and the NVA contingent made their way up to the edge of the perimeter to infiltrate the camp. The enemy moved cautiously as the north and south sentries were still in eyeshot of the western perimeter. So far, the infiltration of the perimeter remained successful, until four VC peered down toward the ground and screamed at the top of their lungs - bamboo vipers had slithered up their ankles onto their shins! Two marine sentries in eyeshot of the congregated VC shouted, "VC!" "Enemy! Nine O'clock!"

The sentries opened up, firing their M-16's on full automatic, dropping several of the enemy.

POP! POP! POP! POP! POP! POP!

Enemy limps flung and bounced, jolting in uncontrolled gyrations, with torsos lifted completely off the ground from the impact of the M193 rounds of the M-16, until dropping backward onto the ground lifeless and torn to bits.

The VC returned fire toward the sentries almost in unison.

RATATATA!

POP! POP! POP!

80 or more enemy weapons fired simultaneously, nearly cutting the sentries' bodies in two.

In a split second, every marine in the camp came alive in their hole, slumped down into their makeshift trench, returning fire in prone positions on the ground firing projectiles back toward the muzzle flashes of the Viet Cong weapons.

Heard over all the noise and commotion were orders from Smith and Rockford.

"2nd Platoon, COVER THE RIGHT FLANK!" ordered Rockford.

"Kiehl, Shaw, ready the grenade launchers!" came another order from Rockford.

"Ready the grenade launchers!" Jones screamed.

Those marines electing not to dig a foxhole for the sake of gaining additional sleep now begged for mercy from God to spare their lives. The exposure to projectiles from enemy fire came tenfold for those who didn't dig a foxhole. Many marines, if not all, slept in their uniforms, ready to fight at a second's notice when attacked by the enemy.

With his helmet secure on top of his head, Buchanan peeked over the edge of his hole, witnessing a battle ensued with an array of lights. The barrage of projectiles and bullets came from every direction imaginable, displaying the tracers from weapons bearing every conceivable color in the tracer line, though many tracers were green. Still dark, the streaks of light from the weapons glowed brightly. The flickers from the weapons welcomed the early morning with sunlight. The simultaneous firing of weapons, adding the tracers coming from all directions of the perimeter, and combining the rainbow of colors popping up from all directions, numbed Buchanan. The experience plastered a permanent memory for Buchanan in the deep crevices of his mind. Years later, he described the experience to fellow veterans that he felt as if he fell in the middle of a science fiction movie surrounded by intergalactic weapons firing in all directions.

The sudden combat wore Buchanan to an immediate beat down. The cacophony of weapons deafened all within the perimeter.

All the while, Jackson fired his M-16 toward the enemy, yelling to Buchanan, "STAY DOWN CHAPLAIN!"

He faintly heard another voice within the chaos, the voice of Rockford who ordered, "West perimeter. FIRE! FIRE! FIRE!"

Within the discord of weapons fired, inaudible voices and familiar combat noise were all about. Buchanan loathed the most familiar sound of combat more than any other – the screams of wounded and dying. By now in his tour, the screams became permanent reverberations forever etched into his brain. Though the symphony of fired weapons rang loud, Buchanan heard the faint orders of battle. The screams of the wounded seemed to drown out the firing of weapons and orders given.

From Buchanan's perspective, he had a front-row seat to the whole attack. Regardless of the fact he wished to be anywhere else but in South Vietnam, he found himself in the middle of a severe firefight. For just a mere few seconds, his thoughts shifted to a steak joint in Los Angeles he and his wife grew fond of. Oh, how he wished he could be in LA right now, chopping down on a juicy steak, instead of in the middle of a stringent, deadly firefight.

His heart pounded a mile a minute. He turned abruptly in all directions, catching every spurt and barrage of weapons blasting away.

The Viet Cong suddenly came rushing through the perimeter, one after the other, blasting away firing their AK-47's. The VC dropped dead just as quick entering the perimeter following a barrage of bullets into their Communist flesh. One VC after the other ran in firing his weapon, one pawn after the other to lay his life down for a cause Buchanan loathed. The attack seemed endless.

Buchanan's thought in his foxhole hit him hard - 'It's sheer suicide.'

POP! POP! POP! POP! RATATATATATA! POP! POP! POP! KABOOM!

The assault seemed to be a never ending number of VC emerging from the jungle. Terror struck Buchanan inside and out. He glanced toward Jackson, still wailing projectiles toward the VC, barking out to Buchanan, "STAY DOWN chaplain! STAY DOWN!"

While overwhelmed by the moment, Buchanan froze from the sheer weight of the situation unfolding before his very own eyes. It scared him to death.

RATATATATATA! POP! POP! POP!

Buchanan now heeded, catching the sight of grenades thrown at the enemy from a marine grenade launcher. What horrified Buchanan came the sight of incoming grenades from the enemy, three times as many. He caught sight of grenades thrown by marines in every direction, even over his head. The unbelievable devastation, along with the taking of life from grenades, horrified Buchanan. Later on in life, he described to friends grenades were 'nasty' in the heat of battle.

KRUNCH! KABLAAAM!

ZZZZzzzzz BrUmmP!

The screams of the wounded emerged thunderously amid all the chaos.

"Corpsman!"

"DOC!"

"Oh God, I'm hit!"

"Why Me!"

And "MoM!" - the shriek Buchanan hated most of all!

As the screams grew louder, the firing of weapons seemed to subside.

Muzzle blasts diminished as the enemy dead laid all about. Buchanan, from remaining flickering flashes of battle, caught sight of American casualties peppered throughout the battle scene. Some dead, some wounded. His first instinct pushed him to run to the wounded, but danger thwarted any attempt to bolt toward any injured.

Jackson again reminded the chaplain, "Get down! GET DOWN!"

Buchanan stayed down, but tempted to watch the rest of the attack unfold, which he did.

As weapons unleashed projectiles, Buchanan noted a most shaking, reverberating noise in great volume and strength in the distance - yells and screams, hundreds of voices in unison, almost harmonious, screaming at the top of their lungs. Blood curling screams reflective of an army of demons, set to carry out havoc and mayhem in its path.

In a split second, the screams seemed more sporadic, coming from all directions, broken from the unison harmonious tone. Suddenly, Buchanan heard the yells and screams drawing closer and closer.

Next Buchanan heard more isolated, distinct individual screams near his and Jackson's foxholes. Another voice even closer. Then another, and another. The darkness of the previous night dissipated, welcoming the early light of the morning, which emerged quickly. Buchanan could now see the Viet Cong and hearing their screams. He caught himself catching flies at the sight. The VC ran into the perimeter with a knife, bayonet, or a machete in hand, possibly a weapon in both hands. Buchanan caught sight of the VC's expressions as murderous, evil killers, the very reflections of the VC in his dreams.

Buchanan watched screaming Viet Cong sprint toward Americans to run a marine through. He himself perceived a shriek too close for comfort. Turning abruptly to his left, he caught sight of a VC running straight at him, with only seconds to spare. In a split second, he turned his head toward Jackson to seek help. Laying his eyes on Jackson, he felt his stomach hit the ground. In total astonishment and horror, Buchanan spotted Jackson in a violent fight with two VC and a third coming in fast on his right. His first instinct pushed him to jump out of his hole and aid Jackson in his fight against two of the devil's legion.

Buchanan yelled, "Philip!"

Turning abruptly back around, Buchanan looked straight into the eyes of the Viet Cong, aiming himself straight toward him - the eyes of the Devil. The sight in front of him possessed the determination of a malevolent, depraved, demented lunatic to kill the American in front of him. His eyes bloodshot red. His mouth was wide open, screaming, showing all of his teeth with slobber and spit spilling about, demonic and mad holding a machete in his right hand, with an expression of the demon representations of VC in his dreams.

Buchanan knew full well the image of a marine about to take the life of another human being, but never had he witnessed a Viet

Cong this close in the middle of a fierce skirmish. The horrifying sight resulted in terrible nightmares from years to come.

Within seconds, the Viet Cong would be upon Buchanan to kill him.

In just a few seconds Buchanan had to decide what to do, with a thousand thoughts running through his mind. The most pertinent thought at the moment came in a question, 'What do I do? What do I do?'

Buchanan, still crutched down into his hole, stared at the VC coming toward him, grabbing his knife lying in the hole on his left, his right hand grabbed his shovel. Standing up abruptly in a defensive position, he waited for the collision of two human beings to tear into one another.

The closer to Buchanan he came, the faster he ran.

With Buchanan's never ending stare into the VC's eyes, he clinched his teeth and gripped his knife and shovel, ready to confront the VC and kill him. The Communist came running toward him with blistering speed, possessing an uncontrollable, lunatic scream, and was just a mere 5 feet away.

Within a millisecond, Buchanan heard a 'CRACK!', seeing the VC's head disappear. Blown away from a marine who had his sights on the VC intending to kill his chaplain the whole while.

The VC's torso, with limbs attached, fell violently hard just in front of Buchanan, close to falling on him, and still holding the machete in his right hand.

Buchanan turned his head to two o'clock on his right and saw Dobbs, breathing heavy and blood soaked, with his M-16 pointed toward the once murderous VC killer.

Buchanan and Dobbs caught one another's eyes in a split second. The brief glance shared nothing but a thankfulness in Buchanan's eyes, while nothing but respect spoken in Dobbs' eyes.

The skirmish continued. Dobbs suddenly turned to his right to face a VC insurgent in a vicious fight.

Buchanan heard Jackson grunt hard. Turning his head expecting the worst, he instead caught sight of Jackson in the aftermath of stabbing a Viet Cong in the stomach, holding the VC with his left arm and with his right hand stabbing the VC in the stomach, whose limbs were dangling downward and his head falling backward. Jackson, still pushing the knife in, grunted with each thrust. Jackson at 6'3" holding the Viet Cong insurgent who was only 5'3" happed a jaw dropping scene. Jackson stood surrounded by seven lying, disfigured, crumbled up VC. The eighth VC held in his grasp, deader than a doornail. Blood and human flesh spilled everywhere. A gruesome sight for the average civilian.

In lightning striking speed, Jackson quickened himself to Buchanan's side. At last, Jackson is ready and perfectly able to eliminate any threat coming their way. He bunched himself up against Buchanan, moving right and left, with his bayonet in his left hand, and his KA BAR in his right, shifting his eyes right and left, scanning with his 20/20 vision all directions the conniving enemy might approach.

By this time, nothing but hand-to-hand combat ensued within the perimeter.

In the foreground of Jackson's fox hole, Buchanan set his eyes yet on another scene.

Of the combat experiences Buchanan had witnessed, none compared to what he saw 50 feet beyond Jackson's foxhole.

In the chaos and initial panic of the brief, though violent battle that ensued, Sergeants Jurgensen and Smith partnered up the opposite end of the perimeter to defend against the major attack of the VC. At the same western end of the perimeter, the sentry fell asleep and exposed the entire perimeter to the enemy.

Jurgensen fought on the left, Smith on the right. The sergeants held a knife in one hand, while Jurgensen held a wooden, small log he picked up during the engagement in his left hand. The men shared the same hootch in Camp Love and bivouacked alongside each other in the bush. The pair were inseparable in the jungle and a whirlwind in combat, essentially a killing machine.

One VC after another came out from nowhere, attacking the pair, hidden in the bush's vegetation.

Surrounding the sergeants were a dozen or more VC lying about. At least 10 to 15 additional enemy combatants lied 20 feet in front of them, possibly killed by the sergeants M-16's.

Buchanan yells, "Machete left Gunny!" Jurgensen swiftly turns left, catching the sight of a Viet Cong bolt from the brush with a machete held back behind his head rushing toward him yelling blood curling screams, taking a downward swipe at Jurgensen which missed. The Gunny quickly punched the VC smack square in the face, shattering his facial bones, sending him twirling airborne onto the ground. Flying high, the VC descended quick onto his own knife, plunging into his own stomach. Buchanan caught in his ear a slight "Augh!" from the VC.

"Another Gunny, 12 o'clock!" Buchanan screamed.

Coming straight at Jurgensen with a Russian issued assault knife, the Viet Cong insurgent conveyed sadistic expressions, determined to take the life of the Gunny.

Before Jurgensen killed the next VC, two more VC simultaneously surfaced out of nowhere, growling and yelling in English, 'Imperialist Pig', with M3 trench knives in both hands, running towards Jurgensen.

The sequence of events happened so fast, Buchanan failed to warn Jurgensen of the next two Viet Cong.

Jurgensen, on his knees in front of the fallen VC, grasped the machete and pointed it toward the encroaching threat, running the point of the machete straight into the VC, practically tearing him in half at his belly button. The M3 trench knife nearly cut Jurgensen in the arm, but fell onto the ground. The VC fell on top of the initial VC carrying the machete. In front of Jurgensen lie two dead Viet Cong, as he breathed heavily from exhaustion.

He swung the machete around swift toward the VC encroaching on his right, slicing his stomach open and falling on the ground beside the other two fallen VC. Still alive, he yells out, "dau!" Laying in agony, the VC cried out, asking for help in Vietnamese, "giup toi!"

The VC on his left came cross slicing his knives running straight at him. To protect himself, Jurgensen literally picked up the dead

VC, who landed on top of the first VC insurgent and threw the corpse towards the oncoming VC, knocking him violently hard to the ground. Before the VC regained his senses to defend himself, Jurgensen popped up on his feet, rushing toward the VC. Grabbing his hair backward, he swung the machete around hitting the VC's head, killing him. The VC crashed onto the ground with a thunderous boom.

All the while, Buchanan observed from a distance yet another fierce fight. Smith, caught in the middle of an entanglement himself, faced six or seven Viet Cong, hanging onto every part of his body, attempting to slam him to the ground and run him through. The VC attempt to carry out the coup de grâce came to no avail.

Smith was no Teddy Bear, exhibiting a most convincing grizzly bear display of tremendous strength, giving no quarter this day. Mad as hell and cornered, he faced the Viet Cong voracious. When cornered, grizzly bears emerge from their cave with a vengeance. As Buchanan watched the fight unfold before him, a Viet Cong hung on each leg of Smith, one hanging piggyback, while another wrapped his arms and legs around his torso like Velcro. Most agitating for Smith hung the nagging VC hanging on each arm, one scratching and clawing to tear the knife out of Smith's hand and the other fighting to immobile his left arm. The seventh VC circled the entanglement of human beings to grab onto any piece of flesh he could take hold of. Somewhere, underneath all the entanglement, Smith endured the leeches attached to his frame.

Buchanan fell spellbound, watching Smith take matters into his own hands. He frees himself from the leeches attached to his body. His football days now bore fruit, as he possessed the strength of an ox. He kicked and slammed his left leg onto a fallen tree, throwing one leech off his leg, knocking the wind out of him. Thrusting his knee up into the tail bone and backside of the VC hanging onto Smith from the front, sending him to the ground in pain. Jumping up off his feet, airborne, Smith swung himself backwards onto the ground. With a deafening crash, 'BooM!'. The impact onto solid ground came a crushing of the piggyback Viet Cong, who thus let go of Smith along with the others hanging on his arms.

Four of the Viet Cong popped back up to tangle with Smith, challenging him for another go around. Smith simply reached out and grasped two of the VC by the neck, slamming the two together at the shoulders with a loud 'thud'. Slowly and sluggishly, the VC pulled themselves back up to stand. He clasped onto a third VC by one leg and grabbed him under his arm with his other hand and rushed to a pointed dead tree branch and skewered the VC, who screamed out a painful "Ahhhhhhggg!" as his arms and legs went limp.

The last Viet Cong just watched, catching flies. He turned and briskly hightailed it back into the jungle. The remaining two VC stood back up just in time to catch Smith skewer their comrade. They too turned about and sprinted toward the jungle, fleeing from a certain death at the hands of Smith. Fortune failed to fall on the two VC this day as marines tackled the two, who were now prisoners of war. POWs are a treasure trove of intelligence for enemy movements.

The battle now entered the final stages.

And now the cries no one ever wants to hear will fill the air.

"Medic! I'm hit!"

"Oh my God! Mom! Help me!"

"Chaplain Buchanan!"

"God help me!"

Hearing the pains from the young men struck an immediate nerve within the spiritual team, who raced immediately to the cries of the wounded.

Jackson, who fought hard but running on an empty tank of adrenalin, set himself to hurry with Buchanan to minister to the dying and wounded, but came close to collapsing.

Stopping abruptly, Buchanan grabbed Jackson's arm, asking, "Philip. Philip! Ya alright?"

Buchanan gave Jackson a quick look over for wounds. With an absence of wounds on his loyal bodyguard but noticing him breathing heavily, Buchanan said, "Philip, I fail, thank goodness, to locate any wounds. But you need to rest, right here, now. You're plum out of energy. Please. I'll go to the wounded. You can join me later."

Jackson attempts to grin. "OK, sir."

Buchanan holds Jackson's arm as he assists him to the ground slowly. He scanned the perimeter from one end to the other. In a matter of seconds, Buchanan laid his eyes on the aftermath of the battle, thoroughly flabbergasted. He stood stunned by what laid in front of him. The scene seemed unbelievable. Human remains spewed all over the perimeter. The beautiful shades of green vegetation of Vietnam turned red with blood. The battle scattered marines about, screaming in pain and agony. Isolated marines wandered about in shock and glassy eyed. The dead and wounded laid mangled together, both friend and foe. Smoke lifted from the heat of weapons fired and the aftermath of grenades exploding. The oodles of isolated fires sprinkled about ignited from the multiple weapons fired. The brunt of savage hand to hand combat resulted in a ghastly sight of death. The smell of the dead will follow Buchanan for the rest of his life. He knew civilians would never believe the carnage he just experienced unless they witnessed it firsthand. All he wants to do is collapse flat on the ground and do nothing but weep.

He thought better of it.

His calling from God to walk side by side in the bush with marines who so desperately needed his spiritual presence trumped his personal needs in this dire moment in time.

Buchanan dashed to the nearest wounded marine.

"Oh God, Padre. It hurts. Help me!" pleaded the young grunt.

With multiple wounds peppered throughout his torso and limbs, Buchanan realized the most severe wound came at the lower torso on the left near his intestines. Buchanan stopped the bleeding with a hand towel, suppressing the wound while he cleaned his face with his shaving towel.

"HOLY MARY, MOTHER of JESUS!" came another cry from a marine just a few feet away.

"Hold on, son. Medics will be here soon." Buchanan said with assurance.

In a matter of seconds, medics arrived to administer medical aid.

"Thank you, Padre. We'll take it from here." said Petty Officer David Crowley.

"Bless you Petty Officer Crowley."

"Petty Officer Sigmanson! Bring the other two emergency packs with you!" yelled Crowley.

The medics worked on the wounded marine, while Buchanan hastened to the young man calling out to Mary, the mother of Jesus, recognizing him as a member of Charlie Company, but failed to remember his name. The young man took part in Communion services, but seemed distant and introverted, reluctant to befriend fellow marines.

A corpsman rushed up to the doomed young marine, hastened to work on the young man.

"Chaplain Buchanan." pleaded the marine.

"Yes, marine." acknowledged Buchanan as Jackson, filthy and riddled with blood stains, finally joined Buchanan on his right.

"I'm here son." said Buchanan.

"I'm here too, Carl. It's Jackson. Philip Jackson." Jackson, who knew the dying marine, reassured the young man of another presence in his desperate time of need.

Buchanan looked up toward Jackson, relieved at last his assistant kneeled beside him once again. Looking back down toward the marine, he noticed wounds throughout his limps and torso. Turning back up toward Jackson, he shivers his head no.

The marine, riddled with shrapnel and bullets, bled profusely from head to toe. All the color from his complexion drained from the loss of blood, as white as a sheet. The fight layered his uniform and face with dirt and grim. The condition of his body, grisly, displayed the pitiful sight of a doomed man.

"Chaplain. Chaplain! Pray with me." pleaded the marine.

"OK, marine. OK, son." Buchanan stared at the young marine in his mid-twenties, fighting back his tears.

"Oh. Oh! - Oh! Jesus! Can't ya see him?" insisted the marine, who stretches out a scantly smile.

The spiritual team glances up over their shoulder, seeing nothing. Jackson reflects a fleeting heart, frowning from deep sadness.

"P-Pray with me. Chaplain - Chaplain." beseeched the marine, growing weaker with every second passed, holding onto life with the negligible sum of energy left within his being.

Jackson holds the young man's head upright in his right hand, holding his other hand with his left. The corpsman attempted to stop the bleeding as much as possible from the other side of the severely wounded young man.

Buchanan held Carl up in his arms and recites the Lord's Prayer with him:

"Our Father, who art in Heaven
Hallow'd it be thy name"

"Na.... thy n-n-na-." said the marine as trickles of blood stream from his mouth.

"Oh my goodness, Philip. He's attempting -" said Buchanan, striving to keep control of himself. "He's attempting to recite the Lord's Prayer."

"It's OK, chaplain. Just keep going. He needs us." encouraged Jackson, holding back his emotions.

Buchanan continued the Lord's Prayer,

"Thy Kingdom Come
Thy Will Be Done
On Earth
as it is in Heaven
Give us this day
Our daily Bread"

"Mom." blurted out the marine.

Chaplain Buchanan pauses, then continues:

"And Forgive Us our sins
As we forgive those who have
Sinned against us"

"Je -! Je-Jesus!" called out the marine, staring into the Heavens.

Chaplain Buchanan gawks down at the young marine, grinning as best he can as he continued the Lord's Prayer.

"Lead us not into temptation
But deliver us from evil
For thine is the Kingdom
The Power
And the Glory.
Forever and Ever."

The marine forces an attempted smile.

Chaplain Buchanan then quotes the Beatitudes to the dying marine.

As Buchanan quotes the fourth Beatitude, the marine's bloody head becomes limp, while his hand squeezes Jackson's left hand. His breathing slowly ends.

Chaplain Buchanan then prays a personal prayer over the young marine. The spiritual team stare at one another intently in the brief, but disheartening moment.

Buchanan whispered, "He's gone. He's really gone."

"Yes, he is, sir."

Buchanan glances back down at the young marine, shocked and sad.

"War takes life so quick." asserts Jackson.

The men pause momentarily, assessing all the chaos of the morning which snuffed so much life away in such a minuscule amount of time.

"Dad saw it in World War II. He hated it in the Pacific. I see it now in this war. And I hate it today in Vietnam." said Jackson.

Jackson gently and carefully laid Carl's head on the ground, closing his eyes.

The spiritual team just sat on the ground for a moment of silence, attempting an effort to make sense out of all the insanity the men just witnessed this morning on January 28, 1969.

Solemn, the men stood up while marines came to gather up Carl's remains. The marines respectfully carried Carl's body to an open space of the perimeter's center, lining up his remains with the other KIAs. His remains to be placed in a body bag, picked up soon by a Huey helicopter, and finally to the 'cooler' for identification.

Buchanan kneeled before each KIA, delivering a brief prayer over the remains.

Suddenly, Buchanan, Rockford, Jackson, Skawinski, and others failed to contain their emotions any longer as the men broke down and wept. Any attempt to stop weeping came thwarted by the loss of friends and the emotional strain the battle inflicted on the marines.

The marines gathered the wounded in one triage area, with corpsmen tending to their wounds, while Bravo and Charlie Companies strived to recuperate from the mental and physical stress of the battle just experienced in the jungle bush.

For four months, Buchanan served as a Navy chaplain. Today he experienced a first degree dose of combat in Vietnam and the literal destruction of a human being in war.

The spiritual team left the KIAs, stepping to Jurgensen and Smith's spot the men defended within the perimeter.

Marines made their way to gather up the remains of Jurgensen and Smith. The sergeants laid in the blood-soaked ground beneath them, flat on their backs, covered with dirt and grim. The men were barely recognizable.

Obviously, the sergeants' will to fight to the death came clear with the condition of the two brave platoon leaders.

Many marines surrounded the two fallen heroes. Emotions ran high as the men wept abundantly. Bravo Company lost two highly competent leaders, impossible to replace.

As the marines gathered up the remains, Buchanan squatted ground level, saying with certainty, "They're alive. They're breathing!"

"Chaplain. Please. They're gone." replied Rockford. "As much as I regret it. They're with the Lord now. Look at'em. They're gone."

"Sir." Buchanan said with assurance, "They're exhaling and inhaling. Look."

"Chaplain, they're gone." Rockford stared at Buchanan with pity.

Rockford continued, but spoke rapidly with confidence, "But I'm certainly going to search and destroy in the next few weeks."

Looking back down at Jurgensen and Smith, Rockford reassured his friends, "I can assure you of that. Those sons of bitches are going to pay for this. The VC is in -" Rockford interrupted himself, glancing down at the two sergeants. He ordered the marines not to touch the two sergeants, as he stooped low to survey the men.

"I do see'em breathing. Chaplain, you're right!" yelled Rockford. With glee, he proclaimed to the Heavens, "Hallelujah! They're alive!"

An astonished Kowslowski declared, "They are alive, sir!"

"Corpsmen!" yelled Rockford.

Sims and Kiehl added, "They're alive! Thank you, Jesus."

Noticing Sims' reaction to the wonderful news, Buchanan perceived a sign in Sims he was coming closer to joining the family of God.

The remaining marines chimed in, "They're alive!"

Buchanan gazed at the bodies, smiling. He thought, 'the killing machine's engine was just in low gear'.

The corpsmen arrived to work on the sergeants. The dirt, blood, and grim covered all the life within the sergeants, who fell from complete exhaustion. Life within the killing machine was far from over. It simply needed a tune up in the Da Nang hospital to recover, to re-energize its engine to run in high gear on all cylinders.

Jackson gently placed his hand on Buchanan's shoulder and said, "Amen."

"Amen." replied Buchanan.

Buchanan never recovered psychologically from the most violent, ferocious hand-to-hand combat he witnessed in Vietnam. Hope and faith, along with much prayer, provided spiritual guidance to cope with the violent combat he witnessed today in the bush. Buchanan preached Hope and Faith softened the hardships of this life to the men, a message he himself leaned on throughout the rest of his life.

The discovery of Jurgensen and Smith alive served a shot in the arm for building a spiritual uplifting and a rebuilding of morale for Bravo and Charlie Companies, especially for Bravo in the aftermath of the bloodiest battle Buchanan witnessed in the bush.

Following the pickup of the wounded and the KIAs by Huey Helicopters, Rockford ordered to saddle up. The mood of marines displayed nothing but melancholy. Dejected from the losses, the marines obeyed orders regardless. The marines conducted themselves as if 'Semper Fi' meant something.

As the marines prepared to saddle up, the marines recognized one prisoner as a shoe shiner in Da Nang who had shined many a marine's shoe. The marines left the encampment site furious, with the South Vietnamese young man having the audacity to take part in Viet Cong activities. The efforts of officers and non-commissioned officers alike, along with the spiritual team, to talk the marines out of handing the young VC over to the ARVN came painstaking and plenty full of supplication. Labeling him a traitor came naturally. Bravo Company had served with ARVN military personnel in the war and grew to respect them.

The marines were in a foul mood. Bravo and Charlie companies suffered from the results of the ambush. The companies endured 15 KIAs and 36 WIA. Recognizing the shoe shiner as a Viet Cong terrorist didn't help matters. Knowing the casualties inflicted upon the enemy, 69 KIA and 168 WIA, lightened the foul temper.

Over the next 50 years in Buchanan's life, the battle flew past frequently in his memory, contributing to many flashbacks for the rest of his life.

He prayed when falling asleep tonight, his dreams will be void of nightmares of Carl dying in his arms, witnessing Jurgensen and Smith kill the Viet Cong in mass or seeing their lifeless bodies lying on the ground. Or possibly the worst memory of all - the VC rushing toward him displaying the most enraged demon from the deepest depths of the earth.

The killing machine fought in high gear this day. The sergeants would heal and again lead Bravo Company.

Though Buchanan prayed the war would end soon one day, the devil's efforts to prolong the war heightened, extending human beings' efforts to oil and maintain their killing machines in high gear.

An Unforgettable Service

January 28, 1969

In the midmorning hours, five Huey helicopters arrived in open space to pick up the 15 KIAs. After the careful loading up of the KIA's, the Hueys hightailed it out of coordinates AT 965766 and AT 972753.

As Bravo and Charlie Companies watched the five Huey helicopters fly out of sight, the men's emotions ran uncontrolled with the loss of 15 brave marines.

Another wing of Huey helicopters came five minutes later to pick up the wounded.

As the helicopters disappeared from eyeshot, Rockford ordered to make the trek back to Camp Love, "Saddle Up!"

The arrival in camp came at 0930 hours sharp. The exhausted men assembled haphazardly in front of the dentist's office, filthy, dirty, covered with grim, mud, soot, and blood. Rockford, standing on the top step of the dentist's office, delivered the men a positive word of note, considering the circumstances.

"Keep your head up. This day we want to forget. We lost good friends." Rockford paused. "But as Chaplain Buchanan has said time and time again, it's all about what's in here." Pointing to his heart over his chest, he gives the marines a good solid stare of confidence. "Remember that. How you view life helps a heap. Don't get down.

We'll show the enemy 'what's for' sooner than you know. I promise ya that."

Rockford informed the men to clean up, eat, and get some shuteye. A note no one sought to hear from him next came the list of those on the duty roster to be posted later in the day.

After cleaning up and some chow, the men literally fell into their cots, falling asleep.

The spiritual team seemed no different. At 1045 hours, the team caught some shut eye themselves, praying for pleasant dreams.

Jackson reminded Buchanan of the Tuesday chapel service in the camp hall at 1300 hours. He cringed at the thought of it.

"It's just sleep, sir."

Buchanan grimaces and says, "At 37, two hours of shut eye just fills my tank half full."

Jackson grins. A couple of hours of sleep sufficed until the evening.

Buchanan usually looked forward to having chapel services on Tuesdays and Thursdays, for it provided a semblance of a home for the men. A sense of being in 'church' instead of military service in the 'boondocks' did everyone some good. But this day of all days, Buchanan longed for nothing but sleep, and shunned within himself as much as possible any antagonistic attitude toward conducting the services. Stepping from a horrific battle into a chapel service came difficult and painstakingly challenging. The spiritual team pushed a strong-willed, determined, orientated ministry. The Lord's presence enabled the team to survive the gauntlet of evil throw at them.

1200 hours came quick. Time to rise and shine. Buchanan crawled out of his cot, getting a little under two hours of shut eye and donned his uniform. Sluggishly and lethargically, Jackson pulled himself out of his cot, dressing himself.

Arrived at the chow hall a moment prior to Chaplain Buchanan, Jackson stood morass and uncharacteristically slothful.

Walking up to Jackson, Buchanan smirked. "Well, Sergeant Jackson. As I've heard in my nearly 15 years of military service, it's just sleep."

Grimacing, Jackson glanced slowly toward Buchanan as if he had gone half crazy. As the men walked into the chow hall, Jackson asked, "Are you out of your mind, sir?" He pauses, reminding Buchanan of the past 24 hours, "You remember the fight we were in last night? Don't you, sir? Whew." Jackson, shaking his head at Buchanan's goofiness, half grins.

"Yes, Sergeant. I do. You said it just a few hours ago yourself. Remember?" added Buchanan, in his familiar accent.

Jackson shrugs his shoulders, grinning.

In a slothful voice, Buchanan said, "Just trying to lighten a mood drenched with sorrow this noonday."

"Yes sir. I understand."

The team stepped in line to receive chow, sitting down to eat a noonday meal. They gobbled down their food quickly. Buchanan possessed not an ounce of tolerance being late for anything, and the time had raced to 1233 hours already.

Everyone and their uncle in the chow hall asked about the fighting just hours ago. The spiritual team's reluctance to discuss the matter appeared obvious. They were in no mood to talk about the gory details. The team simply gorged their food down to their stomachs and dispatched themselves quickly out of the chow hall.

When finally stepping out of the chow hall out of earshot of the chow line, a surprised Buchanan commented, "Can you believe those people, Philip? I can't emotionally speak of those things right now. I held a boy in my arms as he passed."

"My sentiments exactly, sir. My sentiments exactly."

The team scurried to the camp hall to conduct the chapel services.

Arriving to the hall at 1251 hours, the team stopped suddenly as Buchanan looked at his watch intently, and said, "Holy crap."

Jackson snaps his head, grinning toward Buchanan, in shock and wide-eyed. He never heard a word of profanity come out of Buchanan's mouth, period. The reference to 'crap' is the closest to profanity he had heard out of Buchanan yet.

"I mean Holy poop. I mean – well. Holy – Listen, we've got -", looking down at his watch, "nine minutes to set the rows of chairs, and place the service manuals on the chairs. Let's get to it. Hubba - Hubba."

Jackson smiles, stepping into the hall.

"I've got to wing it with the sermon anyhow." said Buchanan.

Stepping into the hall, Jackson is taken aback as he removes his cover and says, "Look here, sir. The chairs! The benches! Someone or somebody has already placed them for chapel."

"Sure did, Philip. Sure did." responded Buchanan, removing his cover slowly out of surprise.

"Wow! Look there." added Buchanan, pointing down at the chairs and benches.

Not only were the chairs and benches set for chapel, someone placed the service manuals on each chair and bench.

The team stood in place, cherishing the moment. The emotional shock of the Christian love displayed would be thought of as silly by most civilians. But no one but those who took part in the fight early the previous morning would know how much the preparation of the service meant to the spiritual team. They were most appreciative of the esprit de corps of the Marine Corps shown. The spiritual team needed something good to happen, and it did. Someone showed some charity in this exhaustive war.

Buchanan's grin wavered as he thought of a problem. Looking at his watch, he says, "There's nobody here. It's 1254 hours. And there's nobody here."

Biting their lower lip, they worried no one would show up for services. The team asked silently what would explain the absence of congregants. Without a word, the team concluded in their hearts the feelings within the camp fell into a damp and melancholy mood. The men might need some isolation to overcome the battle just hours ago.

Attendance for the Tuesday chapel service gathered robust numbers of participants every week. The men loved Buchanan.

"Well, sir. We can worship, can't we? You know what the Scriptures say, 'Wherever there are two or more gathered, I will be there with you.'" said Jackson with enthusiasm.

Buchanan turned to respond but held his tongue as the team perked their ears towards voices. Could it be participants coming for the service heard from a distance? The volume of the voices increased with distance nearer to the camp hall.

"Could it be, Philip? Could it be?" asked Buchanan with enthusiasm.

"I think it might, sir. I think so! Let's go see."

They scampered over to the camp hall wall next to the supply building, looking out the top half of the hall window space.

Many buildings in Camp Love had a wooden half bottom, and an open space which was enclosed with a clear and netted canopy attached on the top of the edge of the ceiling inside to keep insects, pests, and snakes out of the buildings.

Sure enough, 15 to 20 men made their way toward the hall.

They dashed to the other side of the hall, peeking out through the open space, and discovered additional men coming from all directions of camp.

"Hurry Chaplain. To the door. To the door to shake hands." said Jackson.

"Yeah. *Yeah, Sergeant.*" replied Buchanan with fervor. As he made his way to the door, the first marine stepped in, Lieutenant Colonel Lucas.

"Good Afternoon! Yes, sir. Good to see ya today, sir." Buchanan said with excitement as he extends his hand to the Skipper.

"It's *very* good to see you here as well, chaplain. Very pleased." responded Lucas as he took Buchanan's hand.

Lucas patted his right hand with his left just to let Buchanan know his support for the chaplain's office. The commanding officer wanted him to know he carried out his duty as chaplain with fervor and bravery in the firefight.

"Amen." Buchanan swallowed hard. "Thank ya, sir."

Lucas nods his head as Buchanan focused on him walking down between the two sets of rows of chairs, sitting in the front row. 'Great!' thought Buchanan.

Buchanan's afterthought was, 'The Skipper attends services occasionally and of all days to attend, he comes today, a day I have to wing it with the sermon.'

Dozens of marines followed suit into the hall.

The XO Major Carroll stepped confidently through the entrance door, stepping up to the front row, sitting beside Lucas.

There were elements of Companies B and C, Skawinski's combat engineering squad, and Alpha and Delta companies present for the service.

Doc Delaney and a representation of corpsman were present, including Crowley.

Adkins, in Camp Love for an officers' call, Burns, Burnside, and even McElrath attended the service.

Buchanan looked over the hall. Standing room only.

'Wow!' he thought.

The service came through like flying colors. And though Buchanan might have winged it, he delivered one of the most eloquent sermons on spiritual rewards from Heaven Jackson ever heard him convey to the men. Every word spoken from Buchanan came from the heart. Words the camp desperately needed to hear. Camp Love lost 15 friends and fellow shipmates, including a couple of KIA's of Navy explosive experts assigned to Skawinski's team for three months.

The words of Buchanan calmed the wearisome hearts attending the service. The Devil threw evil from every direction at Camp Love for the past 24 hours. Buchanan's zeal to squash all attempts on the Devil's part to prevent the marines and sailors from accomplishing their mission elevated to an all-time high.

Buchanan caught a sudden, healthy dose of fervor to confront the evil one.

Close to the end of the order of service, Jackson stepped to the podium, asking everyone to stand and responsively read the closing Scriptures in the service manual.

Suddenly, in the very back row of benches next to the entrance doors, Jackson noticed several marines jumping about, a few stooped down toward the floor. Every single eyeball glanced back to give a look-see at the commotion, as a marine laughed, blurting out, "Just go ahead with the Scripture reading Sergeant. It's secure again back here."

Buchanan smiled curiously as Lucas and Carroll followed suit. Lucas thought, 'If someone is trying to be cute, that marine is going to work the head and clean uniforms for the duration of his tour.'

Jackson completed the responsive reading as Buchanan stepped up to the podium to deliver a closing prayer to end the chapel service.

The spiritual team swiftly stepped to the back of the hall, not only to shake hands with departing marines and sailors, but to inquire of all the commotion toward the end of the service.

Once Buchanan made his way to the entrance, not only was Buchanan relieved, but mutually terrified at his discovery, a dead bamboo viper with his head cut off.

"I hate those things." admitted Buchanan, followed by marine laughter encircling the chaplain.

"Me too, sir." replied the marines.

With the alertness of visiting ARVN troops, along with Sims and Kiehl, an ARVN soldier sliced the head off of the bamboo viper. The snake's presence heightened the service to be unforgettable.

Buchanan snapped a picture of the skinny reptile with the ARVN soldier who killed it, holding the snake by the tip of its tail. He used the photo to tell the story to many others in years to come.

Pleased with the afternoon, Buchanan's chosen words during the service inserted a solemn atmosphere in Camp Love, especially after the stinging battle left permanent scars on everyone. The standing room only service brought a therapeutic cure for the men, along with an outstanding sermon delivered with comforting words bringing about a calm in the aftermath of a bloody battle. Buchanan felt nothing but shock at his positive words expressed within the sermon since he winged it. Even the Skipper remarked the sermon he heard came as one of the best preached on spiritual rewards of Heaven he ever heard from Buchanan.

The topper turned out to be the snake, bringing a bit of reassurance God is still protective of His children, even amid a chapel service.

On top of all that, Chaplain Buchanan's appreciation for the individual responsible for arranging the hall for the services cheered his heart to no end. No one set up the hall prior to today. The hall found itself prepared for worship every Tuesday and Thursday for the duration of Buchanan's tour. The gratitude felt from the spiritual team overflowed from the benevolence shown with the preparation for the services, though the team will never express their thankfulness by word of mouth.

Whoever the person might have been, he yearned to be anonymous.

PROTECTING THE CHAPLAIN

FEBRUARY 5, 1969

Buchanan displayed nothing but 'gun ho' for the day. After a shower and shave, he read a military history book, waiting for Jackson to carry out the day's agenda.

Buchanan hit the road running at 100 miles an hour at 0500 hours. The spiritual team set an early agenda for the morning to embark on a mission to replenish the candies distributed to the children when visiting villages and CAPs or randomly to children while in the bush. The team scheduled a drive to the Da Nang base post office to receive the new supply order of chocolate sweets, hard candies, and gum requisitioned from an anonymous donator of monies given to the general fund. Unfortunately, the appropriated funds for candy ran out for the quarter, and an undisclosed individual 'out of the blue' contributed a considerable amount of funds to purchase the sweet 'treats', as Buchanan referred to them. The team possessed a bull headed will to run through whatever gauntlet which might lie in front of them to prevent the children the pleasure of indulging the sweet treats. The team had committed themselves long ago to suffer whatever consequences might come and push through the unexpected gauntlet that comes their way to provide candy to the children.

The spiritual team discussed that children in the western world thought life in all four corners of the world seemed comparable to western life. The team rolled their eyes, thinking of children in the west, with no worries for their wants and needs compared to the children in South Vietnam, who wondered where their next meal might come from.

The candy brought great joy and pleasure to each child. Buchanan's bull headed will even pushed him to go as far as traveling deep into the Arizona Territory to ensure the spiritual team provided the children the special treats.

Sleep came scarce last night. Even Burns' selection of Brahms 1st Symphony, a piece of music written in four movements and in the same key as Beethoven's 9th Symphony, failed to bring any solid sleep.

The spiritual team rendezvoused at 0700 hours to eat chow, then headed toward Da Nang. The six-mile trip on Route 1 to Da Nang became a favorite for Buchanan, who thoroughly enjoyed the Vietnam landscape. The drive presented a panoramic view of Marble Mountain and Monkey Mountain, a breathtaking experience of the beauty of Vietnam.

Foremost on the minds of the spiritual team, questioned the identity of the donor for the candy money. Many individuals came to mind, but the team was clueless of the benefactor.

Scratching Porch's name from the list of donors came naturally. The notion he donated money seemed out of the question.

The trek back will fill the jeep and a small supply trailer Buchanan requisitioned from the auto department full of candy. Jackson brought his bungee cords to tie down the mountain of candy in the jeep.

As discussions shifted to the An Ngai Tay CAP and the next ministry in the hamlet, both men were ever cautious of the danger of snipers along the road, keeping an additional eye out for ever present booby traps traveling the road.

"Maybe Doc Delaney can instruct the villagers on hygiene and provide cleanliness lessons to the citizens in the hamlet?" suggested Jackson.

"Great idea, Sergeant. I love it!" Buchanan paused, thinking. "Maybe include a few Scriptures emphasizing the care and maintenance of your body as a Temple of God."

"Yeah. *Yeah*. Great addition, sir."

Buchanan asks, "What if we ask for hygiene products? The villagers are always asking for toothpaste, brushes, other items. We have an elite group of benefactors in Camp Love and in Da Nang."

Jackson added, "What about cotton swabs, cotton balls and pure alcohol? What do you say, sir?"

"Sounds great, Sergeant." said Buchanan as the men smile with the new idea.

Jackson came upon a curve in the road with an over brush of tree limbs covering the highway. He slowed down to make the turn in the road, turned the steering wheel as the jeep approached the curve. He adjusted to the gradual deviation of the direction of the road as it increased, saying, "Chaplain, would it be too much of a hassle for us to have a field day type of -".

"AHHHHHHHHHHH!" - yelled the spiritual team.

Like a bolt out of the blue, a 25 pound primate, a Red-shanked douc, fell between the two men from the tree limbs over the road.

Immediately, Jackson lost control of the jeep, swaying back and forth on the road. He glared forward, then onto the monkey, then back onto the road. Back and forth he went. Flustered and a bit confused, he barely kept control of the jeep.

With the discovery he jumped into a jeep with two human beings, the monkey went nuts, jumping up and down in every direction. Scared and terrified, his eyes were as wide as the ocean view. He jumped onto the centerpiece of the floorboard behind the gearshift, roaring 'ECKKKKKK!!' as loud as his little lungs could muster. Showing his sharp teeth, he spread his arms with an arm span reaching the sides of the jeep, giving the illusion of him looking two, even three times his actual size.

"AHHHHHHHHHHH!" the spiritual team yelled.

Jackson reaped the agony of another intimidating showing of teeth, with the head of the Red-shanked douc pushing forward, causing him to sway the jeep farther to the left and right.

"STAY ON THE ROAD! STAY ON THE ROAD!" yelled Buchanan, as he foolishly attempted to grab the monkey.

"I'm trying sir! I'm trying!" insisted Jackson.

"He's going to bite me! He's going to bite me!" yelled Jackson. "Please, Sergeant!"

Buchanan again foolishly attempted to seize the monkey to toss him out of the jeep alongside the road onto the ground. He hit a streak of luck, considering he didn't get bitten or ripped up by the primate's sharp nails.

The monkey gave Buchanan a turn of showing his teeth, sharpened fangs and all, as Buchanan shrieked, "Uhhhhhhh!"

"He's going to bite me! He's going to bite me!" screamed Buchanan. "Uh-huh! Chaplain! See there!"

With all the commotion, Jackson continued to sway the jeep.

"You're driving off the road, Sergeant!"

"I can *see* that, sir!" replied Jackson with sarcasm.

The primate grabbed Buchanan's helmet strap, pulling him straight down toward the monkey eye to eye, as Buchanan strained, grunting "Uhhhhhh!" He felt an unbelievable strength from the small primate pulling his helmet strap.

In different circumstances, Buchanan might have admired the magnificent beauty and strength of the Re-shanked douc, but in his present circumstance - the monkey is a killer!

Unbeknownst to Jackson the monkey took hold of a clipboard in the back seat knocking it back and forth from on top of Buchanan's helmet, to the back of his seat, then swinging it back toward Jackson, slamming it on the back of Jackson's head hitting his combat helmet. Feeling the impact of the clipboard, Jackson felt the momentum and velocity of the collision jarring his senses.

Jackson attempted to slow down, but in haste at the impact of the clip board upon his head, he pressed onto the accelerator instead of the brakes and sped up, with the primate still all over them and the jeep.

The jeep sped up just as they came upon another curve, too late for Jackson to discover his mistake to press on the breaks, until he was on the curve, turning sharp and wide. Both men tilted with the jeep rounding the curve, hanging on for dear life, still yet having to push the monkey off of them simultaneously.

"Ahhhhhhhh!" screamed the men.

With the jeep pushed on its side, the thought of tipping over was very much on their minds, though it was only seconds to think of it.

Luckily, the road straightened from the curve and the jeep slowed down from the fluid pressure of the jeep and Jackson, who broke free from the primate, pressed the brakes, drastically slowing the jeep down.

As the speed decreased, the Red-shanked douc soared out of the jeep.

The men froze, shocked, catching flies as they kept their eyes glued on the primate, throwing himself out of the jeep, airborne into the air until he landed on the ground, scurrying back into the jungle. The spiritual team now realized the primate had been just as startled as the humans were, glaring at the primate as he scampered back into the bush.

The jeep coasted at a good 15 miles per hour and the two men breathed heavily, glaring at each other, catching flies and shocked, thinking not in a million years what just happened to them would have ever occurred. But reality set in as the jeep coasted to a complete stop.

From sheer shock, the men laughed hysterically. They laughed and laughed. And laughed some more.

The men had experienced violent war, fatality, and much sorrow in Vietnam, including facing death personally more than once. That's a fact. And here a simple monkey jumping into their jeep, possibly causing a fatal flip of their vehicle, humored them to no end.

Following the moment of jocularity, the men composed themselves. The recuperation from 'the monkey visit', as Buchanan referred to it in years to come, reminded them they still had a mission to complete. The candy still awaited the spiritual team in Da Nang. They continued their journey, but with a considerable bit of trepidation.

Jackson sped the jeep up to 45 miles per hour to make up for lost time.

The team did indeed arrive in Da Nang and picked up the candy at 0955 hours in the base post office. The team traveled the rest of the journey without another unexpected 'Bonzo', as Buchanan referred to the primate - a reference to one of Buchanan's favorite Ronald Reagan movies.

The route to Da Nang ended up an adventure, but the candy was worth the trip.

The team strapped the candy onto the jeep with the bungee cords and filled every nook and cranny of the trailer.

Departing the post office, the team passed through the main gate, turning onto Route 1 back toward home.

Two miles down Route 1, Jackson asked, "Funny, ain't it? Your bodyguard, me, protected you from a primate on the way in. Not a sniper or the VC with an explosive. Not even a road hijacking. But a monkey."

The men smile at the thought.

"I think the monkey got the best of you, though." said Buchanan, smirking.

"Funny. *Funny,* sir."

Buchanan laughs, reminding Jackson of the monkey's use of the clipboard. "The clipboard proved lethal. He gave you a pretty good beating on top of your head."

Jackson grins.

Peering out into the countryside, Buchanan said with conviction, "Truth is Philip - I owe ya my life. You've been my protector. You've saved my life on more than one occasion."

Jackson nods. "Even with a pesky monkey, huh?"

Buchanan smiles.

He says, "Yeah."

Cowards and Bystanders

February 7, 1969

Stuffing his tobacco pouch back into his lower right pocket of his fatigued jacket, Buchanan, along with Jackson, stepped out of the jeep at An Ngai Tay hamlet at 0800 hours in the morning.

Doc Delaney and a team of corpsmen arrived in An Ngai Tay to reach out with the prognosis of many members of the hamlet from the past four weeks. Lieutenant McInally, the camp's dentist, came to administer dental check-ups.

Buchanan made his presence known as often as possible with the medical CAP.

Buchanan had in hand plenty of candy and chocolate for the children. The trip to Da Nang two days ago proved the danger had been well worth it, even if a Red-shanked douc accidentally caused a fatal accident for the spiritual team.

Two trucks from Camp Love, one occupied with a platoon from Delta Company to secure the perimeter and another with Delaney's corpsmen, along with a jeep transporting Doc Delaney and Senior Chief Petty Officer Gross, drove directly to the gate of An Ngai Tay.

Marines secured the perimeter while Doc Delaney and his corpsmen administered their medical skills.

With a pinch or two of tobacco in his mouth, Buchanan mentally gained confidence against the pesky worms, gaining confidence of the potency of the tobacco barring any infiltration of the grotesque invader. At least the tobacco set a mental state of health for Buchanan.

As the spiritual team stepped toward the gate of the hamlet, Jackson points downward toward Buchanan's fatigues right pocket, and says, "You're going to give the citizens of An Ngai Tay the impression you're addicted to that stuff."

Jackson smirked. "You've even gotten sick from unintentionally swallowing the juice, sir."

Buchanan responds with assurance, "Well, getting sick was early on and besides, I haven't gotten those nasty you-know-whats."

Buchanan found it difficult even to say the word, as he found tape worms revolting.

"You mean tapeworms, sir?" said an inquisitive Jackson, smirking even more. "You know, Chaplain -"

"I know, I know." Buchanan said, interrupting Jackson. "There's no scientific proof that tobacco has any chemical substance to kill the, well, ya know."

"*Huh*. HAHA! Chaplain?" said Jackson.

Buchanan points with his index finger, shaking his head sarcastically, saying, "I don't care about sci-en-ti-fic evidence. The tobacco makes me feel better."

Buchanan spits tobacco juice into the defensive perimeter surrounding the hamlet.

Entering the hamlet, Buchanan says, "Come on. Let's go make our rounds of visitation with the villagers, Sergeant."

Jackson smiles, thinking, 'I can't get enough of this man. He humors me to no end.'

Buchanan noticed added scissor barbed wire to the original perimeter, along with an additional perimeter trench. After further Viet Cong nocturnal activities in the area, the ARVN and Seabees strengthened the defenses.

Once in the hamlet, the team visited the citizens of An Ngai Tay.

With every visit to An Ngai Tay, Buchanan cultivated a stronger trust with the villagers. The team visited the hamlet frequently since October 1968. Buchanan possessed a genuine and considerate personality, and people enjoyed his company, especially after the massacre in December. American military chaplains gained respect and trust of South Vietnamese Catholics, but the respect and trust for a chaplain did not materialize overnight. The time to nurture a building trust and relationship over time required patience, an innate trait Buchanan possessed from birth. He established trust and respect quickly in his first three or four months and bent over backwards locating Catholic Navy Chaplains to conduct Mass, an effort noticed by hamlet leadership. The humanitarian efforts pursued by Buchanan solidified a genuine Christian undertaking to meet the wants and needs of fellow believers in Christ. The villagers in the hamlet opened up to Buchanan once he convinced the villagers his efforts were not there to proselytize Roman Catholics to the Baptist faith.

Buchanan added his efforts to a solid core of chaplains dedicated to fulfill the Navy chaplain corps motto – 'cooperation without compromise'. Buchanan's labor in An Ngai Tay, An Ngai Don, or any other CAP or endeavor, came fulfilled without compromising his own Baptist doctrine. Every exertion and effort on Buchanan's part to meet the spiritual and physical needs of the South Vietnamese exerted itself out of a spirit of the Great Commission.

After visiting the people of An Ngai Tay, the team joined Doc Delaney at the end of two lines of waiting patients to be examined.

Patients in line had suffered injuries from a normal work routine of the day in the rice patties and farming.

The wounds varied due to age or from the responsible role of the villager within the hamlet. A young boy suffered from cuts and bruises on the bottom of his feet working in the fields. An elderly lady had calluses from broken bones after falling on a blown up tree trunk along the Perfume River from artillery shells.

Lieutenant McInally checked the elderly and the condition of their teeth.

Buchanan's eye opening experience in South Vietnam revealed many truths of poverty-stricken peoples of the third world, especially the rural elderly who had never seen a dentist until the Americans came administering humanitarian aid to the South Vietnamese. Buchanan had little room to talk, with the fact he himself did not experience a dentist working on his teeth until he reached 22 years of age while enlisted in the Air Force. His teeth deteriorated over the years, as the Air Force dentist warned the young Buchanan to watch carefully how he treated his choppers.

The first time Buchanan ever experienced a dentist performing surgery of any sort in his mouth came from the result of a bar-room brawl he found himself in the middle of. To this day, he can't remember if he had started the bar-room brawl or not, but he remembers receiving a violent blow onto his chin, a collision from either a beer bottle or a tightened clasped fist with knuckles harder than steel.

Delaney and McInally finished the follow-up visit fairly quickly at 1015 hours. The two MeDCAP visits a month were making inroads. The villagers sensed a healthier populace within the hamlet with the medical attention given to them. The villagers grew to appreciate the Americans' efforts to improve their health.

As the medical examinations came to a close, the spiritual team distributed candy to the children. The team then leaped into the jeep, venturing even further into the bush to visit Alpha Company, accompanying the Seabees repairing pontoon bridges along the Perfume River two miles farther west from An Ngai Tay. The Viet Cong heavily damaged three bridges the past two days in night attacks and the bridges were vital supply routes to replenish the men in the field. The distant relationship between the ministry team and Alpha Company resulted from Company A's orders with sweeps and operations on the opposite ends of military sectors and sections when Buchanan received orders with the other three combat rifle companies a dozen miles away in the other direction. Failing to formulate rapport and develop relationships with the marines in Company A gnawed Buchanan, but certainly no fault on him. Alpha Company's assignments were deep into the jungle, with extended patrols, which amounted to schedules for days on end.

A quick visit to Alpha Company will instill a vital connection with the men to maintain a link of ministry. Jackson reminded Buchanan of the tight schedule and the necessity of returning home for the Friday night social. Besides, Buchanan looked forward to watching the first movie of a cavalry trilogy starring John Wayne.

Alpha Company fell under the auspices of Buchanan's responsibility and fell obligated to minister to the whole contingent of Camp Love.

After patching up the damage done of the first pontoon bridge, the Seabees, along with Alpha Company, were repairing the second of the three bridges to overhaul, at coordinates AT 898813 and AT 907576.

Arriving at the first bridge, the spiritual team discovered the Seabees had repaired the pontoon bridge. Jackson then drove the jeep to the adjacent road parallel to the Perfume River to the second bridge, where Alpha Company established a perimeter to guard the Seabees as the sailors worked on the damage done from the hands of the Viet Cong.

As Jackson pressed on the brakes, the jeep squeaked to a halt. Buchanan, without delay, dumped his can of tobacco juice onto the heat soaked ground. As Buchanan sat his can on the floorboard of the jeep, six to eight riflemen of Alpha Company dashed to the jeep, excited, yelling enthusiastically, and talking simultaneously. Neither Buchanan nor Jackson understood a word, but hearing a remark or two within all the gibberish.

The spiritual team just nodded their heads in disarray and placed their hands up in front of them as if to ask, 'What?'

The team heard only words in isolation within the discord of simultaneous voices speaking at once, words such as 'incredible', 'coward', 'brave', 'Jansen', 'Rodriquez', 'hand-to-hand', but incapable of putting any words together with any coherence from the marines talking all at once.

Communication came a bit more coherent as the marines slowed down a bit.

"Listen chaplain, he was incredible last night." said one marine.

"Rodriquez was unbelievably brave." expressed another.

And yet another marine blurted out, "I bet his hand-to-hand combat skills are unmatched in the camp."

"Jansen and McElwaney are just cowards." insisted another marine.

Buchanan spit tobacco juice onto the ground, and motioning with his hands to talk one at a time. "Slow down. Slow down, men. We can't understand ya."

Jackson, who put his hands up as if to say stop, said, "One at a time. One at a time."

Simultaneously, the marines again started talking all at once.

"Guys, Guys. Hold up. Hold up." said Jackson with authority.

Jackson knew one man, Corporal John Mark Truman, from Jackson Missouri and kin of President Harry S Truman. Jackson pointed straight at him and said, "Truman, tell us what happened."

Buchanan interrupted, asking Truman even before he could speak, "Hey, aren't you kin to President Truman?"

"Why, yes. Yes, sir. I am." said Truman proudly, wearing a grin from ear to ear.

"Yes. *Yeeeees.* President Truman's one of my favorite Presidents. You'll have to visit me and we'll have a talk in my hootch of your kinfolk." insisted Buchanan with a bit of anticipation in his mountain accent voice.

"*Sir*? About last night?" asked Jackson, glaring at Buchanan.

"Oh. Sorry, Sergeant." apologized Buchanan, smiling toward the men with a bit of embarrassment.

"OK. Now let's hear it Truman. *What happened*? Something about Rodriquez?" asked Jackson.

"Man, is it all about Rodriquez!" said Truman. The other marines added, "Yes it is, man."

"It went like this Padre." spoke Truman, glancing toward Buchanan sternly. Turning back toward Jackson, Truman said, "Sergeant. 1st Platoon, Bravo Company accompanied Skawinski's combat engineering team as usual the past two days along Route 540, which stumbled upon us last night on their way back to Camp Love, so Lieutenant Smith bunked down with us for the night. Their party seemed pooped from the patrols and sweeps searching for mines and booby traps the last couple of days."

The spiritual team listened intently.

Truman continued, "Well, 1st Platoon Bravo took the north perimeter to bed down and guard that end of the perimeter. As the night went on, most to all of us were asleep except those on watch. There might have been 5 to 10 minutes left until sunup, when all the sudden, the VC were on all sides of our encampment firing away. AK-47's blasting and grenades thrown inside the perimeter from all directions."

The spiritual team stood transfixed, catching flies as they listened to Truman's account of last night. "The only infiltration of the perimeter came from the north. And a few Viet Cong actually ran in. Luckily, we seized the seriousness of the situation and we secured the north perimeter. And the fighting didn't last all that long. It seemed to us, though, it was just a hit-and-run attack."

Truman paused, taking a deep breath as he continued his account of the early morning attack.

He turned to Buchanan. "But this is the part that's great, chaplain. Padre, the s-sun was just coming up, and you can barely see. But *you* can see, you know that time of the morning. It's *just* when you can catch a glimmer of sunlight. In the glimmer of light, you could see the north perimeter and where the VC could infiltrate the camp. And do you know – do *you know* – what we saw?"

The spiritual team nodded no.

"We saw no one other but -" and with great anticipation, Truman said, "Rodriquez. Yes, sir. Rodriquez."

Marines surrounding the spiritual team smiled, chuckling ever so softly.

One marine said excitedly, "Tell'em. Tell'em. Tell'em what Rodriquez did, man. Go ahead."

"I will, if ya shut up!" Truman said. He turned to Jackson, saying, "Sergeant, he'd already killed three or four with his bare hands and with his bayonet knife. They were lying beside him, all around him. Two or three others were running his way, and he killed each one of 'em. One after another. And his expression on his face was - was, well, as you say, Chaplain Buchanan – 'savage' like."

By now, the team's mouths were wide open. Buchanan asked, "Private Rodriquez! He's O-OK. Isn't he?"

"Don't worry, sir. He's fine. Fine. Shaken, but fine." replied Truman.

"Whew!" said the team.

"But as Rodriquez is kicking the VC's ass, we see something else. Rodriquez is not all the story. Listen to this. *Listen* to this....sir. The two of you will not believe this part of it." said Truman, turning to Buchanan.

"Guess what we see in the glimmer of light, sir?" asked Truman.

"*I don't* know, corporal." replied Buchanan with a slight grin, motioning with his hands, 'Just tell us!'

"Right, Padre." says Truman. Excitedly and methodically, Truman finishes up the story of Rodriquez. "We see in the dim glimmer of light, off to the side somewhat off into the brush, sits - low and behold - two marines sitting on their backsides, leaning back toward the ground, and holding themselves up with their hands, and they are -" after a moment of pause, Truman finally lets loose the names of the two mysterious marines and says, "Jansen and McElwaney."

The team is speechless, overwhelmed by the news.

Sergeant Jackson stares at Truman, attempting to picture in his mind the images Truman described in his account of Rodriquez.

"Yes, Sergeant. It's the truth." Truman said.

"Yes, it's all true." said another marine.

Buchanan comments, "After that 'big mouth' talk of how great of a warrior the two of 'em are. The talk of invincibility in combat, and this happens."

"Yes sir. Jansen and McElwaney apparently froze and didn't lift a finger to assist Rodriquez, sir." said another marine.

Truman says abruptly, "Rodriquez saved many of us from getting killed. Maybe all of us."

Another marine added, "Jansen and McElwaney just stared at Rodriquez, fighting with scared stiff and terrified expressions on their faces."

"Yeah, the two of 'em were just whimpering and crying like babies, man." added another marine.

"They just kept staring at Rodriquez, fighting to protect the north perimeter." commented a marine who was friends with the Michiganders.

"That's not all, sir." comments Truman.

With intensity, Truman continued, "This all took place on account of Jansen and McElwaney committed the unforgivable - the two of 'em, well - fell asleep on guard duty."

The marines observed an immediate double take from the spiritual team.

The attack accounted for 14 Viet Cong killed and many wounded. The three VC prisoners captured to interrogate for intelligence added a bonus to the bounty of victory. The attack accounted for 2 KIAs and 9 marines wounded in the firefight. An unprovoked and unnecessary firefight brought on by two cowardly idiots falling asleep on perimeter duty.

Truman continued to explain, "After the fighting all ended, Jurgensen lambasted Jansen and McElwaney for their cowardly actions, not lending a hand to Rodriquez. We thought he was going to literally kill 'em - *Kill 'em*!"

Buchanan tilted his head downward, staring in disbelief. Truman mentioned, "*Really*, sir. Describing him as furious is understating his anger. He turned livid."

Turning toward Jackson, Truman explained in further detail, "But when he's informed of 'em falling asleep on guard duty, WoW! I'd not seen anyone in Vietnam go as ballistic as we saw Jurgensen go off on Jansen and McElwaney. He went nuts. Cursing, flying around, mumbling many things, talking to people no one knew - who weren't even there. People who were back home in the states, we guessed."

Truman laughs and adds, "He'd say, 'Can you believe it, Uncle Charlie?' or 'Idiots, Marvin! Idiots!'"

Jurgensen held Jansen and McElwaney responsible for the casualties, and rightly so.

Another marine interjected, "Sir. And I'm not kidding, sir. It literally took eight to ten men to hold Jurgensen off of Jansen and McElwaney."

"Yeah, they were just standing there in shock, bewildered as Jurgensen went off." commented yet another marine.

The marines clued in the spiritual team the remaining morning's account.

Lieutenant Smith radioed in Huey helicopters for a MEDVAC to pick up the KIA's and wounded, ordered the men to eat some chow, then prepared the men to saddle up for Camp Love. As the marines finished up informing the team of the remaining sequence of events, the team then made the rounds visiting the troops and the Seabees, including Adkins, a pleasant surprise for Buchanan.

The spiritual team reckoned the visit to Alpha Company a success. To arrive in camp in time for the social, Jackson drove the team home.

Just a few miles from Camp Love, the spiritual team sat mute, as thoughts were of Rodriquez and his mental state. The drive to camp flew by quick. The team drove through the main entrance noticing straight away two men at attention, standing erect just an inch or two from touching the camp's flag pole. The two men standing at attention with their noses just one inch from the pole stood Jansen and McElwaney.

"Someone must have talked Jurgensen out of corporal punishment for the two." joked Jackson.

Buchanan stared sternly toward Jackson, smirking. Turning back toward the two cowardly marines, Buchanan felt a swift dose of embarrassment thrown forth from the flag poles because of the candy-asses actions. He felt sorry for them.

Nodding toward Jansen and McElwaney, Buchanan says, "Well, I guess that's what you're in for, if you're a coward and a bystander - *huh*?"

Jackson shrugs his shoulders, nodding in agreement.

Buchanan stares out in the distance toward the two cowards and confirms for himself, "I guess what they say of a coward is true - 'A coward's courage is in his tongue.'"

The Birthday Party

February 7, 1969

Stepping out of the jeep in front of Buchanan's hootch at 1245 hours, the spiritual team made their way to the chow hall for a pick me up of energy.

After chow, the men spent some well-deserved rest in their own hootches. After a good rest, they would later meet at 1700 hours in the camp hall to prepare for the Friday Night Social.

Going in opposite directions, the spiritual team thought of nothing but the Michiganders. Buchanan found himself between a rock and a hard space. The two marines were still members of his base ministry. He felt compelled to show some concern for his 'parishioners'.

Stopping abruptly in his tracks, Buchanan thought for a moment the possibilities on his part to show concern for the two 'ashamed cowards.' Nothing serious enough to rock the boat, just a show of subtle interest in the men.

Buchanan pondered a means of showing an element of consideration toward the men and a light bulb went off. He ambled toward the flagpole without delay.

When Buchanan arrived, he stood next to the pole, looking out into the vast perimeter of Camp Love. Without laying his eyes on them, he spoke to the men, "Marines. I've heard your state of circumstances and just simply want you to know good can always come out of what has been an awful experience." He thought to himself, 'What am I saying? This is ridiculous!' He again spoke to the men,

"If you ever want to just come and talk, you know I have an open door policy. To make amends in life can come easy. Just have to take the first step forward. Just a thought."

With that, Buchanan said, "Good Afternoon, men." He turned, stepping towards the direction of his hootch, spotting Rodriquez on the way sitting all alone just outside his hootch on a defensive embankment, a knob of impacted dirt in an oval-shaped redoubt as a defensive barrier to intruders. Smiling, Buchanan parked himself beside Rodriquez, saying nothing.

Returning a friendly, but melancholy smile, Rodriquez turned back toward the jungle, staring into the depths of the ever present green vegetation of the bush. Buchanan sat with the young marine, hoping his presence alone provided a sense of security and encouragement to Rodriquez. The brave marine sat struggling to discern some rationale of what happened to him earlier in the morning.

After a moment or so, Rodriquez finally spoke. He turned toward Buchanan, saying softly, "Funny how life treats people. Makes you think. Doesn't it, Padre?"

Nodding, Buchanan said, "Yes. It certainly does, corporal."

Turning back toward the tree line, the men stare once again in the distance. Neither man had anything to say. But the many thoughts in their minds ran wild and rapid.

Buchanan wondered all the while about the young marine's feelings and thoughts. Nothing could trigger a thought or a feeling for Buchanan to comprehend the young hero's feelings. Only Rodriquez knew how to cope with his own difficulties experiencing the combat. The young marine took the life of many enemy combatants, securing the north perimeter. He saved the lives of many marines and sailors from a sudden death. Loads of emotions ran through Rodriquez's psyche.

Following a few moments, Buchanan spoke, "Listen, Corporal Rodriquez. If you need me for anything, the door's always open. Ya know that."

Rodriquez nodded in the affirmation.

With that, Buchanan padded Rodriquez on the shoulder and departed for his own hootch.

After an hour of reading his Bible and European history, fatigue finally caught up with him, dozing off in his chair.

Buchanan dreamed while snoozing. In the dream, he was only 15 years old. The colors of fall were in full bloom, revealing themselves in the middle of October. Buchanan had been playing on the stiffening girders and suspension cables of the bridge crossing into Mason, West Virginia from Middleport, Ohio, with his brothers late at night. An activity of play, if caught, assured curative punishment from his father in real life. The boys were having fun climbing the bridge. Suddenly, the boys walked over to the West Virginia side of the Ohio River. The panoramic view of the river and the hillsides along the river banks presented a stunning scene in the dream, with the various colors of the fall reflected off the river's service. The beauty came from all directions - from Ohio, West Virginia, and the Ohio River. The feeling of warmth felt within Buchanan with the view of the river valley on the bridge overwhelmed him, catching flies looking onto the beauty of southern Ohio during the fall. As Buchanan admired the beauty, Jansen and McElwaney suddenly rushed up to Buchanan, pushing him over the edge of the bridge as he descended, falling without end. As he dropped, he headed toward plummeting into the Ohio River. The remaining of the dream amounted to nothing but Buchanan screaming at the top of his lungs and falling straight into the depths of the Ohio. The screaming never ending.

His dream came to a thankful end with a knock on the door.

Buchanan popped up, befuddled from his snooze, dreaming. He contemplated in mere seconds the meaning of his dream. He composed himself and asked, "Yes. Who's there? What?"

"It's Ski and Private Kiehl, sir." answered Skawinski.

"*Yeah?* I mean, yes, come in." replied a disoriented Buchanan. He overheard Skawinski make the comment, "He dozed off."

Skawinski and Kiehl chuckled as the men stepped into Buchanan's hootch, greeting Buchanan with hand shakes.

"Yes, Corporal. I accidentally dozed off." said Buchanan. "And, yes, ya know how I feel about sleeping between reveille and taps, Ski."

Skawinski stood with his hands on his hips, grinning.

Sensing the visit is not a social call, Buchanan asked, "What can I do for you men?"

The marines, fidgety and anxious, stood silent at a loss of words to ask Buchanan their request.

Peeking at his watch Buchanan said, "Men, it's 1455 hours and I have to prepare for the social tonight here soon with Sergeant Jackson. What is it?"

Kiehl chimed in, "Well, that's what we're here for, sir. The Friday Night Social."

"Oh?" replied Buchanan.

"Yes sir. See sir, well, we want...well -" stammered Kiehl.

Skawinski took over explaining their request to Buchanan. "Well, sir. What we want to do, and we know ya don't like to interrupt the routine of the Friday Night Social, but we want to do something for Rodriquez tonight."

"And?" asked a curious Buchanan.

Skawinski answered Buchanan. "Well, you're not going to believe this, sir. But it's his birthday today, of all days. And if you haven't *heard*, well - Lieutenant Smith put him in for a Silver Star for his actions this morning. He really did."

"Wait a minute. You're not suggesting a birthday party, are ya?" Buchanan asked with an inquisitive tone.

"Well - yes sir. We are." answered private Kiehl.

Buchanan paused and said with some trepidation, "Men - I don't know if that's a good idea." He thought a bit more and added, "I sat with him for a while this afternoon, men. And he's struggling. I was going to check on him before I departed for the hall to prepare for the Friday social. I don't know, men. This might be too quick for him."

Skawinski said with concern, "Sir. You and I have talked many a time. Haven't we?"

"Yes. We have, Ski."

"Well, ya know as well as I do," said Skawinski, sitting in the soft chair, "I handle stressful situations by talking someone to death. And it's usually you." The three men smile wide knowing he spoke the truth with his approach to recuperate from combat experiences. "For others, and I guess myself occasionally, after a fight, sit by yourself. To be left alone. But sometimes, and especially after a vicious fight, something positive or *anything* that brings joy in life and is uplifting, helps someone deal with the combat he experienced." He paused. In a convincing soft tone, Skawinski lobbies for a party, "Sir, this birthday party would be a positive shot in the arm for Rodriquez. We know him."

More than once, Skawinski returned from a harsh firefight. He only regained his sanity following a good therapeutic talk with Buchanan in his hootch.

Every marine coped with the aftermath of a firefight individually. Skawinski preferred to talk about anything but the war to calm his nerves with Buchanan. The talk of sports or politics. Or living an agrarian life. Even the participation in church activities. The marine just laid in his cot thinking of home and his family farm.

Most often, for Skawinski, the rejuvenation of a healthy mental state came from talking with Buchanan.

For many, isolation soothed the soul. For other marines, music or reading calmed the nerves to cope following a firefight. Just spending time with fellow marines in personal hootches enabled a setting of recuperation.

As Buchanan listened to Skawinski plead his case for the birthday party, he considered Skawinski's plea. Rodriquez maintained a perfect record of attending the Friday Night Socials, voicing his loyalty and devotion to John Wayne. He loved the Duke. The young man considered himself the Duke's number one fan.

Buchanan assessed further the benefit of a birthday party doing some good for Rodriquez. He peered toward Kiehl, grinning from ear to ear. Kiehl's expression spoke loud and clear, screaming for Buchanan to give the go ahead with the party.

"Sir, it'd be good. Trust us, sir. He'd really appreciate the extension of a hand of friendship." said Kiehl.

Buchanan sighs heavily and, with a deep, soft voice, says, "OK. As long as ya think it won't unnerve him in any way."

"It won't, sir. It won't. Trust us, we know. Thank you, sir. Thank you." said Skawinski.

Skawinski and Kiehl literally charged out of the hootch, enthusiastic and gun ho to throw the surprise birthday party for Rodriquez.

The time was 1540 hours. And not much time to attain a cake or to come across a gift or two to present to the hero of the day.

Rodriquez wholeheartedly supported the Chaplain's office. He gained a respectable reputation in camp, endeared by all within the ranks of Bravo Company. His MOS given in his files is an infantry rifleman. He fulfilled his role in camp, contributing to the success of Camp Love ever since he stepped foot into the perimeter of camp 6 months ago. He immediately took part in the chaplain's office endeavors. It became evident from the start of Rodriquez's tour, his loyalty to the fervent group of believers in Christ within the camp stood rock solid. These two adherent traits Skawinski deemed worthy going to bat for Rodriquez every single point in time for whatever motives. Following the heroism of the early morning, his life changed forever and marines in camp never thought of Rodriquez the same again.

1930 hours comes quick.

The spiritual team had prepared the food for the men to enjoy during their time of fellowship. The movie projector sat on the small table with the first of a trilogy of cavalry movies starring John Wayne, ready to go. Skawinski and Kiehl scurried about in camp to stumble on a gift or two to present to Rodriquez, round up friends to welcome Rodriquez, and make a deal with the chow hall personnel to conjure up a cake of some sort.

The Friday Night Socials centered in on John Wayne, and for good reason. But tonight celebrated the actions of a brave *Teufelhunden* who carried out in battle the foundation of character for individual marines: honor, courage, and commitment. The character traits supply the mortar, which ties together one generation of marines to the next, molding marines into fighting warriors.

Delaying Rodriquez's arrival up to the time of the social, Sims distracted Rodriquez until 1930 hours. Sims strolled about the camp discussing dog care with Rodriquez, asking tons of questions regarding dog maintenance and Sims' Labrador Retriever living with his mother back in Los Angeles. As a dog lover, Sims served as the perfect distraction for Rodriquez, until time arrived to step into the hall for the social.

Glancing at his watch, Rodriquez asked, "Shouldn't we walk on over to the hall? It's 1930 hours. And tonight Chaplain Buchanan is showing the first of John Wayne's cavalry trilogy. I don't want to shatter my perfect record of attending the social. The movie is a perfect means of normalcy. You know what I mean?"

"Yeah. Yeah, I do, Manuel." answered Sims. "And you're right, man. I love that John Wayne movie. It'll do us some good." Sims laughs, patting Rodriquez's shoulder.

Rodriquez grins. "Let's go." Sims nods as the men bolt toward the hall.

Rodriquez entered the hall, followed by Sims. "Surprise!" yelled his fellow combatants and friends. Thoroughly surprised, he froze. Taken aback. He stood speechless, as he had not been given much attention on this level in his life.

Following the initial surprise for Rodriquez, stepping into the camp hall, the men sang 'Happy Birthday' to Rodriquez, obviously embarrassed, to greet him. The men in the bush who witnessed his heroism first hand were present, singing louder with zeal.

Marines and sailors vital in Rodriquez's life committed themselves to attend the social this night, making the night one for him to remember for the rest of his life. Lucas. Skawinski. Buchanan. Adkins. Jackson. Pokorny. Chaplain Kensington even showed up following Buchanan's explanation to him of Rodriquez's heroism of the early morning. Dobbs, of all people, showed up out of sheer appreciation and respect from witnessing Rodriquez's heroism. Delaney and McInally's presence gave him a shot in the arm. Sailors and corpsmen who know Rodriquez showed up - Sigmanson, Crowley, Gross, Jenkins, Jackson, and Dingus. Many others joined the cluster of friends. Jurgensen. Shaw. Varnes. McElrath. Carroll. Frost. Rockford. Johannsson.

Skawinski stepped from hootch to hootch, frantically searching for gifts prior to the social to present to Rodriquez. He finally accumulated three gifts Rodriquez opened at the party. The gifts were A Guidebook for Bird Owners and a San Diego sports team t-shirt, used, but Rodriquez didn't care. He paraded the t-shirt throughout camp days to come. The third gift, Skawinski mooched off Chaplain Buchanan - chocolate candy, a favorite of Rodriquez's, and an extra cross to reveal his faith baring his dependence on the Lord when in combat. The monetary value of the gifts valued little in Skawinski's estimation. It's the thought that counts.

Rodriquez unwrapped each gift enthusiastically, as friends noted a genuine surprise out of Rodriquez's expressions, discovering the contents of each gift, catching flies.

"Thank you. Thank you." expressed Rodriquez as he unwrapped each gift. When finished unwrapping the bird book, he declared to the group of friends assembled, "Oh, a book every homeowner should have in their home library."

A roar of laughter erupted throughout the hall.

Rodriquez reflected a kid opening gifts on Christmas morning.

Buchanan, pleased with the outcome of the evening, now knew the idea of the party strengthened the resolve of Rodriquez.

The attendance soared for Rodriquez's party.

Following the opening of gifts, the feasting of food began in the hall. Every morsel and crumb of food consumed, even the birthday cake, disappeared by night's end.

Following twenty minutes of 'fellowship', the men found a seat in chairs and benches for the main event of the evening - John Wayne and a film based on the United States cavalry.

The night will be one of the most cherished moments in Rodriquez's memories, forever etched in his mind and remembered for the rest of his life. Few human beings depart childhood without experiencing at least one birthday party. Rodriquez was one of them. The event inspired him never to doubt himself or to compare himself with anyone else again.

The young man Camp Love recognized as a timid, intelligent, reserved, and mild-mannered young man now knew, though these traits still held true, he carried himself in combat as a ferocious warrior, a man the enemy learned to avoid in the bush.

Rodriquez experienced in one day the confrontation of the most horrific event a human being can experience, along with the most pleasant day a human being can encounter in their life, a birthday. The party lifted his spirits like no other event experienced in his life.

The immense reflections of the last 24 hours overwhelmed Buchanan as he took a crack at putting the events of the day into perspective.

The day's events convinced Buchanan that Rodriquez, though a young man, proved destined to fulfill his dreams in life. Buchanan prayed God's mighty armor and protective shield will follow Rodriquez for the duration of his tour.

Now a mentor to fellow young marines, Rodriquez showed human spirit and Marine Corps 'Esprit de corps'.

A hard lesson Rodriquez learned today reflected a truth about Buchanan's grandfather, who partly raised him, taught him about labor. The truth learned working on his grandfather's farm in southern Ohio applied to the events today. His grandfather taught him every bit that is a part of a human being, the portion that excels and overcomes the trials and tribulations in life is the human spirit!

Buchanan's grandfather instilled in him a work ethic to labor beyond what others expected from them.

Earlier in the day, while reading, Buchanan came across a quote from General George S. Patton. The quote tied an uncanny sense to Rodriquez's experience. He recalled the quote in his mind, 'Battle is the most magnificent competition in which a human being can indulge. It brings out all that is best; it removes all that is base. All men are afraid in battle. The coward is the one who lets his fear overcome his sense of duty. Duty is the essence of manhood.'*

Rodriquez fulfilled his duty. A human shield protecting his fellow marines from death who overcame his fear, leading to his best despite all the danger. The threat of death to rip the life right out of him hovered over him, yet he turned the table on the enemy, ripping the heart out of the life of the Viet Cong.

He embodied the character traits of the United States Marine Corps - honor, courage, and commitment.

He held his head high.

For he proved himself a marine.

And showed forth his pride.

Falling Asleep

February 21, 1969

The music Burns selected last night amounted to the worth of the last two months of music put together. His family sent him an album of John Wayne movie themes. Buchanan soaked in every note, every measure of music as he laid on his cot, reminiscing about the movies music, and harked back sitting in a theater enjoying the acting of his iconic hero growing up.

The next day brought about another Friday Night Social.

The first two nights of the John Wayne movies in John Ford's cavalry trilogy generated the highest attending socials.

The attendance pleased Buchanan to no end. The social paid off dividends for boosting morale and ever increased a higher status of Esprit de corps.

The past two weeks of the war combined many sequences of events which created an all-time high level of political and military actions amounting to an all-time high of United States involvement in the war. The social aspect of the war provided a pause from the weight of the war.

At 0900 hours, Buchanan attended an officers' call to brief Camp Love of the military status and progress of the war in South Vietnam, along with orders for the camp's departments. Lieutenant Colonel Lucas led the briefing, while the XO Carroll reported the camp's personnel reports.

As usual, Porch and his cronies gave Buchanan a good smirk as he arrived at the briefing. And as usual, Buchanan threw a smug, confident smirk back toward Porch and his crony officer buddies, planting himself in a seat with his fellow officers.

The usual order of business for an officer's call started with a monthly report. The monthly report updated the camp of the military status up to that point for the month of February, especially the past two weeks of the South Vietnamese government's contentions that one million more citizens of South Vietnam lived under the 'relative secure' control status. The South Vietnamese government claimed further that nearly two-thirds of South Vietnam now lived in a 'relative secure' political environment. The news advocated an accomplishment of particular pride for the 7th Engineering Marine Battalion. The battalion conducted mine sweeps in and around pro-American hamlets and villages, building an infrastructure of transportation, including bridges and roads. One of the proudest achievements of the battalion's long list of bragging rights located and eradicated enemy Viet Cong cells in the Quang Nam Province. The goal for 90% of South Vietnamese citizens to be secure by United States and South Vietnamese government officials increased daily. The battalion took part daily in that attempt to achieve a 90% level of security, a fact the marines in Camp Love are acutely conscious of.

During the briefing, talk amongst the officers of President Nixon's troop reduction placed a lofty goal on the new administration, and a reduction only after progress in peace talks took a turn for the better. Reduction of troops formed a top priority for the President. Buchanan thought of it as an interesting concept, a conversation which he continued with his friends.

Negotiations between the North and South Vietnamese governments brought about a decrease in fighting because of the diplomacy taking place between governments. South Vietnamese Vice-President Nguyen Cao Ky represented the South Vietnamese delegation who demanded a political settlement with the Viet Cong would only come to fruition if North Vietnam withdrew NVA forces giving the liberty of the South Vietnamese government to settle their own problems.

On 15 February, 1969, the Viet Cong announced a seven day Tet cease fire. The allied forces on their part announced a 24-hour ceasefire on the 21 February 1969. The cease fire opened up the door for the idea and hope the war would eventually end and invite a resolution to end the fighting. However, Lucas reminded the officers in the briefing the seven day Tet cease fire of the Viet Cong ends on 22 February 1969. They braced themselves for the evil guerrilla tactics of the Viet Cong once again when the cease fire ends at midnight. The irony of the 15 February 1969 date of the seven day Tet cease fire is the date the United States announced allied troop strength reached an all-time high of 1,610,500. The updated briefing to the Marine and Navy officers showed the fighting was probably far from over by any stretch of the imagination.

The briefing reported the previous month's activities and duties fulfilled, along with a report of Chaplain Buchanan's CAPS, a report from the medical and dental CAPS, and the list of engineering projects expected in March.

Lucas ended the meeting, relieving officers to depart to individual duty stations.

Buchanan caught Burns on his way out. "Major Burns! Hold up! Hold up!"

Burns glanced over his left shoulder, smiling as Buchanan briskly approached him 15 feet back.

Buchanan catches up with him and enthusiastically says, "Major! Major! Major! You made my night last night. It didn't take me long to remember the first piece of music and the movie score for the film. I recognized the music and the movie after the first two measures. The music lifted me up!"

Grinning, Burns commented, "Well, Chaplain, time called for something different. The selections last night definitely inspired the men. And I know the music was uplifting for at least *one* member of Camp Love."

Smiling wide, Buchanan boasted, "Amen to that, Burns. And I say a hardy, Amen!"

"Many positive comments of the music this morning from the men, Chaplain. As you said, Amen!"

"Again, thank you for the music, Major Burns. Good day." said Buchanan.

"Good day, Chaplain Buchanan. See you at the social."

"Yes, sir." replied Buchanan.

Buchanan headed for supply to check on a requisition he submitted for additional Communion manuals. On his way to supply, a marine sprinted up to Buchanan, nose to nose, pushing him backward, talking haphazardly. His discombobulated manner displayed a desperate marine. Talking a mile a minute, he said, "Sir. Sir! You've got....well - stop him. Got to stop him. Help me. H-H-Help me. Hide me. Help me. He's going to kill me."

Buchanan raised his hands, appealing to the marine to calm down. In his deep mountain accent, he pleaded, "Slow down, marine. Slow down. I can hardly understand you."

Buchanan paused. "Aren't you Corporal?....Westcott? Daniel Westcott. You're the kid from Columbia, South Carolina."

"It's David, sir. And I am Westcott. Listen, sir, I need -" Buchanan interrupted, saying, "The preacher's kid. The Baptist preacher's kid."

"Yeah - yes sir. But, sir?"

"Now what's this you're yammering about?" inquired Buchanan. "Something about somebody wanting to kill ya?"

"Sir. It's Jurgensen. He caught me and another marine on guard duty asleep and he's out, well - well, out looking for me. He's going to kill me."

Buchanan lowers his shaking head in amazement. Bewildered, Buchanan looks back up toward Westcott square in the face and says, "Westcott. You can't go to sleep on guard duty."

"I really wasn't asleep, sir. I-I was just resting my eyes."

Buchanan stares hard into the young marine's eyes, knowing he was lying. "Sure, Westcott. Sure."

Westcott shrugs his shoulders, expands his hands outward, cocking his head sideways as if to say, 'Oh well.'

"Well, listen Westcott. I'll do what I can. Let's go talk to him."

From time to time, Westcott had found himself in trouble, nothing serious but enough to find himself in front of the Skipper.

Infractions such as being written up for an uncleaned weapon or disregarding military protocol in the upkeep of his government issued equipment. Other minor infractions issued to Westcott contributed to his reputation of conducting himself as a 'goof ball'. Not a bad kid, just a goof ball. Enough of a goof ball to pick up the nickname 'The Loafer' in camp.

As a chaplain, Buchanan constantly performed a juggling act. The dilemma for Buchanan choosing either to talk to a superior on behalf of a marine or not; or to be the go between for a marine and the authority over him or not placed him between a rock and a hard place. Buchanan rarely chose the former. He relied more on in house problems dealt with in house leadership. Westcott proved to be one of the rare occasions, as he sustained himself in battle more than once. The discussions in private between Jurgensen and Buchanan posed an obvious question, 'How can The Loafer, a goof ball in camp, be such a ferocious warrior in battle?' In the bush, he displayed a fierce, incredible point man for Bravo Company 3rd Squad 1st Platoon, and expert in almost every weapon imaginable. As a country boy from South Carolina, he asserted himself as a weapons expert. Far from the poster child for 'hose heads' or even the 'PVT Schmuckatelli's' in camp, Westcott's superiors in camp still considered his record shoddy.

A fine line existed for a chaplain to intervene in any situation in a combat zone. The judgment call to intervene posed a decision wagering high staked risks of threatening morale or chain of command, especially when a chaplain felt obliged to intervene in a situation. As an enlisted airman in the Air Force, Buchanan bore in mind chaplains in the past sticking their nose in everyone's business, which disrupted military protocol and high morale. Now a Navy chaplain, he committed himself never to put his chaplain status over morale.

Buchanan rarely intervened in discipline situations, but Westcott's record in the bush outweighed his undisciplined 'Loafer' self. In the bush, Buchanan sought competent and courageous men of confidence when encountering the enemy to defeat the enemy.

Buchanan stepped with Westcott over to Bravo Company Headquarters' office, searching for Gunnery Sergeant Jurgensen.

The pair checked every hootch and Quonset hut hunting for Jurgensen. For five to ten minutes, Buchanan searched high and low for him. Finally, he approached Staff Sergeant Frank Smith of Bravo Company in his hootch.

Peeking into the hootch, Buchanan spotted the sergeant in a chair just inside the hootch. "Sergeant? Sergeant Smith?"

"Yes. It's me, sir. I'll beat ya to the punch, chaplain. I can give you Gunny's exact location. He's sitting across from Westcott's hootch, waiting for him."

"Oh. He is?" answered Buchanan, playing dumb.

"He figured Westcott went running to ya." Smith grins.

"*Yeah*. He came running up to me this morning. Just as I was exiting the officers' call."

"Falling asleep. Serious business, Padre." stated Smith.

"*Yeah. Yes*, sergeant. It is." responded Buchanan. "Whose hootch is he waiting in?"

"His friend, Sergeant Haskins of Charlie Company."

"Thanks, sergeant. You waiting for somebody yourself, Sergeant?" asked Buchanan.

"No, sir. Just thinking of how to find a way of ridding ourselves of the pests getting in our supplies at night."

"*Pests*, sergeant?" said Buchanan curiously. "*Ohhh*. Those pests. Yes, nasty creatures."

Smith smiles with a bit of banter in his eye.

"Thank ya, sergeant." said Buchanan.

Smith nods. "Good luck, sir."

Buchanan immediately bolted over to Haskin's hootch, the first of Charlie Companies hootches, 35 yards away.

When Buchanan arrived, he cautiously stepped toward the entrance of Haskins' hootch. In the dim darkness of the entrance, he spotted Jurgensen sitting in a civilian lawn chair, staring. He waited patiently for Westcott.

Haskins' friends, his hootch mates, are sitting with Jurgensen just inside the entrance drinking cold beers, cooling themselves from the atrocious heat of the day.

At a loss for words, Buchanan squatted on his knees, thinking of the words to speak.

Staring into the distance, the Gunnery Sergeant beat him to the punch. "Westcott went to sleep. That kid put us all in danger of getting killed, Padre. And he's - he's going to pay for it." The calculation and resolve in his voice spoke loud and clear.

Jurgensen paused. "I know ya like this kid, Padre, and his record in the field is exemplary. But enough is enough. He's a hose head when not in combat. I'm going to put an end to it."

The men in the hootches next to Haskins' stared intently. Buchanan continued to squat in front of Jurgensen, sitting patiently just inside the hootch, in the shadows of the canopy covering the entrance.

Jurgensen did most of the talking until Charlie Company personnel from a distance finally observed Buchanan deliver a few spoken words. The words spoken were inaudible to the men, but lengthy. The men noticed the spoken words of Buchanan swayed Jurgensen's demeanor shown from his shift of mood. Company C stared intently as Buchanan stepped into Haskins' hootch to speak to the Gunny more directly.

After five to ten minutes discussing Westcott's situation, the two men emerged from the hootch with Jurgensen, ending his search for the hose head marine who fell asleep on guard duty.

Sure enough, the Gunnery Sergeant granted Westcott a second chance. However, Jurgensen felt obligated to place him on report for falling asleep on guard duty and face a Captain's Mast or a Non-Judicial Punishment as the Marine Corps referred to a disciplinary hearing. Jurgensen postponed his personal punishment for the time being. Charlie Company sat in their hootches, impaired with the distance of the conversation. Whatever words Buchanan said to Jurgensen held enough weight to ease off Westcott and to impart him a break.

Jurgensen, as a non-commissioned officer, along with the chain of command, considered guard duty the most serious matter in camp. Buchanan knew, along with others in camp, if a marine fell asleep, the danger of Viet Cong slipping into camp by the dozens, if not more, quietly and undetected could cause tremendous numbers of casualties.

Over the past five months, Buchanan had heard of eye-opening scuttlebutt told of Jurgensen's first tour in 1967. One incident of scuttlebutt from 1967 spread throughout camp which described Jurgensen catching a marine on guard duty falling asleep. Fed up with marines dozing off on guard duty, he made an example out of the poor, unfortunate young man. He called a surprise muster of Bravo Company into formation. The Gunnery Sergeant placed the marine smack dab in front of the men, suddenly going ballistic on the young marine in front of the whole company.

"Do you know what this idiot we caught doing last night?" Jurgensen paced left and right in front of the whole company, embarrassing the marine. He paused in his rant, permitting the question to sink into the minds of the grunts.

"Sleeping on guard duty. Yes, this marine…." pointing his finger straight at the guilty marine, "endangered all of you because he needed his beauty sleep!"

Jurgensen, incensed and infuriated, stepped in front of the marine, placing his nose a half an inch from the marine's ear and yelled, "And from the looks of his face, HE NEEDS IT!"

Nothing but smirks and giggles came from Bravo Company as the marine stood exposed, completely humiliated.

As Jurgensen took a step or two from the marine, he turned back swiftly, reared back his arm and with one resolute, forceful swing struck a solid blow on the marine's jaw, sending him plummeting backward hitting the ground with a loud thunderous 'thud'.

Jurgensen took a step forward, gawking down at the marine, smirking to find out the physical condition of the thumped jarhead.

The battered marine teetered his way back up to an erect position at attention, swaying back and forth from the force upon his jaw, striving to position his boots at attention. All the while, Jurgensen, with his hands on his hips, observed his efforts to stand at attention.

He stood with blood on his lips, cheeks, and chin from afar. Jurgensen gave notice to Bravo Company in 1967. He meant business from an obvious blow delivered from his iron-tightened fist. A man who falls asleep on guard duty will have to answer to him.

Flabbergasted at Jurgensen's display of force, Bravo Company bowled over with the show of physical words of warning, convincing every member of Bravo Company the last person anyone wanted to cross in a combat zone turned out to be Jurgensen. "Let this be a message to you all. Marines *don't* fall asleep in my company. Ya do, you'll pay for it."

He moseyed his way back to his hootch to drink a cold beer. Lounging in his civilian lawn chair, he read his recent political science book written on Federalism.

Dismissed from formation, marines went their separate way in shock.

Nobody back in 1967 dared go to sleep again on guard duty in Bravo Company. Jurgensen assured himself he instilled the wrath of God in every single member of Bravo Company, never to go to sleep on guard duty again.

That was then. This is now - 1969. Jurgensen had changed little in two years. After hearing the scuttlebutt of Jurgensen, Buchanan convinced himself the Gunny sought young Westcott for a public display of discipline. To humiliate him in front of Bravo Company, reminding those in Bravo Company in 1969 no one goes to sleep on guard duty.

Buchanan rushed to Bravo Company headquarters informing Westcott he will put him on report for falling asleep, but off the hook with Jurgensen at least for the time being.

Westcott sighed. "Thank you, chaplain."

Buchanan set some guidelines for the jarhead marine. "You're going to have to be on your toes, Westcott. No more snoozing on guard duty. Make sure you keep your eyes open on duty. I'm going to bat for you, and I'm going to be disappointed if you don't walk away hitting a home run."

"Yes sir. I promise, I'll bat a thousand for you." replied Westcott with assurance.

"Come by my hootch later on and I'll give you some pointers on staying awake. Remember, I once wore an enlisted uniform and stood duty myself." Buchanan paused. "Jurgensen assigned you, along with the other marine falling asleep with you last night, perimeter duty in the west fighting hole together again tonight."

"What? Y-Yes sir." trembled an alarmed Westcott. The worried young marine hurried to his hootch. Time stood at 1145 hours.

Buchanan headed for the chow hall, forever thankful Westcott had left for the day from his presence. He got on Buchanan's nerves. When finally arriving at the chow hall, he found Jackson standing patiently for him.

After chow, the two set out for Buchanan's hootch for two counseling sessions, one ordered by Lucas for a marine dealing with disciplinary issues at 1300 hours and a second session with a marine confronting combat fatigue at 1400 hours.

Buchanan felt comfortable with Jackson present in the counseling sessions, though Jackson occasionally excused himself to protect the privacy and confidentiality of the individual marine. Jackson convinced himself that his absence from counseling sessions maintained an open environment with a sense of liberty for Buchanan to speak with the men. Regardless, Buchanan maintained Jackson's presence added an enlisted perspective of the war Buchanan did not understand or embrace. Jackson related to marines as an enlisted man. Besides, Jackson gained a standing with the men as a strong shoulder to lean on in war. Of course, confidentiality of any discussion within the chaplain's office, Jackson swore to secrecy and had to use discretion in communicating with military personnel outside the chaplain's office of any personal circumstances and spiritual situations a marine might divulge to Chaplain Buchanan.

The scheduled sessions arrived on time, though the second session took a bit more time because of the nature of the visit. Again, Jackson's presence in the second session heightened the sense of contentment, one that consoled the marine dealing with combat fatigue.

Time stood at 1550 hours. Plenty of time to visit camp departments prior to preparing for the social.

The spiritual team walked the camp full circle, visiting each department starting with the headquarters building, which offices were next to the camp hall. The team ended visiting the men at 1700 hours, dropping in on supply, which reflected a hardware store back home in the States.

With just two and a half hours away from the social, Buchanan sensed an urge to prepare for the night. The first two of the trilogy cavalry movies drew enormous numbers in attendance. Buchanan looked forward to the third night of the cavalry series, convinced the night will break attendance records. The third trilogy movie co-starred John Wayne's opposite favorite actress, red-headed and full of Irish spunk. She possessed a commanding presence in every movie she ever starred in. She became Buchanan's favorite actress to work with. Her presence in the third movie strengthened Wayne's character as a Lieutenant Colonel in the United States cavalry. The chemistry between Wayne and the actress brought the film alive on the big screen. As an adolescent, Buchanan worked in a movie house in the 1940s in Middleport, Ohio, remembering her movies fondly.

The spiritual team prepared the food, arranged the movie in the film advance mechanism of the projector, and straightened the chairs and benches for the men to sit in. The team finished the errands for the social at 1840 hours. The two men sat and talked about every subject under the sun but the war until 1930 hours.

The initial intent of the social spurred an effort from Buchanan to instigate a settling down from the war, diverting banged up, over stressed minds from the war, at least for a few comforting hours.

The marines trickled in about 1910 hours. Buchanan thought, '1910 hours? Really.'

Buchanan leaned toward Jackson. "What in tarnation are they here for this early?"

"I guess the men are looking forward to the third movie in the trilogy." answered Jackson with a grin.

"I guess so, Sergeant."

Buchanan could never be more pleased with the attendance, 129 total counted for the night, an astounding number for the event.

As always on Friday nights, John Wayne exhilarated the men, boosting morale for enlisted and officer alike! The third movie in John Ford's trilogy deemed a gratifying termination for the last day of a ceasefire with the Viet Cong.

The presence of John Wayne's opposite on the white screen provided a fiery personality in the film. Her role played mesmerized the marines regardless of the fact the actress' red hair remained hidden throughout the black and white film. When the Duke worked with her, she naturally complimented Wayne's role in whatever film the pair worked on.

The marines prolonged the night as late as possible. The social was again a success, as the men longed for the night to never end.

As always, Buchanan insisted on leaving the hall as he found it. An attitude of gun ho inspired the spiritual team to arrange once again the hall for table conferences for tomorrow's workday. Skawinski, Adkins, along with other friends of the chaplain's office lent a hand.

Time stood approximately at 2130 hours. Every ear in camp shared the music Burns selected for the evening - Franz Schubert's 2nd Symphony, a speedy, emotional piece of music. The air in the camp flowed with the melodic, inspiring piece of music. After the marines set the conference hall back in order, the men sat in chairs to continue conversing farther into the evening, listening to Schubert.

As marines departed for their respective hootches for the evening, the last movement in the 2nd Symphony had begun. The marines prayed for a night void of any turmoil or annoying disorders, especially an attack from the Viet Cong. At least the night began with ease, viewing the John Wayne movie and ending listening to classical music.

The spiritual team required a good night's sleep. The next morning, the team's agenda schedule a trip to the bush to hold Communion Services for Alpha Company on a Saturday.

Buchanan reminded Jackson, "Remember sergeant, 0530 hours, breakfast. 0600 hours, off to the bush and Communion service."

"Yes, sir. Up and at'em at 0430 hours. See you at breakfast." Jackson said with enthusiasm.

"Thank you, Sergeant."

At 2325 hours, the spiritual team turned toward their separate hootches for a good night's rest.

Every ounce within Buchanan's body heaved with exhaustion, though he and Jackson spent the whole day in camp absent from the jungle. A heavy weight of weakness within Buchanan grew from the mental stress of the emotional counseling session with the young marine dealing with combat fatigue Jackson sat in.

Buchanan walked to his hootch on the scenic route to give the camp a quick once-over for security's sake. From the first day out in the bush, the risk of infiltration by the Viet Cong gave him the creeps. He just wanted to give the camp a quick look see before retiring for the night. He had covered in Reynolds wrap and paper towels pieces of fruit from the social stuck in his lower right pocket of his combat fatigues for Arthur and Churchill for a treat. Buchanan strived to reward, a top priority, his reptile friends for protecting him.

The fourth movement of the 2nd symphony came close to winding down, written in a gallop tempo and in 2/4 time. A rapid movement appropriate for what Buchanan will soon discover in Smith's hootch.

Buchanan walked, listening to the final moments of the music, as he stepped close to Sergeant Smith's hootch of Bravo Company. He noticed a dim light glimmering out of the entrance, with a shadowy image in the light just inside the hootch. Curious of the origin and purpose of the dim lights, Buchanan stepped closer to the hootch entrance. Illuminations in Camp Love were out by 2300 hours to conceal any movement within the perimeter from the Viet Cong, who were just five to ten feet inside the treeline.

With apprehension, Buchanan approached Smith's entrance and slowly peeked in, noticing candle light in the heavy darkness.

Buchanan, taken aback by what he envisioned, felt a quick dose of fright. With the utmost ogle, Buchanan glared at Smith sitting on his backside. Leaning his back on the hootch's bulkhead, Smith balanced his .45 caliber on his right knee toward the opposite corner of the hootch where supplies were stored.

In the dim light, Buchanan looked in the hootch, catching a sight in the corner of his eye, what Smith took aim of with his .45 caliber. Pests Buchanan loathed – rats. Colossal rodents indeed. Buchanan set his eyes on the most massive rats he had seen in his tour, displaying snarling teeth and razor-sharp claws.

Buchanan leisurely stepped toward Smith, whispering softly, "What are you doing, Sergeant?"

A long pause from Smith seemed an eternity for the unnerved Buchanan.

Smith shattered the silence. "I'm gonna to kill 'em. They've pestered us to a frenzy. I'm shooting every damn one of 'em."

Buchanan swallowed hard, shaking his head gently. "Sergeant, don't fire that weapon." Swallowing hard, fear overwhelmed him. The fright and trepidation shook him from head to toe. The pandemonium which would follow if Smith fired his weapon at night in camp made his blood run cold.

The moment required Buchanan to ponder carefully the words to speak to Smith in order to prevent a trigger within Smith to carry out the execution of a hated enemy. An event inviting a chain reaction of chaos and friendly fire in camp inflicting many injuries.

A nervous Buchanan gave a shot at talking some sense into Smith. "If you fire your weapon, the camp will go nuts. You fire your .45, all of our friends will spring out of cots and hootches and kill each other." Following a moment of pause, Buchanan said, "Think about it, Sergeant."

Two minutes passed and not a word.

Smith once again broke the ice of silence, grumbling to himself. He pointed his .45 caliber upward, switching his weapon to safe mode, slowly rising to his feet. He stepped toward his holster hanging on a hook fastened on a wooden plank as part of the bulkhead and placed his weapon back in his holster. Hanging on an adjacent hook beside his .45 hung a machete. Smith methodically drew his blade weapon out of its sheath. Ambling his way over to the rats, he prepared himself to slice the throats piecemeal of each rat.

The racket of rats in the last moments of the coup de grâce by a knife or machete against the throat of a rat being slit became all too familiar for Buchanan. As Smith made his way toward the rats, he seized each rat, slitting the throat with one swift slice. The familiar squeaks a rat bellows out when approached turns to hisses when realizing the danger encroached upon them. The hisses turn to growls when snatched by a marine to do the last deed. Smith carried out his duty one rat after the other. Five rats in all, flinging each rat outside the hootch with pleasure.

Buchanan excused himself from the coup de grâce, waiting outside the hootch. He hated rats. But he made his heart grow fonder by patiently waiting outside the hootch. He found himself at odds wondering which came worse - witnessing the rats enter 'rat heaven' or the pile of dead rats accumulating outside Smith's entry with each fling of a rodent corpse. As Buchanan stood, one rat after another came flinging out the entrance of the hootch onto a growing pile of cut up rats. He slowly felt nauseated from the grotesques sight.

When finished, Smith whispered, "Thanks, Padre. Thanks for your help. Machete felt better anyway."

"Ahhhhh." sighed Buchanan. "Anytime sergeant."

Buchanan continued to step to his hootch, following the harrowing but gratifying eradication of the filthy rodents. He prayed. "Lord, thank you for intervening with Smith. Continue to intervene. Amen."

Arriving at his hootch at 2355 hours, Buchanan desired nothing but a good night's sleep. As he was about to step onto the bottom level of steps to enter his hootch, he noticed in the darkness a human figure within the streams of moonlight reflected off the small tree leaves fronting his hootch.

Buchanan froze in place. Struggling to identify the stranger lurking in the darkness, he felt his heartbeat turn rapid. He stood numb. An uncontrollable haste of uncertainty overwhelmed Buchanan, confronting a shadowy stranger.

He thought 'Who was it?' 'An intruder?' 'A friendly marine? Jackson?'

The dismay felt dissipated as the figure slowly emerged from the solid darkness of night. As the shadow like stranger shifted in the darkness, Buchanan recognized a combat helmet, then a M-16 the darkened figure held in his hand. Finally, as the mysterious figure blearily appeared in the full moonlight, Buchanan suddenly recognized the shadowy wanderer - a well known enlisted man familiar to the chaplain's office.

The cagey figure emerging from the darkness featured none other than Corporal David Westcott.

A bewildered Buchanan asked with a bit of curiosity, "Westcott? Is that you? What are you doing here?" The speechless young marine stood frightened. Buchanan could read a temperament of worry and astonishment all over his timid expression on his face. "Well, sir. I, well - My-My duty partner and I, well...fell asleep again."

Before Westcott could utter another word, Buchanan stepped up to the knucklehead jarhead, clutching his t-shirt vigorously, nearly ripping it at the shoulders. Pushing Westcott back onto the side of the hootch near one beam supporting the foundation, Buchanan pressed him hard against the wooden beam.

Stepping up to Westcott nose to nose, eye to eye, Buchanan fought within himself an anger he shed when his heart changed to live for Jesus. An anger full of rage which settled problems through fighting and reaping revenge onto others. He let loose of this boiling rage through his Christian conversion.

Breathing rapidly, Buchanan turned red from Westcott, betraying him. By now, his saturated sweaty uniform added more moisture resulting from the anger. Rarely did Buchanan lose his temper since becoming a Christian.

Tonight will be a night of exception.

The mental and physical shock of Westcott witnessing conduct unbecoming of Buchanan stunned him. He knew a chaplain who took pride in having complete control of himself.

Westcott let go of his M-16, as it nudged Buchanan's leg crashing onto the ground. The duty clipboard followed, slamming the earth's surface.

Buchanan rebuked Westcott. "I went out on a limb for you. And you let me down, boy. You could've gotten us killed. Gunnery Sergeant Jurgensen has all the confidence in the world in me. You might have damaged that confidence. And I don't like that." He paused, panting, and said, "Let's go."

"Where?" asked Westcott.

Tilting his head, Buchanan said, "To Gunnery Sergeant Jurgensen, who else?"

"What?" Westcott caught a sudden dose of fear, wide-eyed with the thought of having to face Jurgensen.

Buchanan pointed his finger straight between Westcott's eyes. He said with poignancy, "You fall asleep again, and *I'll* kill ya."

Westcott read people well. In his heart, he knew Buchanan meant business.

Buchanan retrieved Westcott's M-16 and duty clipboard, shoving the clipboard into Westcott's hand. Taking a stronger grip onto his t-shirt from the front of the neck, he pulled Westcott all the way to Jurgensen's hootch.

Westcott dared not to speak a word on route to Jurgensen's hootch, terrified of the punishment to come.

Buchanan muttered to himself every step of the way to Jurgensen's abode how far he went out on a limb for this imbecile and how far Westcott fell short carrying out his word.

Buchanan grumbled and complained all the way to Jurgensen's hootch.

"Pathetic." he fumed. "Disappointing."

"Lord, forgive him." asked Buchanan.

"Never again,!" Buchanan swore.

Buchanan, pulling Westcott alongside him, finally reached Jurgensen's hootch. Waiting in his hootch playing cards with friends, the Gunny anticipated Buchanan's arrival.

"I see you're here, chaplain." Jurgensen looks over his shoulder toward Buchanan. "It's not your fault, Padre. It's the hosehead's."

Wide-eyed and catching flies, terror struck Westcott. Though presumptive, he knew better to say even one word.

Buchanan briskly shoved Westcott toward Jurgensen. "*Here* he is, Sergeant."

"Thanks, Padre."

With a deep sense of betrayal, a perturbed Buchanan left Westcott with Jurgensen with considerable consternation.

The young marine taught Buchanan a lesson in the middle of his tour – never cover for a knucklehead marine who attains a habit of falling asleep on guard duty.

Buchanan never set his eyes on Westcott again, and at no time inquired of Jurgensen of the young marine's whereabouts.

The mystery of Westcott's outcome crossed Buchanan's mind daily, a steady mull over deliberating what Jurgensen might have done with him.

The scuttlebutt Jackson picked up in camp claimed Westcott found himself back in California. But his time spent passed by sitting on his butt in the brig. Rumors spread he fell asleep on guard duty more than twice. The young marine jeopardized the lives in Camp Love way too often. The decision to send him back home became imperative. The second chances mounted high for Westcott, falling short time and time again.

Buchanan learned a hard lesson from Westcott. Never again would he concern himself with marines and their superiors when falling asleep on guard duty. When marines fled to Buchanan for help, he simply marched the marine straight back to his Gunnery Sergeant, and let his superiors settle it in house.

Westcott evoked Buchanan's curiosity at night to second guess his sense of security and safety when retiring at night, fearing a marine on the edge of the perimeter will dose off on guard duty endangering the lives in camp. Buchanan loathed the thought. He found himself before falling asleep at night asking, "Has a marine gone to sleep on guard duty?" He hoped and prayed defenses Skawinski and other combat engineers set in place would suffice even before the enemy reached the sleeping sentry.

Sleep came scarce on unnerving nights.

Buchanan abhorred nightmares, but especially dreams of enemy infiltration. They were the worse. The fear of infiltration in his dreams hopefully will never emanate into reality.

After Westcott, a fear of attack and enemy infiltration soared within Buchanan's heart and soul. His inner self enacted a vulnerability and a sense of defenselessness at night in the camp for weeks on end. He sensed the fault for his deep insecurity laid at the feet of Westcott.

Buchanan just shook his head, saying to himself, 'Thanks a lot, Westcott.'

HOMESICK FOR BUCKEYES

FEBRUARY 22, 1969

Four months. Twenty-two days. And six hours in Vietnam. Just under five months into Buchanan's tour, and he still longs for home. Especially after Corporal Westcott threw at Buchanan a chock-full dose of insecurity. A sense of vulnerability that the enemy can now infiltrate the camp at their leisure overwhelmed him emotionally. A sense of danger Buchanan wished he could brush aside at will. Unfortunately, combatants in a war lack the luxury of clairvoyance into events not yet seen.

Never in his life had Buchanan witnessed human beings hate each other more than the last five months of service. The innocents butchered and slaughtered by the hands of the Viet Cong for no other reason but cultivating a friendly relationship with Americans. United States forces retaliated ferociously, resulting in high 'body counts', a tactical measurement of success for the American government. Marines were gun ho, out for blood to avenge for the atrocities and mistreatment of friendly South Vietnamese, especially the elderly and children.

On top of the violence, Buchanan threw his hands up out of frustration with the progress, or lack of, winning the war. He loathed the passive strategies implemented by the Johnson Administration in winning the war. The frustration by United States forces ran high conducting maneuvers to drive Viet Cong and the North Vietnamese Army out of an area or sector. American forces were required to withdraw from the area or sector after securing the land, handing the responsibility of the conquered territory over to the South Vietnamese to maintain. This gave the VC and the NVA the liberty to infiltrate the same sector they were driven out of initially. Buchanan considered the tactics lunacy. The Johnson strategy for winning the war made no sense to Buchanan. The ARVN sustained conquered territory for as long as possible. For many, Buchanan seemed a simple chaplain. Though true, he estimated the war as a losing effort, with tactics implemented with no final strategy. The United States government pussyfooted around, costing American lives every day. This angered him.

Buchanan's frustration knowing the VC and the NVA could flee and cross the borders into Cambodia and Laos without giving the liberty of United States forces and her allies to pursue the enemy violated every traditional military strategy and tactic in winning a war. To deny the United States forces the right in wartime to pursue the enemy and to annihilate the same enemy results in a losing cause in every single engagement. Military strategy and tactics from military historians Buchanan had respect for called for the total destruction of the enemy. The negotiation of a peace followed the complete annihilation of an enemy, not prior to.

Buchanan convinced himself the Johnson administration wavered in defeating the North Vietnamese government and the Viet Cong, possibly out of a fear of widening the war, which invited a broader role for the Russians and Chinese governments.

Buchanan deemed losing a war to the Communists unacceptable.

He abhorred the Viet Cong, taking part in any sort of treaty of any kind. Buchanan believed the terrorist guerrillas lacked any grounds or rationale to convey any design for peace. The tactics conducted by the guerrilla group mirrored extremist behavior. Buchanan considered them nothing but terrorists. As an eyewitness to the atrocities committed to friendly South Vietnamese citizens, he didn't trust them. He considered them nothing but 'Commies'.

He understood the President's fear of an expanded war outside the borders of South Vietnam if the government granted the military the liberty of winning the conflict with a Declaration of War.

Buchanan and the President Johnson had one thing in common - a mutual hatred for Communism. The two men cherished the fruits abundant living life in the western world. Communism squelches freedoms lived in the west. Neither desired a life of suppression.

Buchanan just sought to win. Though he disagreed with Johnson's strategy, he understood the hesitancy of the President allowing military forces to pursue the enemy proper. The odds of Chinese and Soviet Union governments escalating their efforts to assist the NVA and the Viet Cong seemed inevitable if Johnson broke the earlier agreements to prevent military personnel from pursuing the enemy across a country's border with Vietnam. If Washington DC extended the liberty for the military to win the war, United States generals would not pussyfoot around.

Steps in winning the war required the bombing of North Vietnam. To win the war required the complete annihilation of the Viet Cong in the field. The notion stood contrary to Johnson's strategy. The bombing of North Vietnam would increase student protests and demonstrations all over the United States, a situation Johnson certainly did not desire to escalate. Buchanan could careless about the protesters, thinking to himself - 'Let 'em protest. The United States will just win the war, and history will just paint the little agitators for what they really are – spoiled, arrogant little nonconformists and Commies.'

Buchanan sensed the anti-war movement back home dead from the neck up. He viewed the efforts of the protesters as an endorsement for a total Communist domination of Vietnam and even southeastern Asia.

The sharp disagreements with Johnson on how to win the war showed obvious, but the support in Buchanan's heart to contain Communism leveled on par with the President's. Though the President's efforts were to prevent the spread of Communism, the world discovered six years later what Johnson's efforts accomplished – a total Communist takeover of South Vietnam and the atrocities which followed. The world became conscious of the evils Communists inflicted upon other human beings. Six years later, the Communists revealed their evil hearts in committing murder, imprisoning democratic minded South Vietnamese, and butchering anyone who threatened the new Communist regime.

The protesters of the 1960s turned a blind eye to Communist atrocities six years later. They were mute in protest of the murders and mistreatment of the innocents, saying not a word. If living in a Communist state reflected the treatment of human beings from the North Vietnamese and the Viet Cong, then Buchanan did not want to have anything to do with communism.

Johnson's strategy mirrored a sluggish process. Johnson's strategy of winning the war required a long, drawn-out struggle, which many in the United States, including conservatives, were hesitant to support.

To win a war, the military requires a free hand in implementing strategy and tactics, and Johnson impeded military generals, knowing the expansion of the war would inflate like a balloon. Buchanan's prayer for the newly elected President, Richard M. Nixon, had been to impart the liberty of implementing a winning strategy to the new Deputy Commander of Military Assistance Command, Vietnam (MACV), Commander of Vietnam forces Creighton Williams Abrams Jr., replacing General William Westmoreland.

Frustrated, Buchanan favored winning the war.

In a Huey helicopter flying high, the spiritual team eyeballed the stunning beauty of Vietnam on the way to Firebase Six Shooter in the Quang Nam Province for two days to lead services. Buchanan, head over heels to minister to the marines in the firebase, looked forward, giving the men a sense of normalcy. Marines who had not laid their eyes on a chaplain close to a month. The spiritual team had been visiting wounded in Da Nang with a friend and colleague, Lieutenant Commander Chaplain Charles Brennan, a New Yorker from New York City. His family owned a city wide pizza business and came from a proud Irish family background. Buchanan grew up knowing few Catholics in the mountains of Kentucky and Ohio until he enlisted in the Air Force in 1949. He grew to respect and love Catholics, placing his Christian brothers in high regard. If any one individual Catholic who possessed the personality to talk Buchanan into becoming Roman Catholic, Chaplain Brennan would be the one to persuade Buchanan to change course in midstream. Buchanan loved the time spent with Brennan, finding his personality type entertaining. And besides, the marines adored and respected him. The chaplains were in their mid to late thirties. The men considered the chaplains father figures to the men, especially the 18- and 19-year-olds. The relationship bonded further as the two served proudly as Korean veterans.

Brennan's bodyguard and assistant, Corporal Carl Angelhoff, accompanied the chaplain to Six Shooter located deep in the jungle, a considerable distance from Camp Love. Buchanan thought the location was 'spooky'. The marines stationed at Six Shooter were members of H Battery, 3rd Battalion, 11th Marine Regiment, 1st Marine Division, arriving eight weeks earlier. Only once in the past 56 days had the men seen a chaplain and led in Communion.

The spiritual leaders were just a mile away now from the firebase.

Buchanan stared down into the heavy foliage of Vietnam. He thought, 'I wonder what's underneath all the foliage? Snakes, other reptiles? Centipedes? Insects? Leeches? Wild animals? Rats?'

"Yuch!" blurted Buchanan, reaching for his tobacco pouch.

"What?" responded Jackson inquisitively.

"Probably the bumpy ride. He still hadn't gotten used to the fun rides on these things." Brennan smiled. "Well, could be his love for the slithering." Brennan then chuckled.

Buchanan shakes his head in the negative.

"What then?" asked Jackson.

"Nothing. Nothing that requires inquiry, Sergeant." replied Buchanan.

Jackson smiles.

Pointing to the tobacco pouch, Jackson says, "I say yuch to that!"

"Amen Sergeant!" responded Brennan.

Buchanan asserted, "Well, you know what Ben Franklin once said."

"No, what?" asked Corporal Angelhoff.

Buchanan glances at everyone. "He said and I quote, 'Forewarned, forearmed.'"

All laugh.

Jackson shakes his head. "What in the heck does that mean?"

"To be cautious. Cautious! I'm a very cautious person." replied Buchanan.

The men chuckle, shaking their heads.

"I just love you to death, sir." said Jackson.

Buchanan grins with assurance.

"Franklin hit the nail on the head on many assumptions, chaplain. But tobacco ain't one of them." Jackson smirked with sarcasm.

"I just drink beer, sir!" said Angelhoff with a smile.

"I don't drink!" responded Buchanan, grinning.

Buchanan peeks over toward Angelhoff puzzled. "How does beer kill off the worms?"

Angelhoff smiles and says, "It's the hops in the beer, sir!"

Buchanan shakes his head, baffled.

The men grin, thinking the Lord sure did a great job putting Buchanan together.

The helicopter finally arrived. The flying machine preceded its descent on top of the landing pad at Six Shooter Firebase.

Noticing the dense foliage surrounding Six Shooter, Buchanan pinched a lump of tobacco, placing it into his mouth. Buchanan made a point. "The firebase sure is out in the boonies. Isn't it? Kind of spooky?"

Feeling the landing skids touch the ground onto the landing pad, Chaplain Brennan agreed. "Yes sir. Sure is, Robert. As you say, spooky."

"The Lord's with us. That's what assures me." noted Angelhoff, glancing up into the skyline. "But it sure gets dark out here at night, sir, this far out into the bush."

The chaplains threw glances of consternation toward Angelhoff, who caught a quick dose of the heebie-jeebies. The clerical leaders were far from their home bases with 'critters', as Buchanan referred to them, crawling about.

Whether in the boonies or not, the religious party arrived to provide spiritual guidance for two days and lead in Communion services. The marines were hungry for spiritual guidance, denied for weeks religious instruction.

The fire support base situated itself on Hill 327 Division Ridge. The geographical position set the hill miles south of Route 542 - the main route of transportation for military and civilian travel. Positioned in Happy Valley, north of Elephant Valley, the firebase blocked enemy advances in and around Route 542 through Dai La Pass, heading toward Da Nang. The firebase protected the Da Nang Air Base and a vital helicopter base on Marble Mountain. An additional responsibility for Six Shooter supported operations in the valley by bombarding the enemy threatening infantry camps and other bases. Buchanan enjoyed the topography in and around Marble Mountain, frequently stopping at a marble cutting business. He visited with the friendly Vietnamese owners who worked with marble extraction from the mountain.

The exhaustive list of duties for the firebase added yet another role which prevented enemy attacks on the III Marine Amphibious Force and 1st Marine Division, a center for Navy administration and logistics, ammunition dumps along with petroleum tanks. Six Shooter prevented the Viet Cong and the NVA easy access to a prisoner-of-war camp.

Located five miles west of Da Nang, Six Shooter strategically served as a vital component of defenses for the Da Nang area.

The components of a firebase consisted usually of 8 parts: 1) a command and communications bunker 2) usually 5 to 7 gunpits 3) a medical bunker 4) a central gunpit to receive ammunition and guns from Chinook helicopters 5) a Fire Direction Center (FDC) to orchestrate the direction of projectiles toward the enemy 6) a perimeter trench surrounding the firebase comprising small bunkers with intervals of 20 to 30 yards 7) a barbed wire barrier surrounding the perimeter trench, and 8) a helicopter landing zone, though several firebases lacked a landing zone

The standard weaponry in gunpits were: 1) a M101 15mm emplacement 2) a M102 105mm emplacement 3) a semi permanent 105mm SP howitzer emplacement 4) a towed 155mm howitzer emplacement 5) a 155mm SP howitzer emplacement, and 6) a heavy artillery emplacement – an 8inch or 175mm. The marines placed the guns either in a square or triangular formation.

Occasionally, firebases positioned tanks within the perimeter.

A soft redoubt of sandbags encircled each gunpit, serving as a protective line of defense in case the pesky Viet Cong infiltrated the firebase. An integral gunpit within each layout of a firebase supplied the artillery ammunition. Adjoining pits in a firebase included an ammunition rack, a storage bunker, a bunker for the crews and artillery, powder pits and bunker, along with a shell bunker. Kitchens, chow halls, bars, and recreational rooms complemented selected firebases in the bush.

The primary function of a firebase fired projectiles from pieces of artillery and mortar in a direction to support infantry patrols and movements. A firebase also supported the transportation of military personnel in convoys on roads and other firebase perimeters with artillery fire. In a secondary role, artillery employed harassment and interdiction or H&I fire. H&I fire bombed enemy movements, especially when the enemy massed together for major offensives against the United States and South Vietnamese forces. The troops referred to H&I fire as 'killing trees'. The marines in the firebase plotted the direction of armament off on a map with no sort of intelligence reports to aim artillery projectiles.

With the threat of being overrun, firebases released a series of fusillade fire at close range to defend itself.

Interested in military strategy and tactics, the firebases fascinated Buchanan. His understanding of firepower from a firebase came in October 1968, his first month in the bush. When accompanying a patrol with Bravo Company, Buchanan witnessed a firebase level in the space of two football fields following a radio request from Rockford for artillery support. Buchanan indeed witnessed the potency of a firebase.

The chaplain personnel stepped off the helicopter and immediately noticed the firebase perimeter defenses were incomplete. Buchanan's stomach hit the ground, laying his eyes on a soft buffer encircling the firebase. He loathed the sudden sense of vulnerability in the deepest crevices of his stomach. The failure of eliminating brush around the firebase provided cover for Viet Cong or NVA infiltrators, practically inviting the enemy to attack. The firebase missed the concertina wire surrounding the interior and there was no barbed wire coiled within the perimeter of Six Shooter as a defense.

Regardless of the incomplete defenses, once Buchanan stepped inside the firebase, he had a peculiar sense of security. Taking a complete panoramic view of Six Shooter, he reckoned his overwhelming, strong sense of protection came from the total sum of firepower of artillery.

Greeting Buchanan and his friends at the firebase entrance stood Captain David Lambert, a long-time friend of Chaplain Brennan's enlisted days and the commanding officer of Six Shooter Firebase. The two friends served together as enlisted marines in Korea and avid Douglas MacArthur proponents.

"Well, how's my favorite chaplain?" Lambert, with his hands on his hips, grinned from ear to ear, flanked by firebase leadership.

"Other than being shot at occasionally, I'm thrilled to be here to let the men know God loves'em." Brennan chuckled, extending his hand to Lambert as the men pat one another's shoulders. The display of loyal friendship lifted the hearts of visitors and hosts alike.

"How's the body guard work corporal?" asks Lambert.

Grinning, Angelhoff said, "Can't keep up with this guy, sir. He's out to break the record in conducting Catholic masses."

Lambert grins at Angelhoff's jest.

Brennan turns to the spiritual team with an extended hand. "Dave, this is my good friend Chaplain Robert Buchanan and Sergeant Jackson. Thought I'd invite them to accompany me, give the Protestants a presence."

Lambert, humored by the inside joke, looked over the visitors from head to toe. With his deep faith in the Roman Catholic Church added to his friendly play of Protestants and Catholics, Brennan jabbed at his friend's loyal convictions of his faith.

Turning toward Buchanan and Jackson, Lambert spoke with confidence. "Any friend of Chaplain Brennan is a friend of mine. Your presence is a shot in the arm for the men."

Brennan said, "Watch yourself, Captain. My friends are Midwesterners from Ohio. New Yorkers they aren't."

The men chuckle.

A sergeant guided the visitors to their quarters for the night. The quarters were a new bunker dug next to the medical aid bunker. As soon as Buchanan stepped down into the bunker, he sensed the space of a Caerphilly Castle. No, the place reserved to gain a night's rest did not reflect the Five Star Huntington Hotel in Pasadena near Los Angeles, but Buchanan felt secure. And that's what counted - a sense of security. Four cots awaited the men, a table for lighting, and a small chair Lambert had placed for leisure.

Buchanan glanced at his watch, noticing the time had raced to 0930 hours. Noting the time, he reminded himself today, 22 February, is the last day of the Viet Cong cease fire. The end of the ceasefire set the firebase on edge. The marines knew not what the future held for the combat base. Within the perimeter, the men heightened their sense of security, keeping their eyes open and their ears perked up.

Buchanan, thankful the trip out in the boonies occurred during the ceasefire, still yet sensed an eerie aura in the air. During the ceasefire, he took advantage of the ceasefire to catch up visiting the wounded in Da Nang, along with several visits to the CAP's Camp Love committed itself to. Besides, Chaplain Kensington and the Catholic priests sought help with additional construction on educational buildings in the An Ngai Don School. The Seabees were ever so pleased to lend a hand.

The sergeant assigned to lend a hand to the visitors, excused himself. He informed the visitors if they needed anything, they could locate him in the 155mm SP howitzer gun emplacement crew quarters bunker.

At 1100 hours, Communion services would begin for the men. With an hour and a half to kill until scheduled services, the chaplains thought time spent should be a quality time with the troops.

Just as the spiritual teams were to visit the men, a little over a dozen marines arrived to visit the chaplains, stepping down into the bunker to greet the visitors. All of them from New York and Ohio.

"Hello, chaplain." The native Ohioans and New Yorkers could not wait to visit with the chaplains.

"Good morning." responded Buchanan and friends.

The marines surrounded Chaplain Buchanan and Jackson, striking up conversations of Ohio, while the remaining marines encircled Chaplain Brennan and Angelhoff to chat of New York.

"So you're from Ohio Chaplain Buchanan?" asked one curious marine.

"Yes marine, I am. From Middleport Ohio."

"Same here, sir. I'm a Buckeye from Washington Court House, Ohio." said the marine.

"Circleville for me, sir. Home of the Pumpkin Show Festival." said another.

"Great. And you men?" asked Buchanan of the other marines.

"Cuyahoga Falls, Ohio, sir." The marine smiled gleefully.

"Dover, Ohio, sir. In Tuscarawas County." responded another.

"Yes, I'm very familiar with Tuscarawas County. My father- and mother-in-law live in the county and my wife's brother, her only sibling."

"I'm from Hilliard, Ohio sir. Do you know where Hilliard is? It's west of the Columbus area." said a proud Ohioan.

"I know exactly where Hilliard is located. The city is near my first pastorate in the Columbus area."

An excited Buchanan felt at home surrounded by so many fellow Ohioans.

With greetings out of the way, the men sat on cots and the dirt floor of the bunker. Buchanan had not jawed with marines in such an informal manner since his arrival in Vietnam. The congenial, likable personalities of Brennan and Buchanan shinned through as the men felt comfortable with the chaplains as they opened up and talked of everything, especially the Ohioans and Ohio State football. Front and center of conversation though fixated itself on food. Every single Ohioan present in the bunker agreed. The one missed common treat amongst Ohioans turned out to be Ohio's famous peanut butter Buckeyes.

Buchanan commented, "I sure can taste a peanut butter Buckeye melting in my mouth right now. One prepared from a German Village candy shop I patronized there in Columbus. Ummm good."

"Yes sir. I know the shop." said the marine from Circleville.

The Dover native threw in his two cents' worth. "I believe you guys don't, and I say *don't,* know the smoothest, chocolaty, perfect Buckeyes made in the great state of Ohio, do you? Their Buckeyes melt in your mouth and dissolve ever so slowly – it's the Amish."

"Aw, yes. The Amish. They prepare a good Buckeye." Buchanan, reminded of the Amish in Tuscarawas County, suddenly fell homesick for home.

Peanut butter Buckeyes is the last thing a marine thinks of in a firebase. But a chaplain's presence brings with it the normalcy of the outside world.

Marines sustained an isolation in the bush, vulnerable from a constant threat of attack from the Viet Cong and the NVA striking the firebase. The continuous talk of the men disclosed the loneliness of the marines. The contact with other marines sealed a connection closer to 'civilization' and normalcy, enabling the men to open up and form a sense of security. The chaplains' personalities and style were similar in telling stories, inquiring of others' lives, laughing, telling jokes, and just enjoying the company of human beings.

The Ohio and New York contingents felt like a dog with two tails visiting with the jovial chaplains and their assistants. The welcomed visit broke the monotony of isolation.

The stress of jungle isolation pressed military personnel stationed in a firebase to deal with problematic issues consistently. The men burned human excrement in diesel fuel in a cut down 55-gallon drum.

Disposing of human excrement implementing the diesel hygienic system stood as the standard in discarding human waste from latrines.

Fighting the local fauna such as lice, leeches, mosquitoes, and snakes amounted to a knockdown drag out fight on a 24/7 daily basis. A battle of human vs nature.

Many other complications arose for isolated marines stationed in a firebase. The excruciating pain from the horrendous heat bore down on the marines 24/7. The regular consumption of C-rations with an occasional hot plate meal posed a challenge working up an appetite. Many marines suffered a sleepless night, struggling to catch some shuteye with the ever present threat of a Viet Cong attack. The unbearable anxiety of living day after day without a shower and shave forced the marines to shove aside the practices of hygiene.

The means of coping with the elements of Vietnam varied widely in the firebase. Men played cards, played baseball, read books and magazines, and listened to Armed Services Radio. Anything to break the boredom.

Spending time with the chaplains and their assistants provided the best means of coping with the tedious routine since the inception of the firebase.

The New Yorkers and Ohioans desired no end to the visit. Time spent with the chaplains was 'Heaven Sent', a God sent medicine beyond measure. The visit delivered a sense of normalcy of home.

Minutes pass quickly in life, and time had sped up to 1040 hours.

Dreading to mention the time, Buchanan said, "Men, I hate to mention it, but it's about time for Communion, scheduled at 1100 hours."

"We'll pick up with the visit after Communion with some chow. But a good time spent talking of Ohio, wasn't it?" Buchanan jubilantly asked.

"Sure was sir." responded the marines.

The men emerged from a cool bunker into the dreaded heat of southeastern Asia. The blistering heat of the sun showed no mercy beating down on every single marine in Six Shooter.

"Whew! It's as hot as hell out here! I can't wait to feel my first snow fall back home." commented the Dover, Ohio native.

"I'd rather be at Niagara Falls right now. It's blasted freezing this time of year." replied a New Yorker.

"Anywhere but here. Whew!" added Angelhoff, himself a native of Coeymans, New York.

Buchanan caught in the corner of his eye Captain Lambert in front of the medical bunker discussing enemy maneuvers for the next 24 hours with officers and non-commissioned officers as the Tet New Year cease fire end today, 16 February.

Unbeknownst to the visitors, intelligence reports alerted the enemy planned and aimed to attack at the strike of midnight with a sledgehammer, hitting South Vietnam hard with no impunity. Six Shooter, along with Observation Post Reno and Hill 327 Division Ridge, ended up on a long list of military posts and civilian targets to attack at 0001 hours from the Viet Cong.

Lambert kept quiet of the danger from personnel in the firebase until the appropriate time to inform them. The captain did not want to dampen the well deserved shot in the arm of invigorating inspiration that Buchanan and his colleagues brought along with them.

"Over here, Chaplain Brennan, Chaplain Buchanan." yelled Lambert. The chaplains stepped smartly to the commanding officer. Lambert instructed the chaplains. "Well, there is no cool spot in the firebase. So, Charles, you lead the Mass with Roman Catholics, including myself, on this side of the medical bunker. There's an elevation for the men to sit somewhat comfortable. Chaplain Buchanan, same for you, Padre - the Protestant men can sit on the slanted dirt embankment on the opposite side of the medical bunker as you lead in the Protestant Communion."

Apologetically, Lambert commented, "It's not much. But it's the best we can do."

Brennan comments, "It's all about the Spirit, captain. And as Chaplain Buchanan constantly preaches, 'It's all about what's in here.'" He nods, touching his chest near his heart. "Remember,

Captain Lambert. As the Scriptures tell us, 'Where ever two or more are gathered, I'm with you.'"

Lambert nods as he concurs with his chaplain friend.

The chaplain assistants distribute the service manuals to the men who share for the lack of. In no time at all, the assistants don the service kits on top of ammunition crates serving as communion tables. Two trucks next to the medical bunker provided a barrier to snipers attempting to take the life of one of the chaplains or the marines.

The chaplains implemented an order of service for Communion. The order followed several steps: a prayer, a welcome, the scripture reading, one hymn, a short message delivered by Chaplain Brennan, communion lead by both chaplains, and ending with a closing prayer. To support Chaplain Brennan, the Prayers of the Rosary followed the scripture reading. The Catholic prayers from the Lay Leader's Handbook followed the distribution of the elements. The addition of the Catholic Liturgy of the day followed the opening prayer. The Communion service this day delivered every liturgical practice available, assuring a spiritual high for those longing for a closer relationship with their Creator.

Except for marines standing guard, practically the whole firebase, roughly 180 men, attended the Communion services. Communion amounted to a 50/50 split down the middle of personnel – half received the Catholic elements, the other half of the men received elements distributed from Chaplain Buchanan.

The chaplains' combined forces in the boonies to conduct a merged service until the distribution of the elements. Dyed-in-the-wool Protestants and Catholics back home in the United States would frown on the consolidated service, but Buchanan and Brennan could careless what that adhered to. Out in the bush, chaplains altered the means to provide spiritual fulfillment to the troops.

The best approach for Navy chaplains to serve communion in Vietnam, especially if a chaplain faced a mixed group of Protestant and Catholic believers, would be to invite military personnel forward and take part in the service. The chaplain simply administered the elements and if a marine denied the elements due to convictions of the individual marine's faith, the chaplain recited a private, short blessing with the marine. The chaplain would then administer the elements to the next marine and so on. Buchanan assisted his Catholic friends frequently and fulfilled the chaplains corps motto – 'cooperation without compromise.' Buchanan mentally and physiologically held onto his own convictions concerning Holy Communion. In a war zone, Jesus superseded all else, including denominational differences.

Catholic chaplains approached Communion similar to Buchanan, though priests were a bit more unyielding regarding the consecration of the elements. The priest simply recited a blessing with a Protestant marine if one stepped forward during Communion. They brushed aside Protestant convictions of the elements simply as symbolic. In Roman Catholic terms, Catholic chaplains knew better. The conviction of transubstantiation - in which the bread and wine converts to the body and blood of Jesus Christ - lived in the hearts of Roman Catholics, real and meaningful to Catholic chaplains. And in the priests' hearts and minds, the elements were more than symbolic.

Buchanan, Kensington, and Brennan were convinced Christians thrived in both Christian faiths – Catholic and Protestant. Ecumenicalism ran deep in their hearts as Navy chaplains. To assist one another in a combat zone seemed to be the right thing to do, regardless of the criticism and wrath they might receive back home from their fellow members of their respected faiths.

Buchanan loved Brennan. Like Kensington, Buchanan considered Brennan one of the greatest Christians he had ever met. Brennan exemplified Jesus' attributes, showing a love for other human beings reflecting Christ.

The vocal, inspired, spontaneous prayers lifted up to God by Buchanan and Brennan to begin the service had been a long time in coming for the marines. The prayers of the chaplains, spiritual mentors to the men, filled the empty, lonely, vacant crevices of each marine's heart.

Buchanan altered the canned opening prayer off the cuff to bring comfort and a sense of God's protection for the men out in the bush.

"Men, let us pray." said Buchanan.

Buchanan prayed, "Heavenly Father, we face enemies every day, throwing temptations our way, to cause us to fall, enemies of war striking at us from the darkness of evil. The principalities, powers, and the forces of evil are against us. We read in the Holy Scriptures forces not of flesh and blood, but of vileness. Surround us with your ever present armor of protection when evil comes our way. Push back the influences of Satan upon those wicked people of this world. Cripple the efforts of those who serve the Devil. Disrupt the sinister and malicious efforts against those who seek your will. Let the Heavenly Legions surround us, preventing the weapons formed against us be foiled. Protect us and let your omnipresence surround us. In Jesus' name, Amen."

'Amens' echoed loud and clear in camp amongst Protestants and Catholics alike.

Brennan began with the Liturgy of the day from the Catholic church followed by Buchanan with a reading of Scripture, Psalm 34:4-18, a Psalm of Protection and Deliverance from Trouble.

4 I sought the LORD, and he answered me,
and delivered me from all my fears.
5 Look to him, and be radiant;
so your faces shall never be ashamed.
6 This poor soul cried, and was heard by the LORD,
and was saved from every trouble.
7 The angel of the LORD encamps
around those who fear him, and delivers them.
8 O taste and see that the LORD is good;
happy are those who take refuge in him.
9 O fear the LORD, you his holy ones,
for those who fear him have no want.
10 The young lions suffer want and hunger,
but those who seek the LORD lack no good thing.
11 Come, O children, listen to me;
I will teach you the fear of the LORD.

12 Which of you desires life,
and covets many days to enjoy good?
13 Keep your tongue from evil,
and your lips from speaking deceit.
14 Depart from evil, and do good;
seek peace, and pursue it.
15 The eyes of the Lord are on the righteous,
and his ears are open to their cry.
16 The face of the Lord is against evildoers,
to cut off the remembrance of them from the earth.
17 When the righteous cry for help, the Lord hears,
and rescues them from all their troubles.
18 The Lord is near to the brokenhearted,
and saves the crushed in spirit.

The penetration of God's presence into the marine hearts and minds in the bush through the reading of Psalms 34 inspired the men to linger on in the days to come, though no end of the war seemed near and inevitable to end with unfavorable terms. The words reinforced a presence of God far from civilization.

Psalm 34 spoke volumes: God will never forsake those who trust in the Almighty.

Next in the order of service slotted The Prayers of the Rosary, with all taking part, including the Protestants. The uplifting of the Prayers brought a smile to every congregant.

Next in the service's sequence called for 'A Mighty Fortress is Our God.' The vocals of the Catholics echoed as pleasant as the Protestants.

A proud Jackson led the men in the hymn. If the Viet Cong looked in or listened from afar, they heard a unifying voice lifting up words of promises from God Almighty, the Protector is never to be taken lightly.

The loudest lyrics sung warned The Prince of Darkness that believers will not tremble before him and that believers depended on The Lord, declaring the Evil one's rage to be tolerated. The promise of doom is sure for the Evil One. Every single marine sung every word, proclaiming to the VC, 'Beware! The Lord is with us!'

The hymn set the tone for the special music performed by a guitar playing marine. Rarely did Buchanan have the means to provide special music in the bush. But this marine furnished an in house means of entertainment for the men playing the guitar in the firebase. The marine's talent broke up the ugly boredom which emerged its ugly head daily. His entertainment served as a vital component of keeping everyone's sanity. The guitar player's post in the firebase stationed him in one of the howitzer artillery teams.

The guitar playing marine stood tall, a good looking, easygoing twenty-two-year-old from Los Angeles, California named Andrew Pedersen, a corporal. His aka, 'guitar', given by his fellow marines he entertained nightly. Buchanan grinned toward the kid, knowing most back home would stereotype him as a 'hippie.' His mannerisms, demeanor, smile, body language, all pointed toward being a hippie. The spiritual leaders smiled as he stepped forward to sing. Buchanan found himself drawn to him, as he sensed Pedersen as a 'people person', a trait Buchanan appreciated. Guitar presented himself as a pleasant, charming human being. Strangers knew instantly Pedersen as a strong spiritual person from his Jesus like demeanor.

Brennan introduced Pedersen and a fellow guitarist in camp to sing. Guitar said, "OK, everybody, my song I'm going to sing today is one we sing frequently around here on long days. You know the words, so sing along. And sing like you mean it, sing to please the Lord. My friend Greg Topping from Los Angeles is going to play rhythm guitar with me as usual. The song we're going to sing is 'Heaven Came Down and Glory Filled My Soul." Guitar paused. "Fill us with your spirit, Lord."

The marines clapped their hands with enthusiasm.

The two guitarists, popular with the men, adjust themselves in their seats. The musicians provided a spiritual uplifting by song. The marines were fond of Pedersen and Topping. The two guitarists possessed a more unconventional personality.

Buchanan pictured in his mind Pedersen and Topping with the long hair, a peace shirt, and holy jeans of a hippie. He thought of the two young marines humorous and amiable. Buchanan found hippies most profound. The hippies he met in the past were searching for the truth, asking questions about what the truth is and where to find it. Key questions Buchanan felt were vital for people to finally believe in Jesus and become Christians. He sought to witness to hippies, introducing Jesus and the Roman Road straightforward to them. For conservatives, hippies seemed rebellious and antagonistic to Christians, and though the guitar players appeared 'hippie' to Buchanan, a conservative, he didn't care. Buchanan enjoyed their company, meeting the two eccentric marines earlier in the day. The marines referred to Topping as 'rhythm'.

The guitarists played to the melody of 'Heaven Came Down and Glory Filled My Soul'. When Pedersen sang, the marines jumped in, singing with gumption, reassuring themselves the Spirit of God filled the air, protecting those of faith.

Buchanan heard nothing sung in Vietnam more meaningful than 'Heaven Came Down.'

With the last note picked on his guitar, Pedersen roared a hearty, "Thank you, Jesus!"

The marines responded with a hearty, "Yay!" clapping their hands.

"We love you, Guitar!" "Another one!" "We want more!" "How about another?" "Guitar!"

The marines wanted nothing but more music.

"Go ahead, Pedersen. Give us another." responded Brennan.

"OK, here she goes." said a contented Pedersen. He asked Topping, "How about the piece we've been practicing?"

"I love it!" answered Topping.

The pair played 'Go Tell It On the Mountain'. A familiar melody immediately recognized by the marines, a common tune performed by Pedersen in the evenings. Today, he sang the song with a folk genre version which he adored.

The sudden applause and deafening "Oorah's" following the end of 'Go Tell It On the Mountain,' reverberating off the sides of the towering hillsides and the mountains of Dai La Pass.

The reception the musicians received for their contribution to the service when the pair returned to their seats came with pats on the back and a well deserved 'Congratulations'.

Brennan then rose to deliver his short sermon, a message centered on God's protection based on Psalms 91. He reinforced all the things said and done in the service with his words in his message - an emphasis on God's protective shield in the bush.

When finished with the short sermon, Brennan concluded with the rites of his faith for transubstantiation to distribute the elements. Buchanan, on his left, began his Communion with the Protestants.

For Roman Catholics, Brennan set the Eucharist for the central focal point in their faith. And for practicing Roman Catholics, the elements to be received during Communion are not to be taken lightly. In Vietnam, chaplains cooperated with each other to provide the spiritual needs of the troops, regardless of the situation.

As each marine stepped up to receive the elements from Brennan, he said, "The body of Christ" as Brennan placed a wafer on each tongue of the marine. The marine would respond with a "Amen." Brennan then presented the chalice to each marine to sip the wine, uttering "The Blood of Christ" as each marine responded, "Amen."

Likewise, Buchanan distributed elements to the Protestant marines.

Brennan offered marine after marine a consecrated wafer and the consecrated wine.

Buchanan blessed the elements and presented them to God. Protestant marines rose for Buchanan to distribute the elements to the men in sequence. The Protestants finished early and sat waiting reverently while Chaplain Brennan administered the last elements to lead the Eucharist.

Marines who have served in the past, knows Semper Fi brings the best out of marines in war.

'Semper Fi' unites. It bonds marines beyond measure. It is a fact 'Semper Fi' underpins the allegiance of marines to support one another's religious faith.

Buchanan held the marine motto 'semper fi' high. His observations of men of various religious faiths in a combat zone, men of many faiths, will protect one another's religious convictions. Buchanan had never seen such a loyal devotion in his life. Though Protestants and Catholics adhered vehemently to their own theological convictions supporting the Lord's Supper, the marines fought to keep one another alive. Though Buchanan and Brennan differed ecclesiastically and theologically, mutual love and admiration in Christian brotherhood merged the two firm believers in Christ.

As the last marine received the elements, Brennan prayed, ending the Communion ceremonies.

With custom, Buchanan and Brennan greeted the marines attending the service as Jackson and Angeloff secured the service kits. The marines from New York and Ohio begged the chaplains to accompany them to chow and to carry on their visit of home.

"Yes. *Yes*! Chow would be great!" said Brennan. His stomach growled from start to finish during the Communion service. He was thankful no one heard his call for sustenance during the service.

"Great, Sir!" replied a New Yorker.

"Talking New York will put me in the mood for a Yankee game or some of our famous pizza." commented Brennan to the New Yorkers.

"Yes sir. Thin pizza!" laughed the New Yorkers.

"Supreme." added Angelhoff with a bit of insistence in his voice.

"Talking Ohio again this afternoon and into the evening will fire me up to go straight to Dover or German Village for some peanut butter Buckeyes when I get back home." said Buchanan, chuckling.

Jackson said, "With a strong peanut butter base for me, sir. Tastes better."

An Ohioan commented, "Yeah. A stronger peanut butter Buckeye is a smoother, mouthwatering Buckeye. Buckeyes that'll melt in your mouth slow."

"Amen!" replied Buchanan.

With that said, the men walked to the chow line to eat. The marines gave the chaplains and the assistants a first place spot in line. It went without saying they were special guests.

The marines guided the spiritual teams in a tour of the firebase, laying out the command post, the bunkers, artillery pieces, and the hootches. Buchanan thoroughly enjoyed the insight of life in a marine firebase.

After chow and the tour, the marines and the spiritual teams visited in the new bunker well into the afternoon. The visit knew no end. The men were hungry to talk of nothing but a life of normalcy. The men talked and talked, homesick for home. Homesick for their natural habitat.

Ohioans longed for peanut butter Buckeyes and German food such as sausage, sauerkraut, and potatoes. Specialty ice cream, special chili in Cincinnati, corned beef, roast beef and mashed potatoes. The native Ohioans longed to attend professional baseball games, eating well known Cincinnati chili dogs. The men dreamed of visiting the dozens of cultural festivals in Ohio with family. The many football fans amongst the Ohioans desired to listen to Ohio State football games in the fall on the radio while grilling in the backyard, including sweetcorn on the cob picked fresh from the local corn field. The men yearned to visit the many museums and historical sites in the state, such as the Train Station in Cincinnati and the Cleveland Museum of National History. The Ohioans went on and on, talking and reminiscing of home.

New Yorkers talked long into the night. The men reminisced about Manhattan clam chowder, New York-style cheesecake, thin crusted pizza, bagels, and pastrami. The corned beef and baked pretzels, along with cultural foods, were favorites amongst the New Yorkers. The food in New York City ranked superb, such as Mexican and Puerto Rican food in Bedford Rock, Italian and Albanian food in Belmont Morris Park, Jewish food in Belmont, West Indian and Jamaican food in Wakefield, and Irish cuisine in Woodlawn. Yankee stadium sat waiting for the New York marines to return home and pass through the gates of the stadium to attend a game in the summer. The New

Yorkers yearned to visit the museums in their home state or travel to Niagara Falls to view the beauty of God's creation.

The depressive loneliness from the depths of isolation in the 'boonies' triggered the men to exchange conversation non-stop to four personalities perfect for lonely men cut off from the amenities others benefited from in Vietnam.

Lonely people tend to talk when given the chance. And the conversation lasted well after midnight. The visitors were 'God sent'. Military personnel in Vietnam fought to sustain their life to return to what waited for them back home.

The only possible thing to end the much needed visit for the marines would be a disruption all present in the new bunker loathed and despised – the Viet Cong.

No More Cease Fire

February 23, 1969

A shadowy, gloomy stillness of night in Vietnam filled the air with a sinister, ghostly aura within Six Shooter firebase.

A stillness of darkness descended onto Six Shooter, a darkness which concealed what lied beyond the jungle of Six Shooter's perimeter.

The shroud of darkness masked the evil waiting in the jungle, to spring forth with hearts of the Devil, to seize the life out of those fighting to bring freedom to those persecuted by the Viet Cong. The stillness of night smacked of an eerie, unnerving gut feeling deep down in the depths of Buchanan's inner soul.

The roar of the natural jungle - insects and wild animals - ruled the night.

Unbeknownst to the marines, the devilry roamed the nocturnal depths of the bush searching for prey, prowling yet again this night, the end of the ceasefire.

Lurking in the darkness roamed the Viet Cong, waiting patiently for an opening to infiltrate Six Shooter.

Firebase lights glowed from entrances of the bunkers and crews' quarters from mosquito repellent candles, LED construction work lights that hooked on the side of bunkers and crew's quarters bulkheads. Outside of the bunkers were the few dimmed incandescent orange lights placed sporadically in the firebase. Keeping the firebase dark intentionally, the marines attempted to obscure any movement of marines from the enemy at night, aiding in the security once the sun went down.

In the early morning hours of 23 February 1969, two dozen undetected Viet Cong sappers unfortunately infiltrated Six Shooter in the darkness.

The holes of the incomplete perimeter came back to bite the marines' ass in Six Shooter.

A platoon of the 25th Sapper Company, part of the 31st North Vietnam Army Regiment, made their way into Six Shooter as quiet as a mouse. The regiment operated its activities west of Da Nang, attacking United States installations with help from the Viet Cong.

Once in the firebase, the invaders hid under trucks in the motor pool, lined parallel with the howitzer line. Patience of the sappers paid off as the intruders waited for the coordinated hit-and-run attacks scheduled against United States installations in and around the Da Nang area.

Six Shooter, Observation Post Reno, Hill 327 at Division Ridge, and Dai La Pass all felt the brunt of simultaneous attacks in the morning hours of 23 February.

The Ohioan and New Yorker marines departed the spiritual team's bunker by 0115 hours, making their way back to their own quarters by 0200 hours.

Buchanan, Brennan, Jackson, and Angelhoff were all tucked away and ready for a few hours shut eye.

"I'm exhausted. I think those marines would have talked our heads off till dawn." commented Buchanan.

Angelhoff sighed hard and long, saying, "I *know* they would've, sir."

"Well, I know they're a bunch of jarheads. But they're lonely, and when you're lonely, you talk." said Jackson.

Turning to Buchanan smiling, Angelhoff said, "Well, it's 0200 hours and we've talked for the past 45 minutes, ever since they left the bunker. Beg your pardon, sir, but you talk all the time too."

"Corporal, I couldn't get a word in edge-wise with this group. It shows how much we need human contact with each other." said

Buchanan. "Besides, I read in a counseling guide the other day a quote from Calvin Coolidge – 'It takes a great man to be a good listener.'"*

"Well, sir. I suppose we became a little greater tonight, huh?" commented Jackson.

Buchanan makes a point. "I guess I know what others think of me then, huh? Can't get a word in edge-wise, can they?"

The men grin at the thought.

Angelhoff said, "You have a tendency to talk quite a bit, sir."

Brennan tilted his head toward Angelhoff. "Well, corporal. You've been with me for the past six months. I'm Irish. I'm from New York. We express ourselves and you know that -"

POP! POP! POP!

What Brennan thought reflected fireworks, yelled - "That ain't fireworks!"

A swift barrage of gunfire and explosions suddenly filled the firebase.

POP! POP!POP!

ZZZZZZZzzzzzzzzweh! Krunch!

PING! PING! KowRunch!

Jackson and Angeloff swiftly grabbed their M-16's and flipped them to automatic.

"DOSE THE LIGHTS!" yelled Brennan.

"Kill that light, sir!" said Jackson to Chaplain Buchanan. He glanced at Jackson with fright in his eyes, full of terror. It ended up being the last image Jackson saw of Buchanan before the hootch fell pitch black from switching the light off.

The chaplains plastered themselves on the dirt floor, crawling in the darkness to find cover behind the crates.

"Corporal, take the left. I'll take the right." blurted Jackson.

Jackson stood confidently, aiming his M-16 in a standing position, Angelhoff in a kneeling position along the bulkhead.

Scared stiff and frightened, the men prepared for the enemy to rush into the bunker, clueless of the action topside.

Gazing up toward the entrance of the bunker, it enthralled the men with the light show of weapons rattling off projectiles in the night, a blend of color reflecting a high-tech laser show.

As terror sunk in, the men felt hemmed in, vulnerable and still unaware of the action above the bunker. The four men transfixed their attention toward the entrance. The nervous men waited, listening.

The reverberations of weapons rattled off increased in volume.

POP! POP! POP! POP! POP!

RATATATATATATATATATATA!!!!

By now, all heard the sounds they grew to hate - agonizing shrieks of men screaming and grunting, men succumbing to their deaths.

But who? Americans? Vietnamese? The Viet Cong? Marines?

Anticipation of what might come in the next five minutes rattled the overwhelmed religious leaders.

Jackson and Angeloff stood firm, prepared to engage the enemy. Yet the men prayed the first human beings at the entrance would be friend, not foe.

Then suddenly the four men heard a loud - KaBOOM!

The tremendous blast muted the simultaneous echoes of war, at least temporarily. The bang had to have come from a main structure of the firebase or possibly a vehicle destroyed from explosive devices, probably from 'Chicom' grenades, short for Chinese Communist. From past engagements, the chaplain assistants recognized Chicom grenades exploding in the fighting above them.

As the fighting died downed, Jackson only heard M-16's firing above. A perfect sign the good guys held the upper hand toward a positive end.

Finally, marine voices dominated the conversation, heard loud and clear throughout Six Shooter. Voices barking out orders, commands to secure the firebase. Buchanan and his friends found the commotion above them rather soothing.

The religious teams heard commands all about the post.

"Corpsman! Watch your left!"

"Sergeant, secure the 155 howitzer!"

"Corporal, secure the ammunition bunker!"

"Reaction Force Team 4 – assemble!"

Hearing orders given topside established a sense of security, as the silence of weapons sounded like music to Buchanan's ears.

The ten-minute attack seemed an eternity.

Then Buchanan heard the optimum words he wanted to hear, "Chaplain Buchanan? Chaplain Brennan? This is Sergeant Nance from Dover, Ohio. We talked earlier. You in the bunker? Your party OK?"

The men heard heavy sighs coming from the darkness of the bunker.

"We sure as heck are, Sergeant!" yelled Buchanan up toward the bunker entrance.

"I'm coming in, sir." said Nance with a bit of trepidation in his voice.

Stepping down into the bunker shining a small flashlight, Nance caught sight of Jackson and Angelhoff gripping their M-16's above their hips out of sheer insecurity.

The chaplain assistants lowered their weapons, spotting the Ohio native, elated they were still alive.

"Stay put till the sun comes up. The VC love a second attack following the first one, attempting to catch us with our pants down. Don't come out till we come get you." said Nance.

"Will do." confirmed Jackson.

Nance expressed his appreciation for the spiritual team's presence in the camp. "Sure am glad the Lord was with y'all tonight. You helped us."

With that, Nance, a devout Disciples of Christ, turned and ambled back up out of the bunker.

Waiting patiently for the sun to rise, the four religious leaders prayed, thanking the Lord for His protection, sitting quietly on the dirt floor, scarcely saying a word. Jackson kept wide eyed, obliged to guard his exhausted colleagues who caved to their weariness with quick cat naps.

Two hours later the sun rose and with a roaring authoritative voice, Nance gave word the camp had returned secure. "OK, chaplain, it's secure. Y'all can come on out."

Emerging from the bunker, the four speechless men caught sight of the attack, flabbergasted by the sight of the destruction. No more did the Fire Direction Center stand proud in Six Shooter, for it succumbed to the destruction of Chicom grenades. The men turned wide-eyed at the sight of debris from the battle spread out all over the ground. Blackened residue laid top of every surface from powder split. The sediment from grenade explosions covered the camp throughout the grounds. The spraying of bullets and shrapnel, with no rhythm or reason, riddled the vehicles, jeeps, and trucks. Littered throughout the firebase laid 22 sappers killed, many ripped to pieces and mangled into a lump of human flesh. One upbeat came in the capture of a sapper, an invaluable resource in collecting intelligence regarding VC and NVA movements west of Da Nang.

What floored Buchanan most came from discovering a manufactured human bridge of the enemy during the engagement of fallen Viet Cong. The sight reminded him of his value of human life, which conflicted with the obvious neglect of the Viet Cong for fellow human beings. The VC's attempt to infiltrate the camp running on a human bridge on top of fallen comrades astonished Buchanan. He thought to himself - 'What kind of people are these Viet Cong?'

The marines suffered three killed in action, including a Navy corpsman, and 15 wounded in the fight.

As chaplains, Buchanan and Brennan made their way to the KIAs, praying over the men. Brennan offered last rites to two Roman Catholic marines.

Stepping toward the KIA's, Brennan found a weeping Corporal Pedersen, Guitar, crouched over Rhythm, Greg Topping, killed in the action. He loved his friend and fellow musician. Brennan turned to a prayer from the combat manual and read with Guitar. Buchanan stood near to support his fellow chaplain.

Holding in his emotions as best he could, Brennan read the following prayer:

"Depart, O Christian soul, out of this world, in the name of God the Father Almighty who created thee. In the name of Jesus Christ who redeemed thee. In the name of the Holy Spirit who redeemed thee. May thy rest be this day in peace, and thy dwelling place in the paradise of God. O Lord, support us all the day long, until the shadows lengthen and the evening comes, and the busy world is hushed and the fever of life is over, and our work is done. Then in Thy mercy grant Greg Topping a safe lodging, and a Holy rest, and peace at last. Amen."

When done reading the prayer, he and Guitar hashed out life's trials for most of the day in solitude. The Roman Catholic priest encouraged Guitar, making the greatest attempt to put in perspective the death of his friend.

Death never comes easy. When war snuffs the life out of a living, breathing human being in a literal second of time, death is especially hard on the human will.

The farthest thing on the minds of Brennan and Guitar tilted toward any talk of Ohio and New York. Nothing but 'fellowship' the previous day. Today, nothing but glum. Foremost on the minds of Six Shooter yearned to sit, reflect, and recuperate. The chaplains presence in the firebase nurtured a mental pick me up for the men. When the time came to talk, the men simply opened up.

After the attack, the firebase sped up the completion of defenses encircling the perimeter. Chaplain Buchanan's earlier prayer to God protecting the men in Six Shooter will be remembered fondly in the days to come – 'surround us with your ever present armor of protection when evil comes our way.'

Face to Face with the Viet Cong

March 2, 1969

"Let's go, Padre! An Ngai Tay's waiting." barked Rockford, outside Buchanan's hootch door.

Buchanan peeked on the other side of the door with curiosity, noticing Rockford decked out in his combat uniform.

"I'm coming! I'm coming! I just have to get my canteens." Buchanan took hold of his extra canteen from his storage cabinet, Rockford stepped into the hootch.

"You just have to have an extra canteen, don't you, Padre?"

"Well, I -" Rockford interrupted Buchanan and said, "Ya loathe the heat, don't you, Padre?"

"Well, it's hotter than hell out there!" Buchanan blurted, with disgust in his voice. "I once heard – 'Coolness and absence of heat and haste show fine qualities.'"

Dumbfounded, Rockford says, "What does that have to do with anything?"

Buchanan sternly asserts, "I don't know, but makes me feel better."

The men smirk.

Rockford adored Buchanan. Of all the chaplains Rockford met in his military career, Buchanan's ministry spoke to his heart more than any other chaplain he had ever known. Rockford admitted to be a hard-nosed, gun ho officer, abiding strictly by the book in the bush. Yet, he possessed an innate Christian heart, providing every means to protect the 'Padre.'

The frailties of ever-present dangers for a non-combatant positioned Buchanan in a state of vulnerability to taste death with every step taken in the jungle. From the beginning of his tour, he chose not to carry a weapon in Vietnam. He did, however, gain courage. As days passed, his resolve strengthened with time spent in the bush. He thanked God for His guidance and direction, bolstering his confidence in handling combat situations with the wounded and those passing into eternity. Though his endurance toughened as months passed, fear still overwhelmed him when facing the trials of the bush.

Rockford revealed the real reason he stopped by Buchanan's hootch. "Padre, I rarely come to your hootch before departing for the bush, but this time - well, we'll be escorting Skawinski's team once again." He paused. "But this time, the enemy's been on a tear since the Post-Tet cease fire. The pests came flying out of Hades on the 23rd of February. They've attacked and attacked. They've killed and murdered hundreds of civilians and US military personnel. It's going to be a little more rough on this trip than usual. Charlie gave you a taste of their tenacity at Six Shooter." Sighing, he added, "I've never seen a chaplain create such rapport as you have with the men."

Buchanan stepped to Rockford, following the completion of packing his field bag. "Well, you only see my shell on the outside, sir. If you knew what's happening on the inside, well, I'm terrified."

Tilting his head, Rockford said, "If you weren't, Padre, I'd worry more about you. You don't want to get cocky. Ya know what I mean?"

"Yes, sir! Amen to that!"

"Well, we better saddle up, Lieutenant Rockford." said a confident Buchanan, smiling. He attached a canteen to his combat belt, placing the other in his field bag, ready to depart.

Secured and all set to go, Buchanan heard a sudden voice from the front of the hootch. "Are ya there, sir?"

"I know that voice. Yes, Ski, I'm coming."

As Buchanan and Rockford stepped down from the hootch, the men caught sight of Jackson and Skawinski with hands on their hips, cracking the widest of smiles.

"You take everything in the bush but the kitchen sink, sir." commented Jackson.

Rockford smirks.

With a confident shrug, Buchanan grins. "Just want to be prepared. And though I was never a Boy Scout, I wanted to be. But they hit the nail on the head – Always be prepared."

Laughing, the men pat one another on the shoulder, pacing quickly toward the entrance of Camp Love.

Once the men arrived, Rockford ordered a muster for B Company and the combat engineering squad. Following muster, he ordered an inspection of combat equipment, along with the combat engineering gear and tools. The mission slotted Company B for a sweep of mines and booby traps along main travel routes, in and around perimeters of friendly villages and hamlets, including An Ngai Tay.

To strengthen numbers, 1st Squad, 2nd Platoon of Alpha Company accompanied Bravo Company for the two to three-day patrol, sweeping sections of Route 540, Route 1, and Route 5.

The mine sweeping, along with defusing booby traps, required patience because of the tedious, painstaking work.

The laborious work in the field will now take on more responsibility and leadership for Skawinski, who made Sergeant in February, a feat he and his family were proud of. His great-grandfather immigrated from Sweden to find financial success from a strong-willed family in agriculture and farming, bringing along with him a strong, determined, and disciplined Protestant work ethic. Skawinski's blood kin held their heads high, living lives in a tradition of hard working Americans in the Midwest. The Skawinski clan sent family members off to war and fight to protect what they had built in civilian life. Fighting in World War I as an enlisted marine, his great-grandfather would have been proud of his advance to sergeant.

In two days, Skawinski's team discovered a significant number of claymore mines and booby traps, disarming the maiming devices the enemy had set to kill an unfortunate victim, unintentionally stumbling upon the eager coup de grâce, a most satisfying end for the Devil's legions who had set the lethal snare.

Rockford's sweeping party completed the travel routes for the mission, including 5 villages and 6 hamlets, ending up at An Ngai Tay. The last assignment to sweep included segments of the Ho Chi Minh Trail, the Red Ball Express. The frequented and active trail served as a route for communications and travel for the Viet Cong.

The terrain to sweep intertwined with sporadic pockets of open farmland and vegetation. The most difficult portion patrolled ended up one and a half miles worth of jungle to trudge through.

The sweeping party ended the patrol full circle, looking forward to travel the many miles back to Camp Love from An Ngai Tay. The contingent of marines would sweep an extension of Viet Cong communication trails.

The party's present location on the map pinpointed Company B six and a half miles from Camp Love.

Rousing up at 0630 hours in the morning on March 4, the men were dog tired from days of work.

To arrive in camp for some shuteye, Buchanan longed for nothing but a quick trip back to camp. Besides, he felt lucky today. Tuesday nights called for playing cards with friends, relaxing with colleagues exhausted from two days of work, draining a considerable amount of energy from the marines and combat engineers.

Rattling off the order to saddle up and head for home, Rockford ordered Private Jaworski and Private First Class PoKorny on the flanks. He ordered Corporal Lipstone at Tail-End-Charlie, the last man to cover the rear of a patrol. Private Shaw preceded Lipstone. Rockford permitted conversation, but in a whisper. To scan the horizons ahead of the patrol, he ordered Corporal Kowslowski at the point.

No one else in Bravo Company possessed a better keen eye for booby traps than Kowslowski while at the point. Skawinski considered Kowslowski superb at the point, for he trained him. After his combat training, Skawinski himself discovered he possessed an innate skill of sensing danger, a canny and sagacious sense of smelling out distant peril in the jungle. A key to survive any patrol in the jungle required a perceptive awareness of the enemy's presence in the jungle's interior. The difficulty came with the dense vegetation and practically impassable terrain.

Accompanied by Jackson, Buchanan landed in the middle of the patrol, protected by Skawinski. The anticipation of playing Rummy ran high as the men paced themselves for the hastened trip back home.

"Well, chaplain. You're going to get hammered tonight. Again, sir!" Skawinski boldly rubbed it in that Buchanan had had a few rough weeks in a row playing Rummy.

"Please, Ski!" answered a skeptical Buchanan in a whisper.

Skawinski appeared confident he attained the winner's circle tonight. "Well, I keep track of the winnings, ya know. Senior Chief Gross is first with just a little under $400.00 dollars won and Burnside's won around $350.00 in second place." Skawinski rubs his chin, looking off sideways pensively, thinking of Buchanan's winnings, saying softly, "And what are your winnings, sir? Uh, yes, I know, around $210.00."

In jest, Skawinski and Jackson chuckle.

"Pst. It's only because we have not caught Gross cheating and Burns is lucky." claimed Buchanan.

"Um." gestured Jackson, grinning. "No sir. It's how they play their cards. They take and throw cards away strategically. And they hold a hand when they know to. Besides, their poker face fools everybody, including you."

Skawinski beamed. "Yeah. Just watch'em tonight, you'll see."

"I'm in the running to take the lead with winnings, eventually. Wait and see. It'll happen." replied Buchanan, with confidence.

The men glance toward one another, shaking their heads out of denial.

Skawinski confessed to his friends, "The card playing is going to do me some good. I'm exhausted. I bet my team disarmed dozens of mines and booby traps. Might be a record. Whew! These VC mean to disrupt life something terrible, don't they?"

Jackson said, "You worked hard, Ski. You might want to take the night off tonight and rest."

"Are you kidding? Rest tonight knowing I'm going to take more money from Chaplain Buchanan, here?" asked a sarcastic Skawinski, smiling at Jackson.

Buchanan sneered at Skawinski's remark. Just as Buchanan spoke up, Rockford abruptly ordered, "Quiet. No more talking."

The patrol advanced close to the communication route, just a mile away. Kowslowski approached a ravine with a small stream flowing in the base. A perfect place for the Viet Cong to travel to avoid exposure. A small inclined hill faced the ravine on the right at a 40-degree angle, while on the left lay a hill measured 15 degrees. The open space bordering the ravine laid heavy with trees for perfect cover for the enemy to ambush a patrol. The route proved the shortest toward home, but not necessarily the securest or least dangerous of routes.

Kowslowski slowed the pace of the patrol to a stagnant advance, sensing danger ahead. Methodically searching for booby traps and mines, Kowslowski meticulously kept his ardent eyes open for any ambush the Viet Cong might have conjured up. His footsteps frontward altered to a slow pace, every step softly stepping on the ground to avoid any booby traps, as if on pins and needles. The spiritual team perceived Kowslowski as if he walked on thin ice above a lake frozen over.

As Kowslowski advanced an additional 25 feet into the ravine, he confidently raised his left arm high with authority for the patrol to stop.

Rockford lifted his left hand to halt, as the patrol crouched in a defensive position.

Kowslowski turned to his left, motioning for Lieutenant Rockford to step carefully up to his location.

In a hunkered position, Rockford made his way up some 15 feet to Kowslowski. He anxiously asked Kowslowski in a whispered voice, "What is it, Corporal? Why ya stop us? You sense something?"

With urgency, Kowslowski softly convinces Rockford something in the air stunk. "I'm positive, sir. I just know we're walking into an ambush. I think we need to backtrack. Back track, right - now."

Skawinski, a phenomenal point man, stares with curiosity straight at Rockford and Kowslowski.

Buchanan stared with as much interest as Skawinski. Turning towards Jackson, he whispered, "Sure wish I could hear what they're saying? This stop sure makes me nervous." Pausing, he said, "You know as well as I do, a stop in a patrol means -" Jackson interrupts, raising his hand gently to Chaplain Buchanan. He whispered softly, "Quiet, sir. We'll know sure enough."

Skawinski, on Buchanan's left, reaches over with his hand in front of Buchanan, poking Jackson's left arm.

Jackson leans forward, glimpses around Buchanan at Skawinski twisting his left hand and asked with his eyes, 'What?'

Pointing to his chest with his right index finger in eyeshot of Jackson, Skawinski then points toward Rockford and Kowslowski.

Jackson nods. Advancing forward in a crouched position, Skawinski steps up to Rockford and Kowslowski.

When Skawinski finally made his way to Rockford, he motioned toward the enclaves on each side of the stream in the ravine.

Skawinski takes an all-encompassing view of the enclaves and ravine, turns to Rockford and Kowslowski, nodding in the negative.

Rockford nods. Raising a bit from his crouched position, he waves to the patrol to back out from the entrance of the ravine.

The whole patrol smartly rose from their crouched positions and walk backwards facing the ravine, with M-16's in automatic in case of a firefight.

As the entire patrol walks backwards, Rockford, Skawinski, and Kowslowski served as Tail-End-Charlie who reach the point of entry of the ravine, when out of nowhere the patrol faced a barrage of 60 caliber machine gun fire, with a spraying of AK-47's from 8 to 10 Viet Cong.

"HIT THE DECK!" yelled Rockford.

The patrol hit the earth's surface with a force of weight that seemed to cause even the elevated hills aside the ravine to avalanche.

The sum of immediate fire from marines toward the muzzle flashes of enemy weaponry delivered a heavy blow upon the hidden Viet Cong.

Buchanan and Jackson within seconds spotted directly in front of them a line of bullets hitting the ground one after the other, each bullet approaching closer and closer, 10 to 12 inches apart. Each bullet hit the ground, jolting up chunks of soil and earth in mini violent explosions. The spiritual team froze, shocked witnessing projectiles coming straight at them. The two men envisioned the end of their lives ending this day in the jungles of Vietnam.

As each bullet hit the ground, drawing closer and closer to Buchanan, his whole life crossed his mind in a matter of seconds. His childhood, his enlisted years, his family in California. Thinking of his whole life pass before him within seconds, his lone thought raced across his mind, 'This is it. It's over. My turn to die. I'm not going home.'

Jackson's life crossed his mind, preparing himself to pass into Eternity..

The bullets gained nothing but momentum, making their way toward the spiritual team, hitting the ground close to their heads, splattering their combat helmets and faces with dirt and tiny particles spent from the projectiles ramming into the hard surface of the earth. A collision of force felt of pin needles penetrating the skin.

The bullets made their way between the flattened bodies of the spiritual team who hugged, practically grasping, the ground underneath themselves as if starting a tunnel to China.

The impact of projectiles on the ground hammered out dirt violently between the men's torsos and legs. The men felt Newton's third principle of motion as projectiles hit the ground. Their gear and uniforms served as a buffer from receiving a wound or feeling dirt on bare skin.

The line of bullets swiftly passed their feet, dispelling several feet behind them.

Sporadic enemy gunfire continued rapidly from pesky terrorists.

In the corner of Buchanan's eye, he caught the violent impact of bullets hitting the ground one after the other, as if peppered from the sky. All the while, Buchanan thought, 'These ambushers suck! They couldn't hit the side of a barn at 50 feet!'

Buchanan, Skawinski and Jackson detected two Chicom grenades fly out from the depths of the jungle in the patrol's direction, one a dud, the other exploding. The grenade which exploded denied taking the life of one of the good guys due to an amateur toss, without precision.

The Viet Cong continued delivering a pestering, harassing barrage of projectiles toward the patrol. Though the severity of fire declined any casualties because of Viet Cong marksmanship, the marines were by now annoyed with the ambush, letting loose hand grenades and a vigorous, furious firing line in the direction of the muzzle flashes of enemy weapons. The combined force of marine fire power eliminated the .60 caliber machine gun, including a grenade delivered pinpoint by Kiehl and Rodriquez from the grenade launcher.

Within moments, enemy fire ceased. Rockford, still tentative, held steady until Bravo Company secured the area.

"STAY DOWN! Stay down, patrol!" ordered Rockford.

Squad and patrol leader's eyes glued on Rockford. He motioned with his right hand to Bravo Company Rifle Team Two, Squad One of 1st Platoon, to move cautiously toward the direction of the Viet Cong ambush positions to envelop the Viet Cong line of attack to secure the area. He gave the same order to Rifle Team Three on his left.

The two teams moved forward, weapons at the ready, until reaching the Viet Cong's extreme flanks. The teams then stepped toward the center of the enemy firing line until the flanking parties met in the middle. The terrain facing Bravo Company egressed secure.

"OK! Everybody up." ordered Rockford. "Gunny, take 2nd Platoon, move forward, make sure Chuck scurried away timidly as they usually do."

"Yes, sir." replied Jurgensen. The Gunny moved forward with 2nd Platoon, while Rockford ordered Skawinski's team to back track, securing the rear.

Rockford ordered third platoon to form a perimeter encircling space occupied by marines. He inspected the Viet Cong firing line with the remaining officers and noncommissioned officers. The spiritual team ambled along with Rockford out of curiosity, laying their eyes on six VC corpses and discovering evidence a half a dozen more VC were present for the ambush.

"Whew! Sure am thankful this crew of Charlie stunk firing weapons. Aren't you, Captain?" asked a contemptible Buchanan, glancing over at Rockford.

"I sure as hell am, Padre." said Rockford.

Jackson commented, "They only look to be 18, maybe 19 years old." Turning toward Buchanan and Rockford, he says, "Pity. Look at the expressions on their faces – sheer terror."

"Probably young men recruited by the Viet Cong with force from nearby villages. Charlie doesn't care how old they are, do they?" replied Rockford.

"Stupid commies." said Lieutenant McInally.

"Yeah. Same ole' threat, probably. Serve us as foot soldiers or we'll kill everyone of your family members. *Pst.* If that's not the Devil's work, I don't know what is." remarked Buchanan.

"*Yes* sir. Nocturnal visits are -" said Jackson, but interrupted by a shocked marine examining the remains of one of the VC, who says, "Oh Lord! Sir! Come here, sir! Look see!"

Rockford made a hurry toward the marine, followed by others. The marine commented, "This kid's from Tung Son Hamlet. His name's Binh Hien. I think it means 'peaceful, gentleman.'"

"*Huh.* He was anything but peaceful and gentle today. He turned on us." said an ungrateful McInally.

The marine said, "I guess so, sir. He farms with his grandpapi. I've talked to this kid in the past about farming techniques. Major 'Mickey', you know Major Sanborn, instructed he and his grandpapi agricultural methods many, many times. His grandpapi is an elder in his village."

Buchanan sighs. "I don't understand, Lance." Buchanan stood beside himself, unable to grab a handle on what just transpired.

Rockford turns to Buchanan with a bit of gloom and says, "Well, Padre. This war stinks. It's nothing I've ever seen before." Buchanan looks down onto the young Viet Cong and says, "Yeah."

Buchanan slightly shifts his head upward a bit and discovers one of the most grotesque sights he has laid his eyes on in Vietnam yet. The sight took a moment or two to recognize. Then he said, "Sergeant Jackson, Captain, look."

Rockford and Jackson turned, noticing a Viet Cong corpse. The men cautiously stepped toward the remains, keeping an eye out for any life-threatening booby traps.

The men kneeled down to examine a little closer the corpse. The remains were mainly skeletal, mangled together after wildlife and insects had had a piece of it. The little flesh left had darkened and dried. A sickening sight, but one Buchanan would never forget.

"He's been here for at least four months." said Rockford.

The men stare for a moment or two. Standing up Buchanan said, "Did the Viet Cong just leave him here?"

"Maybe, sir. The Viet Cong are known to leave corpses behind." said Jackson.

Sighing heavily, the men walked back inside the perimeter of 3rd Platoon.

By now, the reconnaissance parties passed along to report to Rockford of no signs of the enemy.

Miraculously, the marines suffered no casualties or wounded in the ambush. Rockford logically concurred Buchanan's initial estimation with a correct conclusion – the ambushers sucked at marksmanship. Besides, the ambushers were young, inexperienced conscripts.

The spiritual team ambled over to the edge of the east perimeter to survey an encampment deserted, possibly for weeks.

Buchanan walked to two trees, which looked similar to the remnants of a hammock on one end of the deserted encampment.

"Look here, Philip." motioned Buchanan, about to touch a rope attached to the trees. Turning toward the chaplain, he swore to guard with his life, Jackson spoke snappishly, "Freeze Chaplain! Don't move! Stop where you are! Don't move!" He stretched his hands out in front of himself to warn Buchanan not to move even a smidgen.

Scared to death, Buchanan froze. He stood as still as a manikin in a storefront window, not moving an inch. Fretfully, he uttered, "What-What? What is it, S-Sergeant?"

"It's a booby trap." Jackson said with the utmost trepidation in his voice.

Buchanan swallowed hard, shaking ever so slightly, adding all the more sweat to his already drenched fatigues from the scorching heat of the sun. Now sweating ever more from the sudden threat to his life.

"W-W-What do you w-want me to do?" asked Buchanan anxiously.

"Whatever you do, don't touch the rope." Jackson stood ever so cautiously.

Buchanan's eyes widened as he held his breath. And not by choice. Scared out of his gourd, he noticed his fingers just an eighth of an inch from touching the rope.

"I see the strings attached." commented Jackson.

Jackson softly said, "Back your hand away from the rope, sir. Slowly."

Buchanan slowly backed his hand away as instructed.

"Lower your hand down to your side slowly. Slowly!"

Buchanan, edgy, jerked quickly his hand away, when Jackson abruptly said, "Slowly!....Slowly."

Buchanan's hand finally made it to his side.

By now, Skawinski, Rockford, and others noticed Buchanan's predicament. Not one word came uttered in order for Buchanan to hear only Sergeant Jackson.

Jackson scrupulously instructed Buchanan. "Sir. Now I want you to move backward, slowly away from the two trees and the rope, sir. Take gentle, slow, leisurely steps."

Buchanan stepped backwards with deliberate, unhurried steps behind him. After stepping back three feet from the rope and trees,

Buchanan finally stepped back onto the edge of some jungle vegetation. Jackson felt himself full of glee. "You're safe now, sir."

With that, Skawinski and his team made their way toward the booby trap.

The spiritual team gaze toward one another. Sighing heavily, the men grin as if to say, 'We survived another one.' The team, between the treeline of the jungle and the patrol, was by now physically and emotionally drained from the close call. Buchanan came close to meeting his Creator.

He thanked the Lord, saying a silent prayer by quoting Psalms 34:7, 'The angel of the Lord encamps around those who fear him, and delivers them.'

Then suddenly, out of nowhere, a young VC pops up out of the thick vegetation holding a machete upward in his right hand running toward Buchanan, practically frozen out of fright.

Buchanan swiftly turns toward the 19- or 20-year-old kid, both staring at each other in shock.

Buchanan stood face to face with the enemy. Face to face with the VC. His first experience facing the enemy up close and taken aback, terrified to no end. The young kid stopped curtly in his tracks, catching flies, hesitant and motionless in front of Buchanan.

Jackson turns quickly, running immediately toward Buchanan and the young VC, plunging forward with the momentum of a runaway train. Dashing out of the jungle came two additional VC unexpectedly in front of the booby trap and tackle Jackson, knocking his M-16 towards Buchanan.

Marines from every direction ran toward Buchanan and Jackson, when suddenly small arms fire, possibly from six to seven VC, came from the direction of the booby trap.

"GET DOWN!" screamed Jurgensen and Rockford, as marines once again hit the deck.

Scared to death, the young VC felt by now someone dropped him unwillingly into the wrong place, at the wrong time. Buchanan read the inexperienced eyes quickly encroaching upon him. The eyes of the young VC had no desire to attack the marines. He simply dropped his machete, turned and hightailed it back into the jungle.

An additional VC came running out of the jungle toward Jackson, throwing himself into the scuffle. As Jackson fought hand to hand, guerrilla firepower increased as two AK-47's blasted away toward the marines.

By now, Buchanan regained his composure. Dropping onto the ground as fast as his energy drained body could go, he crawled behind a mound of eroded soil.

From the ground, he watched Jackson fight. He witnessed three VC pouncing on Jackson, attempting to plunge knives into Jackson's torso or limbs wherever they could find a spot. Jackson threw the VC off of himself, waiting for an opening to kill the enemy.

Jackson finally found an opportunity as he engaged in hand-to-hand with only one VC while the other two pulled themselves back up off the ground to once again plunge themselves into Jackson.

He quickly squeezed the wrist of the VC holding a knife, which he promptly dropped due to the superior strength of Jackson. He took hold of the VC by one leg with one hand, grabbing the VC's underarm with his other, running towards a sharpened, cut limb of one tree for the booby trap, ramming the VC's torso onto the tree limb leaving him hanging. His arms and legs went limp from the life taken out of him.

After pulling himself up off the ground, the second VC came running straight for Jackson with a snowball effect of momentum with the energy of a steam engine.

Jackson immediately turned toward the VC, zeroing in toward him with the wind at his back, noticing behind the front runner the last of the three VC running as fast as lightning.

All the while, the patrol fired weapons toward muzzle flashes from enemy gunfire in the jungle.

RATATATATA!

POP! POP! POP!

Buchanan heard nothing but rings from the weapons fired, followed by ricochets of bullets. Yet, he watched every move Jackson made, fighting the VC, screaming at the top of their lungs. Silent screams because of the racket of weaponry, but wreaked volumes for Buchanan. He viewed the whole fight.

The patrol dared not to take a risk and aim their weapons at the attacking VC fighting Jackson, but made all the efforts to kill the VC in the bush.

As the VC ran towards Jackson, he kicked the front runner to the ground dropping his knife, with the oncoming third VC with his knife hoisted, ready to plunge it into Jackson's torso. The VC on the ground, shaken by the kick delivered by Jackson, grabbed his knife, taking a swipe at Jackson, ripping his combat fatigues pants but no flesh.

Jackson looked down at the VC, then rapidly turned his head up, looking at the oncoming VC. He lurched himself towards the VC, grabbing his hand holding the knife, pressing downward, pushing the VC back toward the ground. The VC held onto the knife, pushing as hard as he could toward Jackson.

With weapons rapidly fired, Buchanan fixated himself on Jackson fighting the pesky VC.

The second VC stood up, rushed toward Jackson, still holding the hand of the third VC with his left hand, threw him round like a rag doll on every turn Jackson made.

Jackson turned toward the oncoming VC, intended on running Jackson through with his knife, which missed by a mile. He grabbed with his right hand the second VC's hand holding his knife with great strength, screaming at the top of their lungs, as Rockford took out the concealed VC in the bush.

Buchanan the whole while watched, witnessing the unbelievable sight in the front of him. Jackson holding with both hands the VC's wrists who are holding their weapons in hand awaiting with malicious pleasure to kill Jackson if opportunity arises. While the VC, with all their strength pushing forward their knives to kill Jackson with one hand, were scratching, clawing and punching Jackson with the other, bloodying Jackson with wounds.

Jackson twisted and turned to defend himself, throwing the Viet Cong about like rag dolls. All three men screaming wildly.

The spectacle in front of Buchanan shocked him. He found himself even more surprised projectiles had not hit him and his friends.

Distracted with the skirmish that had ensued, Buchanan finally noticed in the corner of his eye Jackson's M-16 he dropped earlier in the fight. Buchanan had had enough. He ran from his hidden spot in the bush, grabbed Jackson's M-16 and turned it toward the enemy muzzle flashes, letting loose a barrage of fire from Jackson's weapon in a kneeling position.

POP! POP! POP! POP!

The skirmish continued with ferocious fire.

RATATATATA!!!!!!

POP! POP! POP! POP!

The marines continuous letting loose of projectiles into the bush weighted down the Viet Cong, incapable of sustaining without loss of life.

RATATATATATATATA!!!!!!!

The moments which followed, few men in the patrol will ever find the words to explain such events about to occur. But as Buchanan fired Jackson's M-16, an overwhelming firepower from the marines weapons toward the enemy came out of nowhere. Firepower, which seemed equivalent to a whole battalion firing simultaneously. Weapons fired out of nowhere.

Vegetation disappeared from the force of firepower, chopping off every branch, every twig of every tree, plant, and scrub. The weight of lead delivered into the bush cleared the vegetation and the Viet Cong.

Smoke and small isolated fires emerged across the firing line of the Viet Cong from the heat of weaponry.

A combination of firepower and a loss of adrenalin forced the VC to concede to Jackson's bodily strength. The two VC dropped their weapons out of sheer exhaustion. Jackson grabbed both by the underarm, slamming their torsos together, causing the enemy to descend onto the ground with a thunderous crash.

Jackson seized a knife and ran one VC through, crushing the ribcage, killing him instantly. The VC caught Buchanan in the corner of his eye, and hurried toward him as he reached down, picking up the second knife, and lunged toward Buchanan. Unbeknownst to Buchanan as he lowered his head from firing Jackson's weapon into the jungle.

Clueless to the VC, Jackson cut him off in stride and grabbed him by the back of the neck, clasped the VC's hand holding the knife, turning the VC's hand back toward his stomach, thrusting the knife into his belly and spilling his intestines all over the ground.

Jackson, panting heavily from defending Buchanan in hand-to-hand combat, along with the VC now dead, found total exhaustion and fatigue from the sheer energy exerted, collapsed on the spot.

As the crackling of weapons ceased, Buchanan scanned the terrain following the skirmish. He will remember this day for a lifetime. A permanent scar never to leave his memory banks. The sight wreaked of war. The blood soaked VC hanging on the tree. Two mangled, bloodied Viet Cong laying dead in front of him, and smoked vegetation burning from the devastating full firepower of marine weaponry. The booby trap Buchanan came close to tripping lay on the ground between the two trees, exposed during the firefight. A booby trap composed of dozens of punji sticks fastened on dozens of two-inch sticks tied together, intending to swing down onto its victim, puncturing all four limbs and torso, killing the human being instantly.

As Buchanan viewed the battle scene, he came across Jackson lying flat on his back. He assumed Jackson is a killed in action. Popping up from his kneeling position to fire the M-16, he bolted as fast as he could to Jackson to check his condition.

Reaching Jackson about the same time Petty Officers Sigmanson and Crowley arrived to treat his wounds, Buchanan looked straight into his face. Buchanan, along with the corpsmen, felt thrilled to pieces to discover Jackson breathing in God's good air He gives every morning he wakes up! Giving a good look see from head to toe,

Buchanan saw with his own two eyes Jackson's torso expand heavily as he breathed.

"Oh, thank God! You're alive! You're alive!" Buchanan shouted to Heaven with all the joy in his heart!

Buchanan cried and laughed.

Rockford, Skawinski, and McInally rushed over to inquire of Jackson's status. Marines doubly secured the area, as the patrol established a broader, more expansive perimeter, ensuring a stronger state of security from those in the jungle longing to take the life of marines.

Following an inspection of the second firing line of the VC, Rockford and squad leaders discovered 11 riddled, torn to pieces dead Viet Cong, who had been heavily armed. The second group of ambushers, ages ranging from the late teens to early mid-twenties, comprised a force to conduct nocturnal visits of the Viet Cong upon local hamlets and villages.

Forced recruitment with the threat of death of young men by the Communists angered the Americans, thought of as inhumane. Rockford returned to Jackson to receive a diagnosis from the Navy corpsmen working on him.

As Rockford paced toward Jackson, Buchanan stepped back from Jackson following an emotional and heart filled prayer. Excusing himself, he marched himself to an isolated spot within the perimeter to recompose himself.

As the time struck 1700 hours sharp, the patrol now sat lethargic and weary. The load of energy for the patrol laid barren, still miles away from Camp Love. Realizing his situation, Rockford radioed Camp Love to inform Lucas of his position. The Skipper ordered Bravo Company back to base, canceling the final sweep of mines and booby traps. Completing the assignment will come another day.

Rockford noticed Buchanan breathing deeply some ten feet away, catching him staring straight up into the sky, praying verbally within earshot of Rockford, quoting Psalms 34:7 "The angel of the Lord encamps around those who fear him, and delivers them." He ambled his way over to Buchanan. "Amen to that, chaplain. I like that verse."

"It's Psalms 34:7. One of my favorites."

"I heard. It's a reassuring verse." Rockford consoled Buchanan. "You must have said a potent prayer days ago when we set out on the sweeping patrol."

Buchanan, puzzled and curious, turns toward Rockford. "What? What do you mean, Captain?"

"Well, you were close to Heaven's Door today by a booby trap, survived. Attacked by ambushers, twice, and survived. Shot at by snipers, small arms, and AK-47's, and survived. Came face to face with the Viet Cong today, survived. And last, no casualties, no KIAs. We all survived. "

Buchanan shakes his head, looks up into the sky once again. "Well, you know there's another verse I like to quote - Deuteronomy 31:6. It's, 'Be strong and courageous. Do not be afraid or terrified because of them, for the Lord your God goes with you; he will never leave you nor forsake you.'"

Buchanan shrugs and says, "This war stinks, but I pray every day for God's presence and an end with nothing but a winning finish for our side. I know the Lord's with us."

Rockford smiles, nodding.

Buchanan lightens the mood, smiling, and says, "I just hope my answered prayers continue when we play cards tonight at camp."

"The Lord's gonna humble you tonight, Padre. That's one prayer that's not going to be answered. You're going to lose." Rockford grins.

The patrol rested for an hour. The corpsmen doctored up Jackson's small wounds, followed by the patrol trekking their way back to Camp Love. The men rested in camp eating supper prior to playing cards.

Sought out more than anything else this night from the men came the strong want of a sense of normalcy. The perfect remedy of relief for Buchanan and his friends from the horrendous day experienced would come from a night playing 500 Rummy.

Lady Luck walked into the supply office with Buchanan this night, for he won big. He learned a hard life lesson with his face to face encounter with the enemy. His deadpan expression playing cards fooled everyone this night. His expression confronting the young VC earlier in the day expressed that he had no desire to fight the young man. Likewise, Buchanan figured the VC read him well enough too. The young kid ran away.

Regardless, Buchanan lived a night of playing cards holding or folding on the advice of Jackson in playing hands earlier in the day. From now on, his cautious approach to playing cards resulted in folding and holding only when his gut called for the right opportunity. His poker face fooled everyone this night.

The day ended. And Buchanan ended the day lifting up prayers of thankfulness to the Lord 'who encamps Himself around those who fear Him, who bestows His protection upon them.'

Captain Frost's Problem

March 5, 1969

Days had passed since Buchanan's face to face confrontation with the enemy.

Buchanan slept sporadically. Sick and tired of sleep deprivation.

To fall asleep nightly risked experiencing nightmares including rats, snakes, the Viet Cong, his face to face confrontation with the enemy, and the Devil himself. Dreams entrenched in his mind for a lifetime.

All of Buchanan's thoughts centered on his near miss in the jungle coming to meet his Creator.

The risk of nightmares fizzled away, however, in the early nocturnal hours of camp.

Odds were against him, suffering from a nightmare of his experience. But Buchanan's masterful display of playing cards, standing in the winner's circle for the night, saturated his deepest innermost thoughts.

Buchanan strutted out of Burns' supply office as top card shark of the world, possessing a self-assurance of invincibility in card playing for the duration of his tour. In fact, his total winnings from Rummy will end up in the upper half of players by tour's end.

Regardless of the sudden emotional high from winning the night of cards, the risk of falling asleep with nightmares, however, gained momentum as fear inundated Buchanan's mental state. Burns' selected music for the evening, Oboe Concerto No. 1 in F Major, opus 37 by Franz Kromme, facilitated even more softened thoughts falling to sleep. Written in three movements, the concerto flowed in a virtuosic, rapid speed of notes racing to the Rondo in the final movement.

Buchanan would indeed fall asleep. And yes, he dreamed, not of nightmares, but of Las Vegas. In the dream, he reigned as the number one ranked Rummy player in the world, playing his hand at the tables in Las Vegas. In time, Buchanan won tens of millions of dollars displaying to the world his expert play, donating most of his money to humanitarian endeavors in Vietnam to improve the lives of poor orphans. One of many oddities in the dream set Buchanan at a table surrounded by famous expert poker players encouraging him with every step of success. Added to the expert poker players were his 500 Rummy card playing friends from Tuesday nights cheering him on. He felt on top of the world.

Waking up at 0430 hours in the morning, literally laughing from his dream, Buchanan found nothing but hilarity with his expert card playing.

Overjoyed he fancied life in a playful setting in a dream, Buchanan conceived the dream as hilarious. On the one hand, he positively assured himself Hades will have to freeze over before he would ever gamble hard earned money away in Las Vegas, risking money on luck. On the other hand, he would never expose himself to risky, addictive behavior controlling his life ever again, especially if it hurt his family. Nevertheless, he had fun with the dream, imagining himself a card sharp at Rummy.

Buchanan snoozed for an hour, dreaming once again of dominating with cards, but this time in camp playing Rummy against his marine friends, winning hundreds of dollars.

Waking up at 0530 hours, he showered and shaved to meet Jackson at the chow hall. Following chow, the team would set out for Tung Son Hamlet.

Buchanan scheduled to meet Chaplains Lieutenant Commander Larry Earnest Thompson serving the 7th Marine Regiment, 1st Marine Division and Ensign John Campbell serving the 9th Marine Regiment, 3rd Marine Division at the Tung Son Hamlet to deliver hygiene products, clothes, farming tools, coloring books, and toys to the people in the hamlet. The 7th and 9th Marine Regiments collected, assembled, and donated the goods to the hamlet.

Lieutenant Commander Thompson, an Episcopalian from North Dakota whose family prospered in the grain and barley business, and Ensign Campbell, a native of Breathitt County in Kentucky, a neighboring county of Pike County. Campbell's family had a long history of earning a living as coal miners. As a Presbyterian, he had much in common with Buchanan. His orders for active duty called him to serve as a reservist from his Reserve Center in Lexington, Kentucky. The two chaplains promoted a vehement, rigorous attempt to gain South Vietnamese support to establish a democratic government in the south. Implementing President Johnson's program earlier in the war to cultivate relationships with the Vietnamese ranked high for Thompson and Campbell.

After breakfast, the spiritual team walked briskly to their jeep parked in front of the chaplain's hootch to travel to Tung Son Hamlet to meet the chaplains at 0700 hours. The trip measured three and a half miles away. The spiritual team looked forward to assist the chaplains in delivering supplies and goodies to children in the hamlet.

After the visit to Tung Son Hamlet, the spiritual team hopped back into the jeep and headed for home.

Wednesdays, a day void of scheduled services, ended up an open day for Buchanan. The day reserved itself to visit troops in camp. The middle of the week also reserved itself in visiting Vietnamese refugees living outside Camp Love.

After a mile or two of travel, Jackson said, "The people of Tung Son, well, the Seabees and the marine engineers sure have done a lot of work there, haven't they?"

"Yeah." Buchanan peeked out into the rice fields on his right. "I just hope it won't be for nothing."

Jackson, peeking out of the corner of his eye, turns slightly toward Buchanan and says, "Yeah. I certainly don't want to think of what the Viet Cong and NVA will do to them if we leave and they're overrun by the commies. What a waste it'd be."

Hardly a word came from the both of them for the rest of the trip back home, thinking nothing but the people of Tung Son and their future.

Finally arriving back home, Jackson drove to Buchanan's hootch, parking at the front entrance.

As they briefly sat in the jeep Buchanan asks, "Lunch?"

Jackson shrugged his shoulders, nodding in the affirmative.

"My stomach's growling." added Buchanan, grinning.

Jackson chuckles. "I think your stomach is a bottomless pit, sir."

"I like to eat. I can't help it. Sergeant. Let's go." Buchanan couldn't believe it, but walking to the chow hall stood one delay after another. The spiritual team ran into every Tom, Dick, and Harry with every possible need imaginable to talk about.

The last individual the spiritual team ran into stood Sergeant Skawinski. But he certainly was not just any Tom, Dick, or Harry. Buchanan would die a thousand deaths for his fellow Ohioan and Christian brother in Christ.

Greeting one another, a jovial Skawinski says, "Good day, Padre." Turning toward Jackson, he pointed his thumb towards Buchanan. Grinning, Skawinski asked, "Sergeant, you keeping him out of trouble, are ya?"

"He's a hand full, Ski. Never a rest alongside him." Jackson set his hands on his hips.

"Well, at least it's an adventure." said an exuberant Buchanan.

Buchanan, with eagerness, briefs Skawinski on Tung Son and the benevolent outreach of Chaplains Thompson and Campbell. Skawinski thought the efforts were most noble. His heart centered on Jesus, though his role in combat called for deadly accountabilities and duties as a marine.

As the conversation turned to cultivating An Ngai Tay Hamlet, a marine corporal stepped up briskly. He said, "Chaplain. The brass wants to see ya. In his office, on the double, sir."

Glancing toward Skawinski, the messenger said, "Fancy seeing you here, Farmer. The Skipper wants to see you too."

"For what?" asked Buchanan.

"I just deliver the messages, sir. Got to get back to the office. I already went the long route to grab a piece of fruit from the chow hall. Later!" said the marine, stomping sharply back to his office.

"What'd I do?" asked Buchanan.

"Let's go see, Padre." answered Skawinski.

Buchanan asks Jackson, walking toward Lucas' office, "Where're you going, Sergeant?"

"You don't think I'm going to let you go to the commanding officer's office and stand all alone in there, along with Ski, do ya? Besides, it might be the stick in the mud."

Grinning, Buchanan said, "Yeah. *Yeah*. And if it is indeed the stick in the mud, at least I'd have the two most supportive enlisted personnel by my side to support me."

"110%, sir. We'd march to hell and back for ya, sir." added Skawinski.

Grimacing, Buchanan nods. "Let's go and get this over with."

All the men asked themselves, 'What in tarnation could the problem be?'

Buchanan thought of only one individual – Porch.

The men finally arrive, entering the commanding officer's office with anticipation at 1345 hours.

Immediately, the men notice a sharp confrontation behind Lucas' door, recognizing Porch's voice in all the distorted conversation.

"Good afternoon, Sergeant Vickers." Buchanan nervously acknowledged the sergeant.

"Very well, sir. Go on in." responds Vickers, winking at the visitors.

Buchanan curiously stepped into the office first, followed by Jackson, then Skawinski. And standing square in front of him stood Porch, compressed lips and all. Standing erect as if to elevate himself over all who entered the office, with his hands on his hips.

Every eyeball peered at Buchanan as he entered the office. Porch. Frost. Rockford. Kiehl. Dobbs. Even Gunnery Sergeant Jurgensen eyed straight at him. Standing in front of the bookshelves on Lieutenant Colonel Lucas's left, the Gunny's presence came about from a request of Lucas for Company B's senior non-commissioned officer to attend the meeting with the potential fireworks letting loose in his office. On Jurgensen's right and left, Buchanan spotted Ludwig, Brahms, and Hans, sitting on bookshelves revealing nothing but haughty expressions, staring straight at the human beings who have disrupted their daily routine - sleeping.

Also present stood Lieutenant Nicolas Napier, the duty officer four days earlier. Not only is he a loyal friend of Porch, but is on record as a resilient critic of Chaplain Buchanan's style of ministry. Few human beings revere uppity individuals. And in camp, Napier's reputation amounted to nothing but being a snob. An uppity, smug Virginian who had a family tree of aristocratic ancestry in England. He considered Buchanan nothing but a country bumpkin preacher. Regardless of Buchanan's education, he measured up the chaplain as nothing but an ignoramus who did not deserve to wear a Navy officer's uniform.

"Well, Chaplain." said Lucas abruptly, glancing over to Porch and Napier on his left. "I woke up this morning thanking the Lord for providing another day of life. I really did. I think it might've even been your sermon last Sunday."

"Well, thank you, sir." responded Buchanan, half grinning.

Nervous with the setting in the room, Buchanan felt uncomfortable, feeling out of place.

"Discussing the talking points of the sermon will have to come another day or hour, Padre." Lucas sighed heavily.

"Why am I here, sir?" asked Buchanan.

The considerable pause of silence screamed for an answer, till Porch broke the hush. "There's been a considerable amount of infractions, Lieutenant. Infractions *you* played a role in."

"What? What are you talking about, major?" A clueless Buchanan felt blindsided. Jackson sensed a bit of irritation in Buchanan's Appalachian mountain accent.

Porch spoke up. "Four days ago, there was an unauthorized break-in -"

"Break-in?" interrupted Buchanan, abruptly.

"Yes. *That's* right! A break-in." insisted Porch.

Lucas interjected, "Listen, major. You might bring some poop up against Chaplain Buchanan here, but you don't have to display any sort of short shrift or disrespect to the chaplain. Do I make myself clear, *major*?"

Porch detects a long and glaring stare from Lucas.

Glancing over at Lucas, Porch begrudgingly apologized. "Sorry."

Lucas expressed nothing but disdain for the nosey parker. Porch quickly corrected himself. "Sorry, *sir*."

Smirks spread quickly across the room, sparing Napier and Porch.

Clearing his throat, Porch swallowed hard. Recomposing himself, he said, "As I was saying, four days ago, there occurred an *unauthorized* break-in of the chow hall in which you, Captain Rockford, Lieutenant Frost, Corporal Kiehl, and -"

"OK. OK - Major Porch." interrupted Lucas. "Let me inform the chaplain of the infractions you've written up, *Major*." He leered toward Porch as if he had won the jackass of the year.

Lucas held the write up high, raising it up toward Buchanan with disdain. "Chaplain, Major Porch here has a complaint, serious complaint against you and Captain Frost." Sighing softly, Lucas spoke with contempt in his voice. "The major here has written in his infraction that Captain Rockford, Lieutenant Frost, Corporal Kiehl, Corporal Dobbs, and yourself, along with Sergeant Skawinski there, broke unauthorized into the chow hall, smashed, and that is Major Porch's terminology...." Lucas sighed heavily, "into crates of chow hall food and again his choice of words, stole, food authorized for chow hall personnel to open and administer that food, and only chow hall personnel."

Caught catching flies, the accused stood in utter silence, shocked beyond belief.

The accused shift their heads toward one another, attempting to make sense of the words just read to them. It took every molecule in their bodies to hold themselves back from beating the poop out of Porch.

"What? What? What?" Rockford stood astonished. Pausing, he spoke with a bit of rage in his voice. "What I should do is take you out back and beat the hell out of you! Listen here, Porch!"

"That's *Major* Porch to you, *Captain*!" insisted Porch. "You lay a hand on me and I'll -"

Rockford stepped toward Porch. He stood erect and held his ground to receive Rockford if necessary.

Lieutenant Frost and Jurgensen stepped forward in front of Rockford to restrain him from kicking Porch's ass.

Buchanan, officer and enlisted friends alike, stood shocked at the confrontation. But all wanting Rockford to beat humility into Porch if it came to a fistfight.

Napier stepped back close to the bookshelves, distant from Frost and Jurgensen. But suddenly hopped back away from the bookshelves, sensing a cat paw swing at him with claws expanded to rip a chunk of flesh from Napier's shoulder, hearing the most daunting cat hiss.

Napier looked back over his left shoulder, eying Hans glaring back down at him, his hair standing on end. The confident Siamese possessed the look of a lion ready to devour his prey. Everyone heard Napier utter to Hans, "You dirty little cat. I get my hands on you, I'm gonna to -" Napier stopped in mid-sentence, turning sharply with every eyeball glaring back at him, including the Skipper.

Lucas sneered at Napier. Buchanan could hear him saying softly with a murderous glare, "You'll not touch my cats."

Napier half grins, looking away.

"Can we get back to the present issue at hand?" insisted Porch. "Read the infractions." Porch glanced over at Lucas as if 'he needs to get on with it.' Lucas fumed at Porch's behavior.

Frost calmed Rockford down. The combat platoon officer simmered within, ready, willing, and able to tear Porch apart from sinew to sinew, and muscle to muscle.

"Yes, please do." Napier wanted nothing but to get it over with.

Lucas twisted his head toward Porch and Napier. "Aren't you forgetting something, Major Porch? Lieutenant Napier?" Tilting his head forward inquisitively, Lucas expected a 'sir' at the end of their request of reading the infractions.

Porch tersely turns his head toward Napier, clears his throat and says timidly, "Uh, yes, sir. I mean, read the infractions." Porch clears his throat once again, saying with more of a confident, deeper voice, "*Sir.*"

Lucas sighs heavily, shaking his head despondently.

Buchanan smirks. Lucas signals towards Porch his failing to keep with the simplest of military protocols of referring to your military superior as 'sir' in communicating with superiors.

Taken aback, Porch and Napier shifted their feet a bit, embarrassed Lucas caught them with their pants down, making a mistake, though an innocent mistake, in front of those present.

"We ought to bring charges against *them* for forgetting to say 'sir.'" said an indignant Dobbs.

Porch and Napier shift their heads gruffly towards Dobbs as others chuckle at the suggestion.

Lucas sharply rebukes everyone raising his head sternly with authority, as the chuckling came to a hasty end. Turning to Dobbs, the Skipper tilts his head to the side, curving his lips as if to say, 'Shut up!'

Porch breaks the pause, saying, "Can we finally have the infractions read to these men, *sir*?"

"Of course, *Major*." responded Lucas.

Everyone listened with anticipation the sorts of charges that could be slapped on five disciplined, patriotic, loyal marines and chaplain.

Lucas rattles the charges off one by one. "The charges are as follows: Infractions against Chaplain Buchanan and Lieutenant Frost by Major Porch, United States Marine Corps - Number One, Section 895, Article 95a disrespect to a sentinel or lookout."

Heavy sighs filled the air as men shake their heads in disbelief.

"That's ridiculous! Sheer idiocy!" shouted Buchanan vehemently, injecting his two cents' worth. "I informed Napier I'd talked to Staff Sergeant O'Bryant the next morning. The men just completed a patrol of several days in the bush! They were as hungry as a month old baby. Corporal McClure always lets me in late at night in the wee hours of the morning, or early evening when the chow hall is closed if men get in from the bush and are hungry. They need some chow after a hard and rough patrol."

"I told you not to enter the chow hall, *chaplain*. I told you to notify the cooks, the food service specialist." Napier insisted Buchanan had disobeyed orders. "Oh, I'm so terribly sorry. But, I told you not to enter the chow hall, *chaplain - sir*."

Napier glanced out of the corner of his eye at Lucas.

The Skipper scoffs toward Napier, reading the second and third infraction. "Number Two, Section 909, Article 109, property other than military property of United States – waste, spoilage, or destruction and Number Three, Section 909, Article 109a, mail matter; wrongful taking, opening."

As Lucas recited each charge, the accused jeered, exhaling heavily with the silliness of it all.

Frost bellowed, "That's ridiculous! Again - sheer idiocy!"

Frost defends himself. "McClure opens fresh crates of food for the hard-ridden men from the bush. He's been in the bush in combat situations. He knows how it is!"

Lucas had had enough. "OK. OK. I'm tired of all this. I want to read the rest of the charges. And I want to hash this out once and for all, so we can get back to fighting this war." The Skipper sighs, adding, "So shut up!"

By now, Lucas concluded Porch has been wasting everyone's time over petty charges.

As Lucas read each charge, accusations as Buchanan referred to them, those who were charged sighed heavily, rolling their eyes, shaking their heads in disbelief.

Lucas read the charges once again, "Number Four, Section 917, Article 117, provoking speeches or gestures. Number Five, Section 931, Article 131f, noncompliance with procedural rules. Number Six, -"

Interrupted by Buchanan, he asked, "Really? Is he for real?" He turned to Porch with disdain.

"Chaplain? Please." Lucas said.

"Sorry, sir."

Lucas reluctantly continued with the charges. "Number Six, Section 933, Article 133, conduct unbecoming an officer and a gentleman."

The accused group responded, "Seriously?" "That's pathetic!" "Ridiculous!"

"All of those charges are by the book!" Porch boasted.

"What? They're bogus and you know it!" Rockford responded.

Skawinski finally chimed in, saying, "The chow hall has never denied the chaplain access to food for the men who haven't eaten for days coming out of the bush."

"*Maybe*." Porch said, sighing. "But the chow hall cooks have always been present and have given Chaplain Buchanan or any other officer, including Frost, access to the chow hall *with* permission. The chow hall does not have an open door policy or a free for all, Sergeant Skawinski, and you know it."

Frost said, "When we dragged ourselves into camp after a beat down of a patrol at 0200 hours, we looked for McClure, O'Bryant, other chow hall cooks in camp. We came across no one. We discovered later on the cooks were in O'Bryant's hootch listening to a Lakers game on Armed Services Radio."

"But that's no excuse for *breaking* and *entering*, Lieutenant." Napier asserted.

"What? It wasn't breaking and entering. I have a key in case of a late night." Buchanan said.

Turning to Lucas, Porch quibbled, "Sir, this is not good. Buchanan shouldn't have a key. That's a security breach. There ought to be more charges. Now, this is an infraction of -"

"I've had it! I have had it up to here!" interrupted Lucas with authority, leveling his hand neck high.

"Now Porch, Napier, about these charges." Lucas holds the papers up, listing the infractions in front of them. "These charges will not hold up in court since the chow hall knew Chaplain Buchanan had a key. I'm sure Chaplain Buchanan has a key in order to minister to the men, to provide a means of service distributing food to deserving men from the bush. It's obvious they trust him with a key. Who else in camp would be more trustworthy?"

The accused shook their heads, knowing full well the unwanted meeting neared the end, while the accusers felt a hard slap across the face knowing Lucas spoke the truth. The embarrassed accusers turned to avoid any eye contact with anyone, tongue tied, while the cats hissed toward the departing accusers every step of the way out the office door.

Walking past Lucas' desk, Porch gently grasped the papers from Lucas' hand, nonchalantly dropping them in the trash basket. Buchanan's disgruntled enemies, disappointed by their efforts, failed to nail him and his friends to the wall, sulked their way out of the office.

Lucas falls back hard into his swivel chair, exhaling a heavy sigh. Reaching in his upper right-hand desk drawer, he grabs a cigar, lights it, and delivers a slow, intentional puff.

"Boy, that feels good." Lucas said, following his self gratifying puff of his cigar.

The innocent accused marines and sailors in the office smile.

"You know what, men?" Lucas said.

"No sir. What?" asked an inquisitive Skawinski.

Standing up, Lucas turns deliberately towards Skawinski, staring straight into his eyes, saying, "Ski, Porch and his crowd, they aren't nothing but a snake in the grass!"

Turning to Buchanan with a smirk, Lucas says, "I remember hearing something in the past, goes something like this, 'Better to keep your big mouth shut to let people think of you as a fool, than to open up your big mouth and take away all doubt'".

Nodding, Buchanan smiles.

Sensing the absence of foe, Hans, Ludwig, and Brahms leap from the bookshelves onto the floor, who confidently strut over to Buchanan and his friends. To inform the humans things are OK now, the cats rub up against the human's legs and boots, a feline means of communicating, purring like a well-oiled engine all the while.

The cats glance upward toward Buchanan with sympathy, gloating with pride and sensitivity, that he held his own in yet another bout in the ring with Porch.

"He lost again, chaplain." Lucas concluded.

Smiling once again, Buchanan nods in approval.

But within himself, Buchanan felt for Porch. He felt sorrow for Porch's antagonistic friends as well, who held deep animosity and malice in their hearts for those who opposed them in life. Enemies come and go in life for all human beings. And Buchanan dealt with them piecemeal as obstacles placed in the way by the Evil One as a barrier to carry out ministry, even if that obstacle claimed to be a believer.

Frost's problem ended up solved with courage and an unwillingness to consent to Porch's ridiculous pursuit of pinning Buchanan to the wall due to his displeasure with Buchanan's ministry style.

Again, Porch attempted to win a battle. And again, failed with his efforts.

Buchanan continued to minister regardless, exerting every ounce of energy to comfort and tend to the men, even to provide food in the wee hours of the night.

One thing was for sure, Buchanan prepared for plenty of sleep tonight.

Surviving another bout with Porch inspired him for a good night's sleep of triumphant dreams.

A Sheep in Wolves Clothing!

March 17, 1969

Matthew 7:15-20 Beware of false prophets, who come to you in sheep's clothing but inwardly are ravenous wolves. You will know them by their fruits. Are grapes gathered from thorns, or figs from thistles? So, every sound tree bears good fruit, but the bad tree bears evil fruit. A sound tree cannot bear evil fruit, nor can a bad tree bear good fruit. Every tree that does not bear good fruit is cut down and thrown into the fire. Thus you will know them by their fruits.

With unswerving work comes great reward. With hard work comes success.

The 7th Engineering Marine Battalion in March worked rigorously, fulfilling work orders with great reward and great success.

Buchanan never ceased with amazement at the dedication and commitment of the marines in Camp Love. 'Semper Fidelis' showed through in every officer and enlisted personnel in camp, from top to bottom in rank. First and foremost, the motto motivated every marine in camp to complete the responsibilities and duties of his own individual MOS. Buchanan witnessed no greater work ethic than these marines in Camp Love during the war.

Every good tree bears good fruit. And Camp Love bore great work.

Buchanan witnessed a dedicated work ethic in March as Company A upgraded Route 545 and 30 for 50 class traffic and Route 540 for maintenance at coordinates AT 899774 to AT 912743. Route 542, Route 544, and Route 10 called for repairs due to the wear and tear of road travel and the devastating effects of war. Alpha Company also provided a platoon of reinforcement assigned to Hai Van Pass responsible for conducting daily sweeps of Route QL-1 at coordinates AT 927842 to AT 886954. And as usual, Company A completed daily sweeps of Route 545. As Company A fulfilled its duty at Hai Van Pass, Buchanan ventured out with Jackson to conduct Communion Services for the men.

Buchanan looked forward to accompanying Bravo Company on patrol most. He cultivated a close relationship with them. He became most comfortable with the vast assortment of personalities in the combat fighting force. In March, Company B improved Route QL-1S for 5 class traffic. The responsibility of maintaining and upgrading Route 4, essential to military transportation and communications, at coordinates AT 056589 to AT 968584 fell at the feet of Bravo. Access to Route 4 in March was inoperable because of tactical situations, but an ARVN Engineer Unit assisted and provided a two lane road between coordinates AT 958584 to AT 984584. Buchanan accompanied many of the daily sweeps of Route QL-1 between coordinates AT 999707 to AT 090555 to provide a presence of spiritual guidance.

Company C, led by Lieutenant Frost, had been busy as a beaver in March enhancing Route 540 from coordinates AT 912743 to AT 926607. The spiritual team ministered much to Frost and 2nd Platoon of Charlie Company at An Hoa. The platoon worked at An Hoa till March 16, responsible for engineer support of a Combat Base being built. Lieutenant Commander Adkins' Seabee unit assisted in the construction of the base. Frost requested Buchanan to accompany the platoon for spiritual support. Company C also conducted daily sweeps between coordinates AT 949707 and AT 926607. In March,

Charlie Company carried out thoroughly everything on their plate, beaming with pride completing their responsibilities.

Buchanan lifted up to God extra special prayers for Delta Company in March with the monstrous duties assigned to the company. D Company's orders assigned were to upgrade Route 540 between coordinates AT 926607 to AT 874460 for 50 class traffic and conducting daily sweeps between coordinates AT 926607 and AT 925533. Delta Company found itself responsible for Route 4 maintenance at AT 968584 west of South Vietnam. Parts of Route 4 east near Hill 37 and west of Hill 65 ended up as unapproachable due to the tactical situations in the area. The numbers of Viet Cong in the area overwhelmed the vicinity of Route 4, creating a most dangerous situation. In the past few months, Buchanan accompanied marines in the vicinity and felt compelled to walk as if treading on Lake Erie's thin ice in the dead of winter. Delta Company's nerves worked on edge as it tiptoed through the Tulips to avoid booby traps in a heavily occupied and dangerous area populated with a profound Viet Cong presence. When a company or platoon ventured far from camp, Buchanan felt impelled to pray more for a safe return home.

At 0630 hours, the spiritual team returned to camp in the early hours of March 17th with Frost and 2nd Platoon of Charlie Company, along with marine engineers, Adkins, and the Seabees from An Hoa. The team had accompanied the large party for five days, cultivating relationships along the way. The team's spiritual presence extended a therapeutic hand in harm's way.

Buchanan arrived in camp in a state of dormancy as slumbering as Rip Van Winkle, while Jackson looked dead on one's feet, pooped from the long hours of ministry in the bush. First and foremost on the spiritual team's mind comprised of sleep.

Following a stout breakfast, the two rewarded themselves to a good, long rest after days of ministry in the bush with little sleep.

Upon stepping into his hootch with his gear, Buchanan immediately caught in the corner of his eye the newly requisitioned candy for the Vietnamese children destroyed by malicious, filthy rats!

Fury filled Buchanan from head to toe!

"Lord, why did you create these ugly, horrid pests!?!" Buchanan yelled. He yammered on, "I hate those hairy, disgusting, flea-ridden hideous heels!"

Throwing a canteen through the air, he hit the corner of his wall shelf, spilling out his hygiene and shaving gear.

The little demons chewed through a soft spot in the wood attached to the door.

With showering and a change of uniform, Buchanan thought twice about going straight to sleep. His thoughts were preoccupied with the candy. 'Where is he going to locate more candy?' 'Who in camp would have stored any of the treats?' He ventured out into camp to acquire whatever chocolate and candy he could locate. The search came at a minute's notice, but Buchanan will permit nothing to come in the way of providing candy to the precious children the spiritual team loved and cared for.

After an hour of searching for a quick fix, Buchanan discovered no luck in finding any candy or chocolate. Frustration set in.

The ordeal with the candy reminded Buchanan a fact he gained over time in Vietnam - he hated rats. Along with the rodents, his hatred for insects flowed within his blood veins from head to toe. The destruction of nature and man made alike which followed the insects everywhere they crawled became a nuisance to the westerners. From time to time, Buchanan became incensed when the insects would destroy candy. But deep down within himself, he seemed to hate the rats more, and with a passion. Buchanan loathed both pests, exerting with all his might to combat these creatures with all the intensity he could possibly muster.

With Lady Luck shining on somebody else today, Buchanan failed finding any candy in camp. He opted to retire to his hootch. He briefly rested to accompany a scheduled patrol, including Skawinski's combat engineering team, to An Ngai Tay for a one day sweep to search mines and booby traps.

Buchanan fretted about making a trip to An Ngai Tay short of candy for the children.

While with Frost in the bush, the candy arrived in the mailroom. The mail clerk delivered the candy in Buchanan's hootch and simply laid the candy down on his desk. Usually, he or Jackson secured the candy, locking it up in an air-tight compartment.

The days spent in the bush with Company C resulted in success ministering to the men. Buchanan felt accomplished and fulfilled as a chaplain. Charlie Company fell conditioned in need of counseling and consoling as the company grieved too many casualties in February. A few of the men killed were popular members of Company C.

Time spent with Company C equaled the all the gold in the world. Buchanan gained a stronger spiritual bond with the company. He brushed aside the temptation of permitting a minute point as trivial as candy to ruin a string of great days of ministry for the spiritual team.

Sitting in his swivel chair, Buchanan stared out his window toward the wide open fields of Camp Love's perimeter. He thought of a resolve for his candy problem.

As Buchanan continued to brainstorm for solutions to his problem, he rotated his swivel chair in the opposite direction, facing the pictures of his family on his desk. Grasping the last family picture taken prior to his departure for Vietnam, he thought of his children. Robert and Dorothy insisted the family sit for one last photo in case the unfortunate happened, entering Heaven eternally with the Lord.

As Buchanan deliberately and leisurely gazed at each and every one of his children, a special memory of each child popped up in his mind.

Thinking of his children, Buchanan wondered what each child might be doing tonight. In the park? Visiting his brother in Anaheim with their mother, Dorothy? Or at home playing with recent toys from Christmas?

He missed his children. Time spent as nurturer and protector of his children is what he missed most. Today, he would give up anything to be with them.

After months spent in southeastern Asia, he witnessed firsthand the children in South Vietnam who lacked all the perks American children are fortunate to be born with.

The excitement, joy, and bright smiles upon the faces of children when given the candy, Buchanan will never forget. Some children never experienced the pleasure of chocolate sweets in their lives until westerners entered their lives.

The goodies offered a small pleasure given to the children from a Navy chaplain, and nothing, including the Devil himself, would prevent him from making available the chocolate and candy to children less fortunate.

The longer Buchanan sat in his chair, the further determined he was to find some candy.

Tersely rising out of his swivel chair to march himself over to Lucas' office for some help, he practically runs into Skawinski, Corporal Jones, and Jackson, who suddenly rushed into his hootch. Panting, the men's laughter came naturally, holding onto each other's shoulder out of camaraderie. In a hurry to inform Buchanan of some sort of news, the men rumbled inaudible words, throwing towards Buchanan audible disconnected phrases which he identified single, isolated words such as 'Porch', 'candy', and 'unbelievable'.

"What in tarnation are you all babbling about?" roared Buchanan in his country accent.

"Listen here, sir. Listen. You're not going to believe it." Jones said.

Buchanan, taken aback at the abrupt entrance, hastened a swift inquiry, "What? Please!" Grinning, Buchanan paused and sharply said, "Enlighten me!"

"Sit down, sir. You need to have a seat when you hear this sir." Jackson said.

Buchanan ambled his way back into his swivel chair, leaned back, and curiously asked, "What? What is it?"

Jackson placed his hands on Buchanan's desk, leaned over leisurely, fixating his eyes on Buchanan with the widest grin he ever saw on his enlisted friend's face.

With a bit of anticipation, Jackson slowly says, "Promise me you'll hold on to your seat once you get the news, sir."

Buchanan shifts a look toward Skawinski, and says with buff, "Ski. Will ya please spill the beans?"

"No, sir." Skawinski stood firm in his silence. "Jackson should tell ya."

Turning to Jackson, Buchanan shoves his hands in front of him, lifting his eyelids asking for an answer.

Jackson finally says, "OK. Here she goes, sir. I myself found it unbelievable, but we saw it with our own two eyes. So, here she goes."

By now in his tour, Buchanan knew the scuttlebutt in camp passed as noteworthy beyond measure.

"Sir, your candy will be here tomorrow. That's right, sir." Jackson said, informing Buchanan of the news with glee.

"Really? Wow! It-It's, well - like a miracle." Buchanan said, with astonishment on his face.

"Sir, it is a miracle! I was working the receiving, you know, and I saw it." Jones said with his thick mountain drawl.

Buchanan, with interest, asked slowly, "Who requisitioned it?"

Pausing, Jackson informed Buchanan. "Well, sir, someone requisitioned candy for replenishment, not even knowing what was going to happen to the candy while we were with Lieutenant Frost." The sergeant finally revealed the marine with some anticipation, "Well, sir, it was…well, it was the one and only Major…Michael...Porch. Yep, there ya go. That's who it was. Can ya believe it?" Jackson, wide-eyed, threw his hands up in front of Buchanan out of total surprise.

Buchanan, catching flies, displayed nothing but shock. He appeared baffled beyond measure.

Attempting a reply, Buchanan said, "What? What Porch?" He paused, asking, "What? What for? I mean…I can't believe it! I just can't believe he replaced the candy. I guess we have a sheep in wolf's clothing, huh?"

Skawinski cut in, saying, "Sir, he's the one who replaced the candy the last time. Yes, twice." Lifting his index and middle fingers up to stress the point he smiled, expressing all the joy in his heart.

"There's something else too, sir." added Jackson.

"Yes, sir. Wait till you hear this." Jones said with a bit of anticipation in his voice. "He's responsible for the chairs in the hall."

"That's right, sir." added Skawinski with enthusiasm. "The chairs and, listen to this, the clothes for the children back in December? Christmas time? His retail distribution company his family owns, they sent all the clothes."

Buchanan's jaw froze, catching flies by now wide-eyed.

Confused, Skawinski asked, "Chaplain Buchanan? How can this be, though? He's such an ass in public. Am I missing something here?"

Jackson said out of curiosity, "*Yeah*, sir. He doesn't fit the mold. Does he?" Jackson presses his right index finger onto his left and says, "Replenishes the candy twice." He then presses his middle finger and says, "Supplies most of the clothes for the children." Then presses his ring finger, and says, "And last, sets the chairs in order in the conference hall for Sunday services." He pauses. "I'm with Ski, sir. He's constantly barking out, 'regulations this, regulations that'. I don't get it either, sir."

Skawinski asked with hesitation, "Sir, is he feigning his spitefulness?" He, Jones, and Jackson all lean backwards into chairs expecting an answer from their chaplain. Buchanan sat perplexed, pondering the peculiar behavior of Porch, across from three bewildered marines waiting for an answer.

Buchanan contemplated long and hard for an answer to Skawinski's thoughtful question, a difficult question to answer indeed.

Buchanan leisurely turned 90 degrees in his swivel chair to a direct view out of his hootch window into the dangerous bush, dangers unknown to those who dare to enter the devil's lair.

Agonizing through the long pause, Skawinski finally asks, "Sir?"

Befuddled, Buchanan said, "I don't know."

Dazed with Buchanan's answer, the men wanted a more definite answer for Porch's conduct.

Buchanan said, "I'm but 37 years old. I've some experience and I've known quite a few people in my day. But I really don't have an answer."

"Then what does it all mean, sir?" asked Corporal Jones.

He rose out of his chair, walking out in front of the men, and leaned back onto the desk to face the three marines, by now leaning forward for an answer.

Buchanan said, "Well, corporal. In life, many people behave for many reasons. Motives on personal grounds. I've known some men who cover up their true self or their real persona not out of shame, but – well, maybe due to what others expect of 'em."

The marines lean backwards, pondering for an answer for Porch's demeanor.

Buchanan said, "Porch just might portray this tough guy role to avoid the perception of being the softy type. I've been here long enough to know that being thought of as soft will not get a marine very far. I know a thing or two of Porch. Facets you don't know about."

"Like what, sir?" asked Skawinski.

Jackson quickly said, "I know one thing."

"Oh, *yeah*? What's that Sergeant?" asked Buchanan.

"Well, sir. He won two Silver Star and one Combat Service Medals in Korea. He also won the Distinguished Combat Award." Jackson said.

Surprised, Buchanan asked, "Who'd you hear that scuttlebutt from?"

"Word gets around, sir. And it's not scuttlebutt, it's the truth." asserted Jackson with a smile.

"Well, listen. How many people know of this requisition being paid for by Porch?" asked Buchanan.

Rising out of their chairs, Skawinski answered, "Just us, sir."

"Well, let's keep this to ourselves, shall we? If this got out, Porch paying for the candy, the chairs, the clothes for the children, he'd be the laughingstock in camp. I just can't let that happen."

"The way he's treated you, sir? And you're going to protect him?" asked Jones.

"Yes, corporal, I am." said a submissive Buchanan.

With a stern glance to each marine, Buchanan knew each man to be a believer in Christ. He instructed the men, "The Lord commanded us to pray and love our enemies. He knows and I know that's how you're going to win them over to your side."

Buchanan nods, saying, "And as much as I hate saying it and knowing it, Porch has made himself an enemy." He implored, "But his billet is in Camp Love and I've made a commitment to minister to *all* personnel in the camp, and that includes that, as much as it hurts me to say it, that, well, at least on the outside - pompous ass."

Buchanan sternly stared into his enlisted friends' eyes. "Y'all are going to have to promise me none of ya will spill the beans of this little tidbit of information we've learned of Porch to the rest of the camp, won't ya?"

"Sir -" uttered Jackson.

"Promise me." declared Buchanan.

Smiling, the men reluctantly concede to Chaplain Buchanan's request. Hesitantly, the men promise, "Yes - sir. We...we promise."

Laughing, the men reassure Buchanan. "OK, OK, sir....we promise."

Smirking, Buchanan says, "I'm going to hold you to that promise."

Buchanan slowly makes his way back to his swivel chair, reaching for his Bible in the lower right-hand desk drawer. "Listen to these words, men. I was thinking of these scriptures as we were talking."

Turning to Luke 12:2, he reads, "Nothing is covered up that will not be revealed, or hidden that will not be known."

He next turns to Proverbs. "And then there's Proverbs 3:5 and 6, 'Trust in the Lord with all your heart, and do not rely on your own insight. In all your ways acknowledge him, and he will make straight your paths.'"

Buchanan then turns to Romans and said, "Listen to this last passage men. It's the clincher, Romans 12, verse 16, 'Live in harmony with one another; do not be haughty, but associate with the lowly; never be conceited.'"

Looking up, grinning, Buchanan said, "He'll come around. Deep down inside, he's a believer. I know it." Leaning back in his chair, he says softly, "The Lord will humble him. We'll leave it in His hands."

The men continue to hammer out an answer for Porch's facade and his little secret.

When the men laid their eyes on Porch in the days ahead, nothing else but Porch's little secret gathered their thoughts. They thought of his life as a sheep in wolf's clothing.

For days on end, the rat - Porch, intended for those he came in contact with to think of him as a rat, comparable to the rats who devour candy. But for the four men in the chaplain's hootch on March 17, 1969, the perception of Porch as a rat no longer existed in their minds.

The men will forever remember him as the sheep in wolf's clothing.

The Death of a Hero

March 19, 1969

"You guys are the Marine's doctors - there's none better in the business than a Navy Corpsman..."

Lieutenant General "Chesty" Puller*

Waking up at 0530 hours, Buchanan immediately thought of last night's well deserved rest of solid sleep as a blessing which flowed over with pleasant and agreeable dreams.

His first of many dreams included camping in the mountains of his beloved blue grass state on a cool March weekend before Easter Sunday. He then dreamed of Niagara Falls, a site he and his wife loved to visit.

The music Burns selected last night hit the spot, Vivaldi's Winter. Several days ago, Buchanan discussed with Burns in the chow hall how satisfying to the soul it felt to sit in the middle of a winter storm instead of this persistent, intolerable heat of Vietnam.

The weather in Ohio and West Virginia in March is the perfect month of the year for those who prefer a four season weather pattern which includes the winter. The end of March fiercely fights the forthcoming spring, dropping an occasional early spring snow from time to time.

Unfortunately, the pleasant morning ended on a sour note.

Buchanan's schedule slotted him for a meeting in Lucas' office. The scheduled visit concerned a marine written up by Captain John

Thomas Massena, a devout friend of Porch, for insubordination and dereliction of duty. Serious charges.

The marine, a rifleman from Delta Company, requested Chaplain Buchanan's presence as he counseled the young man from time to time. He immensely trusted Buchanan, who opened up to him with quite a few personal problems.

Buchanan ranked the attendance in disciplinary captain's mast on the bottom half of his listed duties he handled. He did not look forward to attending such a tense environment in a room. Maybe the apprehension emerged because of facing commanding officers in his own right, busted twice down to E-3 and E-1. The demotions pulled his strips off, knocking him down after advancing to E-5 and E-6. Busted down in rank due to his drinking problems.

Following captain's mast, Buchanan loathed a hundred fold the next duty scheduled for the day - to identify remains in the 'cooler' at 0900 hours. But again, Buchanan acknowledged in his heart loved one's back in the states who wanted nothing more but for their husband, father, or brother's remains to be cared for with respect and tender loving care, regardless of the hideous circumstances of the war.

The day would end on more pleasing terms. The spiritual team scheduled a visit to the new South Vietnamese in the refugee village outside Camp Love. The Viet Cong intimidated many of them. Refugees pushed out of their own villages by the VC.

To impede the inevitable day Buchanan faced, he readied himself with a shower and shave, thinking of his meaningful dreams the previous night above all else in his mind. He hated the cooler, for it depressed him, welcoming anything to take his mind off the cooler.

Regardless, he donned his fatigue uniform, retrieved his notebook to take notes, and made his way over to the chow hall.

Full of a hearty breakfast, he visited the men in the chow hall, making his way to Lieutenant Colonel Lucas' office for the meeting. The provoking presence of Porch in the office with his friend Massena, bringing the charges against the young marine, came close to ruining Buchanan's great start of the day.

The insubordination charge stuck, but the dereliction of duty charge fell off the wall as fast as a dry leaf. The marine's punishment confined him to laundry and sanitation duties. Porch and Massena thought Lucas a softy.

Following Porch and Massena's defiant march out of his office, Lucas said to Buchanan with a smile, "Oh well."

Buchanan grins.

Time stood at 0810 hours. Just 50 more minutes until dreaded cooler duty.

To delay the unavoidable even longer, he visited Jackson's hootch, who now shared a hootch with two members of Delta Company and a Navy Yeoman billeted in supply. Actually, Buchanan dropped by to ask Jackson if he would tag along to identify KIAs in the cooler with him.

Jackson had opened up a Napoleonic history book, thoroughly enjoying the content. Earlier in the

morning, he had read his daily devotion and Bible reading.

"Hello, anyone down there?" asked an inquisitive Buchanan.

"Sir? Chaplain Buchanan?" answered Jackson.

"Yes."

"Well, just don't stand outside, sir. Come on down." insisted Jackson.

Buchanan stepped down into Jackson's hootch. "Good morning, Philip."

"Good morning, sir."

"Where's your roomies?"

"On patrol."

"Oh, OK. Well, I thought I'd come over and, well, visit."

"*Visit*? We visit and fellowship all the time, sir."

Jackson tilts his head ever so slightly for an answer from Buchanan's.

Buchanan finally let the truth out of the bag, his actual intention to visit Jackson. "Well, I just thought I would come visit, well, come visit before I have to go-go -well, to – OK, I'll just come out and tell ya - I'm scheduled to unfortunately identify KIA's in the cooler."

Jackson smirks, now hearing the truth from the horse's mouth.

"Uh-huh. *I* see. You want me to go with ya?"

"Well Sergeant." asserted Buchanan, "Ya know how I *hate*. And I mean *haaate*, cooler duty. I know that's part of my sworn duties – but I *despiiiise* going in there."

"Ya think *I* enjoy going in there, sir?" replied Jackson with exasperation.

"Come on, Philip." Buchanan entreated.

"I'm reading a book on Napoleonic tactics. Your favorite period of military history. You want me to interrupt myself taught education right here and now in the middle of my reading." said Jackson with a self-assured smile.

"Listen, Philip. I'll make a deal with the Scrounger for the combat knives, the extra .45, and the green t-shirts ya want. You know he can get'em. Supply has rejected your requests since October. I promise I'll get'em for you."

"Well."

"Please, Sergeant." pleaded Buchanan, looking down at his watch. "Ya got plenty of time to get ready. It's still just 0845 hours. Come on."

Buchanan tilts his head in anticipation of a 'yes'.

Grimacing, Jackson raised his hand up toward Buchanan, with his fingers pointing at him. "You owe me, sir. I want to see those combat knives within five days."

Buchanan smiled from ear to ear. "Great. Thanks, Philip."

"Ummm." Jackson uttered. He dressed and the spiritual team ambled over to the cooler as Jackson relentlessly reminded Buchanan of the combat knives. He cadged up to the Scrounger.

The spiritual team arrived at the cooler exactly at 0858 hours, waiting up till the last minute.

Doc Delaney welcomed the spiritual team, along with the duty officer, a corpsman, 1st Class Petty Officer Ernest Jackson, and an administrative clerk to complete the distasteful work.

Jackson leaned toward Buchanan, quietly saying, "Well, here she goes."

The identification team entered the cooler, aghast at the sight of the remains, the most appalling corpses Buchanan had seen in his tour. The significant number of corpses resulted from a Viet Cong ambush in and around Route 540.

Sickened at the sight, Buchanan gawked at the mangled remains of human beings torn to pieces. The deceased entangled all together as if holding onto each other, as if they were comforting and consoling one another's heart and soul. The lifeless, motionless young men were mere boys who had just days ago been full of life and energy.

The first boy identified resembled a 15-year-old to Buchanan. His dog tags acknowledged a native from Fort Lauderdale, Florida. The name on the dog tags spelled Eugene Bethel Upchurch, 18 years of age. The enormous hole in his belly appalled Buchanan. Jackson explained later in the day Upchurch's wounds showed his death resulted from a mine explosion or a highly explosive booby trap. Following Doc Delaney inspecting the body, which included listening for a heartbeat, the men placed the remains in a body bag, placing his dog tags in an envelope inside the bag.

The second young man looked just as 15 years old to Buchanan, a 21-year-old from Philadelphia, Pennsylvania. Doc Delaney read out loud the pressed letters on his mental dog tags - 'Michael Nicholas Loudermilk.' His torso and limps received hundreds of small puncture wounds in an upward direction towards his head. Doc explained that more than likely he stepped on a booby trap which instantly killed him. Doc yet again examined the remains and listened for a heartbeat, hearing nothing, and again the men placed him, like Upchurch, into a body bag along with his dog tags inside an envelope.

Two bodies ID'ed. And two bodies too many for Buchanan. He hated the cooler.

Buchanan desired for nothing but to head back to his hootch and read a western. Or maybe a history book, skipping the cooler duty altogether. But again, he thought of the young boy's loved ones back home. Their loved ones would want their son or husband or brother treated with respect and decency, and that thought kept him motivated.

The team ID'ed six more bodies, not that Buchanan tallied the KIAs as the work party fulfilled their duty. He just wanted it to be over and done with.

Doc Delaney examined the next corpse with a bit of intrigue, as Buchanan stooped down along with Doc to inspect the remains, who mutually considered the remains curious. "*Ummm,* interesting." Doc said. He removed the dog tags, reading the name, "Alexander Petya Volkov, from New York, New York. What do you know? A Russian-American from New York City."

The doctor grins, looking up in the direction of the identification team. He comments with a bit of sarcasm, "Russian descent and coming to fight the Commies. What irony, huh? Like my mother's family, who's German. Her family fought against the Nazis during World War II."

Delaney chuckles, looking back down toward Volkov.

The identification team stared at Delaney as if he had lost his mind. They asked themselves questions - 'What's happened to Delaney?' 'Has he lost all compassion and understanding as a human being?' 'Has this war sucked all the empathy out of him because of the day-to-day exposure to a never-ending cycle of human beings dying and the horrific, inhumane atrocities committed against the innocents?' The identification team sensed he grew apathetic toward the horrors of war and death. As if he carried out his cooler duty as routine. Even so, he glances back up to Buchanan with sorrow on his face, sighs heavily, saying, "What a pity."

Taking another look at Volkov, he noticed his probable age. "Wow. He's too young, a kid in his early twenties."

Delaney pointed at Volkov's injuries. "Look here at these wounds."

The men crouched down to view the damage inflicted on his body.

"Volkov's wounds sure are -" Delaney stops abruptly. Every man, including Delaney, suddenly lunged backwards out of sheer fright, descending rearward into deceased marines.

Volkov's limps twitched in every direction, as his torso jerked ever so slightly.

The identification team fell all over each other, tripping over and on top of the dead remains.

Marines and sailors outside the cooler heard simultaneously the most terrifying yells inside the preserver of dead flesh - "Ahhhh!" "Uhhhh!" "No!" "I'm on top of him!" "Help me off of him!"

The identification team, frightened to death, attempted to get control of themselves.

Volkov quivered every which way, screaming in his silence, "I'm alive! Help me!"

Scrambling to stand on their own two feet, the men slipped and veered, skidding on the floor due to the fluid and blood from the deceased.

The first of the identification team to recompose themselves back to reality were Delaney and Petty Officer Jackson. Doc pulled himself back towards Volkov to survey him, along with Petty Officer Jackson looking over his shoulder.

The remaining identification team steadily gained composure of themselves, gathering around Delaney and Volkov.

Delaney swiftly listened for a heartbeat with his stethoscope, as the men detected an unhurried expression of shock on the doctor's face.

Delaney turned harshly toward the identification team and yelled, "This man's alive!"

"Hallelujah." proclaimed Sergeant Jackson.

"This man has a heartbeat! This man has a heartbeat! Get a stretcher! Get a stretcher! Move! Move!" bellowed Delaney.

Petty Officer Jackson stepped briskly to the door, shouting, "Stretcher to the cooler!"

Within seconds, three corpsmen came running from the aid station with a stretcher.

The three corpsmen and a marine ran into the cooler, placing Volkov on the stretcher. Turning, they made their way with haste back up to the aid station.

Delaney and 1st Class Petty Officer Jackson followed suit.

Unfortunately for Buchanan, an unwanted delay push backed the completion of cooler duty until 1840 hours. Regulations required a doctor present when identifying the killed in action. Delaney was the single doctor available for miles. All the while, Buchanan praised the Lord Volkov still breathed among the living.

The delay in identifying the dead came as Delaney worked on Volkov. Doc kept him alive. Six hours

later, a helicopter came and picked Volkov up, transferring him to the Da Nang hospital.

Without further ado, Delaney rushed to the cooler. And for the ID work party, the sight of Doc stepping briskly toward the cooler thrilled each and every heart of the contingent. The men breathed a sigh of relief. They can finally complete the identification of the KIAs hours later.

Hurt, pain, and depression overwhelmed the men. Buchanan endured a whole day, instilled with nothing but total gloom and hopelessness.

The abundant numbers of deceased to identify came to a screeching halt at 2110 hours. The six men assigned to the cooler remembered the day for the rest of their lives.

Two weeks later, reports reached the camp Volkov survived and four months later sent to Japan for further recovery of his wounds, three bullet holes and a dozen shrapnel wounds scattered all over his body.

When the long awaited completion of cooler duty finally arrived, Doc Delaney and Petty Officer Jackson took advantage of Buchanan's open door policy, spending the remaining part of the evening with the chaplain to relax, visit, and talk of anything but the war. Sergeant Jackson's presence lightened the mood further.

Unfortunately, the enjoyment of one another's company came to a screeching halt.

At 2345 hours, a corporal from Delta Company, filthy from head to toe, knocked on Buchanan's hootch door.

"Doc Delaney. Sir? Are you in there? Sir?" asked the corporal.

"Yes, marine." answered Delaney.

"Sir, Lieutenant Kephart needs to speak to ya. He's on his way."

Just as the corporal finished speaking, Lieutenant Kephart of Delta Company approached Buchanan's hootch.

Delaney urgently opened the door and asked, "What is it, corporal?"

The spiritual team stood patiently to hear what news the Lieutenant might have, anticipating bad news.

Sure enough, Kephart reached the group. Stammering, Kephart said, "Doc. I'm sorry. I'm really very sorry...Crowley. Well - Crowley. H-He's - I don't know how else to tell you, sir. He's - Well, he's gone. He's dead."

As still as death, Delaney and 1st Class Petty Officer Jackson stood tongue tied.

Kephart stood describing an account of what happened to Crowley and Delta Company confronting the enemy in a fierce fight. He explained Company D had been accompanying a combat engineering team in An Hoa, 11th Marines, Battery D to search for enemy booby traps and mines. Delta Company's patrol in the battery came under attack by a battalion of Viet Cong and NVA regulars who overran much of the battery. The marines engaged the enemy in ferocious hand to hand combat. In the initial attack, the marines manned the artillery and howitzers, firing back, then forced to face the enemy who had infiltrated the camp from many breeches within the barbed-wire perimeter. Kephart explained the marines, fighting hand to hand, endured many casualties. Crowley jumped from one parapet to another, treating wounds and administering emergency care to the severely wounded under hostile attack.

Delaney and his friends listened intently to Kephart, glued to every word spoken out of his mouth. In minute detail, Kephart described Crowley entering the third parapet, immediately spotting three marines wounded, one severely, which Crowley administered medical aid to. Three NVA jumped dead center in the parapet as Crowley turned without delay, placing himself between the wounded marines, fighting and killing all three of them. Now wounded himself from serious knife wounds, he finished administering the medical attention to the three marines in the parapet. Hopping into the adjacent parapet, he found two more wounded marines. He stopped the bleeding and bandaged the marine's wounds, though he suffered himself. He again made his way to the next parapet housing a howitzer. Again, three NVA leaped into the parapet and attacked the Americans inside. He again killed all three of the enemy. Kephart explained that by now, Crowley carried himself thoroughly exhausted from his own wounds, but the corpsman didn't possess one ounce of quitting in his DNA. The corpsman's dauntlessness instinct again detected more wounded in another howitzer parapet, running to the wounded marines. As he collapsed, running down into the parapet, his refusal of medical treatment until all the marines received medical attention exposed the sacrificial commitment of Navy Corpsmen. Leaping up, he took dead aim and emptied his weapon onto the enemy, running straight toward the parapet. All eyes caught the tossing of a grenade thrown into the redoubt, as Crowley jumped onto a wounded marine, saving his life. An agonizing "AHHHHH" came from depths of Crowley's inner being. Fragments of the grenade laid into the backside of Crowley's arms, legs, and torso. The severe ripping of his flesh from grenade fragments proved too much for him - he died an hour later.

Delaney and PO1 Jackson were by now emotionally distraught. Initially, denial set in, then a regrettable recognition of the truth Crowley will never set a foot into Camp Love ever again.

Today, a single fact of war soaked in for Buchanan. He witnessed Delaney save Volkov's life. And next, he heard the testimony from a teary-eyed marine officer about the account of war taking one of his most beloved corpsmen in the battalion. Doc's day did not set well. He turned from a sad state to one of bitter anger.

Kephart added, "Doc. I know that this will not bring him back, but we're putting in a Medal of Honor for his dauntless, courageous, brave, and sacrificing self. I know he's not coming back, but he showed the finest tradition of United States Navy Service."

Shocked, Kephart and Delaney turned and walked away, by now weeping, straining to hide the unraveling taking place within themselves.

The spiritual team paced themselves a respectful distance from Doc and Kephart, weeping along with them.

When the men reach the conference hall, they step up the stairs with a bit of melancholy into the hall, collapse into chairs and literally cry themselves dry. Even Burns' selection of Beethoven's 5th symphony failed to shatter the sudden grim spirit.

Exhausted, the men return to their personal hootches and attempt to gain some shut eye.

When awoken, the realization of Crowley's death hit them like a punch below the belt, as Doc once again wept. Shattered from the devastating news, Doc again falls asleep for another two hours.

The camp faced a new day, swift and quick.

War took the life of another hero, trying the emotions of marines and sailors. Buchanan prayed a simple prayer for the new day, no hero deaths.

Swimming With the Leeches

April 5, 1969

Psalms 48:14 That this is God, our God for ever and ever. He will be our guide even unto death.

Swimming in a tributary of the Tvy Loan River seemed as refreshing, cool, and invigorating as a tributary in the mountains of West Virginia.

Temperatures climbed to 100 plus degrees in the hottest parts of the day in Vietnam. The coolness of water onto the surface of scorched skin soothed the seething heat delivered from the sun, sending the coolest of sensations into pores of marines' skin.

With the good that comes in life, bad soon follows.

A cool swim in a tributary comes the relief from the scorching heat. But with the comforting coolness of a swim comes the horrid reality of Mother Nature in Vietnam - the ever present bootlicking leeches. Bloodthirsty. Blood sucking. Revolting little slugs.

The sound of the word alone revolted Buchanan to nausea. The bloodsuckers sickened him.

The spiritual team had accompanied Lieutenant Jones in the bush since April 3. 1st and 2nd Platoons of Charlie Company, along with 2nd Squad, patrolled Route 540, guarding Skawinski's combat engineering team. 1st and 2nd platoons of Bravo Company joined the patrol on April 4. Rockford would now take the leadership role of the patrol.

For the past two days, the marines swept a logistical transportation route west of Monkey Mountain, which traveled straight through the jungle, providing much needed supplies for marines and ARVN in several camp locations, including marines assigned to villages and hamlets with CAP programs. The supply routes furnished pro-American villages and hamlets arms and ammunition, crucial to establishing support for the American efforts to win the war.

The day entered the late morning hours as time struck 0900 hours sharp. As temperatures rose to a blistering 100 degrees plus the past few days, Buchanan woke up every morning in a consistent state of perspiring, soaked in sweat.

The patrol came across a path merging with a tributary of the Tvy Loan River. With the searing heat hammering down onto the marines, it didn't take long for the men to choose to take a swim in the wet, cool offshoot of the river.

With a perimeter set, the company shed their sweaty, filthy uniforms, many down to their birthday suits to skinny dip. The spiritual team chose the modest route - shedding down to their skivvies. Buchanan, worn from the heat, flung off his combat fatigues, jumping into the tributary. Modesty won the day, however, as Buchanan held back from jumping into the water butt naked. Besides, the risk of facing an attack from the Viet Cong completely nude was too much for him to handle.

Besides, the shorts served as a barrier against the dreaded leeches.

One marine after the other soared into the air in a fetal position, plunging into the tributary, following the shedding of their uniforms.

"Who hoo!" yelled Skawinski as he jumped into the water!

"Geronimo!" blurted out Dobbs and Kiehl.

"Whoa!" Kowslowski and Rodriquez screamed.

Jackson followed suit, "Wheeeeeee!"

Buchanan took hold of his camera, snapping one slide picture after the other of the men enjoying the coolness of the water. When finished taking slide pictures, he jumped as a cannonball into the water from the top of a high eroded bank, roaring a cheerful holler, "Heeeeeeeeee!" Into the water he went, feeling the coolness hitting his skin. The sudden sensation reminded him of his grandmother placing a cool saturated washcloth on his back following the spent hours under the tropical sun getting sunburned in southern Ohio.

As Buchanan descended slowly toward the bottom of the tributary, he reminisced of skinning dipping in the mountains of Pike County, Kentucky, feeling his heart jumping for joy. How he wished in this moment of time he could be home taking a dip in the deep crevices of the cavernous mountain cool waters of eastern Kentucky instead of in southeastern Asia on this humid day.

Buchanan dropped deep into the water, close to the bottom, as his weight immediately hauled him down to the lowermost of the tributary. He prayed his slow ascension back toward the surface would never end, as the layers of his skin felt a soothing contentment from the water, the greatest of relief upon scorched skin. With every inch of his ascension, he soaked in every ounce of comfort from the coolness of the water. He longed for the slow ascension to last forever, an everlasting respite from the heat never to end. A sensation Buchanan weeks later would long for when the temperatures reached 100 plus.

"Whew! That feels good!" shouted Buchanan, emerging from the water.

The boisterous laughter of marines echoed off the high eroded banks of the tributary, hearing Buchanan's newfound relief from the searing sun, an obvious enjoyment of a cool swim long in coming.

"Nothing like it, is there, sir!?!" asked Lipstone, the reliable radioman.

"Sure isn't!"

The swim served as a pardon from the war, one which all wanted to last for an eternity. Unfortunately, all good things come to an end. There is a war on. A war the marines set out to win.

In the days, weeks, and months ahead, the marines recalled the swim warmheartedly. In the days ahead, the men on patrol will remember the refreshing water, void of any means of relief from the heat of the day.

One marine after the other emerged from the waters.

As Buchanan dried off following his swim, he caught in the corner of his eye a glow and sprinkle on the marines skin. The glow shined from the sunlight, peppered all over the marines, a sight of unusual spots of color reflecting the skin of a fish or the shape and color of a tear drop hanging from the marines torsos and limbs.

As Buchanan stepped nearer to the marines, reality hit him. The tear drop shaped spots were compressed, fragmented bodies of slugs in nature Buchanan loathed – nasty leeches. The bloodsuckers varied in size and length. Slugs of one to three inches sucking blood in every nook and cranny of the marines bodies. The limbs. The torso. Underarms. Neck and groin areas. Marines covered from head to toe with suckers. Regardless of the size of a leech, dark blood flowed fast from the wounds inflicted from dozens of leeches, each with a full set of 200 teeth. The sight nauseated Buchanan to no end.

The marines in earshot of Buchanan grinned from humor who heard him say in his heavy, thick mountain accent, "I hate those things."

To his horror, the methodical look see of his own torso sighted blood suckers scattered all over his hairy chest and arms wreaked a disgust within himself, spotting the detestable slugs from head to toe.

Jackson trailed behind Buchanan, out of the water. And he, too, discovered his torso and limbs littered with the gross specimens.

Buchanan turned abruptly, demanding, "Get'em off! Get'em off!"

"They're disgusting! Disgusting!" yelled Buchanan.

Grinning, Jackson noticed Buchanan's mountain accent most often when he became most agitated or when thrown a bout of excitement. He encouraged Buchanan, "Patience Chaplain. Patience."

"Patience? Get'em off!" demanded Buchanan.

Jackson grins wider.

Walking toward the spiritual team with his cigarettes and lighter, Jurgensen handed Jackson the remedy to Buchanan's predicament. Jackson said, "Here ya go, Chaplain!"

In Buchanan's first month in Vietnam, he took note marines preferred to use cigarettes in removing leeches from the skin than the manual means of removal. The first manual step to remove a leech required a marine to locate the frontal sucker at the lesser end of the leech, placing the index finger on the skin next to the sucker. The next move entailed the marine to smoothly, but steadfastly, maneuver his finger toward the spot where the bloodsucker is drinking blood. The last vital phase called for the marine to maneuver his fingernail with precision to shove the sucker on its side, in the opposite direction from the skin.

The fact a manual means of removing leeches from human flesh called for too many steps, the grunts simply made use of the addictive nicotine cancer sticks, numbering in the millions in southeastern Asia, to burn the suckers off out of pure retribution. Buchanan knew without a doubt, the marines burned the leeches off their skin with the ciggies out of sheer vengefulness.

Jackson lit a cigarette, turning toward Buchanan, saying, "OK, Chaplain. Come on. Let's give these little cusses a singe they'll never forget."

As Buchanan stepped closer to Jackson, his bodyguard pointed his index finger straight up, twirling it round and round, informing Buchanan to turn his back toward him. "Turn around Chaplain, let's start with your back. I noticed the slugs nearer to the muscular veins protruding from your back muscles."

Jackson chuckled.

"Very funny, Sergeant. Just get 'em off!" Buchanan insisted. "Have I ever told you have a warped sense of humor? Warped!"

Jackson suppressed cigarettes on the posterior sucker of the few leeches on Buchanan's back. The bloodsuckers dropped onto the ground one after the other, relieving Buchanan of his horror.

"OK chaplain, turn back towards me." Jackson instructed.

"Let's look for those bloodsuckers hiding in the chest hair of yours." laughed Jackson. He noticed nothing but a frown on Buchanan's face. Smiling, he said, "Sorry, sir. Just trying to lighten the mood."

Starting with Buchanan's torso, Jackson searched his upper chest area, thick hair and all, for the bloodsuckers, working his way down

Buchanan's remaining torso. Next in line for the search and destroy mission required a thorough examination of his head and throat, followed by his arms, then his underarms, and finishing with his legs and feet. Last, Jackson searched his groin area.

Buchanan stood butt naked. Waiting patiently for Jackson to burn the very last of the menacing bloodsuckers off his body, sending the ugly slug onto the ground. Immersed in the marines predicament, Buchanan stood blinded of his own situation, a situation deserving attention, to observe the spectacle square in front of him. What lay in front of him were dozens of naked marines exchanging turns, pressing cigarettes into sordid leeches. Scrupulous, painstaking examinations searching for unwelcomed slugs. The men inspected every nook and cranny on each human body for leeches. To seek for the ominous freeloaders is a rigorous undertaking. In the first place, the Marine Corps trained the grunts to pay attention to detail, never to end a mission in failure. In front of Buchanan were dozens of naked men searching fellow marines, fellow friends in every crevice of their bodies, for the disgusting bloodsucking barnacles. In the second place, no marine ceased searching until every leech fell to the ground, seared from the end of a lit cigarette. The sight of dozens of naked marines examining one another for the bloodsuckers humored Buchanan. In years to come, Buchanan never will forget the sight, bringing a smile to his face. Every marine took the greatest pleasure in their efforts to eliminate the slugs.

Jackson took a tally of the number of leeches dropped from the man he has sworn to protect with his life. Buchanan felt light-headed, knowing the slugs had taken a part of his whole being away from him in just a matter of minutes. After freeing Buchanan of the revolting bloodsuckers hanging from his body, Jackson's turn for examination came calling. Buchanan took great pleasure giving the sergeant a dose of his own medicine, pestering Jackson the whole while after all the tommy rot he received from him. Skawinski jumped in to assist Buchanan to free Jackson of the blood sucking invaders on his body.

Elation ran high as the last blood sucker dropped from Jackson's body. For Buchanan, describing the leeches as 'gross' understated his sentiments regarding the suckers. Time spent examining Jackson ran extensive, as Skawinski and Buchanan discovered three, four, even a six half inch leech, proving to be the most difficult to remove under his arm.

Anger raced through Companies B and C following the attack from the crude spongers, turning to physical retribution as marines sliced the suckers into smithereens with KA-BAR knives.

Rockford broke a record for the most leeches attached to a body, 35 in all.

When the last unwelcomed slug invader fell to the ground, the men donned their uniforms, with orders to saddle up and head for Monkey Mountain. The trek measured four miles to the mountain. The men were eager to complete the sweeping patrol and head back to camp.

With the greatest desire to complete the mission and return to camp, the marines marched to Monkey Mountain in record time to sweep the supply routes next to Route 540.

One supply route sat in the thick, dense jungle between Route 540 and Monkey Mountain, running along small hillsides underneath the mountain in a valley with little room for maneuverability once you enter the impenetrable jungle.

The combat engineering team defused many booby traps and mines along the supply routes, exposing the enemy's efforts to slow up the exertions of the American and ARVN forces to resupply fellow compatriots.

The complete sweep called for three full days to accomplish.

On the second day of the mission, Rockford ordered a short 10 minute break from work to rest from the sun-soaked, exhausting heat. The sweeping party halted below a low, steep ravine down from one of the many sloped hillsides running next to Monkey Mountain, two miles away. Roughly 150 feet laid open space from the hillside to the jungle treeline, with sparse trees scattered in the open space. The patrol flopped onto the ground with the loudest thud either under a tree or up against an eroded mound within the landscape.

"Uh! Oh my!" blurted out Buchanan. "This heat is from the Devil himself."

"Ugh!" Jackson groaned. "You're right, chaplain. Only the Devil could come up with weather this brutal."

Dobbs overheard saying, "I think I'd rather swim with the leeches in the Tvy Loan River, chaplain."

"Just as long as we've enough cigarettes to kill the suckers!" Buchanan responded.

Jackson and Dobbs sneer, laughing.

"There's not enough cigarettes in the world to kill all those suckers, sir!" Jackson declared. "Ya know what they say, - 'The sun slowly beats you down and wrenches life out of you.' Leeches? They *suck* the life out of you." Pausing, Jackson asserts, "They're calculated. Cold. Measured and premeditated."

Dobbs nods. Smiling, he said, "Yeah, you reminded me of how nasty those things really are."

Grinning, Buchanan listened to the conversation. The whole while, he noticed the worn, weary condition of the men. The grunts had had enough of the insufferable heat from the sun. The men sat with heads down on their backsides, leaning against trees on an embankment of a hill, complete with vegetation and trees on its side, offering a bit of shade from the sun. Buchanan noticed towels hanging around the marine's necks soaking in the moist sweat from the heat of the sun. A few men stood, preventing their worn bodies from stiffening up from sitting too long.

Rising from his tucked sitting position to speak an encouraging word to the men, Buchanan took a few paces toward Sims five feet away from him. Just as he spoke to Taxi, he suddenly noticed 25 feet away from him, a marine jerking and convulse in place.

Within a millisecond, Buchanan hit the deck.

The marine, slammed with spraying bullets from enemy snipers, crashed to the ground, vibrating rock and soil beneath him square in front of Buchanan. The memory of witnessing the young kid ripped to pieces will ever be remembered by Buchanan decades to come.

The familiar thud of bullets hitting the ground just inches from the marines caused their hearts to skip a beat, violently hurling up dirt, triggering mini explosions on the surface of the ground.

PING! PING! PING!

RATATATATATATATATATATATA!

POW! POW! POW! POW!

Now came the familiar sounds of projectiles hissing through the air. Then suddenly horrid screams from marines receiving hot lead, ripping the flesh literally off of them.

Unforeseen grenades thrown in mass into the perimeter seemed endless, similar to hail on a hot early summer night in the Midwest.

KaBOOM! KaBOOM!

The grenades flew in the air from all directions, one landing too close for Buchanan's nerves to handle. "No!" he screamed. Fortunately for Buchanan, the grenade ended up a dud. He froze momentarily, catching flies.

All human beings handle combat differently. And all Buchanan could think of at the moment, within seconds, is he wanted to be in Cincinnati watching a Reds game at Riverfront stadium.

Fortunately, swiftly looking back toward his right, Buchanan discovered Dobbs, Jackson, and Corpsmen Petty Officer 2nd Class Philip Jenkins bunched up, crouched on the hill's side. They scampered for cover behind an eroded mound, motioning with their arms for Buchanan to run toward the mound for ample cover, out of sight of enemy gunfire.

Exposed, Buchanan laid flat on his stomach on a slopped incline at the base of the hillside slanted in an inward angle toward the base of the slope. The snipers from above caught sight of the very edge of Buchanan and his uniform within the slopped incline.

POW! POW! POW!

PING! PING! PING!

Confronted with nagging sniper fire, the patrol faced a potential siege with an enemy who possessed the high ground.

"FIND COVER! Hold your position!" Rockford barked. "Chaplain, get out of sniper sight! NOW!"

Buchanan thought to himself, 'Are you kidding me, Lance? What am I to do?' He felt obliged to look left, instantly spotting a young rifleman running toward the hillside for cover. When suddenly three bullets hit his upper left leg, making their way down his limb, shattering his bones into smithereens, exiting through his left foot. Collapsing onto the ground, he yelled at the top of his lungs, "I'm hit! Oh my God, I'm hit!"

Buchanan's instinct kicked in. He rushed to the young kid, along with two other marines, carrying him to safety along the embankment of the hill, as bullets whizzed by the men scurrying toward cover.

The marine screamed, "Ahh! It hurts like hell!", as the agony of the wound grew to extraordinarily excruciating throbs of pain.

POW! POW! POW!

The harassment of sniper fire peeved the marines.

"Corpsmen!" Jurgensen yelled.

PO3 Lawrence Sigmanson darted to the wounded marine to administer first aid.

"Oh dear God! Jesus help him!" Sigmanson blurted, noticing the severity of his wounds. Regardless, he put his superb medical training into practice, working his skills on the shattered leg.

By now, the vast majority of the patrol raced under the embankment of the hill for protected cover, with marines still yet trickling in from exposed sniper fire who had concealed themselves by means of trees and vegetation. In time, the stragglers made their way to safety along the hillside. The enemy forced the marines to either expose themselves to enemy fire by running out in the open to safety or to choose to stay put, positioned behind a thin tree or squatting in vegetation. The wait to be picked off was not a tough decision to make. One by one, marines high tailed it for cover in the hillside's underbrush. Once a marine reached the underbrush, not one of those marines felt the pain of a flying bullet in the air searching for a victim. Every marine ran for cover, safe and sound. Buchanan maintained, later on in camp, 'the VC again either sucked at marksmanship or the Lord's presence protected them.' He liked to think the latter determined the fate of the men.

Buchanan scanned the horizons. He caught sight of three marines down, mangled from bullet wounds and probably dead. Large pools of blood soaked the dirt underneath the brave marines.

At this point in the surprise attack, countless bullets hit nothing but the treeline and the surface of the earth with loud thuds of devastation on impact.

Rockford, the ranking officer, estimated enemy fire came from three separate directions, inflicting a dangerous crossfire. From the cracks and impact of the bullets, he reckoned enemy fire came from one or two .60 caliber machine guns, AK-47's, SKS 7.62 caliber assault rifles, grenade launchers, and SVD 7.62 caliber rifle gunfire. The enemy above possessed heavy armament.

Stepping along the side of the hill out of enemy sight, the marines maneuvered within the ravine on a high eroded bank, which provided ground cover, serving as a cave like structure.

For three grueling days, 100 marines, the spiritual team, and corpsmen tending to the wounded, congregated at the foot of the hill. Bravo Company retrieved five dead marines lying in the open during the night, under the cover of darkness. Trapped at the foot of the hill and with no help to come, the company fell besieged and confined from receiving enemy heat from above.

The combination of a siege mentality and saturated with the heat of the sun delivered an unbearable, torturous pounding upon the nerves. Three days of a siege within a cruel war no civilian back home would ever understand or conceive, unless a civilian witnessed the siege first hand.

Rockford radioed in for help. But attempts to relieve the patrol by helicopter came under attack with nothing but a continuous volley of projectiles.

The open space aligned along the hillside made it almost impossible for the helicopters to drop supplies for replenishment and water. Marines and Navy pilots flew over the open space and exposed themselves to enemy snipers as easy targets.

Rockford positioned one Bravo Company platoon on each flank to prevent any enemy envelopment maneuvers on the bottom incline of the hill. 2nd platoon on the left had showcased splendid flanking tactics in the past, while 3rd platoon showed courage time and time again protecting a flank in previous skirmishes. Lieutenant Jones' 1st Platoon of Charlie Company positioned itself in the center position to support the Bravo Platoon on the flanks. 2nd Squad 2nd Platoon served to booster the center and protect the command at the bottom of the hill.

After three days, headquarters and Camp Love presented strategy after strategy for the best tactics to provide relief to Charlie Company, but to no avail. An air strike of fighter jets or napalm posed too much of a risk of hitting friendly marines. Dropping marines by Huey helicopter randomly in the jungle seemed out of the question with no reliable intelligence to show any hidden enemy in the strategic area. The marines dropped in would be a shooting gallery for the enemy.

With no relief coming, Bravo and Charlie Companies had run out of water after the second day.

Within three days of being stranded, the wounded were sure enough to die, including the marine hit in the leg, if reinforcements failed to immediately relieve the patrol. Sure enough, two wounded marines expired the next morning after the attack, one perished the third day. Of the many duties Buchanan fulfilled in Vietnam as chaplain, holding a dying marine and administering last words to the young man ranked as one of several duties he didn't look forward to. But the marines longed for Buchanan to be present in the bush for this very reason. He meant every word when he prayed with a young man entering eternity, finding the words to speak, showing genuine compassion for the dying. So Buchanan prayed over the three wounded who succumbed to their wounds and quoted Scripture as the young men entered Eternity.

Buchanan cited a prayer for the Protestant marines as they expired, "O Almighty God, with whom do live the spirits of just men made perfect, after they are delivered from their earthly prisons; We humbly commend the soul of this Thy servant, our dear brother, into Thy hands, as into the hands of a faithful Creator, and most merciful Saviour; most humbly beseeching Thee, in the blood of that immaculate Lamb, that whatsoever defilements it may have contracted in the midst of this miserable and naughty world, through the lusts of the flesh, or by the wiles of Satan, being purged and done away it may be presented pure and without spot before Thee, through the merits of Jesus Christ Thine only Son our Lord. Amen."

For the young man who suffered the leg wound, a Roman Catholic, he recited the Catholic prayer for the dying, "O My God, I am heartily sorry for having offended Thee, and I detest all of my sins because I dread the loss of Heaven and the pains of Hell, but most of all because I have offended Thee My God, who art all good and deserving of all my love. I firmly resolve with the help of Thy race to confess my sins, to do penance, and to amend my life. Amen."

Buchanan also administered Baptism in extremis to the Catholic marine. The young kid desired to be baptized. He then took a soaked towel of sweat, his own sweat, and administered it softly upon the marine's forehead. The marines had run out of water. The only possible means of fluid came from his own brow. He provided the best he could do for the dying marine. The Lord would understand the lack of water! While he wetted his forehead, Buchanan repeated these words, "I baptize you in the Name of the Father, and the Son, and of the Holy Ghost."

"Thank you, chaplain. Jesus. I love Jesus." avowed the marine. Buchanan and his friends crouched around him in his last moments in this life. His friends, of course, were incapable of holding back their emotions.

The dying marine smiled the whole while. As a proud native of Omaha, Nebraska, he asked Buchanan, "Padre, you think the Cornhuskers will be any good next year?" Buchanan grinned. He held his emotions in check the best he could, saying, "Nebraska has a great coach. I think they'll do fine."

With that said, the marine smiled, closed his eyes, and took his last breath.

Though many might not understand, a dying man's thoughts in a war stream toward home. Buchanan learned quick in Vietnam, a dying marine's last moments are his, and his alone.

Buchanan half grinned, choking up along with the others.

Few said a word for the rest of the day.

Confronted with another night, the marines wondered who was next in line to face death in the jungles of Vietnam.

Dawn welcomed the marines the next morning. April 9 arrived, the fourth day of the siege. Trapped and frustrated, Bravo Company grew even more agitated with enemy snipers above them, pestering the worn and weary patrol. The enemy threw the marines a constant downpour of projectiles longing to take another life. With frustration setting in, the patrol set their minds on freeing themselves from the siege.

The marines, weary and frail from the lack of water, sought relief from the feeble condition they found themselves in. Deprived of the nutrients of water because of the cruel and godless enemy above, the trapped men felt a deep anger within themselves.

Rockford led three separate attacks in the past four days to outflank the three enemy positions - but to no avail. The attempts to outflank the enemy accomplished nothing but to drain even more essential energy out of the marines. Necessary energy the marines will need in days to come.

The captain estimated from the past few days the echoes, cracks, booms, ricochets of weaponry and the projectiles fired, the enemy possessed a .60 caliber machine gun on the right flank with a few AK-47's, a 12.7mm machine gun in the middle supported with Viet Cong armed with AK-47's, and one SKS 7.62 caliber assault rifle, along with an SVD 7.62 caliber rifle on Company C's left.

Without water, the marines would drop one by one from heat exhaustion and malnutrition.

Rockford had had enough, calling for an officer call, including Jurgensen, Skawinski, and Jones.

The four men crouched down on their knees, drawing lines in the dirt, displaying an intense conversation.

The inaudible conversation conveyed to Buchanan a potential storm brewed soon. The intensity of the conversation startled Buchanan of what might happen in the next few moments.

As the tense exchange of dialog ended, the marines rose from their crouched positions, as Rockford addressed the men.

"Listen, men. Listen." Rockford appealed. With determinism and forthright, he said, "Men. Listen to me. Those devils have trapped us for four days. And I, for one, am sick of'em. The enemy on top of the hill - they're from hell. I plan to send'em back!" Rockford vehemently asserted, "If they don't kill us, we're going to breathe our last under this impetuous hot spell. Deprived of water to quicken our demise if we don't take action."

Buchanan took a hard, long peek at the men, bent on listening to every word spoken from Rockford's mouth. These battle hardened marines were no longer in a mood to be pissed on. The tide will soon turn on the enemy. The marines will soon fight as the aggressor once again.

Rockford reminded the marines with bluntness, "If we don't get some water soon, we're going to drop like flies. Dehydrated and close to death, with heat on top of the dehydration. That's a death sentence. That'll be the end of us. Too weak to defend ourselves."

Rockford's brief speech sunk in, invigorating the marines to fight like a bat out of Hades.

Gawking at Rockford speaking, they knew what they had to do – storm the hill and kill the enemy, their only hope of surviving.

Confidence spread throughout the patrol as none said a word.

Buchanan prayed to himself a quick, immediate prayer, 'Lord, Bless these men. Let these brave marines feel your presence with the advance up the hill. If one should fall, receive each one into your loving arms. In Jesus' name, Amen.'

Rockford ordered the assault teams for the attack. "Sergeant Smith, you'll lead the 2nd on the left flank. Gunny Jurgensen, the 3rd platoon on the right, is yours, while I'll lead the 1st platoon and corpsmen in the middle. And Ski, you lead the combat engineers in the middle to reinforce the flanks and the middle if needed."

"Yes, sir." answered the leaders of attacking teams.

"Lieutenant Jones."

"Yes, Captain Rockford."

"Hold back as a reserve. When you observe which of our flanks are about to overwhelm one enemy flank, rush in behind either 1st or 2nd platoons and reinforce the platoon, then carry out an envelopment movement."

"Yes, sir." responded Jones.

"Chaplain Buchanan and Jackson. You stay put till all the action is done and over with."

"Yes, sir." replied the spiritual team with hesitation. Rockford knew in his heart nothing in the world would prevent Buchanan from rushing toward a wounded or a fallen marine if a man should indeed fall.

Rockford instructed the men. "I'll give you the signal to charge up the hill. You'll know what it is when y'all hear it."

The three fighting platoons, along with Ski's team, set themselves in position, ready for the order to charge up the hill.

The men waited in the uneasy silence, gnawing at the nerves of each marine. An eerie, frightening calm and hush overwhelmed the air, only to end with the order to charge.

The marines, on edge, listened with perked ears for an order to charge up the hill. The anticipation for the men to charge mounted, adding to a boiling rage building up over the pain and agony thrown at them over the past four days. The built up anger from the marines for the torment accrued from the hands of the Viet Cong came due to the stubbornness of the marines to deliver some immediate payback for the misery poured upon them from the VC. The Devil Dogs set out to deliver a heavy hammer, stamping out the VC.

Finally, the silence came to a close as the patrol heard Rockford's voice - "Charge!" He let loose with his M-16 rapidly sending projectiles upward toward the unwanted pestilence.

"Charge!" yelled the team leaders.

"Whoooooaaaaa!" came the marines out from cover, taking aim at the enemy, firing their weapons. The men dodged from one spot of cover to another. A tree, a mound of dirt, a fallen tree, even a lone rock spearing out of the hill, whatever presented itself in front of them.

RATATATATATATAT! POP! POP! POP! POP!

KaBOOM! - a grenade exploded, thrown at the enemy.

KaBOOM! - came the aftermath of a grenade exploding near the marines.

"AHHHHHH!" yells a marine as he's hit.

Buchanan, hearing the yell, rushes to his side.

"GET DOWN, CHAPLAIN!" Jackson shrieks, who hurries toward Buchanan.

Falling to the ground beside him, Buchanan is shell-shocked, as Corporal Jaworski looks up at him, stunned from being hit. The farm kid from Pennsylvania, Sanborn's adjutant, is in total denial. He is leaving this world in just a mire matter of seconds.

Jackson catches up with him from a prone position, firing his M-16 repeatedly upward toward the enemy.

Jaworski attempts to utter words through the blood and saliva pouring out of his mouth, but it is nothing but grunts and inaudible mumbling words.

POP! POP! POP! POP!

PING! PING! PING! The ricochets of projectiles on top of the trees and rocks seemed endless.

THUD! THUD! THUD! Buchanan felt the dirt hit his fatigues, terrified of the thunderous bullets landing close around him. But determined to lie with Jaworski in his last moments in this life.

The prayer asked for Jaworski did not come easy for Buchanan, for he died within a matter of seconds in Buchanan's arms. Buchanan was beside himself as Jaworski lay dead alongside him. Just a matter of days ago, Buchanan had had an enjoyable and enlightened conversation on methods of planting corn and tomatoes with him. And now he's dead.

Glaring down Jaworski's body frame, Buchanan noted nothing but innumerable holes and wounds ripping his torso apart. A horrifying sight.

In the front of Buchanan drops another marine from the heat of VC weaponry, then another body falls violently to his left. And yet another further ahead. Rushing to each marine, he lays his hand on each, saying a prayer for the dead or wounded on the ground.

As the spiritual team rushed to dead or wounded marines, the three attacking teams advanced ahead to carry out the pincher movement on top of the hillside.

POP! PING! POP! PING! POP!

KaBOOM!

RATATATATATATATATATATATA!!!!!

Jurgensen's 3rd platoon reached their objective just under the .60 caliber machine gun pit on the slope of the hillside, throwing grenades by hand and firing grenades from the launcher, destroying the machine gun. His team bravely charged up the hill slope, fighting hand to hand combat with the Viet Cong after reaching the top of the hill. The VC fought to the death, no match for marines as their fury blazed away at the VC, ripping the enemy apart. Taking out the .60 caliber machine gun came with the cost of heavy casualties, 5 dead and 6 wounded. As Jurgensen's men reached the top, securing the right flank, the marines turned their attention on the middle entrenchment of the VC for a complete envelopment of the enemy. Jones' Charlie Company followed up the hill, reinforcing Jurgensen's flanking maneuver.

The VC gun emplacements were now enveloped one gun at a time. The middle first, then on to the left flank.

POP! POP! POP! POP!

KaBOOM!

By now, the 12.7mm machine gun pit received cross fire from Rockford's middle and Jurgensen's right. The middle fell rather quickly, as would the left flank, enduring the same punishment the middle received.

Not a Viet Cong combatant lived through the counter attack. The marines accounted for every one of the VC.

The fierce, violent assault up the slope drained the very last ounce of energy from every single marine, resulting in many marines collapsing onto the ground out of sheer exhaustion. Breathing heavily and longing for a shot in the arm of energy, the marines collapsed amid many dead lying about. The patrol gathered the killed and wounded - 13 dead and 15 wounded.

The rage built up in the past 3 to 4 days in each marine certainly showed in their efforts to fight their way out of an exhausting siege as they inflicted 46 Viet Cong killed in the deadly skirmish.

On top of the hillside, Rockford instructed Sims to radio in for some food and water. As the men waited for helicopters to arrive, they surrounded the KIAs to grieve. Buchanan will ever remember the memory of the marines mourning their fallen friends.

Within an hour, Huey helicopters dropped in the open field between the treeline and the hillside food and water. Running to the essential provisions for nourishment, the marines ripped and tore into the food with fervor, stuffing oneself to the gills. The siege had deprived the men of food for four days. The men ate as if there was no tomorrow.

The cool relief of bottled waters poured over each other's head delivered a sense that Jack Frost paid the marines a visit. The marines drank the water until their stomachs were full.

The men, after replenishing themselves with food and water, gathered themselves around the deceased for a second moment of paying their last respects for their brave friends who entered glory with the Savior, overwhelmed with emotion, dazed and stunned over the past four days of war.

Laid with precision shoulder to shoulder in a hideous display, the KIAs were to be placed in black body bags. Buchanan recited a prayer over each marine, followed by the quoting of Scripture. Most difficult for Buchanan wound up his prayer over Jaworski. Not a dry eye found in the house as men mutually shared the loss of fellow friends at the top of the hill gathered around the remains.

The morning of April 9 culminated as one of many gloomy moments for Buchanan in Vietnam. The spiritual team sat on their backsides, spending the longest time with the deceased attempting to place the past few days in perspective. The team sat patiently for the scheduled Hueys to pick up the deceased to begin the long route back home to the United States for proper burial.

Buchanan stepped toward a young marine distraught over the past few days' events, placing his hand on the marine's shoulder. "Marine. I'm sorry." Pausing, he quoted Scripture. "1 Peter 5:7 says, 'Cast all your troubles and anxiety on Him because he cares for you."

Turning toward Buchanan, he smiled.

"Thank you, Padre."

Turning back toward the KIA's, the young marine continued to weep.

"Why? Why Chaplain?" asked the marine.

Buchanan thought hard for the words to say to such a flustered marine.

He finally says, "I don't always have the answers of why things happen the way they turn out." Pausing, he says, "But those of us left must go on." With yet another pause, he reassures the young believer. "It's hard. But we must. God'll give us strength."

Turning towards Buchanan, he nods. Looking back down towards his friends, he mourns.

After a brief pause, the marine poignantly points out, "We lost 13 good men today, chaplain….13 good men."

Buchanan glances at the young marine, letting go of his emotions.

The spiritual team consoled one another, reminding each other of Dobbs' observation days earlier of favoring the leeches over the brutal heat. Comparing the past few days, the men thought the leeches were more favorable than the firefight that had just ensued. The patrol shared a mutual level of levity swimming with the leeches. Fighting the Viet Cong under the scorching heat remained a memory of perpetuity, unforgettable days remembered with wretchedness.

As the young marine said, "We lost 13 good men today. 13 good men."

HAWAII

APRIL 12, 1969

Wow! A little over six months in the bush and Buchanan woke up this morning still amongst the living! He rose from a great night's sleep to breathe God's given air yet another day! This day in Buchanan's early life, he jotted down as one highlight of many special days throughout his lifetime. The day ended with Buchanan stepping down the airstair onto the tarmac in Honolulu, Hawaii. A layover delay in Okinawa at 0700 hours did nothing but heighten the anticipation of a deserved rest and relaxation. The separation from the war will do him good mentally and physically.

Sick of the war, a 10 day spent with his wife, Dorothy, will serve Robert well.

The four-day siege trapped at the base of the hill served as the tipping point. The siege, still fresh in Buchanan's mind, brought on nothing but nightmares. His dreams plastered the death faces of the 13 KIAs he prayed over, not an easy mental image to be forgotten. Buchanan's heart weighed heavily, devastated with unimaginable hurt.

The exposure to normalcy called him into a world of paradise. The anticipation of his plane's wheels hitting the pavement on the tarmac in Hawaii heightened as time passed.

Waiting patiently in the Honolulu airport in Hawaii sat the dearest, most essential person in his life, Dorothy.

Buchanan loved his wife. He adored her beauty. In his eyes, she defined gorgeous. The very first day he set his eyes on her, she glowed radiantly beyond measure.

The excitement to meet Dorothy flowed over, obvious to every service member on the military flight.

"I'm gonna spend some time with my wife who I've not seen since last year!" declared Buchanan passing by fellow passengers, including his newfound friend seated in the 36th row, seat C. Robert made himself at home in seat B of the 36th row.

Sitting in his aisle seat, he turned to the stranger sitting to his left, saying, "I'm meeting my wife in Hawaii who I've not seen since April 1968!"

"I'm glad, chaplain. I really am." acknowledged the smiling stranger, an army officer who had served in the bush near the Cambodian border, an area known for steady heavy fighting. The officer's tour finally ended. He's headed home for good. And he survived.

"Me too, stranger. Me too." replied Buchanan.

Sighing heavily, the stranger delivered a stern stare toward Buchanan. "I'm going home, chaplain. My tour's over."

"Great, stranger. I'm thankful."

"Me too, chaplain. Me too."

The two officers hit it off.

The visit lasted the whole trip to Hawaii, enjoying each other's company. The army officer hailed from Spartanburg, South Carolina. He disclosed the fact he graduated from the major university in South Carolina, and proud of it.

The conversation addressed every subject imaginable but the war. They had had enough of war, at least for the time being for Buchanan.

During the visit, the scar of war raised its ugly head throughout the chat with body language, though neither uttered a word on the subject. The men talked politics, sports, education, entertainment, religion, anything and everything to distract their minds off the war.

Even with the long flight, time passed quickly.

The plane finally landed, coasted to Terminal 2 gate A. The two newfound friends strolled down the airstair, still conversing even toward the terminal entrance. Shaking hands, the two parted ways as they neared the entrance, knowing good and well the scars of war set permanent upon their hearts and souls forever. Neither one uttered a word of the war, but knowing the pain would never go away.

Glancing back toward the army officer, Buchanan stepped toward the main terminal for mainland flights. He noticed the officer stepping confidently to the main terminal as he silently lifted a prayer for the soldier. It was certainly the least he could do for his newfound friend.

Buchanan turned toward the main entrance passageway, searching for Dorothy, a tall order considering the dense number of patrons in the airport.

As Buchanan stepped toward the entrance, he searched left and right for his devoted, faithful partner in life and best friend.

He walked 10 feet. Spotting within the shoulder to shoulder mass of patrons walking about in every direction, Buchanan set his eyes on Dorothy kneeling against a pillar supporting the ceiling, staring right at him, wearing the widest of smiles.

Nothing in the world existed more beautiful to Buchanan than Dorothy. The last day he laid his eyes on her had been March 28, 1968, as he boarded a Navy plane for Okinawa marine base. Overwhelmed by her beauty, he couldn't take his eyes off of her. He gazed at her hour glassed figure with a new Flick Up hair style. Her lips were full with her favorite red lipstick shining a mile away and wearing a new set of dazzling Dachshund jewelry. Her new dress was full of fall colors and flowers beamed, complimenting the splendor of her shining bright chestnut blonde hair. As a humored Buchanan looked on, he knew she had worn her dress intentionally, noticing immediately the fall colors. Dorothy knew full well he cherished the fall. The fall flowers on Dorothy's new print served as the perfect welcome for Buchanan - the fall and flowers, which happened to be her favorite design on a dress.

The pair caught sight of one another, fixated in a glowing, luminous stare. The apparent, obvious deep love for one another showed as the couple could not take their eyes off of each other. Powerless to hold back any longer, the two briskly paced with great momentum toward one another. Once met, they wrapped into each other's arms, landing the longest kiss to make up for the lost time of the past year.

On cloud nine, in complete bliss, the separation from past months tore at the seams. The Buchanan's love joined eternal, which even physical separation failed to sever. Realization set in for Buchanan that he actually stood in the presence of Dorothy once again. The pair felt the same genuine excitement from 1955 when they first laid eyes on one another back in West Virginia.

Grinning, Dorothy stepped back, turned a 180, posed with her hands on her hips, and asked, "Well, what do ya think?"

Buchanan stood catching flies, giving Dorothy a good look over from head to toe. "Beautiful. You're just beautiful!"

"As beautiful as Alice Macron and Mary O'Bryant? Your favorite actresses?" Dorothy asked, giggling with delight and amusement.

"Them and then sum." answered Buchanan.

"All I can say is - the Lord sure took a pinch of beauty from you and made them, babe." Buchanan replied. Buchanan, laughing, stepped toward her, taking her hand.

Dorothy stares steadily. "Let's get outta here."

"I'm with you, beautiful."

With a quick step, the thrilled couple picked up his gear. The vigorous bolt to the front entrance for a cab seemed a blur to patrons in the airport. It took no time to get out of the airport.

Catching a cab for their beachfront hotel, the couple looked forward enjoying the vigor of paradise for 9 days and nights, a temporary holdover of the war for Buchanan - a relaxation from the crushing of his inner self.

Once they arrived to their room, the forth coming necessity of a change of clothes took just a few minutes, as the excited couple looked forward eating in Buchanan's favorite steak and seafood restaurant in Honolulu, a table service worth paying for. The couple arrived at 1050 hours, ten minutes early for their reservation, eager to eat a formal dinner with one another, an event not afforded them for months.

The mutual delight of sending time with one another magnified beyond measure. For the first time since October 1, 1968, the war for 10 short days passed as the farthest thing from Buchanan's mind. He engrossed his time with Dorothy's presence.

Time moved along with no consequence. Buchanan 'took his time' as time stood still. The meal lasted two and a half hours, as Dorothy updated Robert of the children, his brother Dwight in Los Angeles, and news from family and friends back home.

The sightseeing came plenty in the days to come, so the Buchanan's spent the rest of the day secluded. Separated for months, choosing to spend the rest of the day in the room goes without saying. The pair chuckled at the thought.

The couple walked the half mile back to the hotel, up to their room on the 8th floor of the 32 floor hotel.

Never tested for claustrophobia, Buchanan shunned upper rooms in hotels. He even avoided flying in a plane, only setting foot into a plane out of necessity. He would rather take a boat.

As God intended, intimacy brings spouses closer together, producing a sturdier bond between husband and wife. Spending the rest of the day with one another, alone, permitted them to express the commitment and devotion they had for one another. The realization of the totality of their separation did not hit them until spending time with one another as husband and wife.

Hours passed with leisure. No obligations. No deadlines. No interferences.

Darkness inevitably hit the Hawaiian beaches as time reached 2000 hours. As hunger set in, Buchanan dashed out to a local hamburger joint, bringing back two simple cheeseburgers and fries, tasting just as good as his steak and seafood earlier in the day - well, at least initially.

After the filling meal of burgers and fries, Dorothy suggested the two step out and enjoy the creation of God, taking part in one of Buchanan's favorite pastimes while at the beach - walking the seashore at night.

"Let's go." Buchanan said. Throwing on their beach clothes, the eager couple darted down the steps of the hotel with the energy of 21-year-olds. The gleeful couple set their feet on the sands of the Hawaiian shoreline, awed by the gorgeous horizon of the Pacific Ocean.

While on the beach, the pair held hands, leisurely moseying along some two miles down from the hotel. Time passed with no significance. The obligations of life for 9 days brushed aside, incapable of hindering time spent with each other.

The Hawaiian coasts at night lacked the tourists of the day hours. Beaches during the day gave little room for a person to barely walk a straight line anywhere on the beach. Hawaiian beaches invited the young during the day to tan their fresh skin to a light, tanned surface. Tonight, the beach lacked young narcissist tourists, as Buchanan referred to them, wanting nothing but to bring attention upon themselves. The plenty of room on the beach at night to stroll the shores ankle deep appealed to many couples, some to play with their children in the sand, maybe even venturing out into the water.

As they sauntered down the beach, Dorothy, with inquiry, asked, "Don't you think we ought to turn back?"

"I don't want it to end."

Dorothy, chuckling, says, "OK."

Taking an unhurried glimpse at the water's edge at dusk, Dorothy said, "Beautiful, isn't it?"

Looking out to the water's edge, Robert paused to a standstill with Dorothy. "Yes. The moon's reflection on the moving water - look at that. One of the most awesome sights of God's creation, isn't it?"

Buchanan added, "It's magnificent." He pointed towards the moon and says, "The clouds, in the moon's forefront. Those beams of moonlight in and around the clouds are breathtaking, aren't they?"

"Yes… it sure is."

"Reminds me of China Beach in Vietnam. You'd find it spectacular and stunning. Like you."

Dorothy grins. "Let's go back. It's late and dark."

Robert smiles wide, making a u-turn back toward the hotel room.

The stride back turned out to be as just as enjoyable as the two-mile walk down the strip as the moonlight emerged at nautical dusk.

Buchanan thought of dusk alongside the coast of China Beach in Vietnam, the first recollection of the war since his arrival in Hawaii.

The fierce mental battle in Buchanan's mind to dislodge formidable memories and visions of war he has experienced in his tour and to enjoy his time spent with Dorothy tore him apart inside, unbeknownst to Dorothy.

Though a master hiding his innermost emotions from Dorothy to keep her from worrying as they enjoyed each other's company, he prayed to God Almighty to protect him from experiencing a major flashback or demoralizing nightmare the first full night of his R and R with Dorothy.

Honolulu

April 18, 1969

Six days of fun had passed for Robert and Dorothy as the pair visited Honolulu and Hawaii, the Big Island, and cultural history. They will remember days shared the past week as memorial days lasting a lifetime. All the while, Buchanan snapped off slide pictures for his pictorial record of his tour.

Time spent in Hawaii offered a sentiment of vitality, the energy of 22-year-olds. Spending each day without one another for the past year proved too agonizing for the Buchanan's. But the couple had fun attempting an effort to make up for lost time, as the couple took in all four corners of Hawaii.

Buchanan had the pleasure of showing off his favorite Hawaiian sites to Dorothy, who had never experienced the tropics.

Not since the early 1950s had Buchanan been in Hawaii. And Robert excitedly escorted Dorothy to all the sites - Diamond Head, Ionani Palace, the waterfalls at Ho'omaluhia Botanical Gardens – one of Dorothy's favorite spots, International Market Place, Ala Moana Shopping Mall, snorkeling, and Maui's black sand beach. All the while, Buchanan took slide pictures.

One full day gobbled up visiting Akaka Falls on the Big Island swimming under the Waikaui Falls, a favorite of Dorothy's. Tourist brochures and tourist guides from AAA brought the site to life in pictures. Experiencing the falls first hand, Dorothy, enticed, fell overwhelmed, mesmerized with the breath taking, spectacular chutes.

The day spent on Oahu wound up a fun filled excursion, including swimming with the turtles on the North shore and visiting Waimea Canyon and Rock.

When the next day ended, the pair had a good giggle in their room, thinking of their full day. A day the couple referred to as the nerd tour, visiting the Polynesian Cultural Center and the history museums. Robert valued the history museums, shedding light on the people of Hawaii and their culture.

The morning of 18 April, the pair slept late. After dressing, the pair enjoyed breakfast in a restaurant specializing in pancakes, a particular favorite in the Buchanan household for breakfast, on Ala Moana Street from the hotel. Immersed in pancake Heaven, Robert never relished a better pancake breakfast in his life. He had had enough MREs and chow hall food for the past year in Vietnam to last a lifetime. Not that the MREs were the worst food he had ever ingested, but it *was* food in a combat zone.

After breakfast, the couple spent the day relaxing on the hotel grounds or on the beach. The Buchanan clan were never beach types. The fact the family bared skin as white as a sheet, the clan never visited the beach in which the whole family exited the shore as red as a pepper, painfully blistered to the extreme. The Buchanan's preferred the mountains, familiar territory, a part of growing up as children. And besides, the mountains possessed the cooler climate the Buchanan clan preferred. A day on the seashore required the usual precautions to protect the snow white skin of the Buchanan clan under the blistering sunshine of the Hawaiian beaches. Dorothy suggested applying an extra layer of suntan lotion to avoid unwanted sun burns.

Arriving to the room from breakfast, the pair changed into their bathing suits, grabbed their beach towels, flip-flops, and retrieved the most important item, sun screen. The potency of the suntan lotion read 100SPF level on the bottle. Neither one of them cared about getting a tan. They were happy with their snow white skin. Besides, the Buchanan's perceived sun bathing to gain a tan to be narcissistic.

Following a search for a desirable spot on the beach, Robert and Dorothy finally located a perfect hole in the vast sea of beach goers. Laying out their beach towels, the couple sat for twenty minutes. The sun shining through the clouds in the sky prevented the dreaded scorching heat of the sun from beating down on them without mercy, offering a pleasant visit to the beach.

"This is nice." Dorothy said.

"Yeah. It is. The clouds will keep it at least tolerable out here in the sun." Robert pointed out.

Buchanan snapped a few beach pictures with his new camera, applying his newly purchased, high-tech timer.

"Hawaii sure is beautiful, but it's not for me. I'd always wanted to live on the mainland." Dorothy commented.

"You and me both."

For twenty minutes, the loving couple enjoyed each other's company, taking part in their favorite pastime on the beach, people watching. Robert took a few more shots with his camera.

His best shots were of Dorothy playing in the sand with Honolulu in the background. After the picture taking, Dorothy turned her attention to more people on the beach.

Dorothy, the people watcher, noticed countless families on the beach having fun. Children played in the sand, building sand castles and mountains, and in the distance, a twenty something born with innate artistic skill who shaped a car and a navy ship out of the sand.

"Look Robert, that young man - he formed a car out of the sand. And a navy ship. Wow! It's amazing what you can do with the sand, isn't?" Dorothy said.

Lying on his right side, a smiling Robert glanced up at Dorothy slowly. "Yep. Sure is."

"Well, I might not have that kind of artistic talent, but I always wanted to be an artist." Dorothy commented.

"Yeah, that'd be nice. But the Lord gave ya a musical touch. It's music for you."

"Yeah. You're right. The kid there probably can't carry a note in a bucket." chuckled Dorothy. Regardless, she glanced toward the twenty something, awestruck at the kid's God given talent. People were moving about, admiring the young man's expert skill. As the crowds moved about, obstructing her view, Dorothy caught sight for a split second of another formation built out of the sand, a replica of the Alamo.

"Look!" Pointing toward the artist, she discloses, "It's the Alamo."

Robert popped up fastly, looking toward the young man, surprised. "Wow!" He stared momentarily. "That's amazing. Dorothy!" Catching flies, Robert says, "Let's go take a closer look."

Hopping up, the couple stepped over to the artist's sand structures.

Fascinated with the intricate details of the reproduction of the Alamo, Buchanan enthralled himself with the authenticity of the sand structure. He admired the history and story of the Alamo, a favorite from American history. The military strategy behind the defense of the San Antonio mission in Texas' struggle for Independence from Mexico captivated Buchanan's military mind. In the past, the Southern Baptist couple spent time in San Antonio for ministry conferences, visiting the Alamo. For minutes on end, the couple goggled at the complex detail of the sand Alamo in every nook and cranny of the structure.

"It's incredible." Buchanan said.

"Sure is." added Dorothy.

Following moments expressing a high admiration for the artist's skills with art, the loving couple returned to their beach towels, lying down beside one another.

"I love the beach. It's fun." Dorothy said.

"Yeah, but it's still hot. Can only take so much, Babe." Robert quipped. "Besides, you know what they say, 'Summer heat instills an inner self to endure anything."

Dorothy smirks and says, "That's baloney. You just made that up, didn't ya?"

Robert smiles wide.

Tolerating the sweltering heat for two hours under the sun, the snow white skin had had enough. Daily, Robert had endured the heat in Southeastern Asia for months, saturating every ounce of energy out of him. He had had enough. Gathering up their belongings, the couple headed for their hotel room.

On returning to their room, they took advantage of room service and ate lunch in house. Buchanan took every chance offered to him to simply lounge around and do nothing but watch TV, read, talk, reminiscence of home and family, and whatever else might come to mind. Besides, there are only three precious days left together. Time was of the essence, to be valued for the rest of the R & R.

As late afternoon caught up to Robert and Dorothy, he called room service for supper to be delivered at 1700 hours. Hunger hit the couple hard, following all the energy possessed between the two of them all sucked up from the sun scorched beaches of Hawaii. The Buchanan's set out to have a bellyful. The immense size of the order alone meant to make pigs of themselves. The order comprised two 12 ounce steaks, two loaded baked potatoes, salad, a full order of bread, and cheesecake for dessert. 'Wow!' Dorothy thought. 'I'm due to go cold turkey when I get back home.'

The pair enjoyed each other's company more this night than any other spent in Hawaii. No going out to eat. No going out sightseeing. No going out to a concert. Nothing but the company of two loving spouses, savoring every bite of their meal. Buchanan had had his fill of military rations and MREs in Vietnam, at least for the time being.

For two hours after supper, the pair talked each other's ears off. Everything from family to politics, movies to personal dreams in life, and even the plans for their return to Ohio, if the Navy prevented Robert from staying on active duty.

As the evening turned to night, the conversation never ended. The pair enjoyed each other's company for the short few days left to visit before Robert's flight in three days to transport him back to Vietnam.

Lying flat on the bed, Dorothy stared straight up into the ceiling as she chatted and chatted away, absorbing every minute, every moment left with Robert.

Dorothy said, "Kathleen has grown so much since you've seen her last. Her motor skills are coming along just great. Ya know, my nursing training ingrained in me that the motor skills are critical for the development of a young child. I think too she's resembling my kinfolk quite a bit. But here recently, I'm getting to where, well, she reflects your -"

Interrupting herself in mid-sentence, Dorothy glanced toward Robert, who had dozed off. Exhausted, he had run out of gas.

Out of curiosity, Dorothy glared at Robert for hours. She grew frustrated in her attempts to piece together what sorts of immediate dreams and thoughts Robert might experience as he sawed logs. She only imagined what thoughts emerged within his sleep patterns. Hooked on what might twirl around within Robert's mind, Dorothy froze, captivated by every expression on his face. Dorothy caught herself transfixed on facial features, longing to know more of his experience with war in the past year. The emotional letters she received in the mail from Vietnam revealed a ghastly, horrific firsthand experience of war for Robert. Any initiative on her part to describe his experience amounted to an effortless attempt beyond words.

Running out of energy herself, Dorothy dozed off.

To dream in the Buchanan clan came naturally. It flowed in the blood veins as part of the family's DNA. If a member lacked nights of dreaming, the family would think it odd. As heavy sleepers, Dorothy dozed off dreaming of Ohio. In her deep sleep, the weather reflected an early cool October in Northern Ohio with her parents and brother's family picnicking, a favorite pastime in Tuscarawas County. The family unit enjoyed the cool air in a park full of trees, elaborate fountains, and benches in New Philadelphia, Ohio. The beautiful fall colors appeared abundant at every turn on the leaves and autumn decorations, including the plumb, healthy pumpkins placed by the county in the park for the season. An embankment, abundantly full of trees east of the center park pavilion, displayed the resplendent seasonal fall colors. Of the four seasons, the fall ranked high as one of the Buchanan's favorite seasons. The weather in the dream depicted the perfect climate for a cool October picnic in northwestern Ohio.

As usual, the food gathered mirrored dishes featuring popular chefs on television programs – baked ham, sweet potatoes, potato salad, corn on the cob, green beans, and Dorothy's mother's famous red cake with heavy cream cheese icing. The family enjoyed the bounty of the fall. Each member enjoyed the company of loved one's telling jokes, laughing, lifting each other up, the children playing capture the flag, and expressing love for one another simply by spending precious time together as a family unit.

An oddity throughout the dream sequence, however, had been Robert's absence. Dorothy's parents, her brother and his wife and kids, the family dogs - energetic Dachshunds - paced all about. But no Robert.

Though Robert was nowhere to be seen in the dream, Dorothy's family lived a world of amusement, laughing, enjoying life, and savoring the bounty of the fall, satisfying the hearty appetites of the Mayse's, Dorothy's maiden name.

In Dorothy's dream state, the physical body of family members seemed older, as if in a time warp, but yet maintained the youth of earlier years. Regardless, the dream stressed life without Robert.

As the children of the family played capture the flag, Johanna Kathleen fell, scraping her knees while running and playing.

An immediate cry came from Johanna Kathleen, rubbing her knees to ease the pain inflicted from the rough rocks next to the swing sets in the park. Rushing to Johanna, Dorothy stooped down to comfort her, checking her knees for injury. As Dorothy squatted down, she hugged her tight, letting her nursing training kick in. She thoroughly treated her baby's wounds.

"It's OK, Johanna. It's just a nasty scratch. I'll doctor you up. No worries." Dorothy said.

"No! No! It's hurts so bad!" Johanna cried even louder. Her wounds stung with pain.

"Pain! Pain!" Johanna yelled. "No more pain!"

Dorothy grabbed Johanna's shoulders, staring straight into her eyes, to grasp the cause of such pain. Terror filled Johanna's eyes as Dorothy searched for the source of pain.

Johanna's cries surge boisterously, thundering in volume.

"Johanna! Johanna! What's wrong!?! What's wrong!?!" Dorothy asked frantically.

"Ah!" yelled Johanna.

Dorothy let loose of Johanna leaning back, catching flies in total amazement.

Johanna, by now, is totally out of control. Falling backward onto the ground, she turns white, frantic with pain.

"AAAAHHHHHHHHHH!" screamed Johanna.

"STOP! HELP HER! STOP! STOP IT!" Dorothy shrieked. She leaned back on the ground, helpless to rescue her baby.

The climactic end of the nightmare neared, as Dorothy slowly woke up, pleased beyond words the dream brewed near. Never had she experienced such a disturbing nightmare. Bewildered at a loss for words, she panted, breathing heavy from fatigue.

Slowly gaining consciousness, the screams of Johanna, thankfully, dissipated from Dorothy's mind.

Waking up on her right side of the bed toward the wall of the hotel room, she discovered Robert was missing.

As Dorothy regained her cognitive state, Johanna's yells and screams quickly ended. Only to be replaced by another voice screaming. A scream easily detectable, an outcry belonging to Robert.

A dreadful scream indeed. Robert woke up from a nightmare resulting from a flashback of combat.

Popping up from the bed, Dorothy turned her attention to the screams. She froze, staring sorrowfully at Robert, who, in a fetal position on the floor, fell completely out of control of himself. Hitting the television set on top of a wooden stand at the foot of the bed, Robert seemed as if every muscle in his body stiffened from his control.

Robert's shakes and screams turned bit by bit to innocent childlike whimpers.

As Robert regained his surroundings, he spoke various inaudibles to Dorothy. Finally, she perceived a plea of comfort. "Help me. Please...help me."

Shocked and baffled, Dorothy sat stiffly, dazed at the foot of the bed, not knowing what to do, what to say. She caught herself catching flies, looking down upon her husband in utter amazement.

Slowly stooping down, she gently touched Robert's shoulders and arms with her soft, comforting hands.

Dorothy realized the war had changed Robert forever.

His appearance displayed a pitiful sight on the floor. For the rest of Robert's life, he faced the susceptibility of being confronted with his war experience anytime, anywhere.

Dorothy held a strong constitution within herself, but could no longer hold back her emotion. As she wept at the sight in front of her, she fell into a deep saddened state at what the war had done to her devoted and loving husband. Laying on her backside down beside Robert, she hugged him in her arms, weeping, squeezing her husband. The comfort of Dorothy's warm and solemn presence in the stressful state Robert found himself in soothed his heart and soul, far better than any classical piece of music could ever do.

For five minutes, Dorothy sat on the floor consoling Robert. She then stood on her feet to gently and deliberately guide Robert onto the bed to encourage him to sleep.

"Come on, babe. Lie down. You'll feel better." Dorothy said, fighting back more tears.

Dorothy guided him to bed, lying him on his back. She remained by his side till morning.

"There you go, Robert. Now - Now try to rest. I'll be right here - by your side." Dorothy commented.

Dorothy couldn't take her eyes off of him for the remaining part of the night. Dorothy did nothing but ask silent questions in the dark of night for the cause of Robert's suffering. She received no answers to her questions. She silently asked, 'What in Heaven's name did Robert experience in Vietnam for him to have such a traumatizing nightmare?'

She could only imagine. Was it the first hand experience witnessing the death of human beings? Perhaps it embraced the agony and pain of children suffered at the hands of the Viet Cong he wrote about in his letters. Or possibly the excoriating pain and anguish of wounded marines as Robert prayed over them. Maybe the dying marines, breathing their last, as Robert held them. Dorothy now knew an eyewitness experience of a violent war will touch those who participated in it for the rest of their lives.

With all the efforts Dorothy mustered to conceive a reasonable answer to Robert's experience in Vietnam, she never in her life came close to comprehending Robert's exposure to war.

The lengthy, intent gaze of Dorothy on Robert generated a state of despondency. She witnessed tonight the first of many flashbacks. Suddenly, she felt as if a ton of bricks hit her all at once, realizing the real danger Robert will return to in four days.

The morning came soon. And with daylight comes a new day - a day for Robert to start anew.

The next day launched a turning point in the couple's lives. Every day, in the back of their minds, they knew last night's event changed their lives forever.

Neither one spoke a peep about what happened until Robert returned home from Vietnam.

Dorothy knew one certain fact from now on in her life: war had changed Robert. Changed him forever. War triggered a devastating mental impact on her love in life.

Permanent now in Buchanan's mind stood a mental, emotional state of war.

Robert never faced his flashbacks alone. Dorothy faithfully stood beside him, present in his life to protect and console him following a war memory.

She never left his side.

Saying Goodbye

April 22, 1969

The discord in an airport reflects the cacophony of blended echoes bouncing off walls, vibrating down each terminal. The opus of the countless human tones of voices, fused with the clamor of restaurants and transactions in airport merchandise stores, added to the cacophony of echoes. The incessant clanging of restaurant dishes, restaurant glasses, waiters and waitresses conversing with customers, along with the passing by of passengers all welded together, humming and droning with a numbing result.

Honolulu International Airport never stops.

Robert and Dorothy, genuinely in love with each other, sat at Terminal A, Gate 5, in the middle of the Honolulu International Airport noise. Soon, the couple will face yet another long separation. A parting of necessity, but an uninvited farewell. One of obligation, but voluntary in nature.

The last day of rest and relaxation came for the Buchanan's. Knowing the day inevitably would come, neither one yearned for it to come so hastily. Not a word said from either of them out of fear they would never see each other again, from the trepidation of an unknown future. The last three and a half days spent in Hawaii were ones felt of anxiety and fear.

Ten days in Hawaii flew by, coming to an abrupt end just as the couple began to have fun. Ten days of enjoying each other's company, never to be forgotten.

Over the years, the Buchanan's cardinal rule called for the family to arrive two hours early at the airport for a flight, military or civilian. Never were the risks dared to tempt fate and miss a flight. Not in the Buchanan household.

So, as usual, Robert and Dorothy arrived two hours early for Buchanan's flight to Japan. Two precious hours together prior to Robert boarding a military flight from Japan to Okinawa marine air base, then back to South Vietnam.

Dorothy's flight, number 0604, at 1530 hours to Los Angeles International Airport, shadowed Robert's by 30 minutes at Gate 3 of Terminal C.

Expecting Robert's flight sitting at Gate 5, Dorothy spent time in the airport as she does on the beach, people watching. The different peoples and cultures of patrons observed in the airport passing by aided the monotony of sitting for an airline flight.

Glancing from the corner of her eye at a family passing by, she leans over to Robert, nods says with confidence, "Midwesterners. I'd bet on it."

With a raised eyelid, Robert smiles wide. "How do you know?"

"It's that congenial, good-natured Midwestern appearance - if not Midwesterners, mountain folks for sure. If not mountain folks, southerners, for *sure*."

Shaking his head, Robert chuckles. "You've always people watched in the airport, haven't ya?"

Turning to Robert, Dorothy grins and, with assertion, says, "Yes."

"You love people, don't ya?"

Dorothy paused. "Yes. Yes, I do." Thinking to herself, she says, "Well, I've always enjoyed the company of others. But ever since I became a believer, Jesus changed how I treated 'em. You know what I mean. We've discussed it in the past."

"Yes, yes. I know. I was the same."

The pair glared at one another with intensity and curiosity.

Robert said, "You're special. You are."

Dorothy shrugs and nods her head no. She never in public presented herself as a pastor's wife or a nurse who pranced forward in life smug and uppity.

"Please." said a modest Dorothy.

Robert knew in his heart Dorothy had indeed influenced parishioners with a witness of Jesus.

"When we were ministering in Columbus, the mother in ya and the spiritual leader you are in church made the perfect spiritual mentor in the lives of those members of the church." Robert said. "And the children. They loved ya. The Sunday School lessons and the music you introduced them to, well - will impact them 25 years from now and beyond."

"Stop." Dorothy said, rolling her eyes, smiling. Thinking of full-time ministry, Dorothy admits, "You know. I miss the parishioners. I really do."

The pair hug, chuckling at the great times experienced with the church in Columbus, Ohio.

"Well. You're not so bad yourself. Your sermons are straight from your heart and you're so genuine with your pastoral care."

Smiling, Robert shrugs.

"You know as well as I do, you'd get up at two or three o'clock in the morning to respond to a need or an emergency if called upon." Dorothy added.

The couple continue to people watch, as they extend their conversation.

"Your sermons are great, Robert. Every sermon has a lesson on how to be a better follower and believer in Jesus."

"I suppose." Robert shuffles in his seat a bit, grinning. He insisted accolades and rewards were for those who desired attention. His modesty preserved because of his insistence that he worked for Jesus, not himself.

Dorothy interrupted their conversion as she leaned over to Robert. "Northeasterners. I'd bet on it."

Robert glances sternly toward Dorothy with a half smile, shaking his head.

"How do ya know?" Robert asked.

"Well, Northeasterners. Can't you tell?" Dorothy said, smiling widely.

Robert grins with a stern stare, shaking his head.

Following Dorothy's assertions of the Northeastern family, she spotted a couple she insisted were southerners on their honeymoon.

She interrupted her own thoughts and said, "The marines." Gazing into Robert's eyes with curiosity, Dorothy repeats herself. "The marines. They need you, don't they?"

Swallowing hard, Robert looked out toward the tarmac. "Yes… Yes. My presence has been, well, yes - a positive encouragement for them."

Grasping his hand, she delivers a loving smile straight at Robert, as he looks deep into his loving and beautiful wife's green eyes, holding back the hurt of war.

"It's terrible." Robert said, fighting the emotions.

"Well, God's been with ya. He will never leave you." Dorothy encouraged him with confidence.

Robert slowly grins, knowing her assertions are absolute in the fact God will never leave him.

At 1430 hours, the couple will revere the next 45 minutes for the rest of their lives. The pair longed for the 45 minutes to last for an eternity, as Robert's departure time at 1515 hours will come quick.

Holding hands, Robert and Dorothy spoke of everything from family in the Tri-State area in Ohio to cooking, to sports and even politics, including the great potential Nixon had as president.

Time passes quickly, as the past ten days slipped by them in a blink of an eye.

Before they knew what hit them, the time to depart came about. 1515 hours on this day will soon be history.

What neither Robert nor Dorothy wanted to hear on the PA system came the announcement - 'International Flight 1127 for Japan at Gate 5 Terminal A is ready for boarding. All passengers, please report to Gate 5.'

A state of consternation set in, as the two turned snow white, noticing one another's complexion. The inevitable announcement for boarding the plane resulted in an unwelcome frown.

The pair stood up, clutching one carry-on bag in one hand and holding hands with the other, stepping closer to the gate.

Halting in route to Gate 5, the pair wrapped their arms around each other. Robert fixated himself on Dorothy, giving her a long, loving, and adoring kiss.

All the while, Dorothy held back her tears. She shunned making matters worse for Robert by failing to control her emotions. Keeping her composure in front of Robert aided in the best interest of his sanity.

"I love you." Robert acknowledged.

"Love you too, babe."

"I'll be home in six months. Kiss and hug our babies for me." Robert requested.

"I'll kiss and hug each and everyone of them with your blessings upon them."

The loving pair locked eyes one last time, for old time's sake. They gazed at one another as if it would be the last time they would set their eyes on each other again in this life.

Reality finally hit them with the last announcement for Robert's flight - 'Last call for boarding Flight 1127 for Tokyo Japan Gate 5 Terminal A. All passengers for Flight 1127, please make your way to Gate 5 Terminal A for boarding. Thank you.'

"I've got to go, babe." said a sorrowful Robert. He stepped toward the gate, presenting his ticket to the attendant, who tore carefully the confirmation stub off, handing his ticket back to Robert.

Glancing toward Dorothy, Robert read her lips. 'I love you.' Robert reciprocated the heartfelt expression of love before turning toward the plane for his long trip back to the jungles of southeastern Asia.

The couple threw one last glimpse back toward one another until October, neither wanting the moment to end.

Then Robert turned, walking out to the tarmac toward the plane. As he walked toward the aircraft, Dorothy stood fulfilling another tradition of the Buchanan clan while in the airport - to keep an eye focused on a loved one board a plane, followed up by watching the plane take off before leaving the airport for home. Dorothy spotted Robert the whole way over the tarmac, then up the airstair, as he turned waving to her for everyone to see. Though looking back at Dorothy, Robert stood incapable of sighting her because of the glare of the sun upon the windows of the airport.

She waved back, unaware of his inability to spot her.

Despite the obstruction, they waved regardless as Robert stepped into the plane out of sight of Dorothy.

Instantly, the thought of never seeing her loving husband again made her blood run cold.

The unbearable thought of Robert's name on a KIA list rankled Dorothy daily. The horrifying thought of his babies growing up, never knowing their father ate at her gut bit by bit. The fright of Dorothy knowing her children would lack a father mentor struck her as inconceivable. She just couldn't imagine her children missing out on experiencing Robert's personality and knowing him as a positive influence on them growing up into adults.

As Dorothy observed Robert's plane fly into the sky and out of sight, she turned toward the gate for her flight to Los Angeles. Fighting back her emotion walking toward her gate, she insisted on being strong for Robert's sake, regardless of her situation. Dorothy arrived at Gate 3 Terminal C for her flight 0604 for Los Angeles International Airport to be picked up by a fellow chaplain's wife.

As she settled into her seat at Gate 3, she immediately noticed a marine officer family of five sitting straight across from her. She certainly wasn't ease dropping, but she innocently overheard the family conversation, realizing they were on their way home to Tennessee. His tour in Vietnam ended ten days ago. His family met him in Hawaii for a family vacation following his one-year tour in Vietnam to celebrate his return home. What a loving and close knit family she observed, supportive of one another as a family unit. Laughing, having fun. Each member enjoying each other's company. The talk of Hawaii's beauty and the last ten days spent, relishing the fruits of the islands.

The thought of separation from Robert for six more months will come with great sacrifice for Dorothy. She longed for her family to be together again, such as the Tennessee family across from her. Sitting patiently in her seat for her flight, she said a silent prayer, 'Lord, if it be your will, bring Robert back in one piece. Alive and well. His babies await him. They need his loving presence in their lives. Protect him. Strengthen him. Guard him against the Evil One. Amen.'

As a Baptist, she prayed every day for God's intervention in Robert's life.

Dorothy would indeed board her plane, along with the Tennessee family, to Los Angeles. The mountaineer family just had their seats in the same row as Dorothy. A friendly reminder of the separation from Robert for 192 long, agonizing days. An eternity for Dorothy.

For 192 days, Dorothy will recite the same request prayed in her seat in the airport, even writing the prayer down in her notes section of her devotional Bible.

Though confident God's omnipotence and omniscience in world affairs determined the outcome of human history, Dorothy still knew Robert's fate in Vietnam relied on the Lord's permissive will.

Attaining the finite state Dorothy possessed as a human being, she agonized daily knowing whether her loving husband would ever be home again.

Only God knew.

The Sacrifice of Men

April 28, 1969

Reading the latest reports of the war in his swivel chair, Buchanan could hardly keep himself from throwing up his breakfast all over his desk. Catching up with the recent war news nauseated him to no end. The newspapers Dorothy and his brothers had sent him in the mail sickened him as the press printed the war to fit their own political slant. Without a doubt, Buchanan trusted military briefs far more than those of civilian sources reporting the war. Reading through the reports, Buchanan knew with no doubt the United States had won nearly all the battles, but continued to lose the war with public opinion due to the press. He also convinced himself further the United States had been losing the war because of the bureaucracy in Washington DC, tying the hands of military strategists and generals who knew exactly what to do to win the war in a shorter time period.

Days before departing for Hawaii, Buchanan noticed the war escalating in South Vietnam. On April 9, civilian workers discovered 65 additional victims, murdered by the Viet Cong. The atrocities in and around Hue during the Tet offensive added to the evidence for those who loathed the VC that they were nothing but a bunch of no-goods. Now the number of massacred in Hue rose to 2,200 victims. April 10 and 11 erupted into fierce confrontations between the United States and Communist forces, resulting in heavy casualties in the Mekong Delta and Saigon. Between April 12 and 18, American forces inflicted severe and bruising campaigns against the

Communists, resulting in heavy casualties upon the NVA and Viet Cong forces, such as the pacification operation Washington Green, conducted by the 173rd Airborne Brigade. In March, Operation Menu was carried out over 14 months by bombing the smithereens out of Communist positions in Cambodia and Laos, with devastating results for the United States, though the campaign prevented future enemy movements and operations into South Vietnam.

Buchanan read in the reports the United States continued to hammer away at the Communists, delivering devastating blows onto the enemy with heavy causalities, only to see the Communists charge ahead with even greater numbers of armed combatants only to be blown apart with ferocious fire power. Starting on April 18 through the last day of December 1969, the ARVN's 22nd Division conducted military maneuvers, Dan Thang 69, delivering hefty enemy casualties in the Binh Dinh province. On April 24 and 25, the heaviest bombardment of the war took place from nearly 100 B-52 bombers, centered out of Thailand and Guam, in a border area 70 miles northwest of Saigon. The United States dropped 3000 tons of bombs, causing severe damage. Unfortunately, no appropriate offensive ensued following the bombing of the area. The Communists continued to suffer from substantial casualties from border battles with United States forces, soldiers and marines, on the Cambodian border 45 miles northwest of Saigon. On April 26, 1969, the Communists suffered 213 killed in one day alone and possibly hundreds wounded, with only one American killed and one wounded.

Though many military successes of American forces were in the news, Buchanan sat in his swivel chair seething with the thoughts of politicians interfering in the war, the negative press of the media, and the silly protesters back home, an Iron Triangle of three antagonist hindering the winning of the war and the admirable attempt of United States forces to stop the spread of a suppressive and cruel system of government that exists in Communism.

Contemplating the state of the war in his chair, Buchanan recalled Burns' selected piece of music last night to lighten the mood in camp - Joseph Haydn's Opus 33 number two string quartet, 'The

Joke.' Hayden, known as the 'Father of the String Quartet.', wrote a famous set of four quartets which has lasted in popularity for decades. 'The Joke', the second of the four, appeals to many fans of classical music. For music lovers, the composition's rondo in the last movement presents an intriguing theme of changing contrasting tunes in different keys. The central theme of the piece focusing on joy and interchange. The movement reflects the 'storm and stress' drama in Hayden's op. 20 quartets.

Burns lightened the mood in camp as it eased the pain for Buchanan a bit from reading of individuals, American citizens, and political groups in the United States dead set to see the United States lose the war. Buchanan's interest in reading the military successes of the war balanced out the muck and filth the media dished out of twisted truths. The music relieved Buchanan of his nightmares the prior night.

The peculiar nightmare reflected the agony of war. Dorothy and his children donned military uniforms, armed with every weapon imaginable, on patrol, with Rockford leading them through the jungle, along with Jackson and Skawinski. In the darkness of night and approaching a narrowing ravine, the patrol converged onto a sharp incline that dead ends, with the Devil and the Viet Cong awaiting them for an ambush. Buchanan's presence appeared in the dream, but no one in the dream heard or acknowledged him. No one could see him, for he was invisible. Buchanan's presence failed to stop the ambush. Running to Skawinski, Jackson and Rockford, he yelled nose to nose, pleading for them to turn back. He hollered a boisterous scream to his wife and his children, "Go back! Go back!" He shouted to the marines, "Stop! Stop!" Regardless of Buchanan's pleas, his family and friends ignored all of them. All of his attempts to warn his family and friends to no avail. His last resort, out of desperation, came to pushing on the torsos of his family and friends, but to no avail. Closer and closer the patrol stepped toward the sharp incline, unbeknownst to the Devil and the Viet Cong awaiting them. Panicking, a petrified Buchanan again stood nose to nose with Rockford, Jackson, Dorothy, and Skawinski, yelling at the top of his voice, "STOP! STOP! The enemy's at the end of the ravine." The patrol continued to go forward quietly and cautiously. Buchanan looked on in dismay. All the while, a cackling Devil lie in wait with the Viet Cong, licking their chops, patiently awaiting their prey to step into the trap, wide eyed with the chance to pounce upon the innocent of the world.

Death awaited Buchanan's family, as he watched his loved one's walk into a slaughterhouse, helpless to do anything about it. Buchanan is delirious as he leaps in front of Rockford and Jackson to get their attention. He sweats, pants, and yells for the patrol to turn about and go in the other direction. He shouted one last plea, "Go back! The Devil is over that embankment!" He points toward the sharp elevated ravine, but no one paid any attention. He attempted to stop the slaughter. But to no avail!

He finally falls on his knees, desperately praying to God for help. "Please God! Please, help! Protect my family!" As his family and the patrol advanced toward the ravine with the Grim Reaper waiting, Buchanan continues to scream at the top of his lungs, "STOP!"

The Devil curled his index finger for the sinister Viet Cong, all cackling away, to move forward in his direction. His index finger - long, white, crinkled, and topped with the most grotesque finger nail - circled, methodically teasing the killers to step forward to carry out the nefarious slaying.

The Viet Cong, in an L shaped ambush position, slowly raise their weapons to attack Buchanan's family. By now, Buchanan is paralyzed by what is about to happen. As the Viet Cong were about to fire their weapons, laughter emerged from their mouths, loud and hideous. Buchanan shouts louder, "STOP! STOP! Danger lies ahead of you!" Still, no response from those on patrol in the dream.

To his delight, he woke up. To his dread, he awoke listening to the guffawing of the Devil and the Viet Cong.

Nothing came to mind the past six days for Buchanan but Dorothy, missing her physical presence in his life. Especially after ten days spent together in Hawaii. It's a natural instinct for a husband to think of his wife so far away from home in the middle of a war zone. He only wished for pleasant dreams of Dorothy. Not nightmares with her having a part of his dreams of war.

Buchanan woke up this the morning scheduled for cooler duty at 0900 hours. He had 30 minutes from forcing himself to walk for the duty which he hated.

Buchanan read a letter for the umpteenth time inserted in a thinking of you card received from Dorothy dated the 23th of April to lift his spirits.

Just as he finished the letter, a sturdy knock came banging from the hootch door.

"Yes. Who goes there?" Buchanan asked with curiosity. He heard two marines chuckling from the other side of the door. "Did you hear him? He said, 'Who goes there?'" whispered one marine in a spooky voice.

After a brief pause, Sergeant Jackson answered, "It's me, sir. Along with Ski."

Grinning, Skawinski commented, "Door's locked, sir. Ya got your latch hooked."

"Oh. Yes. I-I was hoping y'all would show up." Buchanan said, as he stepped out from behind his desk to let his two enlisted marine friends in. Unlatching the hook, he opens the door to two smiling young marines looking forward to another day, spending it with their encouraging chaplain.

"Paranoid Charlie's going to sneak in, sir." Jackson pointed out sarcastically.

The enlisted friends strutted into the hootch, sitting confidently in the two chairs opposite of Buchanan's desk.

Buchanan strolls his way back behind his desk, and says in passing, "No, it's not anything like that. The early morning hours always seem creepier to me. The enemy is a little more conniving in the mornings." Buchanan's enlisted friends chuckle, shaking their heads.

"The enemy just thinks we're less attentive and careless in the mornings since we're all waking up. We're more drowsy and less alert." Buchanan said. He insists with conviction, "I'm telling ya the truth."

"Ya know, Padre. You're a bird in this world." Jackson commented, grinning, nodding his head.

"May-be! But we're still vulnerable in the morning." said Buchanan, grinning.

"Well, sir. Ya might have a point." Skawinski said.

"I know I do." said Buchanan, knowing he asserted the truth.

"I love for the two of you to drop by for fellowship's sake. Ya know that. But, -" Buchanan interrupted himself, looked down at his watch, and glanced back toward his two enlisted friends, and asked, "I trust that the two of you are here to accompany me to the cooler?"

Buchanan cringed ever so slightly for an answer, turning his head to the right, as time stood still for him as he waited patiently for a response. Skawinski finally answered, "Of course, sir. We're not going to sit back some place here in camp, knowing good and well you'd be in the cooler all by your lonesome, carrying out a duty you loathe and detest to no end. So, yes sir - we're here to accompany you to the cooler."

With intent, Skawinski gradually smiles.

"Amen!" Buchanan bellowed, with his hands in the air, smiling from ear to ear. He sighs deeply and says, "Thank the Lord."

Jackson adds sincerely, "Besides, chaplain. You've been there for us, time and time again."

"Our support system for one another here in the camp, well, you created it. And in the brief time we've been together, that's impressive. Like no other we've ever seen, sir. And you're a Baptist." Skawinski said jokingly.

"Amen to that, men. Amen to that."

The marines smile.

"Well, let's go and get this filthy, unwanted job done." Buchanan said with scorn.

"Yes, sir."

The men march themselves to the cooler united in heart and mind, practically in lock step, fast and hurried. The quicker the better.

When the chaplain's office personnel arrived in the cooler's front, the required camp personnel to ID the KIAs were already waiting for

Buchanan - the doctor, staff officer, the corpsman, and the administrative assistant. All present to carry out the grisly task ahead.

The disinclined group hesitantly entered the cooler shocked by the massive numbers of KIAs, two to three marines piled high, from one corner of the cooler to the other.

From his first encounter in the cooler, Buchanan's first impression most permanent on his mind pertaining to the corpses, was the last expression of the deceased displayed, left on his face when taking his last breath of this life. Expressions of shock; of surprise; bewilderment; anger; and of puzzlement.

The cooler this morning never displayed more lifeless remains of human beings, leaving a permanent, lifelong imprint upon Buchanan's mind, taking it with him when he leaves for home, never to depart his memory.

Just under two long, grueling hours, the identification team fulfilled their duty, ID'ing the remains of the fallen. Men once full of life and loved by kinfolk and friends back home. The breaks from ID'ing the KIAs came frequently this day! The unbearable stench alone prompted the men to step out of the cooler for a breather. Even the tough and strong Jackson and Skawinski struggled with the stench of the mangled, destructive condition of the remains.

The relief of winding-up the repulsive cooler duty delivered a better mood for Buchanan for the remaining part of the day. The camp knew full well his hate of completing his responsibility of ID'ing deceased service personnel in the cooler. He knew without a doubt no one back home would ever understand the experience of ID'ing deceased human beings from a fierce firefight with the enemy. Years later, he intentionally held his emotions inside regarding the cooler, withholding the excruciating pain of being subjected to so many dead marines.

After ID'ing the KIA's, Buchanan hustled his way back to the hootch with his enlisted friends, Jackson and Skawinski, who visited with Buchanan out of sheer morale support. The visit strengthened the Christian unity shared between the three men.

As the men paced themselves toward the hootch, Skawinski said, "Well, that's just one more cooler duty out of the way, sir. I know you hate doing it."

With a slow glance and pointing backwards with his thumb, Buchanan said, "The men back there – they were brave young men, who gave their lives for what? For what?"

Walking alongside Buchanan, the marines gave him a sharp gaze, taken aback with Buchanan's statement. It definitely came across as atypical of Chaplain Buchanan. Rarely did anything come out of his mouth that wasn't to support fighting the war to win and providing the South Vietnamese to live free and to prosper with western ideals of freedom. A perplexed Skawinski and Jackson walked, stunned at Buchanan's utterance.

Buchanan pondered for an answer to his own question. "I remember a quote of President Roosevelt I came across the other day, and it went like this, 'Those who have long enjoyed such privileges as we enjoy forget in time that men have died to win them.'"*

Looking out into the middle of camp, the words of President Roosevelt sunk in. Buchanan said, "They gave, no – they sacrificed their lives for others to live such privileges."

The men finally arrive at Buchanan's hootch.

The heart felt moment reminded Jackson and Skawinski the purpose for fighting in South Vietnam, which lied in the principle of establishing democracy in a country who faced living under a Communist state. Buchanan served as a source of assurance and confidence for the men in the bush fighting the war. His presence and source of strong morale gave many marines a reason to continue the effort to fight and win a war, regardless of how many Americans back home would rather see the people of South Vietnam live under a Communist government.

The essential necessity to rest ahead of eating chow to regenerate the heart and soul of the men came immediately. The men required sufficient perseverance to stomach any sort of grub following the past two hours of hell on earth. The well-deserved rest in Buchanan's hootch paved the way to satisfy the longing for any nourishment into their systems.

Following the rest, the men paced themselves to the chow hall and ate till their heart's content, making their way back to Buchanan's hootch to further their well-deserved rest.

The day was young as time stood at 1130 hours sharp.

The mental strain of cooler duty gnawed in the gut of Jackson and Skawinski who were pooped, flopping themselves onto the small couch exhaling a convincing sigh, "Ahhhhh!", while Buchanan collapsed onto his cot, bellowing out, "Whew!"

"Am I dog-tired?" Skawinski commented.

"Amen!" responded Buchanan.

Jackson conceded with a deep-felt, "Amen!"

"15 minute nap men? Whatyasay?" asked Buchanan.

"Then lunch?" answered Jackson, glancing Buchanan's way.

"Yeah. More chow!" Skawinski replied, smiling.

In no time, the men sawed logs, sound asleep. A deep sleep indeed. The mental and physical strain of the cooler took its toll on the men.

Time fleets as the men snored away.

After an hour of solid sleep, Jackson awoke and glanced at his watch, nudging Skawinski. As he wakens, disorientated by his surroundings, locates Jackson in front of him, who says, "Holy Cow, Ski, it's 1250 hours. Aren't you to muster at 1300 hours near Delta hootch headquarters for a sweeping patrol?"

Looking immediately down at his wrist, Skawinski read his watch - 1249 hours exactly. He quickly says, "No chow today!"

Buchanan regains his consciousness and says, "Men?"

As Buchanan spoke, Skawinski jumped up, and like a blur runs out of the hootch, uttering, "Catch ya all later!"

"W-What was that-that all about? That's not like him. Is he alright?" asked a drowsy Buchanan.

"Well, sir, Ski's due for a muster at 1300 for a patrol to sweep Route 1 and Route 540." answered Jackson with a bit of surprise in his voice.

Alarmed, Buchanan asked, "What? What time is it?"

Jackson, looking back onto his watch, answered, "It is now, according to my watch - 1250 hours - exactly."

"What? You're kidding? We slept for over an hour? In the middle of the day!?! That's nothing but laziness! As Mrs. Buchanan would put it, 'Shear, unadulterated laziness!'" Buchanan bellowed.

Jackson, now upright on the couch, chuckles at Buchanan's response to the time. "Sir. It's OK! People sleep during the day every day. They do it all the time. Men coming in from patrol. Men who have had duty all night. Believe me, it's OK!"

Buchanan steps onto the floor of his cot, looking down at Jackson. "Yes, but I have to set an example. Sleeping during the day was a big no-no during my enlisted days and in charge of men. It's still the rules."

Buchanan adds, "I've not overslept or slept during the day since I arrived in Vietnam. This is a first!" He points his finger at Jackson to make his point loud and clear. "This will be the first and the last time. You can be assured."

Jackson slowly rises out of the couch. "Sir. We're in a war zone. It's OK! They're just some rules to be broken."

With a grin, Jackson says, "You know who you're beginning to sound like....you-know-who."

"Who's you-know-who?" asked a hesitant Buchanan. And with an abrupt response says, "The pompous ass?"

"Yep. The pompous ass!" Jackson said, responding with a sarcastic chuckle.

"Yuch!" answered Buchanan with disdain.

Porch will be the last person on earth Buchanan desires to emulate. The only person's demeanor he wanted to imitate was Jesus'.

"Well, maybe I am overreacting." commented Buchanan.

"Just a bit, sir. Just a bit." Jackson said. "How about some more chow, sir?"

"Amen to that, sergeant! Eating some grub might do us some good."

Though Buchanan's day found plenty of mental inferences – news of the war, classical music, frightening nightmares, the nap, oversleeping, displaying Porch like behavior - he failed to dislodge the permanent, implanted memories of cooler duty and the men who sacrificed themselves for the freedom of others.

THE DUMB JOCK

APRIL 28, 1969

Buchanan will end the day with a hearty chow with Jackson. The spiritual team rested for most of the day prior to chow to prepare for a scheduled bush patrol to conduct Communion services.

Turning slightly, Buchanan reminded Jackson, "See ya in a little while for some chow. Remember, tomorrow morning Sergeant, 0600 hours sharp to eat breakfast. Then, head for the bush to conduct Communion with the men!"

"Will do, sir! Will do! I'll be ready!" answered Jackson gleefully.

"Bye, Sergeant!"

"Bye-Bye, sir!"

The spiritual team departed early in the day, 1515 hours, for their respective hootches to rest. The jungle patrol scheduled the spiritual team for several days in the bush to conduct devotions and Communion services in the field. In his time of leisure, Buchanan hoped for the prospect of reading some history and prepare his devotions to lead the men spiritually. After some reading and rest, he pondered the thought of popping in on Jackson to convince him to visit the camp departments.

Keen on reading the several history books on hand, Buchanan felt obliged to fulfill a promise made to Arthur and Churchill. Pulling from his jungle dungaree pockets, he drew three rather large bundles of napkins full of fruit and vegetables, smuggled out of the chow hall. He felt sure his amphibian friends appreciated the frequent treats brought from the chow hall. It was the least he could do for his two lizard friends protecting him over the past few months from the annoying pests in the jungles of Vietnam.

He looked forward to relocating his amphibian friends to southern California as pets, great additions to the family to protect the Buchanan clan from pests in southern California, along with the family Dachshunds.

Buchanan stepped to the small bookshelf, reaching down toward the wall of the hootch under the bookshelves, spreading the fruit and vegetables onto the floor along the wall for his two reptile friends to feast upon. With daylight and all the commotion, Arthur and Churchill might be skittish, emerging from hiding until darkness. Nonetheless, come the next morning, the treats would be gone. All he cared about had been to reward his reptile friends a bit more for the security they rendered in a mysterious and dangerous part of the world full of poisonous reptiles and aggressive predators, let alone the massive numbers of insects.

He stood up, ambling his way to his swivel chair. "Whew!" Buchanan sighed, falling back onto the seat of the chair.

Glancing down on his desk at a book on European military tactics during the age of Marlborough, he opened the book up where he left off last, beginning to read.

Just five minutes into reading, two distinct knocks came from his door.

Buchanan yearned to say in jest, 'Who goes there?', but thought otherwise and asked, "Yes. What can I do for ya?"

"It's Staff Sergeant Jack Roberts. You don't know me, but I know you."

"Come in. Come in. Please come in, by all means."

As the hootch door flew open, Buchanan gawked, catching flies. He gulped hard as he laid his eyes on one of the biggest, dumbest looking Neanderthal, 'dumb jock' football players he had ever seen in his life.

The marine stood 6'4", with a robust 235 pounds to go along with him.

Buchanan thought to himself, 'Oh great! Everything this week has brought, and now this specimen of a meathead.'

However, a sudden second thought emerged in Buchanan's mind of this mountain of a man, 'Jack Barnes sure could make a heck of a tight end out of him at Ohio State.'

Anyone close to Buchanan knew full well the contempt he held inside for the silly blonde sorority queens and the goofy, grunting – 'I can't think' – football dumb jocks. Buchanan loved football, but never seemed to come around to think too much of a football player's ability to constructively advance and enhance western civilization.

With every step of the massive marine toward his desk, Buchanan felt the hootch shake from side to side with earthquake tremors. From the hootch door to his desk, it took but one step for Roberts to reach the desk, and with an extended hand, introduced himself, "Chaplain Buchanan, it's a pleasure to meet ya."

Smiling from the humor he found in Roberts, Buchanan stood up, extending his hand to his new friend.

"Good to meet ya, Sergeant." Buchanan said, straining himself to hide his discomfort from the strength of the marine's grip. "Jack Barnes sure could use you on the offensive line at Ohio State. Or maybe even a fine tight end."

"Yes sir. Thank ya, sir." replied Roberts, releasing his grip of his hand. An inaudible "Whew" came from Buchanan's mouth with the relief of the handshake.

"No sir, I didn't play for Ohio State. Though I did play for a major school of technology in Georgia. I'm from Georgia." said Roberts in a deep southern accent. Buchanan offered him a seat. "Please sit down, Sergeant." Roberts fell back into the chair in front of the desk.

Buchanan prayed the chair's cuffed foot leg strength withstood the weight and size of the massive muscular body Roberts displayed across from him.

Buchanan feasted his eyes on the specimen in front of him. The only word popping up in Buchanan's mind to describe Roberts seemed to be 'gigantic'. Robert's physique shielded the manchette side supports and the chair itself. The sight presented Roberts sitting in midair. All Buchanan saw in front of him seemed to be a clumsy, dumb jock with a goofy smile on his face. Giving the hootch a good panoramic view, Buchanan assumed Roberts occupied half the space in the hootch, creating an optical illusion of the hootch appearing half the size.

"Haha haha." laughed Buchanan at the sight he saw across from him.

"Did ya hear a good one, sir?" asked Roberts with a bit of curiosity in his voice.

"No, *no*, Sergeant."

Buchanan certainly didn't want to hurt his feelings. "I was just thinking of the last movie I saw prior to your arrival with a favorite English actor who plays a clumsy police detective. You enjoy English humor, don't ya, Sergeant?"

"Yes, sir." answered Roberts with energy. "I love English actors. I especially love English war movies as well. Movies such as those portraying the Zulu Wars and World War II. I love'em. The World War I movie on the life of Lawrence might be my favorite."

Buchanan gaped at his new dumb jock friend, speaking of his favorite English movies, culture, and history as if an intellectual.

In life, first impressions spoke volumes for Buchanan, and his first impression of this big dumb jock presented him a man of intelligence.

He thought, 'Wow! And he's a dumb jock.'

"I love those movies too, Sergeant. I couldn't agree with you more. Lawrence's biography movie is my favorite too. I love when the networks broadcast those films for the movie of the week."

"Me too, sir." commented Roberts.

Roberts, noticing Buchanan curious, interrupted his own self to inform Buchanan the real reason he dropped by his office, to Buchanan's delight.

"Sir, you're probably wondering who I am. Aren't you?" asked Roberts.

Buchanan nodded.

"I'm from Company D. I work with the Seabees, and I know your friend Lieutenant Commander Adkins."

"Yes. *Yes*. He's my friend. *And* I remember you in the bush. You stand out, ya know?"

The men smile at the thought.

"My MOS is construction and we're in the bush quite a bit working with Seabees. You probably have noticed me attending Communion services when you lead in devotions for my company and the Seabees. Lieutenant Commander Adkins informed me you maintain an open door policy, well, just to talk. So, here I am." Roberts nods.

Buchanan noticed Roberts' southern accent. "Sergeant. You say you're a southerner? From Georgia was it? Because you sure gain not only a southern accent, but your demeanor speaks volumes of southern Appalachian culture."

"Why *yes*. Yes, sir. *I* am a southerner, from Fort Oglethorpe, Georgia. It's in Catoosa County."

"The Tri-State area?" asked Buchanan.

"Yes sir. Many of my kinfolk have married folks from Alabama, from Tennessee. I played football and graduated from a major school of technology in Atlanta. While working my civilian job, I ended up being called up for active duty out of my marine reserve unit to serve in Vietnam. I've been out of school for five years now. My family has worked for Coca-Cola – my present employer - for 40 years now. I'll retire from the company someday, like my loved ones in the past."

Roberts paused. "And I'm Southern Baptist, like yourself."

"Amen!" Buchanan quickly responded. "A deacon from a Southern Baptist church in Mobile, Alabama led me to Jesus."

"Yes. Lieutenant Commander Adkins informed me a bit of your past, sir. Alabama possesses some of our most evangelistic congregations."

"I can attest to that." confirmed Buchanan.

Roberts noticed the military history book lying on his desk. "I see you have an interest in military history, sir. Looks like you're brushing up on your European military tactics of the Seventeenth century. The enveloping tactics of the 1600s fascinate me most of that century."

Roberts unleashes himself, outlining his military assessments and interpretations for minutes on end, chatting of military tactics and strategy of the Seventeenth Century.

Sitting in front of Buchanan, Roberts epitomized the stereotypical dumb jock, the shell of a simpleton. Buchanan had set for himself in his own mind for decades that dumb jocks were nothing but a dopey ignoramus. But here in front of him sat this athletic, massive man who spoke words of an educated and enlightened human being, possessing a mind of the social sciences.

Roberts said, "I love that era. I earned my masters in military history from a small university in Tennessee."

Buchanan asserted his convictions for the era. "The Seventeenth century through the Napoleonic Era is my favorite centuries of European study of warfare. Especially the Napoleonic Era. My favorite discussion of study is the line versus column debate in the French Revolution and during Napoleon's reign. Terrain has been a contributing factor in discussing the tactics and strategy on the battlefield for centuries and how to fight in that terrain in either a line or column."

"Yes, sir. I would've loved to have seen who the victor would've been with many a battle if the terrain would've been flat."

"Yes, me too, sergeant. Me too."

With that said, Roberts found himself incapable of holding it in any longer. He shared the contents of his heart. "Yes. *Yes*, sir. My chosen interest in any era is the never ending debate of line versus column. We've something in common. My master's degree, however, was written on a theory of combining the proper implementation of artillery and cavalry simultaneously on the battlefield in the center and the flanks. I revealed that nine out of ten times, the victor employed artillery and cavalry concurrently during the battle."

"Outstanding! I love the study of artillery and cavalry support in battle." Buchanan admitted.

Roberts opened up to Buchanan, as if to unleash all that had built up within him for weeks. "Now with the line versus column debate. Sir Charles Oman's study of the Battle of Maida* gives the best insight of which is most effective in battle – line or column.

And Richard Glover's book on the Peninsular Wars* back in 1963 has an interesting point. Have you read his book on the Peninsular Wars, sir?"

"No, I haven't read that work yet." Buchanan answered.

"Ya need to, sir. It gives great insight into the subject. Of course, David G. Chandler, a new and upcoming military historian, has given the topic some well-deserved attention. Now, from the British point of view, a good read is -" Roberts went on and on and continued to elaborate on sources pertaining to line versus column.

Buchanan sat back in his swivel chair, listening. He simply reveled listening to Robert's intellect. What he marveled most of had been Roberts' expansive base of military history. He found himself taken aback by the sentences coming out of Roberts' mouth. He finally found a man in camp engrossed in military history as much as himself. And a dumb jock, of all people.

As Buchanan cocked his ears listening to Roberts, he thought, 'maybe the Lord's teaching me a lesson today that not all dumb jocks were so dumb.'

He smiles at the thought.

".......and I pretty much pitch my tent in the line camp, sir. I admit, coming from English ancestry, I usually take the British side of view." declared Roberts as he chuckles at his biased statement.

The two men sat mostly for two hours immersing themselves in conversation about military history few men in the camp would have wanted to take part in. The two men engaged in a subject both had longed to discuss since arriving in Vietnam. Though Roberts immensely enjoyed the chat, he finally broke down after delaying as long as possible his true reason for visiting with Buchanan.

Having been in the bush for close to four months on construction and maintenance missions, he had seen much action. The skirmishes and small firefights Roberts encountered in the bush had badgered his psyche to no end. He himself had taken part in many, if not all, of the engagements. He described in chronological order his experience in the bush from start to finish. The construction and maintenance missions were methodically described, with the combat added to his account of the missions. The worst aspect lodged in his memory bank from the combat were the deaths of young men and the suffering of the wounded.

Roberts struggled throughout his depiction of his construction missions. "Chaplain Buchanan. I-I need your help. There's a lot of anguish and pain. I - well, I inflicted much pain and suffering on the enemy myself. I killed many of the enemy, sir."

He dropped his head, beginning to fight his emotions. With time, his hurt turned into an uncontrollable weep.

"I need your help." Roberts pleaded.

Buchanan, overwhelmed, appeared taken aback.

So here is Buchanan who had had an engaging visit on a mutual, common subject for both men - military history. Neither Buchanan nor Roberts had enjoyed a better time in Vietnam than the last two hours, though they were in the middle of what seemed an endless war that could be won quicker if carried out properly.

It would not be the last conversation together on their favorite subject. But for the time being, Roberts sat in the front of Buchanan who suddenly and without warning broke down right in front of him.

Buchanan felt his pain. He himself never took another human being's life, but he himself had held another human being in his arms as he read or quoted Scripture in his last moments, or prayed with a dying marine as he went into eternity.

Buchanan rose out of his swivel chair, grasping his Bible on his desk. He stepped around the right side of his desk toward Roberts.

He snatched the vacant chair on his right, placing it beside Roberts. As he sat down, he placed his right arm around Roberts as far as he could, patting his right shoulder. Buchanan actually patted his upper torso, for Roberts possessed a robust physique.

Buchanan encouraged Roberts the best he could with purpose. "Listen, Sergeant Roberts. God, he - well, He understands. He's with you as a service member."

With phenomenal composure, Roberts asked, "How?"

Buchanan explained. "Well, there are many Scriptures that concern the subject. Here's a few."

Buchanan, from the outset of most sessions counseling marines who took the life of another human being, found himself at a loss for words at the front end of a session. But he recuperated as time passed, sitting with a marine. With Roberts, hearing God's Word will provide the therapeutic need to comfort his inner being.

Buchanan turned in his Bible to Luke 7:1-10.

"Listen to this, Sergeant Roberts. It speaks volumes on how military personnel are lifted up by God, even in ancient days. It's Luke 7:1-10. 'After he had ended all his sayings in the hearing of the people, he entered Caper'na-um. [2] Now a centurion had a slave who was dear to him, who was sick and at the point of death. [3] When he heard of Jesus, he sent to him elders of the Jews, asking him to come and heal his slave. [4] And when they came to Jesus, they besought him earnestly, saying, "He is worthy to have you do this for him, [5] for he loves our nation, and he built us our synagogue." [6] And Jesus went with them. When he was not far from the house, the centurion sent friends to him, saying to him, "Lord, do not trouble yourself, for I am not worthy to have you come under my roof; [7] therefore I did not presume to come to you. But say the word, and let my servant be healed. [8] For I am a man set under authority, with soldiers under me: and I say to one, 'Go,' and he goes; and to another, 'Come,' and he comes; and to my slave, 'Do this,' and he does it." [9] When Jesus heard this he marveled at him, and turned and said to the multitude that followed him, "I tell you, not even in Israel have I found such faith." [10] And when those who had been sent returned to the house, they found the slave well.'

Roberts listened intently to every word in Luke, and with every word, a small glimmer emerged in his eye.

With assurance, Buchanan makes a valid point. "Jesus recognized this man, a soldier, a *Roman* centurion, even a pagan to the Jews, to have possessed the greatest faith in all of Israel. That speaks volumes, doesn't it?"

"Yes."

Buchanan adds to his commentary, "Roman centurions in Roman cohorts didn't rise in ranks without proving themselves worthy.

Sergeant, here is a man who more than likely took the life from others in combat, and Jesus is lifting him up as having the greatest faith in Him than any other in Israel, including his own folks, His fellow Jews! Remember when the authorities came to arrest Jesus?"

"Yes. I do."

"What did Peter have strapped on him? You remember, Sergeant?"

"A sword. For protection." answered Roberts, glancing over to Buchanan, who slightly smiles.

"Yes. *Yes*. A sword. Peter was prepared to take the life of another to protect his Lord Jesus, his friend. If it wasn't so, Peter wouldn't have had the sword."

Buchanan then reminded Roberts of Joshua. "Then there was Joshua. Ya remember, his military prowess and his strong faith in the Lord. All his military expertise and skill amid a war-torn environment during the entrance of the Promised Land would've never happened if Joshua didn't lean on the Lord for leadership. The Hebrews took the land from their enemies with precision and accuracy. None of it would have happened if Joshua would have leaned only on his own skills."

Buchanan's words sunk in with silence.

"Joshua was a man of God, Sergeant. He killed. He killed to, well - protect. He killed to take the promised land, promised landscape to the Hebrews, which never would have been taken without a fight."

"And we as believers, we believe Joshua and the approaching Hebrews coming out of Egypt had a right to the Promised Land."

Buchanan turned to Joshua 1:9. "Listen to this, Sergeant. Joshua 1:9 says this – 'Have I not commanded you? Be strong and of good courage; be not frightened, neither be dismayed; for the Lord your God is with you wherever you go.' This included going into battle too, Sergeant. The Lord sanctioned Joshua and his military conquests."

Roberts nods. "Yes, sir. Thank you, sir."

"Let me finish with some isolated Scriptures. You don't mind, do ya?"

"Of course not, sir."

Buchanan turned to each passage and rattled every one of them off, one by one.

The first was Psalm 56:3-4, 'when I am afraid, I put my trust in you.

4 In God, whose word I praise, in God I trust; I am not afraid; what can flesh do to me?'

Next was Philippians 4:13, 'I can do all things in him who strengthens me.'

The third passage read came from Psalm 29:11, 'May the LORD give strength to his people! May the LORD bless his people with peace!'

Buchanan smiles, consoling Roberts. "I only have two more passages. But I think reading Scripture always helps to cope."

Grinning, Roberts says with assurance, "Yeah."

"Here's the first. One I know you are familiar with. It's Ecclesiastes 3:1-8, entitled 'Everything Has Its Time', listen to the words -

'For everything there is a season, and a time for every matter under heaven:

2 a time to be born, and a time to die;
a time to plant, and a time to pluck up what is planted;
3 a time to kill, and a time to heal;
a time to break down, and a time to build up;
4 a time to weep, and a time to laugh;
a time to mourn, and a time to dance;
5 a time to cast away stones, and a time to gather stones together;
a time to embrace, and a time to refrain from embracing;
6 a time to seek, and a time to lose;
a time to keep, and a time to cast away;
7 a time to rend, and a time to sew;
a time to keep silence, and a time to speak;
8 a time to love, and a time to hate;
a time for war, and a time for peace.'

Roberts shakes his head, smiling with every word spoken.

"Amen!" said Roberts.

Buchanan wraps up reading the scriptures. "Here's the last one, Sergeant. It's one of my favorites, Psalm 46. In fact, Sergeant, and - well, I haven't expressed to anyone till now – but I read this chapter, word for word, every morning when I wake up, ever since I arrived here in Vietnam. It secures me. This Psalm offers me a sentiment the Lord is present with me when accompanying the patrols in the field. In fact, the Psalm provides a presence of the Lord for you men as well."

The two men fight the emotion, as Buchanan reads Psalm 46,

> "God is our refuge and strength,
> a very present help in trouble.
> 2 Therefore we will not fear though the earth should change,
> though the mountains shake in the heart of the sea;
> 3 though its waters roar and foam,
> though the mountains tremble with its tumult.
> 4 There is a river whose streams make glad the city of God,
> the holy habitation of the Most High.
> 5 God is in the midst of her, she shall not be moved;
> God will help her right early.
> 6 The nations rage, the kingdoms totter;
> he utters his voice, the earth melts.
> 7 The Lord of hosts is with us;
> the God of Jacob is our refuge.
> 8 Come, behold the works of the Lord,
> how he has wrought desolations in the earth.
> 9 He makes wars cease to the end of the earth;
> he breaks the bow, and shatters the spear,
> he burns the chariots with fire!
> 10 "Be still, and know that I am God.
> I am exalted among the nations,
> I am exalted in the earth!"
> 11 The Lord of hosts is with us;
> the God of Jacob is our refuge."

As Buchanan finished, the men think in silence of home. Of family. Of sports. The mountains. And friends.

Neither man spoke of their thoughts. But somehow the men knew what lied in each man's heart and soul.

Buchanan pensively stood up, stepping to his desk to retrieve a Chaplain Capadonno crucifix from his lower desk drawer, handing it to Roberts.

Untangling the necklace, Roberts gives the necklace a look over with reverence.

"Thank ya, Chaplain. Thank you very much."

"It's a cross Chaplain Capodanno gave to the men prior to his death. He wanted the men to feel closer to the Lord with a crucifix around their necks as they went into the field of battle. I like it."

Roberts placed it around his neck. "Yes sir. It's just right." He tucked the necklace down into his t-shirt, wearing the necklace for the duration of his tour. In fact, he ended up wearing it till his dying day.

Checking the time on his watch, Buchanan comments, "It's 1815 hours. Enough time possibly for some chow and afterwards, visit the men with my trusted friend and assistant."

"Yes, I know of Sergeant Jackson, indirectly. But I know of him. He's a good man."

"Correction Sergeant – a great man."

"Yes, sir. A great man."

"Amen!" said Buchanan. "Hey. Why don't ya come along with us? I'd be good for you. Chow, then visit the troops. You've been with the same old folks for five or six months. Come on?"

Roberts hesitated, then relented, tagging along for the night.

"OK, Chaplain, I'll go."

"Amen! Come on. We'll pick up Sergeant Jackson and make our way to the chow hall."

After a well-deserved supper, the party of three service personnel visit hootch after hootch, department after department. The visits brought a semblance of customary life to the men.

The visiting party popped into many hootches during the evening, including Delaney, Carroll, Sanborn, Burns, and Rockford's.

While tagging along, Roberts enjoyed immensely a night meeting men from diverse states and backgrounds. He stood back and just watched the spiritual team do their thing - minister to the men. Minister in entertaining the troops with jokes, telling stories, and encouraging the men to convey stories of home - Buchanan's favorite encounter with the men. The spiritual team laughed and joked. The night of visitation never ensued without any talk of sports, football, and food. Buchanan always insisted culture be a part of a conversation with the spiritual team's visits to the men.

Captivated with the spiritual team's rapport with the men, Roberts learned quickly Buchanan became a grunt's chaplain. Never had he seen a chaplain own such an innate personality and precise skill in communicating with individual marines from hootch to hootch. The knack of Buchanan to generate a love for living and a desire to laugh in the middle of a frustrating war of attrition was a sight to behold.

The men loved Buchanan. They treasured the laughs and jokes with their chaplain and his assistant. Marines opened up to the spiritual team, divulging stories of home. To see family and friends again one day proved to be one of the many prompts to fight and stay alive. To live and see home again ended up being the light at the end of the tunnel.

With such a state of euphoria for home, Buchanan's mood shifted to the point even to visit Porch and his fellow officer friends. Officer or enlisted, Buchanan showed identical care and concern for even the stick in the mud and his friends.

Out of earshot of Porch's hootch, Jackson commented, "Well, that visit was as cold as ice, colder than the ice in the chow hall."

The men chuckle.

"Well, you know what the Scriptures say, 'Love your enemies and pray for them.'" said Buchanan.

"Only way to win them over, sir." added Jackson with a smile.

"Amen!" Buchanan affirmed.

The spiritual team shared a fervor for the betterment of the men. Top priority for the team certainly laid in the fact the pair possessed deep within their hearts a zeal to win unbelieving marines to a saving relationship with Jesus. Jackson's hidden crooked past from Buchanan served as a motivator to witness to others. The road of destruction and sure death at a young age laid in front of Jackson with self-inflicted abuse, physical and mental, upon his body. But Jesus changed his life on the straight and narrow. He wanted nothing else but to see Jesus do the same for other young men headed down the wrong road in life.

Witnessing the spiritual team go to work in the hootches this day planted a permanent memory of the war for Roberts, who discovered Buchanan a 'people' oriented minister. He attempted to talk Buchanan into moving to Atlanta, Georgia after his tour in Vietnam and work in the Public Relations department at Coca-Cola, but to no avail.

By the end of the night, the three men made a complete round about of Camp Love visiting the men. The three men finally made their way to their respective hootches for a good night's rest.

Roberts arrived home to his own hootch, exhausted from the weeks of bush work. After brushing his teeth, he read his Bible and said his prayers, laying flat on his cot, staring straight up into the canvas of his hootch.

The evening raced quickly to 2135 hours, five minutes into Burns' music, a piece that seemed hand-picked for Roberts – Mozart's Sonata no. 17 in C major, a favorite of Burns' and a shot in the arm of 'joyful tunes' as he put it. The young Georgian thought of his life as the delightful music soared throughout camp. He especially thought of Chaplain Buchanan, a superb source for a marine to talk problems out. The words and Scriptures Buchanan shared calmed his inner self, helping him to provide a good night's sleep. Dreams ran rampant in Roberts' sleep of home, the mountains of northern Georgia, and the solitude of Catoosa County.

Not only would Roberts sleep with a different mindset tonight, so did Buchanan. He fell asleep discovering dumb jocks aren't so dumb after all.

The Baptism

May 1, 1969

The spiritual team stood patiently some 10 feet from the main entrance of Camp Love, erect and poised, ready to send marines into the bush with a shot in the arm of spiritual affirmation. The visit with Roberts a few days ago was fresh on Buchanan's mind to spur the spiritual team on. The military history enthusiast reminded him the marines departing will deal with Roberts' pain in a matter of hours, possibly minutes. Buchanan stood with his devotion and prayer book, as Jackson held a full box of crucifixes to distribute to marines departing camp to patrol, ready and able to shake the hand of passing marines instilling confidence to every marine stationed in Camp Love. Jackson's enthusiasm stemmed from his desire for every marine in the field to embrace a physical presence of the Lord while fulfilling their duties with a cross hanging around marine's necks, serving as a humble representation of his Lord and Savior.

Alpha and Bravo Companies received orders to the field to accompany combat engineers, including Skawinski, for booby traps. Viet Cong activity increased in a dozen mile radius around Camp Love. A primary duty and responsibility of the 7th Engineering Battalion rested in the security of vast territory the enemy heavily infiltrated, including An Ngai Tay. Charlie and Delta Companies arrived simultaneously as Companies A and B were to depart.

Patiently waiting for the men to arrive, Buchanan commented, "I wish we could go with them, but the schedule's full - chapel services and devotions here at Camp Love. Besides, the Skipper insisted we conduct services here in camp for Delta and Charlie Companies arriving back from patrol. I guess he's right. We've been out in the field here recently."

"Yes, sir. But maybe we can hop in the jeep tomorrow morning, visit the men out in the field before the Friday night social. Whatyasay?" asked Jackson.

"Yeah. Let's do. If time permits."

"Yes, sir."

Dissatisfied with Buchanan's answer, Jackson wished for a more confident response. Experiencing the bush as a grunt, he knew full well from his firsthand experience the feelings of deep fright and the venture into the unknown jungles of Vietnam.

"Maybe we'll take them some chocolate and candy." Jackson suggested. Noticing Alpha and Bravo Companies approaching, he said, "Uh-oh. Here they come, sir."

Alpha and Bravo arrived following musters, as the spiritual team set themselves ready, willing and able to receive all who desired a blessing from Buchanan and a cross from Sergeant Jackson.

As the men passed by, Chaplain Buchanan recited a quick prayer and blessing, lifting the men's spirits and conveying a word of encouragement in advance, entering the Devil's Lair and the evil marines will face in the jungle.

Buchanan supplied a simple and routine greeting for the marines returning or departing from patrols at the entrance of camp. Typically, the marines departing approached Buchanan who placed his left hand on the marine's right shoulder, lifted his right hand in the air with the cross, and humbly prayed a blessing by paraphrasing Psalm 46, "Father - Bless this brave, courageous marine with your strength and presence. Amen." Buchanan spoke personally to individual marines he knew. Jackson handed a cross to many a marine if so desired. Jackson merely said, "God be with you, marine."

Jackson took particular interest in seeing the men off. In prior tours, he left his base of operations for the bush, terrified. Many instances in his previous tours as an unbeliever, he departed for the bush without a chaplain to see him off. Unbelievers entered the bush with terror in his heart. In his previous tours, he knew if the unfortunate happened to him, he would find himself in Hell.

"Be strong." added Jackson as he graciously handed a cross to the young men, patting the marines on the shoulder, smiling.

Marine after marine requested a blessing and prayer from Buchanan, many beseeching a crucifix from Jackson.

Skawinski, towards the back in of the elongated line of grunts, finally reached Buchanan, who gently placed his hand on Skawinski's shoulder and prayed, "Father - Bless this marine with your strength and presence. Amen." He added, "Lord, shield Adolphus from the enemy and their evil intent. Amen."

The mutual believers, enlisted and officer, smile, confident of the Lord's omnipresence.

Skawinski expresses his gratitude. "Thank you, Chaplain. See ya when we get back, sir."

"You know it, Sergeant." Buchanan said as Skawinski began to walk into the perimeter of the camp. Buchanan smirks. "Remember, it's cards night the next day ya get back."

Skawinski looked back towards Buchanan, grinning. With confidence, he says, "Be prepared to lose some more money, sir." He turns from Buchanan, who implores a silent prayer, 'Lord, please. *Please* take care of him. He's special. Amen.'

Buchanan nods, confident of the Lord's presence will be alongside Skawinski, regardless of what may come.

Several marines followed Skawinski, requesting a blessing and prayer from Buchanan. The last marine in line to walk out of camp ended up being Rockford. Marching himself squarely in front of Buchanan, eye to eye, shoulder to shoulder, he stared with hesitation and trepidation in his eye, intense with fear. The demeanor was uncharacteristic of Rockford.

With uncertainty in his voice, Rockford said, "Chaplain, well – I, well…" Buchanan inquired, "Lieutenant. What is it? How can I help? What is it?"

"Well. You're not going with us." Rockford said. "That's right. The men and myself feel more comfortable, ya know - more secure when you're around. Better protected. Besides, if, as you put it, the unfortunate happens, your presence with the casualties and those who might, well - you know, won't make it, you'd be there to pray with them in their last moments."

Rockford pauses. "I know. I know - I heard. The Skipper wants you here to lead in regular scheduled services for the camp personnel."

"That's right, Lieutenant. I'd love to go out with you - but, ya know, the responsibilities in camp. Many marines here in camp requested time for counseling and such." Buchanan half grins.

With averseness, Rockford reluctantly agreed. "Yes, sir."

"Let me pray for you and the men, Thomas." Buchanan motioned towards Jackson to step forward and pray along with him. He placed a hand on Rockford's left shoulder as Jackson laid his right hand on Rockford's right shoulder, lowering their heads to pray.

Buchanan prayed, "Father, we come humble and thankful before your throne of grace. We ask for your protection and strength, and your power to be bestowed upon each marine of Alpha and Bravo Companies and the combat engineers. Let your Spirit speak to every man's heart. Let no weapon of the enemy cause harm or injury. May your presence abound amongst the brave and courageous marines. Amen."

Confidently lifting his head, Rockford glared into Buchanan's eyes a second time around with a bit more gleam in his eyes.

Rockford delivered a confident hand shake to Jackson, expressing thanks. "Thank you, Sergeant."

"The Lord be with you, sir." responded Jackson with certainty.

The Lieutenant stepped away to join the patrol, looking back towards Buchanan with emotion as if for the last time. "Thank you chaplain. The Lord will be with us."

Buchanan nods with assertion. "Amen! I know he will - without a doubt."

"So long." Rockford said, hurrying toward the last man in line leaving camp.

"See ya. See ya when you get back." said Buchanan out of earshot of Rockford.

In no time at all, the men received a prayer, blessing, and a cross.

Regardless of motive, Buchanan stood at the camp's entrance for every departure of a patrol to witness the last marine fade away out of sight. He insisted on carrying out his routine, either out of superstition or simple sentimentality. What mattered most sat deep within his heart of his sense of obligation, seeing the men off into the bush.

Rockford, the last marine in file formation, finally disappeared, treading over the small knoll about a mile away, as the spiritual team turned, striding back to the chaplains quarters.

The spiritual team were as busy as bees the next three days ministering, visiting, counseling, and conducting Communion services in camp.

Buchanan learned quickly in Vietnam marines eagerly longed for Communion services returning from patrols which were frequent each and every day since Rockford left on May 1.

The spiritual team conducted a whopping 39 communion services in just three days. The spiritual team reckoned the men desired a closer presence of God when venturing out into a world where the Devil reigned and his evil head emerged without notice, abruptly attempting to bite the life out of a marine.

Three days passed with many a prayer lifted up for zero casualties inflicted upon Alpha and Bravo Companies.

As life passes by, so does time. And May 4, 1969, came as fast as any other day.

The spiritual team awaited the return of marines home to their safe haven. They welcomed all the men back to camp graciously with a firm handshake and a hospitable smile.

With the absence of casualties, the men returned, receiving a firm handshake and a welcoming smile, thrilled to return home.

Three men, above all, returned seeking Chaplain Buchanan.

When finally spotting Buchanan at a distance, Private John Sims, from Los Angeles, said, "Yes, yes! There's the Padre." He bolted out of line with excited energy, running past those in front of him to talk to the chaplain.

Nervously making his way to Buchanan, Sims practically tripped over his own two feet, as Jackson reached out, grabbing Sims' arm to help him keep his balance. His clumsiness offered the men a good laugh.

With his hands on his knees, Sims huffs and puffs, attempting to catch his breath from running so erratically. He briskly speaks to Buchanan. "I-I'm ready sir." Pausing, he says, "I'm r-ready. Yes, sir. Whew! It's-It's time."

Glancing toward one another, the spiritual team smiled from ear to ear. The team thought, 'What in tarnation could all the hoopla be about?' Placing a hand on Sims' shoulders, the team attempted to help him catch his breath.

"Catch your breath, Private Sims. Ya must have ran 200 feet full speed." said Buchanan with a bit of jest.

Sims finally raises up, declaring with self assurance, "I want - I want to be, well - to be baptized. It's time." He grins as wide as the ends of the ocean.

Pleased, the spiritual team smile. "Amen!" they shouted.

Jackson said, "It's answered prayer, John."

Sims revealed, "I know. I know. You've been praying for my Salvation. Well, it-it happened while we were out the past few days."

Skawinski stepped up to join in the good news of Sim's conversion to a believer in Christ.

"So you've heard the good news, sir?" Skawinski asked.

"Yes, Sergeant Skawinski. Amen!" said Buchanan.

"Yes, sir. Amen." Skawinski replied.

"Ski and I talked while out in the bush, sir. I owe a lot to him, assisting me in deciding to become a believer." Sims commented.

As the men talked, a notable change in Sims' behavior came immediately. He changed overnight. His speech, his body language, his entire presentation of himself. The marine who departed Camp Love three days earlier came back as a unique human being. Sims accepted Jesus as his Savior. Buchanan could spot a new convert a mile away. Jesus provided joy and life in his own life. And now he witnessed it occur in Sims' life. No longer did Sims serve the Evil One. He now chose to serve the God who made him.

Sergeant Remington and Private Pokorny had by now stepped up to the small group forming at the gate, just as excited for Sims. The spiritual team had been praying for the men for months.

"It's time Chaplain. It's time." congregated the men around Buchanan. With glee, they added, "I want to be baptized, sir. It's time, it's time."

Excitement flowed from the men with no end. "We've found Jesus. We've found Jesus."

"Amen!" said Buchanan, heard in the ensemble of voices speaking concurrently.

Members of Alpha and Bravo companies walked past the assembled group of believers observing nothing but exhilaration. Though many of the men were unbelievers, clueless of the deep emotions new converts experience in the desire to be baptized.

Buchanan never felt more spiritually pleased in Vietnam than on this day. "OK, men. OK. Clean yourselves up and eat some chow, then come by my hootch and we'll talk about the baptism."

"We'll do, sir. We'll do."

Sims affirmed with buff, "Give us a half hour, sir."

When out of earshot, Jackson said, "A half hour? They really want to be baptized, don't they, sir?"

Grinning slowly, Buchanan attested, "They sure do. And I say, Amen."

"Amen sir." said Jackson.

Bringing up the rear of the patrol came Rockford, walking through the front gate. Stopping to speak to the spiritual team, he informed them of the patrol's experience while in the bush. He briefed them on several close calls from the past three days in the jungle. Many casualties mounted onto the marines inflicted from Viet Cong attacks. The constant barrage of harassing VC assaults turned to a nagging series of actions interrupting the combat engineers' work for hours, but no KIAs. In skirmishes encountered, Sims and Remington displayed superb conduct under fire, saving several marines' lives with flanking actions. Pokorny ran in the open under enemy fire raining down on him, saving several wounded marines exposed just outside the treeline of a rice field, carrying the wounded to a small knoll for cover. Rockford informed the team he has intentions to apply for citations for bravery for all three men.

Sims' story revealed a spiritual experience. According to Rockford, Sims insisted Jesus spoke to him audibly during a firefight, speaking directly in his ear encouraging him as projectiles flew in every direction. "It's OK. I'm with you. I'm your protector, your shield."

"No one else could hear the voice, Padre. But Sims insisted he heard it." Rockford said. "Ski's been talking to him the past two days about his experience in the bush. He's helped him."

Buchanan deliberated in his mind the story, remembering Skawinski heeded Jesus for safety and encouraging him in a firefight. Ski's experience validated Private Sims' encounter in the bush.

Buchanan thought the voices must be real. Ski and Sims were not the first or the last marines to inform him they heard voices in the heat of battle.

Firsthand accounts of combat from military personnel levied a bit of verity to the experiences of auditory hallucinations and mattered to Buchanan. The experiences were genuine for him. The Lord reminded Buchanan of Paul's experience on the road to Damascus when confronted by the Lord. Many brushed Paul's encounter aside, discounting his account. For Buchanan - it did indeed happen.

When departing, the spiritual team prayed for the patrol. Now Rockford requested a prayer of praise lifted for the safe return to camp from the team. Following the prayer, the team made their way back to Buchanan's hootch, awaiting the marines. As promised, Sims and his friends arrived 30 minutes on the dot to the chaplain's hootch. Jackson remained for moral support. Buchanan asked his routine, thorough questions to assure himself the men truly converted and accepted Christ as Savior before he baptized them.

When the formalities ended, Sims promised Buchanan he would paint him a picture of the Ohio River reflecting fall colors and the autumn season. He looked forward to Taxi presenting him a portrayal of home Ohioans' treasure in their hearts.

"You'll be proud of my work, sir." Sims acknowledged.

"I know you'll put your heart and soul into it, Taxi." Buchanan said, grinning.

The next day, May 5, 1969, Buchanan baptized the marines in the Tvy Loan River, a day most exciting in Sims' life. A day the men will tell and retell again through the decades.

When hearing of Buchanan's baptizing a member of the Roman Catholic Church, Porch fell in a fit of fury with the notion.

As always, Porch searched for anything and everything to harass Buchanan. He accused Buchanan of proselytizing a Catholic to the Baptist faith. Of course, Porch requested Buchanan, Rockford, Sims, Jackson, Pokorny, Remington, and Skawinski to report to Lucas' office as witnesses to charges of proselytizing and infringing on the religious freedom of a citizen of the United States, dragging everyone of them into Lucas' office to inquire into the baptisms.

All charges were dropped when Pokorny admitted to Porch he intended going back home and informing his Catholic priest in his home parish what happened to him in Vietnam, requesting to go through Catechism once again due to his affirmation of his Salvation experience in Vietnam. Pokorny's awareness of his spirituality is what Baptist might refer to as a 'rededication of Faith.' He felt as if he was just going through the motions of religious rituals with his relationship with his Savior. Buchanan just guided Pokorny in coming to grips with his spirituality. He professed to be a Roman Catholic. And he intended to remain a Roman Catholic. He in no way intended to join a Baptist congregation. His family was Roman Catholic, going back hundreds of years. The baptism simply served as a reaffirmation of his faith, to express his new life, his new beginning. Pokorny's expressed excitement at his outward assertion of Jesus living within him merely showed forth to his fellow believers in camp. And possibly even more vital, the excitement of Jesus expressed to unbelievers in camp.

For Porch, he departed Lucas' office, once again losing yet another battle to Buchanan.

For the rest of the men departing Lucas' office, they felt Porch left a more humbled man, at least temporarily.

Sims, Pokorny, and Remington lived differently for their rest of their lives. Combat experiences facilitated the men to examine their own spiritual lives to change their hearts and minds for the better.

Pleased with the results of the past few months of ministry, Buchanan ended up convinced the Lord's Spirit thrived in the presence of the marines and sailors in the bush regardless of their chaplain's presence or not. In the past few days, Buchanan's prayers were certainly answered, the Lord's presence prospered with the men in the bush.

ECUMENICALISM

MAY 8, 1969

Buchanan lived life as an idealist. He envisioned achieving accomplishments for the Lord in years to come. He envisioned winning many individuals to the saving grace he experienced in Mobile, Alabama in the early 1950s, turning his life over to Jesus. Though raised a Presbyterian and attending a Lutheran Seminary, he lived his faith as a Baptist through and through. And as a Baptist, he vehemently held strong a fundamental Baptist principle - all things are possible through Jesus, who reigns and sits on the right hand of the Father in Heaven. A powerful tenet of the Baptist Faith. For Bible believing Baptists, a far-reaching Faith and a complete trust in God goes a long way in believing things that are scientifically impossible are possible.

In the finite world, the efforts of former President Johnson and present President Nixon to win over any South Vietnamese citizens still doubting the benefits of western democratic principles through CAP's, especially the medical, remained to be one of the many efforts Buchanan strongly supported and intensely believed in. The efforts would work if implemented properly both by the United States and South Vietnamese governments.

The spiritual team traveled today to An Ngai Tay to meet nurses Lieutenant Nancy Burleson and Lieutenant Commander Veronica Reagan to administer medical care to the villagers. Doc Delaney, his corpsmen, along with the dentist, joined forces with the nurses to render medical care and provide dental check ups.

As usual on Thursdays, chapel and devotion services were held at 1300 and 1900 hours respectfully, and the spiritual team will be forced to depart the MedCAP early to lead services in Camp Love.

Along with the MedCAP in An Ngai Tay, Buchanan contacted his Roman Catholic chaplain friends Lieutenant Brennan and Lieutenant Commander Marino to lead in Catholic Mass for the villagers, devout and dedicated Roman Catholics. Buchanan invited friend and fellow Southern Baptist chaplain Lieutenant Daniel Fontaine Anderson from Cartersville, Georgia, out of sheer morale's sake. Anderson conducted himself as a man of God who dearly loved human beings. Buchanan knew Anderson prior from past denominational conferences and meetings. Besides, Anderson's ministry billeted him with the 5th Division Marines, overlapping with the 1st Marines ministry zone, including Camp Love's CAP's.

The spiritual team visited with villagers while Doc Delaney carried out the medical examinations. Following the examinations, the spiritual team assisted with the Roman Catholic Communion scheduled at 1000 hours. After the Communion, the spiritual team will head back to camp for services.

The scheduled day for work began at 0800 hours. Two platoons of Company D, the company least familiar to Buchanan in Camp Love, accompanied the medical and clergy personnel for perimeter support while in An Ngai Tay.

The spiritual team greeted the visiting chaplains and assistants, as Jackson guided the visiting religious personnel to the center pavilion for the Catholic Mass.

"Good to see ya, Dan." Buchanan said, shaking Chaplain Anderson's hand.

"Good to see you as well, Robert."

"It's been months since we've seen each other."

"Too long." answered Anderson. "I see you're doing well. I got to tell ya, Robert, you never quit working, do ya? Always visiting. Always ministering. Always cultivating."

"Can't quit." Buchanan answered, smiling.

With a stern glance, Buchanan admits with emotion, "If I did, I'd-I'd lose it. Ya know what I mean?"

Anderson ponders the thought. "Yeah. *Yeah*, I know what you're saying."

The fellow chaplains show nothing but weariness in their eyes, as if they had had it.

Interrupting the reunion, Buchanan heard over his shoulder familiar voices behind him.

Unbeknownst to the spiritual team, Skawinski, Rodriquez, Sims, Dobbs, Pokorny, and Remington all jumped out of two jeeps bringing up the rear to surprise the team.

"Well. What a surprise! Seeing y'all today!" said Jackson, with a bit of approval in his voice, walking back from the pavilion.

"Amen!" Buchanan declared.

"I know the people of An Ngai Tay are blessed today! They'll certainly see Jesus through y'all, that's for sure!" Buchanan said in his deep mountain accent.

"Yes, sir." responded the group.

The new found life living for Jesus exhibited out of Sims revealed a new demeanor in him. Evidence of Pokorny and Remington's life rededicated to live more of a reflection of Jesus' principles showed through with their efforts to meet the needs of others instead of their own. The spiritual team delighted in the changes. And to see Dobbs in the mix floored the team as shocking, but an encouraging sight to behold.

Buchanan thought, 'Is Dobbs coming around to our side?' Dobbs had come a long way since the first time he laid eyes upon the young marine in October 1968. Maybe the fact Dobbs witnessed first hand Sims' conversion experience and Remington's change in life served as a catalyst for Dobbs to think of his own spiritual condition.

"Well, let's get to work, men!" Buchanan ordered.

The spiritual team brought along plenty of boxes stacked on the passenger seats and floor board of his jeep filled with hygiene products, new shoes, Catholic Bibles in Vietnamese and English, and toys. In no time at all, the team, along with help from their friends, distributed boxed good and services to the villagers.

Sims and Remington brought the Word of God, Matthew 28:18-20, alive through the hearts and actions of two new found believers. The thrill of Buchanan witnessing the excitement of new believers fulfilling the Great Commission always brought joy to his heart.

The medical personnel joined in the cultivation of relationships with the villagers when completing the medical examinations.

Chaplains, Protestant and Catholic alike, sought God's Will with the villagers of An Ngai Tay.

Visiting with the villagers, playing with children with the new toys, reading the new Bibles with the villagers, or just simply discussing the weather indicted as a sure sign to the villagers the Americans were on their side to live a more democratic way of life, especially their religious freedom.

The pro-American position of the villagers in An Ngai Tay hamlet stemmed from devout, heartfelt Roman Catholics in the hamlet who fled North Vietnam in the 1950s. The villagers fled atrocious religious persecution from Communists, who had unlawfully taken over North Vietnam. Winning over South Vietnamese citizens to support a government system bestowing western freedoms instead of a suppressive socialist, Communist system proved an arduous task indeed. The energy generated from Americans to give and impart the love of Christ to just one village or to display an effort of Americans attempting to make the world better was one thing. Showing utter disrespect coming from other Americans by protesting in the streets in the United States about a war they knew nothing about turned out to be something else altogether.

Time passes quickly as 1000 hours came in a blink of an eye. The villagers and Americans alike congregated under the pavilion, built by the Navy Seabees led by Lieutenant Commander Adkins and marine engineers, to take part in Catholic Mass with Chaplains Brennan and Marino.

Jackson lent a hand to Brennan and Marino's assistants to set up for Mass.

The villagers were extraordinarily pleased to see Catholic priests. An Ngai Tay had not taken part in Mass for three and a half weeks. Buchanan, serving in the past with Catholics in the military and ministering with priests through the ministerial associations back in the states, came to appreciate the incredible dedication and unity of faith Roman Catholics possessed worldwide.

The one hour of worship lifted up and praised the Lord in Catholic Mass. One hour of complete spiritual bliss for each villager and Catholic military personnel who partook.

Each believer in Christ saturated every verse read out of the Scriptures, every song sung, every piece of liturgy spoken, and every moment in taking of the elements. Believers let every moment sink in as the Lord spoke to His children through worship. Those present discovered their relationship with the Lord strengthened.

Buchanan, who he himself and other Protestants present, participated in all the order of service within the Mass except taking of the elements, felt a powerful presence of the Lord this day and His blessings upon the Communion service. The Vietnamese villagers welcomed his occasional "Amen!" during the Communion service, shaking their heads in affirmation.

Buchanan had visited An Ngai Tay enough for villagers to know that when Chaplain Buchanan bolted out an "Amen!", there was a good reason for it.

As Mass ended, marine personnel departed the village to report back to camp between 1215 and 1230 hours for afternoon muster. Chaplains Brennan and Marino headed back to the 5th Marine Headquarters to continue to fulfill their respective duties. Nurses Burleson and Reagan saddled up their gear, climbing up into their truck to travel back with the marine escorts in jeeps to Da Nang Air Base via Route 1.

Buchanan will remember the day as one of Ecumenicalism, a spiritual priority for him. Carrying out the motto 'cooperation without compromise' ranked high as an indispensable component of a Navy chaplain's ministerial success during the Vietnam War.

The Bridge

May 8, 1969

War is evil.

And today, May 8, 1969, will yet be another day of war memories. Buchanan's recollections of war embedded permanent pictures and visions never to forget. The imprint of just one occurrence is forever indented in the mind of a veteran. The mind of a veteran often remembers, habitually recollecting what evil war might bring.

For those who witnessed what occurred this day, they forever desired to forget the incident. Regrettably, never would anyone who witnessed what would happen forget. The event permanently etched into the memory of every witness, forever haunting the minds who experienced the evil event of war.

Buchanan hopped into his jeep for the trek back to camp, following the Communion services in An Ngai Tay.

Jackson invited Skawinski and Remington to travel back to camp in Buchanan's jeep, to talk of hunting and exchange tracking tips to hunt game in the mountains of Kentucky. The distance to camp, seven and a half miles away, provided plenty of time to talk of hunting, as Buchanan himself enjoyed the sport. He eased dropped on the discussion.

Jackson drove back to camp on Buchanan's favorite scenic route, Routes 540 and 537. Buchanan took plenty of slide photographs of Vietnam's typography on the trek back to camp, making for a great slide presentation someday for family and friends.

Some two miles away from An Ngai Tay, Buchanan said with glee in his eye, "Stop. Stop, Philip! I want to get a shot of the mountain there, Monkey Mountain! Look at it today. The sun beating down onto it. Beautiful!"

The enlisted simply smile at one another, stepping out of the jeep taking in the sight of Monkey Mountain.

Buchanan took a couple of shots of Monkey Mountain, smiling. "Those shots are going to be beautiful. Just beautiful. Listen, men. Gather yourselves together and let me get a shot of you all with Monkey Mountain in the background. Go on, go on."

"Oh sir. Let's go, I'm tired." Skawinski said, beaming.

Jackson said, "Chaplain, you're always getting people to pose for pics. Can we -"

"No!" interrupted Buchanan with urgency.

"Don't make me order y'all." Buchanan insisted with a slight grin.

"OK. OK, Padre." said Skawinski.

"One condition though, sir." commented Remington.

"What's that?"

"Next time I go hunting in the morning, you eat whatever I bring back for chow." answered Remington.

Pausing, Buchanan hesitantly swallowed hard. "Well, I-I…OK."

"In that case, I can see him bringing back a huge Boa Constrictor." Skawinski said, grinning.

Buchanan sighed heavily. "Ski, if that's what he brings back, I'd have to be horse tied and hogged tied, then force fed!"

The men laugh, posing for the picture.

The young marines place their arms around each other's shoulders as if they were in the mountains of Kentucky in a hunting party stalking game. The men poked and jabbed one another as if no one else was around who mattered. Oddly enough, the friends at any moment could be zipped up into a body bag addressed to be shipped back home. The picture taking momentarily took all the attention away from the war, oblivious to the men as war boomed in and around them.

Buchanan enjoyed the moment immensely.

"Say cheeeese!" Buchanan blurted out.

"Cheese!" responded the men.

"Great shot men. Can't wait to see the slide one day. We'll all sit, view the slides, and reminisce together this moment. This moment in time we had together today."

As Buchanan headed back to the jeep, he commented, "It's been a great day, hasn't it?"

"Sure has, sir." Remington said. "I can't wait to get home and hunt in the mountains of Kentucky again. It's going to be great."

When secured in the jeep, Jackson once again drove toward Camp Love.

An added thrill for Buchanan traveling through the scenic route came with crossing the Liberty Bridge. The bridge always brought something to behold for Buchanan, accounting for the longest and largest bridge built in Vietnam by American military engineers and the Seabees, an astonishing engineering feat. A complete masterpiece of engineering.

As Jackson drove toward the security gatepost of the bridge, the guards noticed the sticker on the windshield, saluting Chaplain Buchanan. The guards motioned Jackson to proceed across the bridge.

As the jeep crossed the bridge, Buchanan said with pride, "Incredible, masterful job the engineers and Seabees built, isn't it?"

"Yes sir. Incredible. Masterful job." replied his enlisted friends.

Looking out of the corner of his eye at Buchanan, Jackson grins. "But it just about makes you sick going across. Doesn't it, sir?"

Gazing toward Jackson, Buchanan grins, knowing the ride over is not the most pleasant of trips.

When finally over the bridge, Skawinski sarcastically says, "I hope the nurses from the base are still in the vicinity. I need some help after that rocky trip."

The men laugh.

Grinning, Jackson suggested, "OK, Ski. I think the Padre has had enough digging with the bridge."

Driving onto Route 537, Buchanan noticed the contingent from Camp Love, including Sims and others, along with the nurses and their assistants, stopped, visiting the boys from neighboring villages. The same group of boys who hang around the bridge to visit with the marines looking for free gum, chocolate, and candy from the spiritual team. The nurses yearned to get a quick look-see at the boys' health. Looking a little ragged, the nurses desired to doctor the boys up for their own sake, to provide immediate medical care to the young innocents. The nurses were having a friendly visit, laughing and interacting with the youngsters.

When Buchanan's party drove up, Jackson parked the jeep some 15 feet from the nurse's truck. The boys immediately recognized the spiritual team, running toward the jeep to greet the chaplain and friends.

"Xin chao! Xin chao!" said Buchanan and his friends from the jeep. He had practiced his Vietnamese for months and the one word he knew for sure by now ended up being 'Xin chao,' meaning 'hello' in English. He realized a friendly 'hello' in any language is a sure way of gaining new friends, regardless of cultural barriers.

Stepping out of the jeep, the boys greeted the men, tagging on their uniforms and smiling immensely at the Americans, yelling "ban be! Ban be!" The men responded with "ban be! Ban be!" 'Ban be' meaning 'friends' in English. Buchanan attempted admirably to converse with the children in Vietnamese, but to no avail.

A South Vietnamese officer traveling with the nurses chimed in, letting the young children know the nurses wanted to finish their examinations with the boys. Buchanan asked the officer to inform the boys he had gum, chocolate, and candy to fill their tummies, but only if the nurses could finish their work. Enthusiastically, the boys sprinted to the nurses to finish the examinations.

In no time, the nurses medically tended to the boys. The compassionate caregivers longed to return in the future to travel to the boys' villages to treat them with follow-up visits with the permission of course of their elders to enter and conduct any medical assistance.

The youngsters jolted fervently back to Buchanan and friends after the examinations. The Americans distributed heaps of candy to the boys from the back of the jeep, lighting up the faces of the children from the joy and deep satisfaction indulging in all the pleasure of the sugar.

"So co la! Keo! So co la!" declared Buchanan and his friends.

Buchanan set as a top priority the access to chocolate and candy for children. From the first day he stepped foot in Vietnam, his thoughts relentlessly reminded him of how fortunate American children in the western world are spoiled with all the perks of western life, including chocolate and candy. Many of the Vietnamese children never experienced chocolate and candy in their life until the Americans introduced the sweets to them out of common courtesy. The sweets certainly brought about pleasant and joyful smiles onto the faces of Vietnamese children.

As the children ran 25 feet away toward the bridge to eat the candy and chocolate, Buchanan and his friends conversed with the nurses and Da Nang personnel. The discussion centered in on the essential medical care the boys obviously needed, a lack of many rural Vietnamese, including villagers in the North.

Buchanan chatted with the nurses, discussing the role of the chaplains in the area and how they could minister to the boys and their villages. Distracted, paying no attention to the bridge, Buchanan failed to observe the convoy of several trucks full of marines tuckered out after exhausting patrols in the bush drove to the end of the bridge.

As the first truck stopped at the security post to talk to the duty sergeant, the boys sprinted to the first truck smiling, greeting the marines in the truck, along with a few older boys out from behind the supply hut some 40 yards from the bridge. The boys were seeking additional 'treats', approaching the trucks to request candy from the generosity of the marines.

Glancing over his shoulder, Buchanan smiled, noticing marines stretching down from the trucks to offer candy to the boys, who in return stretched with all the strength and distance a little boy could muster.

Once the boys clutched the candy, all ran to the end of the bridge to eat every piece of candy one piece at a time, slow and with precision, savoring each ounce of sugar. The young chocolate connoisseurs enjoyed every ounce of sugar 'treats', soaking in the pleasure with every piece of candy and chocolate.

Glancing back once more, Buchanan noticed the boys making their way back to the first truck, then scooting down to the second and even to the third truck, reaching up for more candy.

Humored, Buchanan and his friends chuckle at the sight.

"Man, those boys are just like my baby brothers and sisters. They just can't have one or two pieces of chocolate." Remington said, grinning.

"*Yeah*. My younger brother, same thing, man. Has to eat the entire bag!" commented a smiling Sims.

As the rather large group looks on, Buchanan shakes his head in bewilderment. "I hate to end all the fun, but it's time to go." Pointing with his fingers at his watch, Buchanan says, "It's 1215 hours and we have chapel services at 1300 hours." By now, Jackson knew Buchanan well enough to know that when Buchanan pointed to his watch, agitation had kicked in for Buchanan.

"You're right, sir. Let's get going." answered Jackson.

As the spiritual team and the nurses turned toward their vehicles, all glanced over their shoulders almost in unison for one more glance at the boys on the bridge requesting more candy.

Just as Buchanan turned his head from his last glance toward the boys, he caught in his ear the most blaring, deafening explosion he had heard in Vietnam. As he felt his body lifted off the ground violently, he realized instantly a tremendous force had thrown him back fiercely 15 to 20 yards, firmly landing on the earth's hard surface.

Dazed, numb, and temporarily immobile, Buchanan thought in a matter of seconds - 'What bang?' 'Where did it come from?' 'What just happened?'

Slowly stepping onto his own two feet, Buchanan stood dazed and deaf, hearing nothing but a numbing ring in his ear.

Dumbfounded and traumatized from the bang, Buchanan regained his senses, horror-struck and aghast at what lie in front of him at the bridge. He and his friends faced an unbelievable sight. And unfortunately, an unforgettable sight. What lay in front of Buchanan is forever etched into his mind, a haunting, unconscionable scene.

What Buchanan witnessed today in a millisecond will forever haunt him in his dreams. The Viet Cong blew themselves up with explosive devices in combat situations in the past, but never children. The older boys concealed explosives attached to their torsos. The scene for Buchanan amounted to a bloody sight of scattered remains of young Vietnamese boys, a few dead marines, and minimal damage to the bridge, though excessive damage hammered the security post at the entrance of the bridge.

Surviving marines attended to the wounded, attempting to bring some calm from the mayhem.

Buchanan, still discombobulated, felt the grip of Jackson, Skawinski, and Sims' hands and arms holding him. His enlisted friends slowly and gently guided him to a knoll to sit and calm his nerves.

Buchanan, sitting comfortably on the ground, caught sight of the nursing assistants, left and right of him attending wounded marines from Delta Company hit by shrapnel from the blast. He noticed to his right Lieutenant Burleson on the ground, bloodied all over from shrapnel.

In the few minutes which passed, his heart hurt.

Just mere minutes ago, the nurses, marines, and Buchanan were enjoying life with the Vietnamese boys. Now all hell broke loose.

Never will Buchanan forget the children who took their own lives for a cause they knew nothing about.

The infamous day of May 8, 1969, started as one of his best in Vietnam.

The end played out as a horrendous day, haunting his memory for the rest of his life.

Carl's Missing

May 11, 1969

The Communists in May erupted into an offensive frenzy, attacking hundreds of villages, hamlets, United States and South Vietnamese military bases, even major cities in South Vietnam. United States and South Vietnamese forces responded to the heightened military activity of the enemy with a roaring counter offensive. One specific military counteroffensive, Operation Apache Snow, was conducted in the western Thauthien province. The primary objective of Apache Snow intended to conduct an envelopment action in South Vietnam, specifically to sweep the Ashua Valley close to the Laotian border clean of the Viet Cong and destroy Communist supply lines. Principle troops in the fighting close to the Laotian border were the United States 9th Marine Regiment and elements of the 101st Airborne Division, who fought gallantly. The campaign resulted in a success, pushing the Communists out of the territory, killing thousands of Communists. In comparison, the Americans and South Vietnamese suffered minimal casualties from combat. One specific engagement, however, fought between 13 May-20 May, 1969, absorbed some of the most fierce fighting of the war in the capture of a Communist stronghold, Apbia mountain. On the 11th assault, the allies overran the stronghold with a thousand 101st Airborne Division soldiers and 400 South Vietnamese troops. The Communists lost nearly 600 killed, while the allies lost 56 killed and 420 wounded in the engagement. The fierce fighting resulted in many casualties. Future generations referred to the battle as 'Hamburger Hill.'

The month of May from start to finish brought an intensified ambiance of combat in the war. Military personnel in South Vietnam felt the heightened efforts of brunt Communist offensives from one end of South Vietnam to the other. Within all the violence of the war, Buchanan experienced a more calm, composed setting within Camp Love's perimeter. Following the incident at the bridge, he and his friends required a pause of calm.

Last night, Burns treated the camp with a favorite, Brahms Symphony no. 2, putting Buchanan's mind at ease as he fell asleep. His night of dreams was of home, riding a roller coaster at Disneyland with his children. His dream presented a pleasant, heartwarming memory for years to come.

Following a shower and a close shave, Buchanan made his way to the chow hall to eat an early breakfast with Jackson. The enjoyment of a morning breakfast reinforced his tranquil night of rest. His content overflowed as the spiritual team made their way to the gate entrance of camp to set Sergeant Remington off to hunt game in the bush. To their surprise, the team spotted Sergeant Remington at the entrance early – ready, willing, and able to enter the bush to hunt at such an early hour in the morning before dawn. Remington considered departing before dawn a cardinal sin. But today, the Lord's Day, he entered the bush through the treeline in the dark, a first for Remington.

The men meet at the gate, greeting one another cordially.

Remington said in his strong Kentuckian accent, "I'd invite y'all to tag along with me to hunt this morning, but I know y'all have services to prepare for today. This is the Lord's Day."

"That's right. Busy day for us. Besides, it's Mother's Day." said Jackson with a bit of excitement. "And I know ya don't want to miss the service."

"Yep, it's Mother's Day. I'll be back before services start. I'll be there as usual. Save me a seat."

"Well, let me bless you, Carl." interjects Buchanan.

"Thank ya, sir."

"Lord, protect Carl as he enters the jungle to enjoy his most treasured leisure in life. In a month, he'll be home hunting in the United States. Be with him. Lord. Amen."

"Thank ya, Padre. I have a feeling I'm gonna track a good one today. Maybe even a wild hog. Ya know, that might be my favorite here in Vietnam....the wild hog."

The spiritual team grin.

Pausing, Remington peers beyond the perimeter and says, "Maybe it's like tracking the VC. Maybe...maybe it's my way of, well, letting loose of a lot of...anger."

An eerie silence unnerved the spiritual team. The team froze. Tongue tied, at a loss for words.

The men say not a word as Remington turns and heads toward the treeline of the bush to cope with the war in his own way.

"So long. See ya at chapel service."

"So long, Carl." responds the spiritual team.

Buchanan, as usual, kept an eye on Remington every morning, entering the treeline step by step, until he walked out of sight. But this morning, he and Jackson lose sight of Remington because of the darkness, catching only a glimpse of Remington from time to time from the moonlight, eventually losing him entirely.

The spiritual team turn back toward the conference hall worried, as Buchanan looked over his shoulder one last time toward the treeline lifting up a silent, yet earnest prayer for Remington's safe return.

Jackson said, "Better get to the conference hall, sir, to prepare for services this morning."

"Yep. 0900 hours will be here before ya know it."

The service ended up a standing room only due in part to the bridge incident and Mother's Day, a day Buchanan looked forward to every year.

Buchanan's eldest son's birthday was today – ten years of age. There is nothing Buchanan is more proud of in his life than his wife and kids. A fact heard loud and clear in the service.

The phenomenal service ended at 0955 hours, spiritually fulfilling - but still no Remington.

Many a Sunday, Remington moseyed into camp late, entering through the conference hall doors to attend the 1100 hours' service with no worry. Today, 1100 hours came in no time and still no Remington. Though worried, Buchanan continued with the service. Again, a full house of congregants. Jackson thought of nothing but Remington for the entire hour.

When the 1100 hours' service ended, Lucas provided a special surprise Mother's Day meal for the men in the chow hall.

The men made their way to the chow hall, enjoying the meal immensely. The well prepared meal consisted of roast beef, mashed potatoes, various cooked vegetables, salad, rolls, and carrot cake. Lucas pulled some strings to provide the food and the carrot cake. Buchanan appreciated Lucas' efforts to provide the carrot cake, one of two of his favorite cakes.

The men, appreciative of the meal, thanked Lucas again and again. Lucas definitely embodied a 'gun ho' approach, but he knew the primary motivator for any human being – food.

Eating the meal along with the overall euphoria of remembering mothers distracted every single person to forget, at least temporarily, of Remington's absence.

Following the meal, Buchanan gave the men a chance to open up and say a good word of support for his respective mother.

The emotional public recognition of how much the men loved and missed their mothers proved too much for the men, for they failed to hold in their emotions. Even Lucas spoke. "I was fortunate to have the most loving mother in the world. I guess she had to be to put up with me." A response of laughter followed from the men, knowing Lucas portrayed himself as a no nonsense marine officer.

Many marines spoke up. Not a dry eye in the chow hall.

After the uplifting words, though a rather odd moment for some marines, the verbal praise from marines lifting up their mothers started a conversation of home once again.

Unbeknownst to the marines, time had run late to 1550 hours and still no Remington.

Four hours from the end of the 1100 services, two hours from the end of the afternoon's Mother's Day special meal, and still no Remington.

On Sundays, the men leisurely fellow shipped till 1600 hours. A dozen marines out of a little over 100 men left early, but most stayed on. A great day in the bush for the congenial, normal life. A day distant of war though blazing away just mere miles away, possibly with the Viet Cong lurking about outside their own camp perimeter.

At 1600 hours, marines moseyed their way back to their respective hootches for the rest of Mother's Day.

The cleanup of the Mother's Day meal concerted an effort from the cooks and chow hall personnel. The spiritual team looked forward to enjoying the rest of the day, reading, and meditating. Enjoying the day's festivities immensely, Lucas departed from the chow hall with Buchanan, Jackson, and Skawinski chatting, continuing the 'fellowship'. The rare moment offered a glimpse of Lucas in a 'normal' life setting as a human being. Lucas humored the marines.

Just as the men strode about 20 yards from the chow hall, a corporal abruptly stepped up to Lucas. "Sir, good afternoon, sir. Sir? Uh. I'm Corporal Topping. Lance Topping. Sir, I'm-I'm....well"

"Yes, yes. I know you Topping." said Lucas.

"Sir, I-I, well, I -"

"Well, spit it out, son. *What* is it?" Lucas insisted.

"Well, sir. I'm a friend of Sergeant Remington. And he-he's not come back yet, sir. And I'm really worried, sir. No one's seen him since Chaplain Buchanan here saw him off this morning." said Topping, motioning toward Buchanan.

"What?" Lucas, speechless and catching flies, froze at the news. A startled Buchanan, along with his friends, stood worried.

Following a brief pause, Topping says, "He usually arrives back at or around 0900 hours, sir. 1000 hours at the latest. I'm *really* worried, sir." Standing eye to eye with Topping, Lucas softly squeezes his shoulder and says with assurance, "We'll find him."

Glancing toward Skawinski, Lucas says, "Ski, muster up your men." Turning to Jackson, he barks, "Sergeant, make your way over to Bravo Company. Brief the Gunny of the situation, tell him to round up as many men from 1st Platoon he can. Spread the news of Remington in camp as fast as you can. We'll muster up at the camp entrance in 5 minutes."

Lucas runs to his hootch, retrieving his two .45 calibers, Ka-Bar 9140 knives, ammunition, and his combat satchel bag. He rushed to the gate entrance in three minutes.

Buchanan sprints to his hootch, grabs his combat helmet and ministry bag that included his chaplain manual and prayer book, making his way to the camp entrance in 3 minutes flat to join his commanding officer.

Lucas and Buchanan scampered up simultaneously to the entrance, in great anticipation of finding Remington.

No one else mustered at the entrance yet. Lucas and Buchanan expressed nothing but a state of worry.

Lucas stared intently at Buchanan. "When we find him, I'm immediately going to give him a hug. Then I'm going to kick his ass."

Buchanan grins and says, "Well, he's probably just in hiding. Cut off from camp due to the Viet Cong. He's just waiting for us to come and get him."

"If anything happens to him, Robert - well, it'll be my fault. Mine. All mine."

"Don't fret, sir. We'll find him."

A minute later, Jurgensen along with some marines from 1st platoon of Bravo Company, a few men from 2nd squad, a contingent from C Company, Skawinski, Jackson, Gross, Sigmanson, Dingus, Major Carroll, Frost, Sanborn, Rockford, and even Porch showed up to search for Remington.

"Alright, let's go. Let's go find him." Lucas said.

The large search party set out to find Remington on the inside of the treeline in a long, extensive line of 20 feet intervals with two men a piece at every interval.

The search party searched for no longer than ten minutes to find Remington. Major Carroll and Petty Officer Sigmanson located the spot of Remington's initial contact with the enemy. It measured some 125 yards into the bush from the treeline next to the perimeter. Carroll and Sigmanson discovered a small circumference of ground flattened out with a boundary of some 10 feet from one side to the other, blood stained and evident from a vicious fight that had taken place.

Word of finding Remington spread quickly down the line, including the spiritual team darting rapidly to the initial spot he encountered the Viet Cong.

Arriving to the initial spot Remington faced the VC, Buchanan knew without a shadow of a doubt he had stepped into a violent confrontation with the enemy. Jurgensen led the spiritual team 25 yards further into the bush. Horror-struck every molecule within Buchanan at the sight before him. A sight imprinted within his memory bank of war experiences and one most permanent for Buchanan.

Jurgensen guided the spiritual team on a pathway of blood and human body parts. Remington's torso, limbs, even his private parts, were evenly laid out some five yards apart, leading up into a haunting sight for the spiritual team, never to be forgotten. At the end of the pathway of human remains stood a pike shoved into the ground with Remington's head impaled on top for all to see. Tacked to the pike read a message written on a sign in Remington's blood: 'Capitalist imperialist pigs! Go home!'

Buchanan fell on his knees with emotion, utterly overwhelmed with shock. Jackson stooped down, putting his arm around Buchanan, consoling him. He himself incredulous with the sight before him. The search party fell precipitously in shock, weeping heavily and losing all self control.

Buchanan's feelings toward the Viet Cong hardened, now convinced without a shadow of a doubt the VC had been Devil sent.

Hatred toward the Viet Cong heightened in Camp Love as high as the Heavens. The VC embodied the Devil reincarnate. The engineering battalion sought out missions not only to secure the area to protect the pro-democracy South Vietnamese, but sought to defeat the demonic forces searching for prey in the jungle. Only demonic powers could carry out such evil, wicked atrocities.

Remington, a camp favorite, loved to hunt. And ultimately, his love of hunting precipitously took his life as he entered the jungle before dawn. Lucas would live the rest of his life knowing his death came under his watch. He grieved over Remington till the day he died.

Buchanan celebrated his eldest son's birthday today, Mother's Day. The men worshiped the Lord on this Sabbath day, lifting up mothers as essential nurturers. Though the day celebrated birthdays and mothers, the festive commemorated day failed to blot out the extreme pain suffered in the loss of Remington.

The means of the murderous attack of Remington is one beyond the Christian mind of Buchanan.

Only the Devil is evil enough to have committed such an atrocity.

Hating the Devil never came so easy.

CAT THERAPY

MAY 12, 1969

The wrath of the 7th Engineering Marine Battalion rained down on the Viet Cong with the weight of a sledgehammer. The Communist never saw it coming. The murderers hit blindsided with fury from the marines smashing heavy blows upon the enemy out of no where. The murder and the dismemberment of Remington provoked the marines in Camp Love to reap a crushing sweep of the VC for miles beyond the camp's perimeter. The murderers payed a heavy price for slaying a most cherished member of the battalion. The next four weeks the marines accounted for hundreds added to the monthly body count of enemy dead. The intensity of the battalion humbled the VC, forcing the enemy on their knees, begging the Americans to halt the onslaught of VC casualties. Ferocious retribution of the marines pounded the enemy without an ounce of mercy. Unfortunately, the VC just kept coming regardless of the devastating American fire power and it's capability of inflicting immeasurable casualties.

Buchanan's impenitence toward the Viet Cong sought a tough retaliation of pounding and hammering away at the enemy, forcing them to beg for mercy. He rationalized the punishing reprisal as simply an act of war. Nothing more, nothing less. The severity of Remington's murder generated a heated zeal of getting even.

Following the murder of Remington, the 7th Engineering Battalion's fervor to extinguish the Communists completely out of South Vietnam seemed to heighten a hundred fold.

The night of dreams on May 11 will be remembered for a lifetime. In one particular dream, Buchanan and Remington hunted in the mountains of their beloved home state of Kentucky. In another fond dream, the fellow Kentuckians attended a basketball game and ate Kentucky cuisine including burgoo stew and country fried steak. The dreams were far from nightmares, but the mental imagery noneoftheless infuriated Buchanan. When waking up from REM sleep, his immediate response felt pain and misery, drenched in a cold sweat. He slept emotionally distraught. Never had he been so angry in his life. The fact he witnessed cruel atrocities and wicked acts of violence against human beings in a war zone, Buchanan's brashness justified itself without saying. War draws emotions out of human beings uncharacteristic of moral men and women.

At 0545 hours, Buchanan, stressed with little sleep, set out to talk to the Skipper. Walking briskly to Lucas's office, he flopped himself on the top step of the office hootch, contemplating the words to speak when confronting his commanding officer with his frustrations.

The first thing Lucas laid his eyes on arriving to work this day would be a long-suffering chaplain waiting to talk of Remington sitting in front of his desk. Usually arriving to work between 0600 to 0630 hours, Lucas reckoned he had the privilege and liberty to go to work as commanding officer whenever he wanted to out in the bush. He could do whatever he wanted to do – he was the 'boss', as Buchanan referred to him.

Buchanan had had enough. His time with Lucas had come, an open and blunt talk with the commanding officer.

First to arrive to the CO's office hootch walked up Sergeant Vickers.

Failing to see Buchanan in the early dawn, Vickers seemed taken aback setting his eyes on him.

"Oh - I'm sorry to have startled ya, sergeant." said Buchanan.

"Oh, no worries. But, why so early in the morning, sir?"

"Well - sergeant…" Buchanan, frozen at a loss of words, shrugs his shoulders and motions with his hands.

"*You're* here to see the skipper, right, sir?"

"Yes."

The presence of Buchanan smack dab on the top step of Lucas' office puzzled Vickers, asking himself, 'What's he doing here so early in the morning?'

Vickers certainly loathed the thought of any trouble with Porch this early in the morning. Porch rattling sabers for whatever reason ran twenty-four, seven all day. At any time of the day, the possibility of Porch causing havoc displaying a pretentious face about camp ran high.

Vickers appeared concerned. "You alright, sir?"

"Just need to talk to the boss."

"OK, sir."

Reaching for his office keys in his pocket, Vickers unlocks the door, noticing Sergeant Smith consoling marine friends of Remington in the early morning light as he enters the office with Buchanan. He now sort of figured Buchanan came so early in the morning to hash out his emotions of grief the whole camp suffered from.

"You can sit here, sir, in the front chair outside the Skipper's office."

"I'll just sit *in* the office."

As Buchanan approaches the office entrance, Vickers said, "Sir. S-Sir. I think. I-I think you better just sit out, well - out here, sir."

"Don't be silly, Sergeant." Buchanan insisted. "I'll wait for the Skipper in his office."

As Buchanan walks out of eye shot into the office, Vickers throws his hands up in the air, dropping them on the sides of his legs out of frustration.

Buchanan marched himself into the office with assertion, still in the early first hours of the morning sitting in one of the chairs in front of Lucas' desk. With all of the turmoil of the past two days, the presence of Lucas' cats eluded Buchanan, sitting in the office staring straight at him. Brahms, as usual, lounged on the bookshelves. Hans, ever so resolute and assertive, reclined in a padded bed on a table sitting opposite in the corner of the office. And Ludwig, the affectionate and gentle of the three companions, laid in his favorite spot on the second shelf of a set of cubicle shelves Lucas used for administrative supplies. The felines just woke up, ready for breakfast.

Buchanan, sitting silently in the dark, turns his head abruptly hearing a hard, loud 'thump' on the floor on his right, startling him. Slowly rising out of his chair eager to discover what might have made such a noise, he thought, 'Was it a small snake?' 'A rat?' or 'A small lizard?'

Wide eyed and catching flies, Buchanan turned inspecting the floor in front of the bookshelves searching for the source of the loud thud.

A second thought for Buchanan rang loud and clear, 'The thud is a cat. But where is he?'

With just a half step toward the bookshelves, Buchanan stops. He noticed now in the dim light shining through the top screen portion of the south wall a cat, Brahms, walking straight toward him with confidence and determination.

As Buchanan leisurely sits back down in his chair, Brahms closes the distance between he and Buchanan who's waiting patiently for Lieutenant Colonel Lucas, who says, "Whew."

Brahms greets Buchanan, rubbing his leg, purring and greeting him with glee with his Siamese blue eyes.

"I assume y'all chase all the unwanted critters away at night, huh?" asked Buchanan.

"Meow." responds Brahms.

"HaHaHaHa!" laughs Buchanan.

Another 'thump!' is heard over his left shoulder.

Spotting yet another cat in the corner of his eye, Buchanan notices Hans approaching him with self-assurance, with a strut of initiative. Hans greets Buchanan with a firm rubbing of his leg, jumping onto Buchanan's lap as he extends his hand to groom the self-confident feline.

Yet comes another 'thump' echoed off the bulkheads of Lucas' hootch in the faint light of the morning. Ludwig finally made his debut. Buchanan peeked over his shoulder, catching a glimpse of Ludwig just below the supply shelves. Ludwig cleverly paces up from Buchanan's right, leaping up on the topside of Lucas' desk. The inquisitive feline flops himself squarely in front of Buchanan, staring straight at him with a bit of hauteur.

In a matter of seconds, Buchanan is surrounded by Siamese cats purring loudly. One laying smugly in front of him. Another lounging on his lap kneading him softly. And a third cat rubbing his leg welcoming him in the CO's office.

Immersed in the presence of Siamese cats, Buchanan felt an aura of contentment and solitude, as if in another world. With an uplifted spirit, he wished for it to never end. Grinning ever so slightly, he now understood Lucas' assertion felines provided therapeutic cures for human beings resulting in friendship and the sense of affection human beings so desperately need at the end of the day arriving home from a hard day working. Buchanan found himself sitting, petting the cats, never wanting the moment to end. Although the feline therapists failed to totally erase the last 24 hours, the melancholy felt inside of Buchanan did indeed soften. The quite room served him a sole purpose of his longing of seclusion. Serving as an illusory, therapeutic moment in Vietnam Buchanan will forever remember.

In the emotive, soothing quietness, Buchanan heard a combat boot hit the bottom hootch step of the office, then the second, a third, then the fourth, and finally hitting the last step of the stairs before hearing the screen door push open and swing back hitting the jamb and threshold of the entrance. With each step taken up the stairs, Buchanan heard nothing but buff and assertion in each step.

Walking through the office door, Lucas said, "Good Morning, Sergeant."

"Uh. Uh! Morning Sir. Sir!" said Vickers, stepping somewhat in front of Lucas preventing him from entering his office.

"Sergeant? Stepping in front of me? That's not like you. What's wrong with you?" asked a puzzled Lucas, glaring.

Lucas again attempted to pass, but Vickers took a step in front of him, raised his right hand to stop him. "The-The, I - Sir. There's someone in *yoooour* office sir."

Staring indignantly, Lucas turned red in the face.

Vickers swallows hard. "Sir, I –"

Lucas abruptly interrupts. "Is it Michael Porch? Major Porch? Is it?"

"W-Well, sir. I -"

"Well, spit it out, Sergeant. Is it?" insisted Lucas.

Vickers swallows heavy.

"It is, isn't it?"

Lucas is infuriated.

"I despise starting my day with the king of knuckleheads ruffling feathers so early in the morning! He knows I never meet with anybody till 0800 hours."

Stepping toward the office entrance Lucas continues his tirade. "Damn you! Damn you, Porch! You know damn well I hate a problem from anybody this early in the day!"

Lucas rambles on as he steps into the office. "Listen Porch, get out! Come back hours from now. Please! How about next week?"

Lucas pauses. "Porch. You're such a pain." He reaches for the ceiling light switch, flipping the switch up, illuminating the room for all to set their eyes on a grieving chaplain. "A pain in the -". Catching a glimpse of Buchanan rise out of his chair, Lucas pauses in mid sentence saying, "Good morning, Padre."

"Morning Skipper."

The Siamese were all over Lucas, greeting their master with boisterous meows, the loudest Buchanan had ever heard from the cats, resembling vibrations of human voices. The cats were fervently brushing up onto Lucas' legs and feet, each jockeying for his attention.

Turning to Vickers, Lucas said, "Why didn't you speak up – tell me it was the chaplain in the office?"

"Well - I tried, sir." Vickers said with a half smile, shrugging his shoulders.

Shaking his head, Lucas half grins.

Distracted in his arrival to work, Lucas seemed to brush aside the needs of the cats whose meows escalated, drawing attention to the empty food bowls. The continuous rubbing of Lucas' legs and feet reminded him the cats were hungry.

"OK. OK, guys. I'm going to feed ya. Give me a minute." said Lucas stooping down, petting each cat, letting them know breakfast is on the way.

Lucas raises back up, gives Sergeant Vickers one last glance prior to closing the door, a glance asking Vickers in body language - 'What does the Chaplain want this early in the morning?'

But Lucas had a good notion why Buchanan arrived to the office so early in the morning - Remington.

Lucas stepped opposite of a table corner to a storing cabinet to acquire four cans of cat food, with three demanding cats following him. Buchanan said, "I'm sorry, sir, the hubbub this morning's my fault. The commotion there with Sergeant Vickers - *all* my fault. *My* fault. I'll take *all* the blame. To be honest, I just, w-well...barged my way in this morning."

"*Oh.*" said Lucas. The cat lover took hold of four cans of food out of the storing cabinet commencing a concert of energetic meows from the cats, humoring Buchanan.

"They sure do let ya know when feeding time is, don't they?" said Buchanan, chuckling slightly. Never had he heard such vigorous cat meows for food since his working days on his grandfather's farm in Ohio and in the mountains of Kentucky.

"Wow! Look at all the food!" Buchanan spotted the storing cabinet full of cat food from top to bottom.

Lucas smiles wide as he takes hold of the cans, placing them on the surface of the table in the corner. Stepping back to the cabinet, Lucas grabs three ceramic plates from the top shelf beside the dry food stored in an air tight tub, as the cats leap up onto the table to smell the cans, lightly pushing the cans on the table surface. Humored with the intelligent, demonstrative felines. He is even more humored with the tender, loving care Lucas displays toward his Siamese friends.

Placing the plates on the floor, Lucas petted the cats, assuring them breakfast is on it's way. As Lucas pulled back the metal tab lid of the first can, the cats meowed away, especially Brahms, standing on their back paws reaching up to touch Lucas's wrist to speed up the feeding. Opening one can at a time, he placed a can of food on each plate, dividing the last can between all three plates.

All the while, Buchanan listened to Lucas give lessons on the necessity of feeding cats full meals of nutrients every day. He clarified a cat's life is extended with nutritional meals and annual veterinarian visits. He asked curiously, "You've got Dachshunds, don't ya Padre?"

"Yes sir."

"Then you know the importance of tender loving care for your pets." Lucas made his way toward his desk, dropping the empty food cans into a trash container.

"Yes sir. I do."

As Lucas sat back into his huge pure oak swivel chair, Buchanan said, "Sir? Uh, sir."

"Yes, chaplain?"

"Can I ask you a question?"

"Sure, Robert. You know ya have an open door policy with me."

Buchanan pondered the correct words to chose to put into a sentence to inquire of Lucas, the 'gun ho' marine, a question bordering on prying into his life. As a tough veteran of World War II and the Korean War, he had already witnessed violent wars and gruesome deaths. Buchanan did not intend to embarrass him in any sort of way by asking innocent questions of his personal life. He did finally ask, "Sir, ya do this every morning? Don't you? I mean, ya do this as a means to deal with the war? Don't ya?"

Rubbing his chin, he stares straight out into camp. "Yeah, Robert. I do."

Pausing, Lucas stares up smiling with emotion at his chaplain. He says with assurance, "I love cats."

Hating the Enemy

May 12, 1969

For twenty minutes, pets and the love of animals dominated conversation.

The Siamese seemed to enjoy the conversation as well, as Brahms situated himself in Lucas' lap. Ludwig groomed himself on the desk. And Hans demanding attention from Buchanan, sitting in his lap, which the chaplain, of course, obliged. Hans took a liking to Buchanan, who enjoyed his presence in the office when present.

Lucas' love of animals included dogs as well, who grew up with canines along with various felines in his household.

Reminiscing of his favorite childhood dog Hoover, an English Boxer named after the President, brought back loving and special memories of Lucas' childhood. Lucas' father adored President Hoover, who insisted the President's administration had been treated vehemently unfair by the press, the Democrats, and his enemies by unforeseen circumstances the President could neither prevent nor avoid. Buchanan smiled, thinking Lucas' dad must have been drunk during the whole Hoover administration. Lucas recalled his mother's animal rescue leadership in the Cleveland area for homeless pets, attending the meetings and fairs, providing an opportunity to adopt a feral cat or a stray dog.

"Oh, that's great, sir." said Buchanan.

"Yes, my mother's insistence in finding homes for feral and strays ended up a twenty-four, seven commitment. To euthanize animals was out of the question."

Lucas let loose a tirade about how reckless human beings conduct themselves in the selfish motives of the euthanization of domestic animals, out of convenience. When finished, he asked, "What about your pets, Padre? You display signs of loving animals. My cats love ya."

Buchanan's experience with pets in his lifetime differed vastly from Lucas's.

As Buchanan petted Hans, he gave Lucas a rundown of his past pets. "Well, sir. We had cats and dogs. Up in the mountains, we fed many a feral cat who killed off the rodents and rats, along with indoor, outdoor domestic cats. My mother, actually my stepmother, has yet to live a year of life without living with a house cat who's spoiled with every perk feral cats only dream of. She usually adopted a pet store or shelter cat for the house."

"What about your dogs? You had dogs, didn't ya?" asked Lucas.

"Well, sir. Many of our dogs in Kentucky and Ohio were family pets and hunting dogs for grub." Buchanan thought to himself, 'Wow! My favorite dog was a mutt compared to an English boxer.' He sat up in his chair straight as a board with exalted pride, describing his dog from childhood. "Jack is my favorite dog as a kid. My father named him after a heavyweight boxing champion. He wasn't any special dog breed, just a mountain dog who just walked up to the porch one day. No one ever claimed him, so we just kept him."

"Sounds like he just wanted some love and a home."

"Yes sir. His fur was pure black. It sparkled so shiny in the sunlight. He sure was a beautiful dog."

Suddenly, the pet talk came to a screeching halt, as the men failed to avert the built up emotion, caving in to the innermost struggle within themselves dealing with the death of Remington.

Buchanan had never seen Lucas emotional until today.

The silence in the room gave way only from the cats' purring and the soft efforts heard from Buchanan and Lucas fighting back the uncontrollable emotion.

The cats spoke to the men as if a well-oiled engine, purring as loud as their little lungs could muster. The cat's purr simply spoke to the men as if to say, 'It's going to be OK.'

The therapeutic talk of pets and the love for animals soothed the mood, following the past two days of war, at least temporarily. The dictated mood in the hootch centered in on the love of animals. The commanding officer and the chaplain of Camp Love intentionally brushed aside the subject of Remington - until now. Buchanan broke the ice. "Sir, I have a question."

Lucas, anticipating the question, prepared himself for the inevitable. "I know what it is, but you can ask it anyway."

A battered Buchanan admits, "William, I-I'm struggling. Have you struggled?"

Lucas shifts in his seat, petting Brahms. He slowly glances up and says, "Yes, I have."

"Skipper, I didn't sleep a wink last night."

"Me neither." Lucas responded.

Standing up, Buchanan holds Hans roaming the office. Hans, loving every second of the attention, takes advantage of the time given to him by such a caring human being.

"I'll tell you the truth, Robert. I haven't thought of anything but the young man." said Lucas stepping to the food cabinet.

The Siamese, including Hans, who jumps out of Buchanan's arms with urgency, run immediately to the doors of the cabinet, with tails erect and ears all pointed in the anticipation of receiving dry food.

Reaching up into the cabinet, Lucas pulls down the airtight dry food container, placing it on the corner table.

As he sat the lid of the container on the table surface, the cats jump on top of the table to binge feed straight out of the container.

With authority and command, Lucas says, "No! Y'all know I don't tolerate eating out of the container. Down! Down!"

The cats all dart off the table surface onto the floor, as Buchanan smiles from ear to ear. Lucas sounded off as if a father scolding his children.

With a food measuring cup, Lucas scoops one serving after the other, dispensing food onto the ceramic plates. Buchanan gazed beyond belief, observing the cats seizing food out of thin air by mouth. The felines purred at the top of their lungs for the food.

Lucas stoops down to pet the hungry Siamese, finally expressing his love for his cats in a broken voice. "The cats here - well, they.... well, they help me get through the day." Buchanan takes a step forward to get a better look at Lucas. He rises, walking back to his swivel chair. Sitting down, he smiles back up toward Buchanan.

"You lose your emotions in the office." remarked a curious Buchanan. "In the privacy of your own confines."

Lucas grins. "*Yeah*. But if you ever say anything outside this room about how soft I am with my cats or you've seen me emotional - I'll kick your ass."

Buchanan smiles widely. "I started many a fight in my wild days, sir, and won many of them. But," Buchanan tilts his head and shrugs his shoulders, "you're twice as big as I am, trained on how to kill other human beings. I *know* you'd kick my ass."

Lucas chuckles.

"I've heard of what you were like before you became a Christian chaplain."

Buchanan sat back down in his chair, slow and deliberate, peeping over at the cats finishing up their dry food. "They sure like to eat, don't they?"

Lucas glances toward the cats. "*Yeah*."

Buchanan stares intently at the spoiled felines. "It pleases me. You have a means to soften the pain for this blasted war."

Lucas gives Buchanan a thorough look see, examining him from one end to the other. He wonders about the chaplain's innermost thoughts and feelings.

With sincerity, Buchanan said, "The music Burns plays every night helps. And yes, spending time with the Tri-State marines and sailors helps. But what really gets me through the day is reading my Bible and my dependence on God."

Lucas, shaking his head, points to the bookshelf. "Yes. My Catholic devotional and Bible are sitting there on the shelf and is the first thing I do every day." He searches all over the office for the cats, names and points at each and everyone of them. "The cat's presence consoles me here in the office as I start my day with the Lord."

Looking back at Buchanan, Lucas ponders the purpose of his early morning visit. “But why are you here today, Padre? *Really*?”

Buchanan stands up, roaming the room. “Well, here it is Skipper.” Tensing up, he breathed harder. “I’m sick and tired of seeing things happen that’s contrary to the prayers I lift up to the Lord.”

Lucas seemed puzzled. “What? Do what? God answers your prayers, Robert. They -”

“No!” interrupted Buchanan with anger. “No, no they aren’t.” Lucas, who by now knows Buchanan is roaming his office to vent, just lets him unleash his anger and frustration.

“My prayer requests seem to be answered by the Devil. Prayers answered on the wrong end. I prayed the first night last year for the horror to stop. But the more I prayed, the worst it got! I prayed for the Lord to provide great things for the village of An Ngai Tay - only to see their chief tortured and murdered and the women and girls raped and murdered by those wicked Viet Cong.”

Buchanan paused.

“I’m hating the Viet Cong!” declared Buchanan, ranting on. “I prayed for those children at Liberty Bridge, only to see them blow themselves up literally in front of my t-two….”

Buchanan’s emotions finally took hold of him. He took a moment to compose himself.

“I prayed for the safety and armour of God to shield these marines from the enemy, only to see many of them fall to the ground, dead from the Devil’s legions’ bullets. I pray every day for my fellow sailors, the corpsmen and Doc Delaney, only to see Crowley die a hero’s death at the hands of the Viet Cong. I’m beginning to hate’em!” He paused. “The hate I feel toward the VC is not me. My family taught me hate was of the Devil.”

Buchanan, struggling to speak his ensuing words, walks over to the front of his seat, sitting back down in front of Lucas. “And I-I prayed for my fellow Kentuckian every morning for the Lord to protect him while he went hunting. Only to see again those malicious….” Buchanan slows down in his speech, and then says with anger and force, “cruel Viet Cong *murder* him.”

Buchanan slouches, breathing hard. He stares straight into his commanding officer's eyes and all Buchanan sees staring back at him is compassion and sorrow out of his skipper's face. Lucas perceived in front of him a man of God. Regardless, a man of God emotionally and spiritually affected from war like all other men. War had done to Chaplain Buchanan what combat experiences had done to human beings over the millennia – crushing the heart, soul, and mind. The very essence of a Christian reflected the trifecta of the heart, soul, and mind of Jesus Christ. And now war confronted Buchanan from within, as it had within Lucas in previous wars.

Day after day, Buchanan endured a violent war hammering away at his heart and soul. Lucas thought of Leo Tolstoy's quote - 'War is a terrible thing.'* Buchanan said, "I want my prayers to be answered by the Lord, not the Devil." Lucas had nothing but empathy for his chaplain.

Buchanan stood back up, roaming the room, voicing his frustrations. "And you, William, and other marines, prevented to do what you need to do to win this war. We practically win all the battles and skirmishes. Johnson didn't permit bombing the enemy in Cambodia. Or in Laos. And the VC and NVA just run across the border after they blatantly hit and run."

Buchanan catches a glimpse of the cats staring at him with his bizarre behavior. He mused the cats' intelligent feline minds struggling to interpret the odd behavior out of this human being they so admired.

Buchanan delivers an added jab. "And Johnson set in place daytime bombing only. How stupid is that?"

Lucas grins, knowing Buchanan's interest in military strategy.

Buchanan once again descends back into his seat, sighing heavily. "And then there's no bombing of North Vietnam! How can you win a war when bureaucrats prevent generals from bombing the enemy? All the books I have ever....read....on military strategy blatantly exerts t-total...." Buchanan found himself exhausted from the energy exerted by his outburst. The cats continue to stare, sensing a worn down chaplain slowing back down to normal. Hans jumped off the third bookshelf onto Lucas' desk, into Buchanan's lap, meowing and purring to console his human friend.

"Feel better?" Lucas asked.

"Yes sir. I actually do."

"Good."

Buchanan grins as the cats now know the humans are now calm and back to normal.

Brahms and Ludwig jump off the bookshelves onto Lucas' desk. Jumping into his lap, the cats deliver a competitive swipe at each other for rank. The cats settle in his lap, though throwing an indignant glance toward one another. Brahms hollered a most stern, possessive warning to Ludwig, "MEOW!"

Grooming the cats in their laps, the men immensely enjoyed their company.

Buchanan asks, "Sir. Is it right for a chaplain to, well, to feel as angry and hateful as I feel right now?"

Pondering for a response, Lucas answers straightforward. "Well, chaplain. This is my third war. And in all of them, I ask, 'How can human beings treat each other in such atrocious and cruel behaviors?'"

Buchanan listened with the utmost concern.

"I've seen many deaths. I've seen in all four corners of the Pacific and Asia violence no civilian would ever understand. And you know something?" said Lucas. "I really don't have a concrete answer."

Lucas heard a sigh of relief from Buchanan.

"The simple answer Padre is, well - Jesus. Many people have hate in their heart, not the love and compassion of the Lord."

Buchanan grins, nodding.

"And your prayers?" asked Lucas. "As I have heard you say in many a devotion – we can't explain why things happen in life, but we know one thing - God is in control."

Lucas turns, looking off into the distance from camp. "Praying for the better things in life is part of our faith. When they don't come, it isn't necessarily God's fault. It's the circumstances human beings have put themselves in, not God."

Lucas sighs, continuing to counsel his battalion chaplain, as Brahms jumps onto his desk to lounge on the flat surface.

"Robert, war is a man-made thing. And as believers, well, honestly, we must spread the peace and love of Jesus as best we can in our war situation."

Buchanan just sat and listened, humored by the oddity that the chaplain, sitting in the commanding officer's office, assumed the role of counselee while the commanding officer shepherded pastoral counseling to the chaplain.

The men sit silently, slowly accepting the death of Remington in their hearts and mind.

Lucas broke the silence. "Let me share something sent from my priest in Cleveland in a recent letter." He pulled an opened letter from his desk, sharing it with Buchanan. "The letter I received from Father McEachin ended with these two passages of Scriptures. The first is James 1:2-3. It reads, 'Count it all joy, my brethren, when you meet various trials, for you know that the testing of your faith produces steadfastness.' The other is Hebrews 12:14, and it reads, 'Strive for peace with all men, and for the holiness without which no one will see the Lord.'"

Lucas permits the Scriptures to sink in. "Robert, we can't control others. But we can control ourselves. Whenever we show peace to anyone, we have planted seeds for others to know what we know in our own hearts."

The words spoken by Lucas sank in for Buchanan.

"You've preached to all of us chaplain. It's all about what's in here." Lucas motioned toward his heart.

Buchanan sighs, listening to words of wisdom.

"Robert, I've thought about Remington sense yesterday. We can't bring Carl back." Lucas glanced toward Brahms, petting his devoted feline friend. Looking up toward Buchanan, he said, "But we can carry on and go forward." Pausing, he said, "Chaplain, as far as Carl is concerned, well, he's motivated me. I'm going to make retribution. I'm going to make amends. Not revenge, mind you, but retribution."

Buchanan grins, nodding in approval.

Lucas says with conviction, "I will not let the VC get away with this. I'm going to push back on the evil."

With a grinding of his teeth, Lucas says with force and determination, "And that evil is the *NVA* and the *VC*. They will not get away with what they've done to Sergeant Remington."

Again, Buchanan grins.

"As you've noticed, they're not very nice human beings. They need humbled."

Lucas clutched Brahms from lounging on his desktop, pulling him to his chest to groom him. A memory of Remington emerged from Lucas's memory bank, causing Lucas to grimace, pointing to his heart. "They don't have in here what you've constantly preached to us all these months we should have - Jesus."

The CO stood up with Brahms in his arms, stepping to the window behind his desk, thinking of Remington.

Staring out into the bush, he scoffs, shaking his head. "The world sure needs Jesus. Doesn't it, Padre?"

Buchanan nods, recognizing a sincere heart in Lucas' voice.

"They sure do, Skipper."

The irony of the day stared Buchanan in the face. His intention to vent to the Skipper and minister to Lucas fell through. The Skipper ended up the pastoral counselor consoling the bereaved. Buchanan just sits, grinning, pondering the thought. The cats never end loving their human superiors, counseling their human friends all the way to the end of the day.

With just months to go in Vietnam, Buchanan discovered an additional source to cope with war. The presence of the Skipper's cats seemed to curb his hate for the enemy.

John Wayne Visits the Friday Night Social

June 27, 1969

Nearly two months had passed since Remington's death, resulting in two months of retribution from the 7th Engineering Marine Battalion. The 7th had accounted for many victories against terrorist attacks in the field, discovering and eliminating Viet Cong terrorist cells. The VC failed considerably to inflict significant casualties and terrorist attacks on the South Vietnamese in the past two months.

The United States' efforts to win the war gained many victories. But these triumphs added little toward ending the war on a winning note because of self-inflicting wounds. The military's restrictions of pursuing or attacking the enemy after they had crossed the border into safe havens of Cambodia or Laos reaped favorable results of hit-and-run assaults by the Viet Cong. However, the United States suffered some of the highest casualties in the five-year war to date. Casualty numbers protesters back home will use for political advantage and smear in the faces of those attempting to stop the spread of Communism. The casualty numbers of the enemy will mount higher than ever before, numbers never seen up to this point in the war. In the past two months throughout South Vietnam, the enemy suffered tremendously.

At 0530 hours, Buchanan showered and shaved early for the busy day ahead. He stepped to his desk to read and catch up with the war news in the Navy Times and recent newspapers Dorothy sent him in her last package.

He first reads an article informing him of a turn for the good in the ground war, delivering a hard, deliberate blow to the enemy. United States military forces and allies set forth an effort to minimize enemy movements on the Ho Chi Minh Trail in the mountains. From the month of May to July 16, 1969, in the northern Quang Tri Province along the DMZ, the United States 9th Marine Regiment carried out Virginia Ridge, a military operation to weaken enemy strength along the DMZ. The enemy will suffer nearly 600 casualties in the campaign.

On May 5, 1969, Commie forces attacked United States personnel 65 miles northwest of Saigon. The Communists suffered approximately 125 killed in action, while Americans suffered nine killed and 59 wounded.

Buchanan next read a piece that hit close to home. On May 9, 1969, marines, some from the 7th Engineering Marine Battalion, engaged enemy NVA soldiers southwest of Da Nang suffering nearly 130 killed and possibly hundreds wounded. The United States suffered six killed and 12 wounded.

An engagement on June 19, 1969, American and South Vietnamese forces fought Communist forces in massive numbers near Tayninh, South Vietnam. The city is dozens of miles northwest of Saigon and about a dozen miles from the Cambodian border, an area dense with an enemy presence. The fighting was one of fierce combat, much of it in the city streets of Tayninh. Again, the casualties for the Communists mounted high, with 146 killed and possibly hundreds wounded. The United States will suffer three killed and 14 wounded.

The papers reported battles and skirmishes fought in the months of May and June, most if not all won by the United States and her allies.

Buchanan shakes his head in disbelief at the overwhelming numbers of casualties for the enemy and a few compared to the United States. Again, Buchanan is reminded of the fact the United States is winning an overwhelming number of the battles, but losing the war coming from many directions.

The day of the Tayninh battle, Buchanan reads a proposed timeline in an article for the withdrawal of United States troops in the next few years by President Nixon's Secretary of Defense Clark Clifford. The proposal offers the removal of 100,000 for the year 1969 and an additional 100,000-150,000 troops in 1970. The article quotes President Nixon's comment in a news conference, "hope that we could beat Mr. Clifford's timetable."*

Flustered, Buchanan shakes his head and says, "what a waste."

The combat most curious catching the eye of Buchanan occurred between May 10-20. The engagement ensued one mile from the Laos border and was part of a campaign to cut off enemy penetration from Laos, harassing the city of Hue in the northeast and Da Nang in the southeast. The campaign, codenamed Operation Apache Snow, set out to sweep the Ashua Valley with approximately 3,000 allied forces to sweep the valley, including over 400 South Vietnamese personnel and the 101st Airborne Division. The sweep caused an attack and destruction of a key Communist stronghold on Apbia mountain, identified as Hill 937. The destruction of the hill is vital in halting the harassing hit-and-run attacks on Hue and Da Nang. The next eleven days added to some of the most fierce fighting of the war. Allied forces conducted 11 attacks to overwhelm the enemy. Major General Melvin Zais commanded the allied forces, ordering many air strikes on Hill 937 to ensure a victory. Finally, on the eleventh attack, Hill 937 fell to the allies suffering many casualties: 56 killed and over 400 wounded. The North Vietnamese suffered substantial numbers of casualties of their own, nearly 600 killed and hundreds wounded. Buchanan rolls his eyes when he read the North Vietnamese army and press reports, claiming they inflicted 1000 United States casualties. Buchanan muttered, "That's the commies for ya."

The fierce levity of fighting, added to the mounting casualties of United States forces, the American public and historians would refer to the battle as 'Hamburger Hill.'

Protesters back home added the battle to their list of motives to mount more pressure on the country to give up the effort to win the war, permitting the Commies to invade the south and wreak havoc on the innocents of South Vietnam. Buchanan still believed the war could be won, if only the politicians just shoved aside all those in the way and just win the war. The first step in winning the war required United States leadership to shove aside the protesters and the Democratic party, who seem to be very soft toward the aggression of Communists worldwide.

Buchanan dropped his hands on his desk while holding the last paper in his hands he had been reading, shaking his head in denial. "Whew." Sighing heavily, he noticed the time - 0605 hours. Grabbing a western novel off the bookshelf written by a favorite author sent a few weeks ago from Dorothy, he read for 20 relaxing minutes when a knock on the door disrupted his brief cognitive respite from the war.

Buchanan thought - 'Great Scott! Just when the book is getting good, someone has to interrupt!' He asks, "Yes! Who goes there?"

Buchanan heard a young marine chuckling. "He said it again."

"Haha hahaha." came more laughter.

Buchanan again asks, "Who *goes* there?"

Again laughter, but louder. "Haha hahaha!"

"Come on, chaplain. It's us! Jackson! Ski!"

The young marines heard footsteps on the wooden floor surface of the hootch stepping to the door, then the rattling of three safety latches unfastened one after the other. Glancing toward one another dumbfounded, the men wait patiently for the door to be opened. Buchanan pushes the hootch door open and there in front of him stood Jackson and Skawinski, smiling with hands on their hips.

"Who goes there?" asked Skawinski. "Isn't that a little too much, sir?"

"No. And yes, I still ask 'who goes there?'. That's what they told me to say in training, and that's exactly what I'm going to do."

The young marines chuckle.

"And three security latches, sir?" said Jackson. "You've added two more latches."

"Yes." answered Buchanan, stepping back toward his desk to sit down.

"Isn't that a little overkill, chaplain? You adding two more latches?" asked Jackson.

Sitting in his swivel chair, Buchanan answers in his deep mountain accent, "Look, Philip. I don't trust these VC characters. They ain't cheerful people. And I mean 'ain't.' They're mean. I'm going to make sure I'm gonna be as safe as, and as the Scots might say, 'meself' can be."

Jackson grins.

As Skawinski chuckled softly, shaking his head, the two men sit in the two stationary chairs in front of Buchanan's desk.

"Sir, all the VC has to do to get in here is just rip the door off its hinges and toss it aside. No three latches are going to protect you anymore than one." said Skawinski, grinning from ear to ear.

Jackson furthers the point. "He's right, sir. Three latches will not, and I repeat, *will not* stop them from entering!"

"Well, it makes me feel better. Besides, I got two .45's in my desk drawer. And that men, well, that will stop them for sure." said an assuring Buchanan.

"Anyhow, sir. Busy day today. You need anything from me?" asked Jackson.

"No, Philip. I'll take care of the memorial service today here in the camp. That's at 0800 hours. After that, we'll need to jump in the jeep and hightail it to the orphanage. Chaplain Kensington is expecting us at 1100 hours with the school supplies donated by the marine children's fund."

"Yes, sir. Remember, the officers call at 1600 hours."

Buchanan nodded, turning to Skawinski. "Ski? You going with us? To the orphanage? Chaplain Kensington likes ya."

"If you're inviting me, sir? Well - *yeah*."

"Good. The more, the merrier."

Skawinski asked, "You'll need some help with the social tonight, won't ya?"

"Sure. Like always." answered Jackson.

Buchanan took notice of his watch. "Men, it's 0625 hours. We better get some chow before our busy day begins."

"Thought you'd never ask, sir." said Jackson, rising out of his chair.

"Amen to that, sir." added Skawinski.

The three men smartly walked to the chow hall to eat a hearty breakfast, as the day indeed will be a busy one.

Buchanan's memorial service remained one never to be forgotten. The four Delta Company marines killed two days ago were born leaders and part of the heart and soul of the company. The men were the epitome of marine esprit de corps. Buchanan had never led a more emotional memorial service. The marines were so distraught arriving at the service, Lucas turned a blind eye to military protocol, as friends of the KIAs seemed devastated with such a loss of four special members of the company.

Next on the day's agenda scheduled the orphanage. The friendly, loving Americans' visit blessed the elated children.

The routine officer's call at 1600 hours briefed the men of the constant reminder of strict adherence to security measures for the camp, maintaining the chain of command to sustain discipline, authority, and responsibility. Company officers conveyed the usual reports from the various departments of camp to the Skipper.

Knocked senseless with exhaustion, Buchanan felt the fatigue from months of constant mental and physical challenges not entirely in coming due to combat, which contributed. The impetus of Buchanan's combat fatigue stemmed from an array of combat experiences. Looking forward to the conclusion of the officer's call at 1700 hours, Buchanan anticipated a time to rest in his hootch, a secluded recess in the day until 1815 hours. Following 75 minutes of rest, the spiritual team eagerly longed to prepare for the Friday night social. The desire for peace and calm asserted itself.

As usual, Porch and his circle of friends interrupted the monotony of the meeting by introducing new points of order the minute Lucas called for new business. The point of order from Porch usually came written as a complaint. In the meeting, the intrusive bore made obvious the blatant exposure of adult men's materials exposed all over the camp. Posters. Magazines. Pictures and photos. Porch wanted to manage and implement a zero tolerance policy toward, as Porch referred to it, the morale problem. Porch and his allies favored a Prohibition approach. Except for Porch and his cronies, the notion flabbergasted the officers.

"What?" Lucas asked with indignation. The irate commanding officer, beet red in the face, stood up and strolled around his office, puzzled. "With the VC possibly just outside our perimeter ready to attack at a second's notice? With snipers all over the place? An ever present NVA threat of attack within a 30-mile radius? Booby traps every ten feet in front of us? Spies roaming around? And you want to pilfer around, like the Gestapo, in marines and sailors' personal effects, to find girlie magazines?"

Following Lucas' lengthy declination of Porch's proposal, the silence in his office deafened. Porch and his colleagues, including Napier and Lieutenant Turley, from Seattle, Washington - felt like dodo birds.

Rockford made the point further. "I think we need to spend our time *just* a little more wisely. Like - *maybe*, spending our time fighting this war we're in, *major*."

Porch seethed with anger.

Hit with a dose of sick humor, Buchanan glanced toward Porch, imagining steam coming out of his ears.

As far as Buchanan was concerned, he loathed the exposure of adult materials as much as Porch did. As an enlisted man, Buchanan knew full well the material dampened the physical attraction away from a spouse and onto a stranger, something he knew God frowned upon. God intended for sexual intimacy and love to blossom between a man and his wife. He knew it. Porch knew it. Both knew adult material caused human beings to shift the direction of genuine love on an entirely different path. But he knew handling the exposure of adult material on par with the Prohibition called for identical results as prohibiting alcohol in the 1920s. Porch's move of zero tolerance would double, possibly triple, the amount of adult materials in Camp Love if such a policy came to fruition.

Buchanan thought the suggestion an oddity. He noticed very little adult materials in camp, though the exposure displayed itself evident throughout camp. Very little exposure showed in the office hootches. And Buchanan failed to observe the overwhelming quantity of materials which indeed existed in the personal hootches within camp. In his estimation, Porch made a mountain out of a molehill. The problem lacked weight to ruffle the feathers Porch had been willing to ruffle. In fact, pondering the thought at his desk later on, Buchanan has observed less adult materials in camp since his arrival in October 1968. Maybe, *just* maybe, he has had some positive influence on the troops. Grinning, he thought better of it. The men loved women. And the fact the men were in the middle of the jungle, absent from the presence of women, reassured Buchanan the adult materials flourished in camp. Buchanan thought possibly the men hurriedly removed the adult materials when hearing him approach a hootch. And when departing a hootch, it all gets nailed back up again, just to protect the chaplain or simply to escape the embarrassment. Regardless, Buchanan still loathed the adult materials. The men's literature and photographs might be against regulations, as Porch vehemently pointed out in the officer's call, but there is nothing he could do about it. Neither could Porch.

Glancing at his watch, he noticed 1750 hours has arrived, just 25 minutes until Jackson's arrival to pick Buchanan up for the Friday night social. For the 25 minutes, Buchanan sat in his swivel chair. Sitting and just thinking of everything and everyone. His wife. His kids. Ohio State football. Kentucky. The war. Sergeant Remington. Chaplain Kensington and the children at the orphanage and school. His thoughts ran wild and erratic. One recurring thought dominated his mind - to stay in for the night. His mood set for isolation. He wanted nothing but to spend the remaining part of the day alone in his hootch. His body felt weak, weary, and worn. The three w's hit hard. His inclination desired to read or to listen to armed services radio. Or to play solitaire at his desk. Isolation from all the war and commotion ranked high for Buchanan. He didn't really know what to think of himself. The Friday night social is the favorite night of the week for the marines, and here he wants to hermitize himself. The night provided a means of 'normalcy' to both officers and enlisted. But tonight seemed different.

The monotony of silence shatters with the impact of boots hitting the steps ascending upward toward the hootch door. Then a familiar voice asked, "Hey, chaplain? Ya in there, sir?" The familiar voice was none other than Sergeant Jackson. Looking at his watch, time stood at 1810 hours. He had five minutes remaining in his pause with the war. From the killing. From the agony. From the death. From everything. Buchanan just smiled and thought, 'All good things must come to an end.'

Buchanan rose, shaking his head, scampering over to the door. "Yes, Sergeant. I'm coming. I know. I know! The door's locked."

Buchanan unfastened the three latches, pushing the door open.

"Ya ready, sir? Sir?" said Jackson, pondering Buchanan's body language.

"Of course I am."

"Ya could've fooled me. Did I disturb you, sir? With something?"

"No. No, Sergeant."

"Well, *then* - let's go." said an enthusiastic Jackson. "I'm looking forward to tonight's film. One of your favorites."

Buchanan follows Jackson out of the hootch. "The film with Robert Mitchum? Yes, it's a favorite. Where did ya get it?"

The spiritual team walked toward the camp hall. Buchanan asked, "I thought that film was impossible for us to receive with all the copyright business and red tape that goes along with it?"

"Well, we hadn't had a new film for a while and besides, I just thought you would - well, want to see a new one, sir. We now have a library of 35 films, and as great of a movie as they might be, we could quote every line of them. We've seen them so often."

"Sergeant? You haven't answered my question. Where did you get the film?"

Smiling, Jackson glances slowly toward Buchanan. "I made a deal or two."

"The Scrounger? Ya made a deal with the Scrounger?" asked Buchanan, in a tone of suspicion.

"Yes." answered Jackson, smirking.

"Well, *Sergeant,* I hope it was a fair deal. If you're not careful, you can find yourself on the short end of the deal with the Scrounger, if you're not careful."

"Believe me, sir. I know what I'm doing."

Smiling, Buchanan shakes his head, wondering what kind of deal he made with The Scrounger.

Reaching the hall for the Friday social, Buchanan steps in first ahead of Jackson. Noticing the hall close to completion to prepare for the social, the spiritual team scanned the hall from one corner to the other. The team spotted Skawinski, Rodriquez, Kowslowski, Dobbs, Gross, Jurgensen, Lipstone, and other enlisted friends loyal to the chaplain's office, setting up chairs, preparing the food and drink tables, and unfolding the tables in the hall's corner. "Wow!" said a pleased Buchanan.

Catching Buchanan out of the corner of his eye, Skawinski stopped working, standing in the middle of all the activity in the hall. Grinning, he asked, "What do ya think, Chaplain?" in an elevated voice over all the clank and clatter of chairs and tables being set.

Over all the noise, Buchanan shouts loud and clear, "Amen!"

What Buchanan expected for every Friday night social is a neat and tidy conference hall. He expected the food spread out onto the tables and the movie ready to roll in the projector. The chairs were positioned in two sections with 10 rows, each with an aisle in the middle, set with six chairs across each row totaling 120 seats in the hall, as Buchanan favored. The men made the drinks from the chow hall ready to serve. All that is required now for a successful Friday night social were marines and sailors to fill the seats.

Just 35 minutes till the start of the social. Initially, Buchanan wanted nothing but isolation this night and to be left alone. But discovering the men's eagerness for the social, the night might be a special evening after all spent with friends, enlisted and officer alike.

As 1930 hours approached, many of Buchanan's friends stationed elsewhere in Vietnam trickled into the hall for the social. First to drop in for the social entered Chaplain Kensington. Buchanan greeted him, conversing for a moment to catch up a bit with the past few days.

Then came Chaplains Marino and Wynn, and their assistants, committed and loyal fellow religious facilitators. Buchanan welcomed them, walking his friends to the food tables, offering his guests some eats. As they enjoyed the hospitality of the 7th, Buchanan caught another friend in the corner of his eye walk through the doors of the hall - Lieutenant Commander John Adkins. What a sight for sore eyes! Buchanan had not seen him for weeks. A pleasant surprise for a man who initially wanted to spend the night alone.

'What's going on here?' Buchanan asked himself. 'His friends showing up in the middle of the bush for his Friday night social, showing a John Wayne movie? Why?' He felt as if he had fallen into the middle of the television show to surprise people.

After Adkins came the XO Carroll through the door. Lucas followed, along with Rockford and Burns. Next walked Frost through the hall doors. Buchanan feels nothing but elation. Many other 7th Engineering officers joined the fray, including Jones, Case, and Doc Delaney. Even Porch made his way to the social, a first for him.

Porch attending a social? 'But why?' asked Buchanan.

Then Captain Johannsson entered the hall.

Scores of enlisted arrived, including Smith, Shaw, Frank, and even McElwaney and Jansen from 'that state up north'.

Space in the conference hall got a little cramped from all the attendees. It might be the largest gathering yet for the social.

The last officer and dear friend to step into the hall entered Chaplain Brennan from Navy Chaplain's School in Rhode Island. A servant of God providing Buchanan a greater appreciation for his Christian friends in the Roman Catholic Faith. Brennan's influence strengthened Buchanan's appreciation for the Liturgical calendar, though Buchanan's awareness of the Liturgical calendar widened ten years earlier while attending the Lutheran seminary.

Again Buchanan asked himself, 'Why all the visitors?' Pondering the question, he noticed one friend who was absent: Lieutenant Melvin Abrams. His absence saddened Buchanan. He loved him. His faith strengthens in Abram's presence. Buchanan had never met a more committed chaplain in the Navy. Regardless of the cause for his absence, he missed his friend's presence. He thought to himself - 'Well, there is a war on.'

With the many unexpected guests and the usual 7th Engineering crowd for the social, the noise struck a level of deafening cacophony, dense with marines and sailors' voices booming.

Everyone and their uncle stepped up to greet Buchanan, acknowledging the social a source of motivation to cope with combat fatigue and to survive the week.

With just five minutes until the allotted time to show the film, Buchanan gave the room a thorough look see. He approved of what he saw. He is amongst friends and colleagues.

As the men in the hall continued to 'fellowship', as Buchanan referred to it, Lucas made his way up to the front, where Buchanan stood conversing with Brennan, Marino, and Wynn.

"Excuse me, chaplains. I don't mean to interrupt, but we're about to start the movie showing." Lucas said. He faced the rather large gathering, and with a hand raised to catch the attention of his fellow service members, the men quieted down as he addressed all who were present.

Turning toward Buchanan, taken aback with all the attention, Lucas said, "Chaplain Buchanan. You weren't expecting any of this tonight, we know that." Pausing, Lucas continued, "We also know you like a low profile and frown on any recognition when getting attention is concerned." The rather large assemblage of men laugh softly.

"But tonight. *You* are the center of attention. We gathered as many friends as possible here for you tonight, Padre. You might not always feel it or always see it. But, we appreciate you very much helping us get through the hardships, spiritually and physically, we experience every day."

Buchanan stands motionless. Embarrassed and caught speechless. Stiff and taken aback, catching flies.

All 175 pairs of eyeballs staring right at him.

Lucas says, "So Padre, this night is one of those times of the week here at the 7th Engineering Battalion that we all are given an opportunity for 'normalcy' in our lives and it is all due to you."

Embarrassed, Buchanan says, "Thank ya, sir." He now appears less tense and appreciative of the moment.

Lucas finally spills the beans. "And with that said. We have a very special surprise for you and the camp. Only myself, the XO, and Sergeant Jackson knew of our special visitor tonight. When he was briefed on your Friday night socials, he insisted on coming and popping in on you."

Everyone in the room scanned all four corners of the hall, pondering who it might be. Buchanan heard soft mutterings all over the hall. Lucas could no longer hold it in. "Chaplain Buchanan, John Wayne insisted on coming to visit. So, without further ado, here he is. He's here tonight, the Duke, John Wayne! Come on in Duke!"

Every head in the hall tersely turned toward the entrance in anticipation of John Wayne walking through the conference hall doors. For a second or two, all 175 sets of eyeballs were glued to the entrance doors, waiting to see if the Duke was actually going to walk through the double doors. The two seconds seemed as if time stood still. The anticipation rose to wishful thinking. The brave, courageous men who have been laying their life on the line every single day in the bush really wanted the Duke to walk through the doors. If it were some sick joke, someone had better be prepared to get their ass kicked!

But suddenly, through the doors, the Duke - John Wayne himself walked into the hall. The night's events proved to be anything but a joke, let alone an illusion. John Wayne stood in the presence of all, in the flesh. The men immediately recognized the Duke, and 175 men pushed inward toward Wayne, shoulder to shoulder, arm to arm, to get a good, firm handshake with the Duke. The men completely brushed aside General John Sands and the adjutants accompanying

Wayne, and the commanding officer of the 1st Marine Division of chaplains. Enlisted and officer alike were excited to meet John Wayne. The men were ecstatic.

Excitement filled every heart and mind in the hall. And the Duke certainly heard the excitement.

"Good to meet you, Duke."

"It's a thrill to see you, Duke."

"You're my favorite actor, Duke."

"Can I have your autograph, Duke?"

"Mr. Wayne, can I have a picture?"

Nothing else lifted up morale more than a visit from John Wayne. This visit wasn't the first or the last call John Wayne would make in Vietnam. The Duke loved the armed forces and nothing would impede supporting the troops through thick and thin.

All the while, the marines pushed harder and harder inward toward Wayne attempting to shake the hand of the Duke, while Wayne and his party from Da Nang pushed slowly forward toward Lieutenant Colonel Lucas and Chaplain Buchanan, as Wayne's party is forced to tippytoe to the front of the camp hall.

The Duke finally reached Buchanan, spellbound by the appearance of Wayne.

As the Duke stepped up to Lucas and Buchanan, the hall suddenly, eerily, fell silent. Quite enough to catch a mouse squeak and scamper across the floor.

Swallowing hard and clearing his throat, Buchanan said innocently, "Hello, Duke....sir."

Wayne bends back, laughs hard, as the men burst into a roaring laughter along with the Duke.

"Well, hello chaplain. So you're the chaplain who shows John Wayne movies on Friday nights, are ya?"

Buchanan stood at a loss for words and was nervous. "I hope ya don't mind...sir?"

Again, a hearty laugh from Wayne and the marines breaks the silence.

"Mind? I love it." Wayne said proudly. "To know that I'm motivating our troops to fight the spread of Communism, well....it's....it makes me very proud you think of me that much, chaplain. Thank you for your citizenship shown to our great country and for being a fan of my work through the years."

A speechless Buchanan swallows hard. "Thank you."

"To show my appreciation to ya, I have three pictures to autograph for you, with frames to go along with them." Wayne pulls from his dungaree pocket a pen, signing each of the three photos in sequence.

Wayne raises the photos up for the men to see. "These are three promotional photos of myself and my fellow actors in Chaplain Buchanan's three favorite John Wayne movies."

A jovial, jubilant cheer erupted from the men.

As the cheer of the men died down, Wayne said, "And tonight I have a signed autographed photo for every marine and sailor in the camp!"

The eruption of even a louder cheer emerged from the men. Euphoria filled the air!

As the excitement died down once again, Wayne announced, "Well, let's get started with what Chaplain Buchanan has wanted all night. Let's watch the movie!"

A third lively cheer leveled the camp, letting the Commies outlying the perimeter know the Duke's presence packed the house.

Every seat in the house, all 120 seats, occupied by a marine or a sailor. A standing room only hall filled with John Wayne fans and their chaplain sitting smack dab in the center of it all. Buchanan sat front and center beside his hero, The Duke.

Wayne turns toward Buchanan. "Ya know. This is one of my favorites myself. You've got good taste, Padre."

"Thanks, Duke." said a nervous Buchanan.

As the film played throughout the evening, Wayne consistently turned toward Buchanan, giving him commentary on aspects of the film. The Duke is having a blast viewing the film with Buchanan.

Wayne's fervor for the film showed with each statement spoken to Buchanan. "This scene is fun chasing the hired gunmen." "It took many takes on this hard scene. It had to be done just right." "The west possessed a slew of traveling entertainment companies, and music was part of it."

Buchanan is beyond belief - completely beside himself. He felt as if he entered another world. Here he is watching a John Wayne movie with the Duke himself. A dream come true. Buchanan is jubilant. For a day will come when he will describe to his brothers back in Ohio the night he and the Duke watched one of his movies together and the Duke providing movie commentary by the man himself. This night Buchanan will remember for the rest of his life.

The end of the film came too quick for everyone in the house this night, for no one desired it to end. Wayne again thanked Buchanan for the honor of being remembered every Friday night.

Following the movie, Wayne visited Buchanan and his close circle of friends for 10 minutes in the hall. The Duke then moseyed his way through the camp, visiting marines on his way to the several Hueys sitting in the field to take the Duke, General Sands, and the rest of Wayne's party back to the Da Nang Air Base. Lucas, Carroll, Buchanan, Jackson, and Burns escorted Wayne to his chopper.

Wayne extended his hand to Buchanan. "Thank you, Chaplain."

Shaking Wayne's hand, Buchanan said, "Thank *you*, Duke. I'll never forget this night. It's been special."

"Well, I noticed right off the bat, you're special. You're a special chaplain to the troops, Padre. Keep up the good work."

"We'll do, sir. Bye-Bye, Duke."

"Good bye, Duke." said the others.

"Good bye, men. Keep your head high and keep fighting for freedom." Wayne said. As the Duke boarded one chopper with General Sands, he turned back towards Buchanan, grinning, saluting him.

With that, all waved goodbye. The several choppers lift off, making their way back to Da Nang.

When Buchanan finally made it back to his hootch for the night at 2345 hours, he walked in dog tired. For the evening tuckered him out.

Buchanan laid in his cot and thought, 'I started the evening craving for isolation. To see no one. To hear nothing from military personnel. And now, I yearn for it to never end.' In this moment in time, Buchanan came to realize he indeed needed human beings more than he thought. Feeling somewhat guilty, Buchanan recognized an inner need for his friends, and his friends desperately needed his presence in their lives.

The day ended even more memorable as Burns topped the day off, selecting music to everyone's delight. Lucas gave permission to Burns to play music, though time raced promptly to 2345 hours. Besides, Lucas contended, "Maybe the music will enlighten the Commies. Maybe soften their hardened hearts a bit." Humored with the thought, Burns ended the day with a memorable selection of an album of western movie themes from his LP library in his office. The men fell asleep listening to the themes, icing on the cake for a great ending of a great day.

Buchanan is informed Wayne had been scheduled to visit Da Nang months ahead to promote the winning of the war. He learned Wayne did not go out of his way to visit Buchanan, but when the Duke heard of a chaplain showing John Wayne movies on Friday nights to lift morale and the fighting spirit in the camp, he definitely wanted to encounter that chaplain, and on a Friday night.

Buchanan could've cared less Wayne just happened to be in the vicinity, if that indeed had been the case. That he never would have been in the camp otherwise. The Duke simply attempted to travel into the bush to meet Buchanan, definitely something to brag about.

And Buchanan bragged about it for years to come.

Luck of the Draw

July 1, 1969

"Me? Cheat? Never!" asserted Skawinski, sitting in Buchanan's hootch. "But again, if I were playing against the Devil, hell, I know I would."

Soft chuckles emerged amongst his friends - Jackson, Skawinski, Rodriquez, Sanborn, and Rockford, who rarely visited Buchanan in his hootch.

"Hell, I forgot about the Viet Cong and NVA! I'd do more than cheat against them. I'd aim a shotgun between their eyes and take whatever cards I wanted from them." said Skawinski with a bit of disgust in his voice.

A louder chuckle came from the group. Laughter from men who possessed in their hearts abhorrence toward the Viet Cong, who in the past two months heightened the number of atrocious, appalling acts committed against the South Vietnamese.

Did Skawinski and the others feel smug and superior compared to the Viet Cong? Did they think of themselves as better human beings? They most certainly did. And 50 years later will tell you to your face they are better human beings than the VC. 50 years later, the men will still maintain the VC were of the Devil.

Changing the subject, Rockford asserts, "I'll tell you, though, Adkins is the luckiest son of a gun I've ever met."

Jackson agreed. "That's because of his membership in the Baptist church. Remember, we Baptists have all the -"

"We know. We know!" interrupted Rockford. "Adkins spews that garbage out of his mouth about how luckier Baptist are all because they're closer to God than the rest of us."

The men chuckle.

"What a bunch of hog wash!" said Sanborn with disdain.

Buchanan grins and softly chuckles.

"Well, John is just a proud Protestant, proud of his faith. That's all." said Buchanan, who leans back in his swivel chair smiling from ear to ear.

Eyeballs roll rampant amongst Buchanan's peer group, grimacing.

Rodriquez says, "We have Saint Christopher to intercede for us." He slightly smiles. "Thank you for asking me to play cards with your group for the past two months. It has been a pleasure."

"You're welcome, corporal." Rockford said.

"*Yeah*. You've settled in well." added Buchanan.

"Thank you, sir." said Rodriguez, glancing toward Rockford. "But, if I clean house tonight. Just remember, it is Saint Christopher interceding for me, not on account of me cheating."

As every head turned ever so slowly toward Rodriquez, half smiling, all waved their hands toward him in disgust. Skawinski says, "Let's go play some cards!"

The group agreed. "Deal the cards!" "Let's go!"

"Get ready to lose some money, Padre," Rockford said, ragging Buchanan.

In unison, the group leaped up out of chairs and the coach, darting out the door quicker than Buchanan could grab his cover and keys to lock his door.

The men looked forward to Tuesday nights almost as much as they did the John Wayne Friday night socials.

As the group made their way to Burns' office, the discussion shifted to the sitting arrangements at each table for the night. The entire group in stride to supply insisted on sitting at Jurgensen's table, who had cleaned house the past four Tuesday nights. The Gunnery Sergeant walked away with over six hundred dollars, which he sent half to his mother in California and spending the other half on custom-made suits, including a mohair fabric single breasted continental style slim fitting suit, popular during the 1960s. Jurgensen spent a penny or two on a fancy, high priced shawl Kent collared shirt, his favorite. The style had been popular in the 1960s from spy movies and singing entertainers. His shoes were a couple of pairs of leather wingtip Oxfords from the leading shoe company of the 1960s and ordered the latest, popular wide rimmed fedora hat, black with a teardrop-shaped crown. He despised the side-dented crown, insisting the hat bared too much of a resemblance to too rebellious of an image, too criminal like.

Arriving in no time to supply, the first marine through the door walked Rockford, who abruptly stops, bends back and says in earshot of his friends behind him, "Woo-wee! Lord have mercy! My friends, you will not believe what I see in front of me!"

Skawinski proceeded Rockford, followed by his friends one after the other. When the men set their eyes on what sat in front of them, they hit the floor. "Oh, my gosh! Our number one spy!" "Gracious! My entire year's salary on one man!" and "Wow! Hollywood's leading man is in the house!"

Gunnery Sergeant Jurgensen sat in front of them. All decked out wearing a custom made mohair fabric single breasted continental style slim fitting black suit, worn over a shawl collared white shirt, walking in new brown and black leather wingtip Oxfords, a Kipper tie with the loudest psychedelic swirls of fall colors tied around his neck, topped off with a black wide rimmed teardrop-shaped crown fedora hat. Vickers described him as 'dressed to the nines.'

"Really Gunny? *Really*?" said Rockford.

"You really think that getup you're wearing is going to do ya any luck on Tuesday nights, Sarge?" asked Skawinski.

"Yep. Just wait and see, Ski."

Jurgensen's friends scoff, shaking their heads, grinning with indignation.

"We'll see, Sarge. We'll see." Skawinski said.

Players sought to sit at Jurgensen's table to win back money lost. The setting of friends drew straws winning the privilege of playing against Jurgensen in the first round of play. Player after player drew a straw. The shortest three won a spot at Jurgensen's table. Those privileged to play Jurgensen in the first round and lucky enough to draw one of the three short straws were none other than Senior Chief Gross, Sergeant Burnside, and Captain Frost.

"OK. OK." Rockford commented. "Not at your table to begin the night. That just means the more money I'll take from you at the end of the night."

"HeHeHeHe! Gunny!" laughed Rockford. "I'm saving you for last - tonight."

Adkins said, "That's right, Sergeant. Dealing with me at the end of the night will not be fun. I might not have been here for the last few weeks, but you people are going to feel the sting of Adkins tonight."

Jurgensen scoffs, looks around the room and says with assurance, "Let's play."

"Let's go!" said his friends.

The time rolled to a quick 1930 hours. The long awaited hour has now arrived.

The night promised to be competitive as the remaining tables comprised Buchanan, Lucas, Burns, and Skawinski at the second table. Doc Delaney, Vickers, McElrath, and Adkins sat at the third table and Jackson, Rockford, and Rodriquez rounded out the fourth table.

Rounds altered this night, with all adhering to the rule change. The night comprised two rounds of six games played in each round, with the top player from each table from the first round to play for the final round. The second round eliminated due to time. The next day called for a major sweep of territory in and around VC infiltration six to ten miles northwest of Camp Love. The elimination of the second round provided additional sleep.

Buchanan began the night winning big, followed with a quick tapering off. After just five games of Rummy, Lucas and Skawinski eradicated him and Burns from the competition. Lucas and Skawinski survived at Buchanan's table and battled it out, back and forth, officer versus enlisted, Ohioan versus Ohioan.

A disappointed Jackson played to elimination immediately, leaving Rockford and Rodriquez at his table. The two battled it out for virtually a half an hour.

"It's your fault, sir. You've been praying to Saint Christopher the moment you walked in the door." Jackson said sarcastically.

"HaHaHa!" laughed Rockford. "*Well*, the jokers *have* been coming my way."

Rodriquez smirks, rolling his eyes. "You've seen nothing yet, sir. You now have a marine who has *genuine* faith in the Saint Christopher."

Rodriquez grins wide.

"That's right Vet. You tell'em. We Catholics have Saint Christopher on our side." Jurgensen said.

"What is all this talk?" blurted out Adkins emphatically. "No praying to a Saint is going to do you any good."

Patronizing grins met Adkins' smug expression on his face.

"It's just a bunch of tommyrot." Adkins said. He shrugged his shoulders, tipping his head forward and down to make his point.

"We'll just see about that, sir." Jurgensen said.

For an hour and a half, Gunny's table fought a grueling battle of attrition. The level of competition ran high at Jurgensen's table, making the night a heavyweight bout none of the participants will ever forget. The table occupied four Rummy juggernauts, hammering away at each other, showing no mercy. Delivering the coup de gras will come with great sacrifice. As players dealt cards entering the eighth game, Jurgensen came away awarded with several hands in a row of two or three jokers. As a skillful card player, he eliminated Sergeant Burnside first. Senior Chief Gross came next in line for Jurgensen to deliver the coup de gras, eradicating the sailor's presence. Captain Frost hung in there to the end, making a last stand, but gambled once too many in holding too many combinations or spreads, which backfired on him, eliminating him from competition.

The risk of holding onto combinations of cards in one hand of Rummy to end a hand in one turn is a risk of putting your opponents in the hole. The risk is high as it pays off going out, though holding onto too many combinations of cards in a hand places the player holding the combinations in a position of going in the hole himself if his opponent goes out first, backfiring on the player. For Buchanan, the success of holding onto cards to deliver a crushing blow onto an opponent consisted of fifty percent of his card playing. For Frost, he did himself in by holding onto too many spreads. Jurgensen even caught him holding jokers when the Gunny went out to end two or three hands in a row, serving as the last head on the chopping block to be eliminated from play at Jurgensen's table.

Crushed in the last hand of play, a disgusted Frost felt the brunt of Jurgensen's coup de gras. "Whew!" sighed Frost, relieved the torturous punishment finally ended.

In the meantime, Rockford eliminated a pesky, competitive Rodriquez. The young marine arrived with a no nonsense attitude, refusing to dilly dally. The aspiring veterinarian came to win, but lady luck smiled upon Rockford this night at the third table. Rodriquez would have to play his hand another night.

Consoling himself, Rodriquez glances toward Jurgensen and says, "Well, you've not faced the card sharp - yet, sir."

"I fear not, Corporal." smiled Rockford. Glancing toward Buchanan, he boasted. "I feel hot tonight. Bring it on, guys."

Buchanan ponders his thoughts and says, "Lance. Careful to trust in things seen. Be doubly careful of things you *cannot* see."

"*Pst.*" Rockford said.

Adkins' table saw Vickers fall out first.

"Well, that's that." admitted Vickers.

Vickers came with $35.00 for the night. He lost all of it at one table. In 1969, $35.00 dollars amounted to a lot of money, the equivalent of about $260.00 in the year 2020.

Delivering the coup de gras onto Doc Delaney and McElrath turned out to be easier said than done. Neither Delaney nor McElrath took many risks playing Rummy, especially holding combinations.

Over time, Adkins created insurmountable leads on Delaney and McElrath, generating desperate moves on their part. One maneuver came in holding onto spreads to catch Adkins, hopefully with a massive number of points in his hand, and going out ending a hand. Catching Adkins with high numbers of points never materialized.

Skawinski won a competitive, high-scoring affair between him and Lucas, the last table to declare a winner. Ending the hard fought, sluggish battle ended as Lady Luck beamed upon Skawinski being dealt multiple high valued cards. Everyone gathered to watch the competitive group play their hands of Rummy. In the end, his strategy often played off the discards of other players to generate high scores paying off for him. The strategy worked superbly against Lucas, generating high scores hand after hand, eventually beating Lucas in a sluggish, heavyweight fight of a dual ending in sheer attrition.

"Ski. I lost, but I'll tell ya. You sure enough are tougher than nails. Tough, I tell ya." Lucas said, complementing Skawinski. "Like everything else in your life. Hard-working farm life. Hard working warrior on the battlefield. You're a tough one."

"No wonder the damned to Hell Commies are afraid of ya." Lucas grins.

"Thank ya, sir. They'd better be. When I find'em, their toast."

The close-knit group chuckle.

The final four winners from each table now played, and the night's winnings were for keeps, not for a charitable cause. The stage for a cutthroat final round has now been set. The men left standing were four of the most competitive - Adkins, Jurgensen, Rockford, and Skawinski.

"Deal 'em. Deal 'em! Hee!Hee!" yelled Skawinski.

Licking their chops, the finalists took a seat facing one another, eager to walk away with the Jackpot. A no quarter mindset sank into the hearts and minds of the four finalists. The hard-nosed Rockford and the gutsy Jurgensen intentionally faced one another for the last and decisive round.

"Let's start this showdown, men." Rockford commented.

"That's *poker*, captain." said Adkins, smiling.

"Well, it's still a showdown." said Jurgensen, sarcastically. "The term overlaps to other games, sir."

Adkins turns, smiling in disgust at his own estimation of Rockford's ignorance of terminology in the world of card playing. Adkins' frustration humored all of his friends, who were present, grinning with the response to the irritated Seabee.

Adkins' friends in Vietnam by now had come accustomed to his a matter-a-fact demeanor and habit of correcting others. In fact, Adkins became dear friends with everyone present, and in time, the men enjoyed his presence immensely, especially in times of leisure as well as work. He humored them.

"Come on. Come on! Deal the cards." Adkins said. "Y'all are out to lose all your winning's you've won thus far tonight." His confidence in winning the night humored the men.

"Yeah. *Yeah*. I hear ya, Seabee! Nothing but a squid!" said Rockford.

"*Yeah*, soon to be a loser of a squid!" added Jurgensen, leaning back in his chair, all decked out in his new clothes.

Laughter filled the room listening to the jarring back and forth from enlisted and officer, Navy and Marine.

The order of turn established for the final round was as follows - Rockford, Skawinski, Jurgensen, and then Adkins.

The final round exploded initially with high scores resulting in the first three games won by individual players - omitting Jurgensen. He could ill afford to lose a fourth game in a roll. Jurgensen now faced being eliminated from play, forcing him in a corner to play undefeated the remaining part of the night. A fourth loss will send him home a loser.

Lady Luck finally smiled upon Jurgensen, winning two games in a row, shifting favor of the night in his direction. Though the games were close, the night seemed to shift into Jurgensen's direction.

Jurgensen now led in the final round with two games won, followed by Adkins, Rockford, and Skawinski winning a game each.

The stage is now set. If Jurgensen wins the sixth game, it's all over. He wins the whole kit and caboodle. He'd clean house once again on a Tuesday night. If Adkins, Skawinski, or Rockford won the sixth game, there would be a best of three overtime.

Jurgensen began the sixth game roaring like a lion as he went out the first three hands on his first play of each hand, placing him in a quick lead with a score of 310 for himself, 185 in the hole for Adkins, 160 in the hole for Skawinski, and 165 in the hole for Rockford.

The fourth hand started out very well for Jurgensen, as he played three combinations playing off the discards after two turns of play, and had a count of 95 points played, including a joker. He held only two cards left in his hand.

No player placed any combination of cards on the table for two turns. Rockford then went out with two spreads of his own, two aces with a joker, three tens, and a play on one of Jurgensen's combinations. Rockford played a combination of 210 points using two jokers in the hand.

The scores with four hands played placed Jurgensen with 375 points, Rockford 45 'for the good' and out of the hole, while Adkins remained 85 in the hole and Skawinski continued to linger with 115 points in the minus.

An elated Rockford welcomed the next three hands in a row, as he ended each hand going out, roaring a comeback in the game. The marine officer jubilantly heard the score read out loud at the end of the seventh hand - Rockford scored 430 points, Jurgensen tallied 420, Skawinski 285, and Adkins rounding out the bottom with a meager 240 points.

Adkins possessed all the luck in the eighth hand of the sixth game, going out in just the second turn, crafting an even narrower game. Adkins suddenly found himself in the lead with 365 points to Jurgensen's 350 second place total, and Rockford on his tail with 330 points.

The close-knit group of friends had not seen a final round this close in many weeks, and Jurgensen dominated the past few Tuesday nights of Rummy. In fact, the sixth game became a memorial night of players hammering away at each other, a tug-of-war leveling off a game of attrition. The tense bystanders looked on edge, awaiting the winner to emerge.

The revved up spectators encouraged friends to thump Jurgensen for the night. Neither marine nor sailor in the room yearned for Jurgensen to win, but one – Rodriquez. He made his way around the table to Jurgensen, patting his shoulder. "Ya can do it, Gunny. Just keep praying to Saint Christopher."

With a smirk, Jurgensen gives a confident glimpse up toward Rodriquez. "Every hand, Vet. We know whose side he's on, don't we?"

"Sure do. Gunny." said Rodriquez, smiling.

Adkins gawks toward Jurgensen, rolling his eyes.

"Let's go Ski!" encouraged Jackson.

"Ya can do it John, just concentrate and don't get greedy holding spreads of play." said Buchanan, encouraging his fellow Navy friend.

"Remember, Rock, play your jokers when you're dealt 'em!" encouraged Doc Delaney to Rockford.

The fourth and sixth games were key contests on Rummy nights. Many a night, the winner of the fourth and sixth games won the night's winnings.

The eighth hand dealt by Skawinski caught Jurgensen confident. Gathering up his cards in a neat stack, Jurgensen viewed his cards one by one out of habit, placing his combinations of cards in precise order one at a time. The Gunnery Sergeant placed his cards face down in order, fan shaped, on the table, waiting for his turn.

Jurgensen had played a good many games of poker in his day, as well as Rummy. Putting his poker face on, he laid his cards down. No one in the room could guess what sort of hand Jurgensen held with his fingers.

The Gunny reached over the table slowly, almost lethargically, to draw a card off the top of the drawing stack of cards. He dragged slowly the card back over the table as close to himself as he could to discover the face of the card.

At a snail's pace, he turned one corner of the card up, glancing at the order of value of the card.

"Come on. Come on, Gunny! Play. Play!" said Rockford with a half smile on his face.

The quiet, eerie pause in the room pushed the remaining card players over the edge.

"Come on. Come on!" insisted the men.

Skawinski called the Gunny's charade. "He's bluffing. He ain't – and I say ain't - got nothing. Don't ya, Gunny." Smiling from ear to ear, Skawinski stared straight at Jurgensen. The room quieted to an unnerving still.

Anticipation mounted as the men edged near, discovering the value of the card Jurgensen drew. He leisurely picks up his cards dealt him, puts them back into a stack and looks at them one by one once again.

Adkins leisurely asked, "Are you going to play....or not, Richard?" The Lieutenant Commander demanded a response.

Jurgensen glanced a smug grin toward Adkins, shrugging. He then gives a direct stare at Rockford, smiling pompously. Rockford grins slightly, recognizing his friend's bluff.

The Gunny needs 150 points to win.

Picking up his card he drew deliberately, Jurgensen slides the card into the combinations of his seven cards in his hand. He pauses intentionally to rub it in, slowly placing the cards onto the table going out, ending the eighth hand of Rummy.

The group erupts in a rowdy cheer, witnessing one of the most competitive nights of 500 Rummy played in Vietnam.

Rockford rises out of his chair, leaning over the table to count the point value of Jurgensen's cards, determining if his spreads are legit. He counted up the value of Jurgensen's cards and sure enough, his combinations were legal and his points scored in the hand added up to an exact total of 150.

"Son of a....bitch." scoffed the marine captain, leaning back into his seat, shocked and disappointed.

A drooping frown replaces Skawinski's smile, while Rockford sits dumbfounded.

Adkins drops his head into his right hand, dropping his cards, shaking his head in disbelief. He had taken the lead late, only to see it vanish before his very eyes, losing a hard fought game.

Jurgensen's points in the last hand amounted to two jokers, three Jacks, and a spread - a three, two and an Ace of clubs. Adding to the 350 points Jurgensen scored in the eighth contest, his grand total equaled 500 points to win the game.

Calm, cool, and collected, Jurgensen takes a panoramic view of the room. He glances toward a smiling Rodriquez, nodding his head in approval of Saint Christopher looking over Jurgensen's shoulder. Rodriquez then smiles at Rockford, folding his hands as if praying, pointing up toward the Heavens.

The Gunny smiled wide, saying softly, "We know, corporal. We know." He topped off his winning night by admitting, "Ya know the icing on the cake, gents?" Jurgensen smirks, professing, "My new suit."

"Please!" responded the Gunny's card playing friends.

The men had 13 more Tuesday nights of playing 500 Rummy left in Buchanan's tour, and tonight Jurgensen stood in the winner's circle for the last time. His winning ways ended on July 1, 1969. No more luck of the draw.

Vickers dominated the 13 Tuesdays winning 4 nights, followed by Adkins and Rockford standing in the winner's circle twice. The remaining victorious nights were dispersed within the group, including Buchanan winning one evening, breaking the record for the highest amount of winnings for a single night.

Regardless of putting faith in Saint Christopher or not, Buchanan and his friends gathered each Tuesday night to play cards and to win.

Buchanan, a Baptist, thought it silly the Lord showed favor or not on a marine or sailor by simply praying to any saint. Cards amounted more or less and nothing less than the luck of the draw.

But though this night ended up being all about Jurgensen, he made it all about Saint Christopher.

Music Calms the Savage Beast

July 1, 1969

Though the evening will be a memorable one for Buchanan, the day is about to end. A day no one desired to end as time struck 2130 hours. The evening of 500 Rummy provided a night of aura for the men as if they experienced the bottom of the ninth inning of a winning home run or a last-second field goal in a football game. The men had fun.

The night settled to a calm in camp. Outside Camp Love's perimeter, the war reflected a savage beast, but tamed this night with peace in the air. The never-ending struggle to find normalcy and escape from the war, at least temporarily, came on Tuesday nights. One of the few moments in the week providing a night of normalcy for the marines and sailors.

The music Major Burns selected for the evening inserted an additional memory for Buchanan. He expected patiently the piece of music selected to add to the thrill of the night's fervor.

Will the camp have the privilege of listening with enjoyment of Mozart? Or a stirring symphony of Brahms from the Romantic Period? Or possibly the great Russian composer, Shostakovich? Buchanan might have been looking forward to a Shostakovich piece, only because of the composer's loathing of Stalin, who Buchanan despised. He awaited Burns' selection each night of music with great expectation. But who's the composer tonight?

Buchanan's love for classical music had expanded, intensifying since October 1968.

As the men were continuing to 'fellowship', nibbling on leftover food, the music boomed through the PA system at 2130 hours.

Initially, the music reflected another era of music entirely, even unrecognizable. Classical music it was not.

Burns brushed aside Mozart, Brahms, and even Shostakovich for music of a different genre, filling every ear in camp, reverberating a contemporary sort.

Drums, stringed instruments, and a trumpet coincided with treble and bass notes perfectly. But who were the musicians?

And suddenly the melody kicked in, and immediately Buchanan recognized a joy to his ear.

"Yes!" said Buchanan. "Can you believe it, men? Burns, he selected Sam Horton and His Famous Horn Players for the night! Yippee!"

"It's quite a delight, isn't it?" mentioned Delaney.

"Sure is." said Skawinski.

Every single member of the group recognized the album *Sugar Cookies and Sweets*, one of Buchanan's favorites.

Buchanan treasured Sam Horton. The appreciation for all music reflected Buchanan's album collection in his hootch.

First on the playlist, *Sugar Cookies*. The album's title track. Buchanan cherished the first track with its rapid, vivacious rhythm, touching the heart and lifting the soul for Buchanan.

From the start, the men sang along with the melody.

Sugar Cookies ended in no time, as the next two tracks played in sequence, *Red Cake* and *Chocolate Kisses.*

The men perked up, listening to the music immensely, with many a man tapping a foot and snapping fingers.

The fifth track, *Butter Caramels*, initiated a sense of melancholy and calm in the room. The men relaxed, sat back, and enjoyed every note and bar of music.

Every fan of Sam Horton and the television show *Searching for Mr. Right* recognized the first bar of music of the ensuing track, *Chocolate Delight.*

The men's voices heightened singing *Chocolate Delight*. Amid all the singing, Doc Delaney says, "I sure miss watching *Searching for Mr. Right* every week, don't you, Ski?"

"I sure do, sir. I sure do."

Rockford declared, "I watch with my brother. He's the good-looking one. We always tease him he ought to go on the show." He chuckles at the thought.

"Is he a better poker player, sir?" Jurgensen grinned with the jab.

Rockford turns sharply toward the Gunny expressing nothing but indignation.

The best two and a half minutes of music any of them had heard in Vietnam yet, *Chocolate Delight*. One of the most popular songs in United States music history.

The next track is even more popular with Americans.

The men bolted into song. Humming after the first two notes played, recognizing immediately the tune. Three minutes of musical bliss, *Peanut Brittle*. The tune filled the airways back home in the United States, and a favorite amongst Sam Horton fans with a bit of risqué to the tune.

As the men sang, a ruckus emerged from one end of the camp, and a few of the men drop out of singing to distinguish what the ruckus is.

As fewer men hummed the song, all ask one another what the commotion might be.

"What is that?" asked Doc Delaney.

Adkins asked, "It's not an attack?"

"Is it music? No, that's not music?" said Buchanan.

"Quiet. Quiet!" said Rockford. The men hush, listening to the ruckus. "That's not a battle noise. That's men cheering like at a ballgame. Come on."

Abruptly jumping out of their seats, the card players marched themselves out of supply, hurrying toward the disorder.

By the time Buchanan and his friends arrived at the source of all the hubbub in the camp, the number of marines had grown too well over 100 shoulder to shoulder to get a glimpse of Oliver Wheeler, dancing, stripping off his uniform to the music. Wheeler, a corporal and native of Burnsville, North Carolina, distinguished himself as a steadfast and fierce combatant in Bravo Company, 1st platoon.

Lucas, most intrigued, caught a glimpse of Wheeler and the racket generated from his spontaneous performance.

Buchanan's party made their way through the immense number of marines amassed to catch a glimpse of Wheeler dancing.

Skawinski, Doc Delaney, Burns, and Rockford made their way up close to the spectacle.

By the time the music ended, Wheeler stripped down to his skivvies.

The marines gathered shouted, "Off!" "Off!" "Off!" "Off!"

Wheeler emphatically nodded his head no. Not even a million dollars would convince him going all the way, exposing himself to all these 'sickies.'

Buchanan caught the last couple of bars of Wheeler dancing to the music, shifting his feet and grinning out of sheer embarrassment. The young marine glanced left and right, noticing his colleagues expressing shock as if to say, 'I can't believe he did such a thing.'

Buchanan grins. He uttered, "These marines are something else, aren't they? I guess when you're out in the bush as long as we've been, you turn to anything for entertainment. I guess even that is out of the ordinary."

The men grin wide.

After a brief conversation, the men depart for their respective hootches for the night. Buchanan arrived at his own hootch, laid out some fruit for Arthur and Churchill, and hit the sack exhausted from his long day.

Dreams were pleasant enough.

In Buchanan's first dream, he and Dorothy spent the night dancing in a competition to win a $100.00. The two danced and danced until the next morning. No one came close to the finesse and dexterity of Robert and Dorothy on the dance floor in the dream. Waking up suddenly in the middle of the night, his dream seemed thwarted. He laid in his cot disappointed, waking up before the announcement of the winner in the contest. He daydreamed Dorothy and he won. Following a few minutes or so, Buchanan fell back into a deep sleep. His dream started back up where he left off, dancing with Dorothy. The dance contestants competed with the winner yet to be declared, which all expected Buchanan and Dorothy to win. With the expectation of the Buchanan's declared the dance winners, low and behold the winners were none other than Porch and his girlfriend, whose facial features were as if hit by a semitrailer truck. She epitomized ugly. Ugly as sin. She certainly didn't display the shallow, hollow centered cheerleader type, beautiful on the outside, ugly as sin on the inside. The girl in the dream came across far from anything reflecting a fashion model. Certainly not the ending of a dream Buchanan had hoped for, especially after the steady, choreographed moves of Robert and Dorothy in the dream.

Buchanan, beside himself, woke up for good at 0530 hours. The desire for any additional shut eye came to a dead end, for Buchanan wished to avoid any further dreams with Porch. Especially if Porch ended up on the winning end of the dream.

He showered and shaved, read his devotion and Bible Scripture for the day. As he sat meditating on his night of card playing and the dream of dancing, he found himself humored. Most of Buchanan's dreams in Vietnam were of the war or of home with family and friends. Last night proved to be a rare evening for he experienced refreshing dreams. The shut eye gained came minus the sopping sweaty, terrifying dreams. The intimate presence of Dorothy alone in a dream eased the pain of war for Buchanan. True, he lost the dance contest, but Dorothy in the dream resulted with the utmost pleasure for him.

Regardless, he seized his cover, dashing over to the chow hall for some breakfast. He next marched himself to Lucas' office to inquire about his assessment of what discipline he chose to dish out to Wheeler. No where in sight is Jackson, even for breakfast. Buchanan assumed Jackson slept in a little late today, since they reserved Tuesdays for services and a devotion in the camp hall. He waited for Jackson for a few minutes at the chow hall. Buchanan longed for him to tag along to Lucas's office for morale's sake. Jackson never showed up, so Buchanan made his way toward his hootch just 100 feet away from the chow hall. Where was Jackson? He rarely missed breakfast in the chow hall with Buchanan!

Half way to Jackson's hootch, he noticed Wheeler in front of him singing the blues. Playing a tune on his guitar, Buchanan recognized the music well. Buchanan took in every note and word of the second verse sung by Wheeler, mouthing the words with the music. Wheeler sang the chorus consecutively, then ended singing an impromptu little finale of his own with his guitar. He glanced toward Buchanan, grinning, with melancholy written all over his face.

"Wow! Wheeler! I didn't know you could string?" said Buchanan with enthusiasm. "That was absolutely phenomenal! Amen!"

Wheeler sat, grinning even wider.

"I didn't know you enjoyed country music? I didn't think you young folks appreciated country?" asked Buchanan, pondering Wheeler's interest in country blues music.

"Few of us do, sir." answered Wheeler.

"Um." Buchanan attempted to read Wheeler's thoughts.

"My father's a musician. He introduced me to the blues. It's his opinion the blues are tops."

"Well, I think your dad's opinion is bullseye on target."

Wheeler glares out into nowhere. "That's how I feel right now."

Buchanan, puzzled, asks, "Like what?"

Wheeler sighs heavily.

Buchanan asks, "You have the blues?"

"Yes, sir."

"I've been to Lieutenant Colonel Lucas' office this morning. He chewed me out something terrible."

"Oh?"

"Yep. Said the large group late last night massed together was a danger to camp security and readiness." Wheeler said.

Buchanan, concerned, half grins out of empathy.

Wheeler grimaces, scoffing. "Skipper said if the VC had attacked us, they could've found us confused and such."

Buchanan sat, listening to Wheeler explain his visit to the 'boss'.

Buchanan is all ears as Wheeler vented. "Besides, he informed me, well - as he was chewing me out - the fact I was a little tipsy, along with my friends, being drunk and all, put everyone else in camp in danger. He said myself and my friends were at a loss of judgment and a loss of coordination resulting in a state of dizziness or even passed out during an attack."

Buchanan nods. "Very possible Wheeler."

Wheeler seemed convinced the Skipper evaluated the situation appropriately. He is far from being a dummy.

"You don't drink anymore, do ya, chaplain?" Wheeler asked.

"Nope. I haven't drunk alcoholic beverages since becoming a Christian." Buchanan professed. "Drinking controlled me. I was on the verge of destroying myself. All I cared about was drinking. I'd practically do anything to get a drink. I'd drink mouthwash, anything that had alcohol in it."

"Whew!" Wheeler said. "That's not good."

"Jesus helps me, Wheeler. Once an alcoholic, always an alcoholic. I want to drink, but I have Jesus now to help me steer clear of that which can destroy me."

"I wish I could do that too, Padre. I really do."

Buchanan grins. His grin speaks to Wheeler that Jesus can help him, if he would just give it up to the Lord.

"You don't see much good in going to the men's entertainment locales either, do ya, chaplain?" Wheeler asked.

"Nope. That really hasn't been a problem with me, Wheeler. And I, well - love and appreciate women like the next guy – but not in a lustful manner. The only woman I want to be intimate with is the woman I love, my wife. I wouldn't, well, want to hurt her in any way. We expect the same thing from each other: trust and faith. Intimacy outside our own would damage that trust and faith in each other. Ya understand Corporal Wheeler?"

Wheeler nods yes.

"Besides corporal, the only thing those women in those honky tonk nudie joints want is your money. Those women could, well, careless about you as a human being. All they want is your money. You're just handing your hard earned money over to them. Just to see them naked. It's just stupid to me. Just senseless and dumb. Most of the men in there would be furious if it was their sister, girlfriend, but especially if their wife was up there naked."

Wheeler laughs. "I see your point, sir. You have your own way of putting things in your own words. Don't you, sir?"

"I guess so, Wheeler."

"I bet you never took drugs either, have you, sir?"

Buchanan shakes and tilts his head. "Had no use for them. It sounds odd, but, you know, and this *sounds* odd coming from a man who abused alcohol quite hard, but I wanted nothing to control me."

"Really, sir?" Wheeler said.

The men chuckle as they ponder the thought of Buchanan's heavy abuse of alcohol in the past.

"Well, sounds odd, doesn't it?" replied Buchanan.

"Yes, sir. It does."

Buchanan turns his thoughts toward Wheeler, still thinking of him suffering from the blues. "Corporal, you never told me the punishment Lucas dished out to ya."

"Oh, *yeah*. I haven't. Well - after giving me the riot act, he confined me to my quarters for three weeks while not on duty." admitted Wheeler with a half grin. Looking away, Buchanan grins widely with the humor.

"He also put me on no beer or any other alcoholic beverages for a month. He ordered Sergeant McElrath in charge to keep me sober for the month." Wheeler scoffs. "Real severe, huh, Chaplain?"

Buchanan chuckles, shrugging his shoulders. Standing up, he says, "Well, I got a long day, Corporal Wheeler. I've got to get busy. See ya later, son."

"Thank you, sir."

"You're going to make it, son. I've seen you work and interact with people here in camp and out in the bush. You're smart. You're level-headed." encouraged Buchanan.

Wheeler shrugs, grinning.

"I'm taking you're not having a conversation with the 'ole red eye." advised Buchanan, leaning his head toward Wheeler with his eyebrow raised.

"Yes, sir."

Wheeler pauses nervously, and asked, "Sir?"

"Yes, Wheeler."

"Well, sir. I - uh, I. Can I come by your office just to talk? Maybe try to help me kick the drinking thing?"

Buchanan stares with sympathy. "Of course, Wheeler. Anytime. I'd love to help you."

Wheeler departed to his hootch, Buchanan then visited offices and hootches in camp with Jackson. Later on, the spiritual team led the camp's devotion and service in the camp hall. Looking back at the congregation in both services sat Wheeler. Pleased beyond measure, Buchanan felt joy in his heart, discovering Wheeler in the pews for the service. Besides, Buchanan enjoyed Wheeler's company immensely. Buchanan, deep down in his heart, considered Wheeler a good man. In his heart, he knew there was good in his heart and soul. He believed in his heart that in no time at all, the young marine would be on the believer's side of things, living a Christlike life, giving up his life living for the evil one.

Buchanan loved track number 10, *Peanut Brittle.* Even more so after today.

AN INFILTRATED CAMP LOVE

JULY 14, 1969

Bastille Day. A significant day in world history. A day Buchanan knew well from his study of the social sciences. The day ignited the spark to set the French Revolution a blaze, throwing Europe into a firestorm. The event triggered a lifelong interest and study for Buchanan's favorite period in military history.

On the eve of Bastille day, Burns treated the camp with a history lesson placing the vinyl record of Dittersdorf's *La Prise de la Bastille* onto the turntable. The piece perked up the history buffs in camp, appreciative of the significance of the date in world history. The music spearheaded a level of motivation and es sprit de corps for the spiritual team. Time spent listening to classical music in the evenings shoved the war aside, though temporarily, for a short, composed moment within all the turmoil, even for those who detested classical music in camp.

The music on the eve of Bastille Day furnished a sum of last moments of normalcy for the spiritual team, scheduled to accompany a three day long mission with Bravo and Delta companies on a three day long mission with Skawinski's team to sweep coordinates BT 037628, BT 032642, BT 040623, and AT 923930 for mines and booby traps, along with two miles of Route 537 east of Liberty Bridge.

The marines woke up to a dead silence on the morning of Bastille Day. Skawinski and combat engineers woke up assigned to secure camp defenses, aligning M18 Claymore mines and booby traps within Camp Love's perimeter. Combat engineers placed the mines in a checkerboard formation within the perimeter. Skawinski, assisted by Shaw who had been promoted to corporal, double checked the security within the perimeter of Refugee City outside the camp for the new refugees. The Viet Cong attacked the refugees in their respective village or hamlet, displacing them from their homes. A real punch below the belt. The VC burned down hamlets of their village out of retaliation for their support of United States efforts to win the war. The hatred for the Viet Cong skyrocketed a hundredfold for the villagers.

The spiritual team devoured breakfast. It would be their last hot meal for three days. For the team scheduled a patrol with Bravo and Delta companies. With an expected long absence from camp awaiting the team, they made a last-minute effort to visit hootches prior to saddling up for the bush, as a time for departure had been set just after the morning dawn.

Buchanan visited the men, lifting their spirits. He had the knack of setting an environment of normalcy of life all longed for in camp, an innate skill few human beings possess. Complimenting and encouraging the men, the spiritual team inquired of their families back home, seeking to assist in any immediate need a marine or sailor might require in the pressing time left in camp preceding their departure accompanying the patrol.

"Good Morning, Corporal." said Buchanan in his strong mountain accent.

"Morning, sir." answered a young marine in Alpha Company.

"Your mom doing better since the last I spoke with you?"

"Yes, sir. Yes. She's doing much better."

"Amen." replied Buchanan.

"Prayers answered." added Jackson. He continued to visit with the young marine, as Buchanan stepped to a Gunnery Sergeant of Alpha Company he knew well.

"How ya doing, Gunny?" inquired Buchanan.

"Just fine, Padre. Just fine, sir." The Gunny smiles.

"Last time we met, your father started a new contract with some folks in downtown Los Angeles, didn't he?"

"Yes, sir. It was supposed to start last Friday, the eleventh."

"Well, I know he has a reputation in the area as one of the best in his field as an architect." Buchanan said.

"Yes, Padre. He's a great builder. He loves building the -"

PING! PING! PING! PING! Ricochets rang left and right of Buchanan.

"DOWN! GET DOWN!" the Gunny yells.

CRACK! CRACK! POP! POP!

Buchanan hit the deck as fast as a sack of potatoes, locating any cover securing himself.

Distant screams and yells from afar just outside the edge of the treeline caught the attention of every soul in camp.

Marines peeked over sandbags, empty ammo crates, and compacted barriers of dried mud and dirt to make out what all the brouhaha is about outside the treeline.

With shock and horror, Camp Love and Buchanan spotted Sergeant Skawinski firing his M-16 in a prone position some 30 feet from the camp's perimeter line, along with Private Varnes firing .45 calibers in both hands. Private 1st Class Pokorny fell wounded some 15 feet inside the perimeter with Claymore mines lying about, bleeding badly from his left shoulder, arm and right leg.

A most terrifying sight Buchanan laid his eyes on focused dead center on Corporal Shaw, fighting ferociously hand to hand with the Viet Cong, grasping knives and machetes in both hands, streaming swiftly out of the treeline one after the other, screaming at the top of their lungs.

As Shaw fought hand to hand, Skawinski and Varnes fired their weapons toward muzzle blasts coming from the treeline.

Marines in camp retrieved their weapons, firing toward the Viet Cong insurgents.

"Stop firing! Stop firing!" yelled the Gunny of A Company. Fear gripped the Gunny. The firing line may hit their fellow marines with friendly fire.

Suddenly, a tremendous bang explosion threw Buchanan and Alpha Company forward against sandbags with vigor with rapid gunfire for background noise coming from their backsides near the camp's entrance, followed by painful screams and hideous yells, preceded by silence.

From the few seconds distracted from the entrance attack, Buchanan's attention swayed back straightaway toward Skawinski and the security team pinned down in the perimeter. He and Varnes continued a ferocious blasting toward the muzzle flashes within the treeline, while Shaw fought hand to hand with the Viet Cong.

From a distance, the marines cheer for Shaw, barking out warnings.

"Look to your right!"

"Go Shaw! Kill 'em! Kill 'em!"

Shaw, standing a towering 6'1", faced each VC charging fanatically from all directions with sharpened weapons at the ready.

Enemy fire from the treeline dissipated, as Skawinski and Varnes picked the enemy off a little at a time.

Shaw faced the enemy one after the other, at times two simultaneously. Buchanan froze, catching flies, witnessing Shaw use his Karate skills to defend himself. The sight flabbergasted Buchanan, as Shaw killed Viet Cong infiltrators at will. Shaw delivered a Gedan Barai and Soto Uke, then came a sidekick leveling a VC. Shaw then grasped a KA-BAR knife, thrusting the weapon into the ribcage of yet another VC. Next came taking down two more fiends with another Gedan Barai and sidekick.

"Go Shaw! Go!" "Give 'em Hell, Shaw!" came more shouts from Camp Love.

Lying about were nine dead Viet Cong encircling a physically drained Shaw, all killed with his bare hands.

By now, Jurgensen and others joined the spectators of the fight, which had ensued.

"Kick the commies ass Shaw!" "Look to your right, man!" "Kill 'em Leonard!" As the marines threw additional cheers toward Shaw, the men realized they were witnessing a feat of valor worth hero status.

Buchanan yelled, "Help him Lord! Help him!"

Jurgensen noticed still sparse muzzle blasts from the edge of the treeline fired toward Skawinski and the security team. He shouted,

"Fire at the muzzle blasts! Fire at the muzzle blasts! Fire into the treeline. Kill 'em!"

Shaw, along with Skawinski and Varnes, hit the deck, holding onto the ground as hard as they could.

The cacophony of weapons returning gunfire toward the muzzle blasts in the treeline spawned a tremendous heat, as massive numbers of projectiles soared in the air, resulting in a violent crash of shot into the vegetation, flattening the treeline edge back some 40 feet.

No vegetation survived the tremendous blast of weaponry into the treeline. No living being could have survived such a strenuous and concerted discharge of firearms, leveling the jungle vegetation.

After a lengthy pause after the gunfire, a last VC infiltrator inexplicably came roaring out from the thickness of the jungle toward Shaw with a machete swung high in a jodan no kamae position with nothing but the Devil in his eyes and screaming, "Con lon!!!" at the top of his lungs, bearing down on Shaw to swipe his head off.

Where did he come from? How did he survive the onslaught?

The marines quickly yelled loud in unison, "Shaw! Another devil!"

In a split second, Shaw soared high, hoisting himself toward the VC with a sky-scraping, gutsy jump in the air toward the VC, tucking his knees in toward his chest in what seemed to Buchanan a human cannonball. In a millisecond, Shaw's leg and foot emerged from out of the human cannonball, kicking the VC in the chest as he neared him, knocking the enemy onto the ground violently hard. The fierce thud of human flesh hit the ground as if a hammer pounding down heavy onto a nail into sturdy oak wood, felt by all in camp.

The Viet Cong, discombobulated and disorientated, sluggishly rose to his feet, weakened to face Shaw. The VC raised his head deliberate, totally erect to confront the exhausted marine. Shaw delivered a jump turn kick on the side of the VC's neck, leveling him to the ground. With a stray knife laying about, Shaw seized the knife yelling, "Commie!", thrusting it with vigor in the back of the VC, killing him. Exhausted, Shaw fell forward on top of the dead Viet Cong.

Heard suddenly from the marines came a thunderous, booming roar of cheers, "Whooaaaa!" congratulating Shaw for his individual feat of bravery and courage, displaying the energy and momentum of the United States Marine Corps.

The spiritual team, spellbound, cheered at the top of their lungs. The team had seen many acts of bravery and valor in Vietnam, but none like today. Shaw showed extraordinary courage. Valor displayed like no other.

Leaning on sandbags, Buchanan stood mesmerized by what he just witnessed. Looking out from camp, he spotted Skawinski and Varnes rush to Pokorny, severely wounded, now sitting on their backsides beside Pokorny out of sheer exhaustion. He caught a glimpse of Shaw pushing himself off the top of the dead Viet Cong he stabbed in the back. Standing up, Shaw fell backwards, collapsing on his backside facing the camp, smiling from ear to ear. Buchanan counted ten VC lying about in the dirt - all taken out by Shaw.

Buchanan half grinned, realizing he witnessed one of the most daring acts of bravery in Vietnam from these courageous and fearless young marines.

As time passed, the medics ran down around the perimeter edge to an exhausted Skawinski and wounded, fatigued marines to administer their medical skills, along with Doc Delaney.

Patting Buchanan's shoulder, Jackson said, "Let's see what the hoopla behind us was all about, chaplain?"

Turning toward the direction of the bang and rapid gunfire behind them during Skawinski's skirmish, the spiritual team discovered 12 to 15 VC at the camp's entrance, all mangled and torn to pieces from gunfire. Buchanan vowed never to take pictures of deceased human beings while in Vietnam, but today seemed to be an exception day. The chaplain snapped 15 slide pictures of the VC KIAs. The grotesque nature of the bodies of this day intrigued Buchanan, showing the slide pictures to viewers of his tour years later to confirm the horrors of war and why avoidance of war should be pursued at all costs.

Recognizing the es sprit de corps of Shaw, the Marine Corps awarded him the Silver Star, the third highest medal given to a service person in the United States military.

One of the proudest days in Corporal Leonard Shaw's life came on the day Lieutenant Colonel Lucas pinned his Silver Star on his uniform in Camp Love. He displayed his Silver Star in a frame years later in his lawyer's office back in St. Louis, his hometown. His lawyer family will highlight his military service over the years.

Buchanan further honored Shaw at one of the Friday Night socials presenting a double feature, a John Wayne marine movie and a World War I movie honoring a Medal of Honor recipient. The night honored Shaw with special films and feeding the men St. Louis cuisine. Gooey Butter Cake, Gerber sandwiches and Toasted Ravioli. In all actuality, the meal comprised nothing but vanilla cake with powdered sugar on top, dried ham and cheese on slices of bread, and frozen raviolis. The efforts with the food had been the best the cooks could do for Buchanan, considering Camp Love's lack of ingredients to prepare anything gourmet out in the bush. As Buchanan reminded Jackson, "It's the thought that counts." At least the food resembled famous, quintessential St. Louis cuisine.

Shaw, taken aback and overjoyed, will forever appreciate the attention given to him.

Whether Shaw is aware of it, the young marine fought today as if it were Bastille Day. A day to fight for freedom and to preserve it.

Indeed, Shaw's violent day of bravery equaled Bastille Day - a violent day to remember in world history. A recorded day in history Buchanan remembers violent in 1789. A day giving birth to a French Revolution ending an oppressive monarchical government. July 14, 1969 in Vietnam resulted as a violent day for a courageous marine defending his camp and fellow marines.

Buchanan and his friends experienced Bastille Day every day in Vietnam. The South Vietnamese fought tooth and toenail, longing to live the freedoms of the western world, freedoms westerners live daily.

Regardless, many veterans of the war, Shaw included, kept their war experiences to themselves. But visitors years later in his law office will notice his framed Silver Star hanging on his office wall, asking, "What's this medal all about?" Shaw mentioned quick to inform his visitors, with pride and humility, his confrontation with the Viet

Cong on July 14, 1969, the day he won his medal, preserving the safety and wellbeing of his fellow marines in Camp Love.

Over the years, the memory of Shaw's courage, stored in the forever memory bank of Buchanan's mind, would mentally reappear for Buchanan every Bastille Day. He would never forget.

Buchanan thought of Shaw fondly. He smiled to himself, crying occasionally, remembering Shaw's tremendous act of bravery on Bastille Day.

ISAIAH 59:17

AUGUST 9, 1969

Isaiah 59:17 'For he put on righteousness as a breastplate, and an helmet of salvation upon his head; and he put on the garments of vengeance for clothing, and was clad with zeal as a cloke.'

Buchanan slammed his fists onto his desk while still holding onto the weekly news dispatch.

The extensive, long list of KIAs and WIAs seemed never-ending, but one name stood out as clear as crystal - Lieutenant Melvin Abrams.

Spelled out in black and white on printed paper listed the general and critically wounded Navy personnel in the weekly dispatch, including his dear friend. The dispatch description read - 'Lieutenant Melvin Abrams, Chaplain, wounded August 5, 1969, 1st Marine Division, 5th Marines.'

His injuries resulted from fighting engaged with enemy sappers and NVA troops assaulting American military personnel with explosive satchel charges strapped onto their bodies. The attacks conducted throughout 1st Marine Division provinces, including Fire Support Bases Russell and Neville.

In the early months of 1969, combat proved lighter than the year before and light compared to the last half of 1969. Regardless, Abrams ministered to marines in the middle of ferocious combat. The Viet Cong and the NVA had returned to sinister sapper attacks strapping explosives to their bodies when penetrating combat outposts in the bush. A Viet Cong tactic Buchanan thought Mephistophelian and diabolic.

Buchanan shot straight up out of his swivel chair, grabbed his chaplains manual and cover, and vigorously marched to Jackson's hootch.

Time stood at 0530 hours in the morning. Buchanan woke up at 0415 hours, unable to sleep because of odd and unnerving dreams.

It took no time at all for Buchanan to reach Jackson's hootch, barging in and, in his Appalachian accent, "Come on Sergeant, get up. Rise and shine. Get up. Get up!"

"What? What?" muttered a drowsy Jackson, surprised by Buchanan's sudden and unexpected visit so early in the morning.

"Come on, Philip."

"Is - is that you, chaplain?" asked a surprised Jackson.

"No. It's Mother Hen waking up all her chicks. Of course it's me. Who else would it be? Now come on Sleepy, get up." Buchanan said.

"Ya know what time it is, sir?"

"I know. I know! We were going to sleep in a bit since it's Saturday morning. But we can't now. Something's come up."

"Well, this ain't you, and I say ain't, sir. Barging in, answering questions later. What's so pertinent to cause such a stir, sir?" asked Jackson as he rose, sitting on the edge of his cot.

"Well, ya - you gotta drive me to Da Nang base hospital."

"What? Today? Of all days? Now, sir? What-What for?" asked Jackson with a bit of hesitation in his voice.

"Well. It's like this. Our-our friend, Lieutenant Abrams was, well - wounded."

"What?" Jackson froze in shock.

"Yes, Melv is wounded. And on the critical list, not just the general list."

Jackson, by now, knew Buchanan well enough to know when he felt anxious about something. He either spoke in a heavy Appalachian accent or he had an obvious worry in his eye. With the news of

Chaplain Abrams wounded, Buchanan possessed both a heavy accent and a worry in his eye.

"OK. OK! Let me don my uniform." Jackson said. "We'll ride along with a convoy going to Da Nang this morning for replenishments. This afternoon, we can tag along back to camp with the convoy."

"What?" Buchanan asked. "They won't leave till -?" looking down at his watch, "at least an hour and 15 minutes from now. Why can't we leave now?"

"Sir, VC and NVA activity here in the last three weeks – well, it's too dangerous right now to go out by ourselves. And ya know, the drive to Da Nang. They love to hit isolated vehicles on that road, anyway. Ya already know that."

"Well, I suppose so. I guess we'll just have to wait." admitted a frustrated Buchanan.

Patience is a virtue. And Buchanan waited patiently for the departure to Da Nang. While waiting, the spiritual team killed some time eating some chow.

Buchanan's robust physical constitution proved steady throughout his life. The tank within himself storing patience maintained a full tank 24/7, which paid off this morning. 0740 hours came quickly as Buchanan found himself on his way to Da Nang hospital to visit Chaplain Abrams, along with Jackson by his side driving the jeep in the usual middle of the convoy, protecting the spiritual team from danger.

The convoy arrived at 0855 hours at the main gate of the Da Nang Air Base. The slow journey of the long convoy resulted from guarding the vehicles from enemy attack. Traveling the roads in Vietnam at fast speeds placed military personnel and civilians in dangerous and hazardous situations. If combatants failed to notice potential mines and booby traps placed by the Viet Cong in the roads from traveling at high speeds, death followed. Besides, the heavy, dense traffic caused a slow and cumbersome trip to Da Nang, providing a safe trip.

The marines replenished supplies for Camp Love, mostly food, ammunition, and office supplies. The visit absorbed three hours spent. Time ended up on the side of the spiritual team, handing them a plenty stretch of time to check in on Chaplain Abrams.

As the convoy drove to supply, Jackson hightailed it over to the hospital, driving the jeep.

"I can't believe it! One of ours got hit." Buchanan said. "Can ya believe it, Sergeant? It seldom happens anymore, does it?"

Jackson pondered the thought. "No. No, I guess it doesn't. The Navy applied measures to protect y'all a little more since the beginning of the war." Glancing toward Buchanan, he says, "And that's a good thing."

Buchanan glances back toward Jackson, grimacing. "It didn't work for Melv - *now* did it."

Jackson assures Buchanan God protected Abrams. "He's alive sir. The Lord was with him."

Buchanan nods.

"I believe that." Jackson said.

"I do to, Philip. You're *right,* he *is* alive." Buchanan raises his fist in the air, and says with assurance, "Alive!" He paused and asked, "Remember the last words he said to us?"

"Yeah. *Yeah.*" Jackson answered. He drove to the front of the critical wings of the hospital, driving into the chaplain's only space to complete stop. Jackson slowly peeks over at Buchanan.

The chaplain reminds his bodyguard, "He said - Stay the path."

Jackson nods, grinning from ear to ear.

Buchanan gawks toward the floorboard, fighting back his emotion, and glances back up toward Jackson. He reaches up, pats Jackson on his shoulder. "Thanks for setting me straight, Philip."

"Me setting you straight, sir?" Jackson asked.

"Yeah. For doubting."

Jackson grins, pleased he consoled his chaplain friend.

"Because *he is* alive. And God *was* with him." Buchanan added.

Jackson fist pumps Buchanan's knee. "Let's go. Let's go see our friend."

Buchanan tilts his head toward Jackson and says, "Yeah. Let's go, sergeant."

As Chaplain Buchanan grabbed his small chaplain's manual, the two men stepped out of the jeep with confidence. The men walked confidently to the entrance of the critical wing of the hospital, comprising several Quonset huts with over passes connecting the huts on the exterior.

"Good Morning! Good Morning, corpsmen." said Buchanan, entering the front entrance. Marines sat in a small waiting room with two desks serving as reception desks manned by a Navy corpsmen, a marine, and a nurse.

"Good morning, Chaplain." said Corporal Liam Welch. The young, green marine just arrived in Vietnam and was only 21 years old from Erie, Pennsylvania.

"Can I help you today, sir?" Welch asked.

"Sure can, corporal. Sergeant Jackson and I are here today to visit a wounded chaplain, Chaplain Melvin Abrams."

"Oh?" said corpsman Petty Officer 3rd Class Andrew Becker, from Rising Sun, Indiana, a small city in Ohio County along the Ohio River.

Becker asked, "Chaplain Abrams? That's who you're here to see, sir?"

Jackson answered, "Why yes. Ya see -" Becker interrupted Jackson and said, "Yes. *Yes*. A great chaplain. I've had the honor to have had a hand in bringing the man of faith back to health."

"That he is, Petty Officer Becker. A man of faith." Jackson said, noticing Becker's name badge.

"Can we see him?" asked Buchanan.

"Sure thing." Welch answered. "The duty nurse is Lieutenant Doris Mayse. She's Nurse Reagan's replacement."

"Yes, we've met occasionally through the MeDCAPs and chaplain CAP's." Buchanan said.

"I'll fetch her, sir. Just a moment, chaplain." promised Becker.

"Thank you very much, Petty Officer Becker."

Becker slipped through a passage way dividing the reception waiting room from beds on the opposite side of the Quonset hut. The spiritual team visited with Welch while Becker fetched nurse Mayse. The team inquired about his hometown and his family. As time passed, Becker stepped back through the passageway followed by nurse Mayse.

"Good morning, Chaplain. Good Morning, Sergeant Jackson. Good to see ya, Sergeant. How are you this morning?" asked nurse Mayse, turning toward Jackson displaying a gleaming smile.

Jackson replied, "Uh, good morning, nurse Mayse. I'm happy to see you as well, mam."

Buchanan nudged Jackson's leg, smiling at nurse Mayse. He knew her fondness for Jackson in more ways than one.

Mayse, who took a liking to Jackson the first time they met, could careless what people thought of her. Naturally shy, Jackson's conscience about the fraternization policy of the military code made him nervous. Mayse could have cared less for military protocol regarding fraternization. She took a liking to Jackson, humoring Buchanan.

Buchanan said, "It's been a few weeks since we've seen you at An Ngai Tay. We thank you for your support with the medical attention given to the people there, especially to the children and elderly, the most vulnerable."

Mayse smiles. "You're very welcome, chaplain. Corporal Becker explained you're here to see Chaplain Abrams?"

"Sure are. We just found out he was in the critical wing this morning. We rushed on over to see him." Buchanan explained.

"Well, that's great. He's had a visitor or two, officers. But seeing Sergeant Jackson, enlisted, will thrill his soul." Mayse said, grinning toward Jackson.

Buchanan again nudged Jackson's leg, glancing over at Jackson, grinning with twisted lips.

"He loves ministering to the enlisted." Mayse said.

"Yes, we know." replied Buchanan, grinning toward Jackson, nervously shifting his eyes on the edge.

"I can account for that, sir." said Welch. "He's been an inspiration for me even in the state he's in."

"Great, corporal! I know you're going to cherish his influence on you for the rest of your life."

"Yes, sir."

"Let's go on back to the wing he's on, chaplain - wing two." Mayse said, turning back towards the entrance of critical bed wing one.

Mayse steps through the entrance of wing one, followed by the spiritual team. The party of three walks in between the beds and the team is stunned at the condition of the wounded men. Hooked up to only God knows how many tubes and machines keeping them alive. The wounded men were black and blue from the many life-threatening injuries located from head to toe. Some even bared the resemblance of corpses.

Mayse turns to her side. "Let me prepare you a bit before we enter his wing. What you're going to see is a fortunate man indeed. His body has *really* taken a beating. Just remember, he's shot up, riddled with shrapnel, and peppered with booby trap shotgun pellets."

The spiritual team grimaced with concern, fretful of the condition of their friend.

Mayse informed the spiritual team. "But he can speak now. It's been days since the attack, but the ability to speak at this point is a miracle in and of itself."

Again, the spiritual team frowned. Buchanan frets, catching flies.

The small party step out of Quonset hut one, turning left toward critical wing two under an overpass built by the Seabees to serve as shade for the wounded and a patio for friends visiting service personnel from all branches.

Stepping to the entrance of wing two, Mayse stops in her steps and faces the spiritual team. Swallowing hard, she said, "Well, here we are. He's in the seventh bed on your right. Remember, he's been through the ringer."

With that said, Mayse half grins, turns and walks back toward the waiting room.

The spiritual team kept an eye on her till she vanished into wing one, almost intentionally, perhaps to delay the inevitable of facing the horrors and forbidding acts of war.

Buchanan turns, stepping into wing two, followed by Jackson. The spiritual team is impressed with the professional medical personnel administering their skills to the critically wounded, nursing the men with compassion and dedication in keeping every serviceman alive. The visit is a ghastly sight from the start. Human beings ripped to pieces, black and blue from wounds. The injuries of the wounded affirmed the ultimate confirmation of war and the exposure of violent acts of combat, sucking the life out of a living human organism.

Though Buchanan felt a sense of foreboding, a bit of doom and gloom in the air, an overwhelming bodily sensation consumed his inner self, a presence within the room of a physical and spiritual struggle between death's call and the hanging on to life which is so precious. Perhaps a fight of a serviceman longing to live to hold his girlfriend once again back home. Or to hug his wife and kids once again. Or a native citizen of Missouri to visit the Arch in St Louis once again, one of Buchanan's favorite cities. Or to travel through the Rocky mountains once more in Colorado during the winter months. The wounded men just desired to go home alive one day.

The nearer Buchanan came to Abrams, the fight ensuing between the final breath in one's life and the fight to live on, to see family and home again, became stronger.

The spiritual team glared intently at each severely wounded serviceman, horror-struck at the sight of cruel and ruthless results of combat. Wounds and gashes on torsos beyond imagination. Limbs severely damaged covered with lacerations, nearly torn out of its socket. Cuts and scratches scattered over the heads of the wounded, reflecting gruesome creatures out of a horror flick. The sight, a ghastly vista of wounded the spiritual team had never witnessed, portrayed a sickening picture poles apart from corpses and deceased from the past, especially those in the cooler. Grim and bleak nevertheless.

The spiritual team finally reached Abrams bed. His condition exhibited attentiveness, but cognizant.

Abrams laid motionless, silent. Buchanan assessed the immobility of his friend, eerie and unbecoming. Devastated at the sight of Abrams' physical condition, he said a silent prayer for his chaplain friend.

As Buchanan developed a friendship with Abrams, he noticed his companion exhibited a human being full of life. Abrams conducted himself as a man with an unlimited amount of energy, pursuing to create a better world. Personality traits no other human being possessed but him, and those who came into contact with Abrams, recognized a great man of faith. Buchanan loved him as a friend and fellow human being. With a loss for words, he knew not what to say. A clueless Buchanan beseeched the Lord's words to utter once he and Jackson arrived at Abrams bedside. A master in choosing words wisely in awkward situations, Buchanan today found himself tongue tied beyond measure, contemplating every word in order to give to his friend words of peace, consolation, and spiritual and physical healing. The energetic, people oriented chaplain froze in a speechless state.

When laying his eyes on Abrams, Buchanan's first instinct in his deepest, innermost self drew him to weep unhindered, witnessing the ripped and torn body which laid in front of him.

Letting his emotions run free would come at another hour, another time and place. Possibly traveling the return trek back to Camp Love, in the privacy of himself and Jackson, alone in the jeep.

Jackson stepped to the left bedside, while Buchanan stood on Abrams' right. He softly, gently placed his hand on top of Abrams right hand, grinning. With the maximum exertion of energy lingering within his fragile and dilapidated self, Abrams squeezed Buchanan's hand with the slightest of a squeeze. Buchanan grinned wider, knowing the squeeze of his hand showed the man he knew possessing an endless head of steam balked at the idea of throwing in the towel and giving up. No one thought of Abrams as a quitter.

A long pause of silence filled the room, when Jackson broke the silence. "We're here, sir."

Abrams shifts his eyes left, staring straight into Jackson's eyes.

The spiritual team heard a faint, inaudible message from Abrams. The slightest movement emerged on Abram's lips, forced from a man who suffered a physical beating from the hands of the Devil's legions. The team reckoned Abrams attempted a smile.

"It's us. Sergeant Jackson and Chaplain Buchanan, *Robert*, from the 7th Engineering Battalion." Jackson said.

Abrams faintly squeezes Buchanan's hand.

In the front of the spiritual team laid a motionless Abrams, torn to pieces. As Nurse Mayse assessed, Abrams suffered from wounds riddled throughout his body, resulting in thoracic trauma and projectile-embolus injuries.

On the inside, Buchanan experienced every emotion imaginable. Though distressed and downhearted, emotions of resentment, anger, and retaliation shrieked within him. His exterior self showed nothing but a demeanor of solemn and serene compassion. Glancing from head to toe at Abrams, the sight sickened Buchanan indeed.

Buchanan lifted up a silent prayer, 'God save him from the clutches of death.'

As the spiritual team remained flabbergasted at the sight of Abrams, the spiritual team bared in mind that just a week ago, the man they knew - full of energy and 'gun ho' to minister to marines – now lie in front of them a motionless, frozen human being. A man idle from fulfilling God's calling in his life.

"Melv, I'm here. It's Robert." Buchanan said, teary-eyed, emotional and softly holding Abrams' hand. He looks intently at Buchanan, blinking from time to time, relaying tons of information he held within himself to Buchanan, but too frail to communicate by word of mouth.

Sensing his desire to speak, Buchanan says, "We'll talk later. Melv. Just rest."

Abrams again attempts a slight smile.

"All the men in Camp Love are praying for you. You're on their prayer list." Buchanan said.

Abrams slowly shifts his eyes toward the direction of Jackson on his left and softly, almost in a whisper, said, "Va-var. Ne-."

"Varnes? Varnes, sir? Oh, yes. He's doing great. He and Johannsson. Told them your status here at the hospital. They immediately put you on their prayer lists." Jackson explained, softly clutching Abrams' left hand.

"They mentioned this morning the last homily heard from you in camp, 'Keep the Faith.' Your Old Testament Scripture hit home, sir."

Jackson felt the gentlest movement from Abrams' fingers.

"Yes, Melvin. I know you remember. It was Isaiah 59:17: 'He put on righteousness as a breastplate, and a helmet of salvation upon his head; he put on garments of vengeance for clothing and wrapped himself in fury as a mantle.'" Buchanan said.

With a moment of pause and calm in the room, the spiritual team's presence strengthened Abrams' resolve to 'Keep the Faith'.

Buchanan broke the pause of silence. "Keep the Faith, Melv. The Lord's with ya. You have righteousness as a breastplate....helmet of salvation.....garments of vengeance for clothing.....and, yes, fury as a mantle."

A visit to critically wounded served as a shot in the arm for any injured military personnel, including Abrams. No one yet from the 5th marines visited. Not out of neglect, but from a major tactical operation in the field prevented the 5th Marines from venturing into Da Nang to visit Chaplain Abrams. He certainly was not forgotten. Two days later, several officers and enlisted relieved from the operation to rest at the airbase came and visited their chaplain.

Nurse Mayse eventually made her way back to wing 2, standing at the foot of the bed.

Jackson peeked back at her, and moving her lips, said to Jackson, "It's time to go." He turns toward Buchanan, nodding. He says to Abrams, "We better go now, chaplain. We figure you better rest, sir, with all this visiting we've given ya."

Buchanan expresses deep fret, glancing toward Jackson. A fear overwhelmed Buchanan, as if the visit will be the last time the two of them will ever see Abrams alive again.

"Melv, can I pray with ya?" asked Buchanan. Abrams moved his fingers. Buchanan closed his eyes and prayed, "Father, Melvin Abrams, is a great friend. A great chaplain. He loves you and Philip and I are better people knowing him. Better Christians knowing him.

We ask you to heal him. Comfort him. Bestow your soothing hand upon him through the skills and talents of the medical personnel to restore his vigor and agility once again. In Jesus' name, Amen."

Buchanan, never letting go of his hand, felt a strong, forceful embrace from Abrams' hand, screaming hope and assertiveness from Abrams.

Buchanan looked upon his chaplain friend. "You don't mind me praying in Jesus' name - do ya, Melv?"

Abrams utters a whisper, practically inaudible, "no."

"What was that, Melv?" asked Buchanan, turning his head to the right, closer to Abrams.

"Friend." said Abrams with more volume.

Buchanan smiles and with emotion said, "Yes, Melvin. Friends."

As Abrams spoke his last to the spiritual team, the men felt the tightest squeeze possible to their hands.

"We're going now, Melvin. Keep the Faith, my friend." Buchanan said.

"Take care, sir. Keep the Faith." added Jackson.

As the spiritual team rose to face nurse Mayse, the two men noticed Abrams' face wore the widest smile he could muster, a smile to say 'Good-bye.'

Nurse Mayse guided the spiritual team back to the waiting room, as Buchanan asked worrying questions the whole trip back to the front. She assured him Abrams was well taken care of, smiling and answering questions with as positive of an answer that she could give. Mayse, the whole while walking to the front, knew full well Abrams' condition stood critical and on edge of taking a downward slope at any given moment.

The spiritual team said their goodbyes, hopped back into the jeep and headed for supply to muster up with the replenishing detail.

After a muster and some chow, the convoy made their way back to camp.

Buchanan might have said two words on the trip back. The vibes thrown toward Buchanan of melancholy from Jackson wore him down an additional notch or two. The spiritual team learned a lesson or two in humility about the perils of war today, knocking the men of Faith down a notch or two.

Abrams exerted nothing but spirit and energy when hundred percent healthy. The energy was ever so present, even in his vulnerable and beaten state lying on the hospital bed. The spiritual team sat traveling in a state of awe considering Abram's state of steadfastness, impressed with a man riddled and peppered with wounds all over his body, who still reflected the words in his last homily delivered in camp. His unwavering will to live, along with his commitment and dependence on God, hardened his self-preservation and desire to carry on with life.

Chaplain Melvin Abrams survived his horrific ordeal. The physical state of Abrams from the results of actions of the Viet Cong had been one hard to swallow from his friends and colleagues, but actions proven inadequate for a man of such resolve and dedication. Abrams confirmed nothing could penetrate, including the conniving tactics of the Viet Cong, a man donning righteousness as a breastplate, a helmet of salvation, garments of vengeance, and fury as a mantle. With all the evil and malice the Devil and his legions could ever muster, it would never be capable of penetrating the armament of God. That same armament of God protected Chaplain Abrams on August 5, 1969.

In the end, Abrams and God will win. The Viet Cong's evil intent to eliminate a God fearing, caring and loving human being came to an abrupt end - a decisive defeat for the Devil and the VC.

Abrams' recovery required an exhausting and grueling period of rehabilitation, but in the end - he won. In store for Abrams came an additional 33 days in Da Nang to recover, time enough to gain sufficient physical endurance and energy for a long flight to Japan for an advanced recovery.

Buchanan dropped in to visit Abrams from time to time while he visited the wounded from the 7th Engineering Battalion the next 33 days.

After the war, Buchanan bumped into Abrams occasionally at chaplain conferences in Norfolk, Virginia for training or other Navy bases. They rarely mentioned the war in conversation. But the camaraderie generated during the war bonded the two men forever with the love of God and a yearning to pursue His will in each of their lives.

Buchanan's lasting impression of Abrams as a man lived in the words of Isaiah 59:17 daily. The impression set a lifelong imprinted memory upon Buchanan's heart and mind. A mentor for Buchanan the rest of his life, Abrams' dependence on God in all of life's endeavors, spiritual and physical, resembled Buchanan's faith in God. Abrams conferred on Buchanan a greater need for a dependence on God, and in Buchanan's spiritual life - Jesus. Abrams reflected a dependence on a different faith, but Buchanan learned much from this man of God.

Buchanan loved Abrams. The men were friends. His recollection of Abrams constructed a permanent memory, never to forget his friend.

The memory reflective of Isaiah 59:17.

Vietnamese Culture

August 21, 1969

The spiritual team's absence in the CAPs had been too long. A visit to the villages ended up being a long time coming. Buchanan's separation added up to several weeks, not out of neglect but due to combat missions and his ministry with the 7th Engineering Battalion.

The spiritual team's surprise visit to An Ngai Tay overjoyed the children. The time spent with the children reassured them the funny American chaplain and his friend had not forgotten them. The team had a great visit with the villages as time raced to 1400 hours in the afternoon. The team needed to depart for camp.

The trip back to camp ended up serving as a site seeing excursion.

The day absorbed three stops alongside the road. The brief social encounters reinforced Buchanan's appreciation for Vietnamese culture to new heights, enlightening his awareness the Vietnamese people were people - human beings, like him.

Buchanan cherished the social sciences, and history, of course, topped the long list of disciplines within the fields of study. But he valued other sciences within the domain, such as anthropology and sociology, taking slide pictures all day long.

The first stop encountered a marble mountain cutter's shop. His second stop visited a rice paddy field with water buffalo, followed by the most intriguing for Buchanan - a Buddhist funeral.

As Jackson drove the jeep, Buchanan noticed ahead of them the marble cutter out underneath his hut working on marble extracted from the foot of Marble Mountain who they had passed by day in and day out.

"Slow down, Philip. Slow down! Look Philip! It's the marble cutter."

Staring straight ahead in the jeep, Buchanan's intense and intriguing stare gazed sharp with admiration for a skill he only dreamed of possessing, as Jackson slowed the pace of the jeep.

"Stop, Philip. Let's stop. Let's see his work."

Jackson smiled as he slowed the jeep to a deliberate but complete stop in front of the marble cutter's workshop. The desire for Buchanan to see the marble cutter's work firsthand can strike one item off his bucket list of site seeing endeavors in Vietnam. In October 1968, Jackson pointed out the marble cutter to Buchanan passing by.

As soon as the jeep came to a complete stop, Buchanan bolted out of the jeep snapping slide pictures of Marble Mountain, with the marble cutter in the foreground, one of many slides in his Vietnam presentation he shared in many a night to family and friends.

"That's going to be a beautiful shoot." Buchanan paused as he took a panoramic view of Marble Mountain, awed by the beauty of it all.

"Hello. How are you doing today?" Buchanan asked in his strong Kentuckian mountain accent.

"Good. Very good. My name is Giang Vu." said the marble cutter, stepping out from behind his worktable, approaching the spiritual team closer to the jeep.

Jackson smiles, hearing the strong accent in Buchanan's voice. By now, Jackson knew Buchanan well enough that when he heard his strong Kentuckian accent flowing from his mouth, the chaplain found himself engrossed in immense excitement with a personal interest or engaging idea or thought. All the while, Jackson grinned.

Buchanan stepped forward toward the marble cutter, one of many South Vietnamese who, in the mid 1950s, fled the north because of religious persecution of Roman Catholics from a new and oppressive Communist presence in the North.

Surprised with the excellent English from the marble cutter, Buchanan mentioned, "The ARVN marine captain we know, Danh Phu, informed us we could stop any time to observe your work."

"Yes, I know marine Captain Phu. Patriotic, loyal."

"I'm Navy Chaplain Robert Buchanan, and my assistant Sergeant Philip Jackson."

"Good to meet you." replied Vu. Given first impressions, Vu displayed Christian generosity and forbearance.

"I know who you are. You're the funny American chaplain."

Buchanan chuckles at the thought. Jackson, turning slowly towards him, shrugs his shoulders with a grin. "You're funny, sir."

Jackson turns to the marble cutter and says, "The captain assures us your sculpture work is phenomenal and unparalleled."

"Yes, I enjoy the gifts God has given me."

"My sons are very talented as well." Vu motions with his hand his sons on his left with pride.

"You speak very good English, Mr. Vu." Buchanan commented.

"Nuns taught me in European type Catholic schools growing up. I know how to read, write, and speak English. *And* French, fluently." Vu said.

"Wow!" Jackson said. "I'm impressed."

"Your marble work is fascinating to me, Mr. Vu." Buchanan said.

Mr. Vu described the excavation process of marble from the mountain, with the help of his sons, and transferring the marble to him and other marble cutters. Walking from one end of his work space to the other, Vu describes with pride the digging and excavation of marble. Spellbound, the spiritual team listens to every word thoroughly out of Mr. Vu's mouth.

"Fascinating. Just fascinating." Buchanan said. Vu completed his step-by-step description of the marble mining process with the full attention of the spiritual team.

"If you like, I could cut the two of you a marble cross." Vu said.

"Amen!" replied Buchanan.

"You can take it back home as something of a souvenir of your military tour in Vietnam." Vu added.

"That would be awesome." said an excited Jackson.

"Come back in three weeks. I'll have them ready for you." Vu said. He showed the cutting of the marble for market sale. Again, Vu described his work with pride.

Buchanan never forgot his visit with Vu. He snapped several slide pictures for his personal historical record of his tour. The 25 minutes spent with Vu, as simple as it might have been, were some of the most pleasant moments the spiritual team experienced in Vietnam.

Three weeks later, Vu handed over the crosses he meticulously shaped and carved with his own two hands to the spiritual team. The surprise and elation of the Americans mounted with overwhelming appreciation. Vu carved the crosses in emerald green, Buchanan's favorite color.

"Amen!" declared Buchanan at first sight of the crosses.

Vu insisted no money exchange hands. He carved the crosses out of sheer Christian benevolence. After all, the benevolent CAPs the Americans established all over South Vietnam increased the overall wellbeing for the Vietnamese. Vu insisted on returning the charity given with the crosses.

The next 20 minutes for the spiritual team, though brief, became valuable time well spent alongside the road near rice patties owned by a family of farmers supporting democracy. Buchanan insisted on stopping, visiting with friendly farmers. Major Sanborn's agricultural CAPs had assisted with their rice farming.

Buchanan stepped out of the jeep, introducing the spiritual team to the farmers.

As the cultivators, in broken English, explained to Buchanan rice farming, the farmers were all too happy to permit Buchanan to take pictures of them and the rice patties. The most intriguing for Buchanan is the use of the water buffalo to farm. The buffalo were a treasured asset to many Vietnamese, considered more than just an animal. To westerners, the water buffalo is just another animal. But for southeastern Asians, the animal provided an invaluable economic necessity for survival in South Vietnam, and even held religious connotations.

Buchanan snapped pictures of the water buffalo, fascinated with the last slide picture taken - a teenager on the back of the water buffalo farming in rice patties. The sight signaled a red flag for Buchanan, as the work presented a great danger to the young lad. Considering the war and the political culture, at least the young teenager spent his time farming and hopefully distant from the influence of the dreaded Viet Cong. Over the years, Buchanan considered some of his favorite slides to present to family and friends were the pictures of the rice patties and the water buffalo.

The last stop for the trip back to Camp Love provided the most fascinating for Buchanan - a Buddhist funeral. For this social science lesson, the spiritual team thought it best to stay put in the jeep. Jackson parked on the side of the road, insisting too many people were present for them to step out of the jeep. Fearing a possible Viet Cong presence within the funeral participants, Jackson avoided any trouble. Regardless, the spiritual team appreciated the anthropology lesson with the funeral procession, finding the sight fascinating.

With an interest in culture, Buchanan dove in head first in learning more of the Vietnamese way of life. A funeral served as one centerpiece of Vietnam's culture. Traditionally, the Vietnamese avoided celebrating birthdays, a concept odd to foreign westerners. The center of family remembrance centered in on the death date and ancestor worship. The remembrance of relatives occupied a family unit in Vietnamese culture. The neglect in life remembering a deceased family member within a clan group resulted in the return of an ancestor as a ghost haunting other family members.

The Vietnamese adhered to animism - the belief of spirits in nature, such as plants, rocks, trees, and even rivers. When a person dies, the spirit will within the person will be pleasant in the after-life. If not, and the person dies a questionable or violent death, the person will have a harsh spirit. The concept threw Buchanan for a loop due to the Vietnamese culture virtually being atheist, living a Buddhist life.

Most Vietnamese are of the Mahayana branch of Buddhism. Hence, the funeral process comprised the family picking a good day on the calendar for the funeral, especially if the person who passed away died on an unlucky day in the calendar. The next required step was prepared for the days of mourning, which dwelled for three days. The first day amounted to the family placing the deceased family member in a casket. The second day necessitated an opportunity for the family and friends to visit and give their condolences, while on the third day, the family planned for the loved one to be cremated, which is the traditional means of burial. Though many Vietnamese chose a burial above the ground in modern, contemporary days.

For burial, the Vietnamese placed a deceased remains above ground and set dirt and rocks above and around the remains for a mound. An odd means of burial in Buchanan's estimation indeed. He just shrugs his shoulders and says - 'To each his own.'

The next step in the funeral process required the lighting of the funeral pyre with the family.

The last phase consisted of Buddhist monks chanting up to and during the funeral.

All the while Buchanan took slide pictures of every step of the procession.

Over 100 people accompanied the funeral procession, the final act of a funeral in Vietnam, showing love and respect for the deceased on the way to their final resting place. The procession proceeded with the remains in a casket carried by family members, as Buddhist priests chanted and sung traditional songs to the final resting place. Family, friends, and Buddhist priests strolled alongside the remains, with priests holding high in the air long inscripted rectangular banners referencing Buddha quotes and prayers. The procession added musicians, complimenting the words with music.

The most intriguing, mind-boggling aspect of the funeral for Buchanan, absent in the western world, numbered the professional mourners hired by family members toward the end of the procession. The professionals placed themselves at the rear of the procession, weeping profusely, as if they themselves had lost their own mother.

"Look at that, Philip. The professional mourners told to us in our chaplains training." Buchanan looked on with intrigue.

"Yeah. *Yeah*. Absolutely amazing." Jackson paused. "And we're witnessing something very few people back home will ever experience."

"We sure are." Buchanan said. He took one last picture of the professional mourners.

Observing the mourners, Buchanan sat in the jeep in shock witnessing the professionals behavior. "Did that woman do what I think she did? Really?"

Jackson chuckles. "Yes, sir. I *think* she did."

"She *really* did smile at the camera." Buchanan said.

The men smile, catching flies.

Jackson confesses with a bit of amazement in his voice, "Yes sir, she did. A professional mourner, just stops in the middle of everything, and nonchalantly smiles at the camera. Then, like a spigot, returns to weeping profusely to mourn for the deceased human being. Unbelievable."

"Well, they're being paid to weep for the deceased."

"I guess." said Jackson, shrugging his shoulders.

Buchanan glares at the procession, noticing the family members. No phony tears from the family - only tears of genuine grief.

Buchanan looked at his watch for the time - 1645 hours. The time is late, no more time for site seeing. Besides, Jackson is preoccupied with a few participants in the funeral procession whose demeanor is deemed suspicious. The glances given to the spiritual team from the wary characters gave reason to hightail it back home.

"Let's get out of here. I didn't like the looks of some in the funeral procession." said Jackson.

"Come to think of it - neither did I." replied Buchanan, with concern in his eye.

"Let's roll sir."

"Amen to that!"

Arriving in Camp Love at 1715 hours, the spiritual team enjoyed some chow and turned in early.

To top things off ending the day, Burns played Aaron Copeland's Appalachian Spring, a cultural, iconic piece of music in and of itself.

The spiritual team enjoyed the anthropology and sociology lessons of the day. From dawn to dusk, the day had been a good one for Buchanan. The team shared a day of enhancing their love for the social sciences.

With just a little over two months remaining in their tours, the spiritual team dreamed and prayed for more days such as today than the ugly, horrific days when men are forced to glance over their shoulders, expecting attacks from the impious Viet Cong.

A Night To Remember

September 9, 1969

Four more Tuesday nights of 500 Rummy in Buchanan's tour. A mere eight to ten more hours to gather for normalcy and fellowship with friends. Buchanan himself is very near being a 'short timer', along with many of his friends. The men will miss playing Rummy on Tuesday nights with colleagues. Years later, the group admitted the nights of playing cards, along with the Friday night socials, both initiated by Buchanan, were contributing factors of aiding each other to survive the war, mentally and physically, while in Vietnam.

The entire gang arrived ready to play Rummy, winner take all. The winnings of the last three nights of Rummy were donated to nonprofit, charitable organizations, including Catholic charities enhancing Catholic ministries near Camp Love.

Tonight's competition - winner takes all.

The built up frustration inside Buchanan the past few weeks kicked in as he received solid bloody noses night after night from his Rummy competitors, winning nothing for two months. Buchanan sensed odds were in his favor to win. Lady Luck smiled upon Vickers, Rockford, and Adkins the last two months, with luck laid in their lap, sticking their noses in the air, winning most of the nights.

"I'm going to win tonight." Buchanan said.

Rockford rolls his eyes. "You say that every Tuesday night, Padre."

"What's so special about tonight, sir? You've been talking to Animal?" asked Skawinski sarcastically.

"As a matter of fact, I mentioned it to Private Rodriquez." A smug grin lays across Buchanan's face.

Rodriquez smiles widely, shaking his head.

Adkins glances toward Gunny Jurgensen. "He's wearing it again, men. The lucky suit. Don't ya think you -" "Listen squid." interrupted Jurgensen. "I'm wearing - well, I - listen. It did me good the first night I wore this suit, and I'm gonna wear it until I win again."

"Fine with us, Gunny." Vickers said. "You've lost every Tuesday night for weeks wearing that getup."

Jurgensen shrugs his shoulders, grumbling to himself. He demands, "Alright, then. Just deal the cards and we'll just see who wins tonight."

With the conclusion of Jurgensen's spill, the night began with the card playing.

As usual, the group members strategically sat themselves at a table of one's choice. Each player sat at a table of better players to eliminate him out of competition, hence, giving him greater odds of winning the next round or to sit at a table numbered with a greater number of lesser skilled players to advance in play. Of course, everyone thought of themselves as a sharpened skilled player, ranked in the upper tier of competition.

When it boiled down to the best players, Vickers, Rockford, Adkins, Skawinski, and McElrath were on the top tier. Buchanan settled in the rankings as a middle of the road, an average type of player, ranked a little higher than the median.

The rule for cheating remained in place - if caught cheating, the player is immediately banned from playing and throw out from the room as a spectator. No one had ever been caught cheating, of course. No one risked taking a chance of being banned from one of the few standing dates in camp during the week for any normalcy in their lives.

Regardless of rankings, Buchanan's silence in the winning column seemed apparent to everyone. He had not sat in the winner's circle for weeks. But this night's final results will settle out differently in the end. The popular chaplain in camp won big - winning $204.89.

Buchanan promised his boys back home new toy train accessories, including some train cars. He received in the mail a new HO scale train catalog, browsing through the catalog earlier in the day. Completing the order form in the catalog of HO railroad accessories, he ordered his sons trees, buildings, figures and landscape. Isolated so deep in the bush, the ordering of railroad accessories out of the catalog inserted some much needed fun he so desperately longed for.

After two and a half hours of playing cards, the men simply desired to fellowship following the competition, as the night remained young and the friends, officer and enlisted, hung around for companionship. Why not? Tuesday nights calmed the war environment for Buchanan and his friends.

As the men chatted, enjoying each one's company, Buchanan glared above himself with hands elevated. He said out of the blue, "Thanks for looking out for me."

Buchanan lowers his hands and head, smiling with the slightest smirk.

"Oh, please!" responded his friends.

"Oh, come on, Padre." said Rockford, rolling his eyes. "You know you were just lucky tonight. You're not the best player in our group - and *you* know it."

"I prayed for him after y'all eliminated me from play." Rodriquez said with a grin.

"Oh, come on man." refuted the group.

"*Really*, Animal? You're going to really assert praying to Saint Christopher aided the Padre here?" McElrath declared.

"I do." Rodriquez responded with even a broader grin.

"Aghhh." countered McElrath.

Suddenly, and without warning, Dobbs unexpectedly entered the room.

"Good evening, PFC Dobbs." Rockford said. "What brings you to this neck of the woods?"

"Well, sir." said a nervous Dobbs.

"You got a problem?"

"Uh. N-No sir." Dobbs replied. "I just thought, well - I need to speak to you, sir." professed Dobbs, turning to Buchanan.

"Oh?" asked Buchanan.

"Well, yes. Yes, sir."

"Well, let's walk on over to the office." Buchanan said.

"Well, wish the winner of the night off, men. You're looking at him." insisted Buchanan with a wide and smug smile.

"Ohhhh please! Get out!" said Buchanan's friends, all half grinning.

"See ya, lucky. Yeah, that's your new name, sir - Lucky. HaHaHaHa." said Skawinski, followed with laughter from the rest of the group.

Grinning, Dobbs glanced at Buchanan with approbation as the two walked out of supply.

Buchanan filled Dobbs in of the night's proceedings of Rummy and his winning night as the men paced towards the chaplain's hootch. Dobbs, of course, listened to every detail, pleased with the news.

Stepping into the hootch, Buchanan made his way to his desk, sitting in his swivel chair while Dobbs nervously occupied a chair across from him.

Dobbs presented himself to Buchanan as anxious. Fidgety, shifting left and right in his chair, he seemed unnerved, sitting face to face with the chaplain. Out of concern, Buchanan asked, "It's 2300 hours, Dobbs. Coming by supply to see me - well, are ya alright tonight?"

"Yes-Yes sir."

Dobbs, still nervous, rubbed his knees with his hands, shifting his eyes left and right, licking his lips.

Buchanan grins. Thinks of what his problem might be and asks, "Private, you have a reason to talk to me tonight?"

"Yes, sir."

Buchanan asks him forthright what his problem might be.

"Is it physical?" asked Buchanan.

"No, sir."

"Is it a girlfriend back home?"

Dobbs chuckles and says, "No. No-No, sir."

"Is it a family problem back home?"

"No, sir."

Buchanan asked a few more inquiries until the last possible problem came to his mind. He asked, "Is it a spiritual problem?"

Still nervous, Dobbs said, "Why, yes sir, it is spiritual."

"It *is*?"

Dobbs grins slowly. "Well, sir. It's like this - I'm ready."

Buchanan, puzzled by Dobbs' statement, thought, what in tarnation did Dobbs need? What did he mean? - 'I'm ready.'

"What do you mean, you're ready? Ready for what, Michael?"

"Well, sir. I'm ready to join the other side. You know, your side."

Buchanan, stunned by Dobbs' comments, catches flies.

"You mean, ya-ya want - to be a-a believer? A Christian?" asked Buchanan in shock and thrilled to death.

""I'm already. I read your tracks and the Scripture quoted in the tracks in the Bible you gave me."

Buchanan shot up out of his seat, raised his right hand, and said in a slightly elevated voice while walking around his desk, "Amen! Amen! Amen!"

"I knew it the first day I saw ya in the bush. Remember - my first day out in the bush." said Buchanan with a broad smile.

"I remember, sir."

"You remind me of myself when I was your age. Jesus changed my life, Michael."

"Me too, sir. Jesus is now my Savior." said Dobbs proudly.

Dobbs stares down at the floor. "I'm tired, sir. I'm tired of fighting everybody and, well, being a troublesome." He momentarily paused. "I'm tired of hating. I'm tired of being angry. I'm tired of picking fights for no reason. I'm tired of blaming everybody else for my problems."

Buchanan turns toward his swivel chair as Dobbs speaks, sitting slowly back into his chair. "I'm so thrilled you came to understanding God's want to know ya, Michael."

The men smile. Buchanan recognizes Dobbs' smile as different, the gleam of a new man, of a new person who now knows Jesus in his heart.

"Michael, let me go through some steps, questions really, with you and establish some conclusions with you. Then we'll baptize ya in the Tvy Loan River."

"Sure thing, sir."

The follow-up questions were to establish finality and to baptize Dobbs. He let down his hair the rest of the evening.

The young marine divulged to Buchanan his life. He fessed up to Buchanan his mother entered the life of a prostitute, running off with a man to Las Vegas, Nevada. She suffered from alcoholism, an addiction Buchanan knew well. She physically and emotionally abused Dobbs as a youngster. Throwing alcohol his way at age ten, she started an immediate addiction, taking hold of the young ten-year-old, hooking him onto a permanent dependence on a stimulant resulting in compulsive behaviors. No one in Dobbs' life considered his mother a good person. The last time he physically set his eyes on his own mother happened on his last day of his sophomore year in high school, catching her departing a bar with two men. Dropping out of high school after completing his sophomore year, he now felt called to live on the streets. Only 17 years old, he failed two grades in elementary school. When Dobbs arrived in Vietnam in February 1968 for his first tour, he heard of his mother for the last time. She worked as a prostitute in Las Vegas, finding herself often in and out of jail for various misdemeanors.

As a 21-year-old serving the Marine Corps in Vietnam, news of his mother's whereabouts slowly faded away, forever gone. Clueless of his mother's wellbeing, Dobb's separation from his mother severed permanently with time and space.

Dobbs revealed to Buchanan his mother never knew the identity of his biological father. He never knew his real father. The young man is no dummy. He recognized the root of many of his problems in life had been the fact he lacked the positive male mentor every boy needs for guidance and direction.

Regardless of his past, the Marine Corps applied an IQ test for Dobbs, resulting in an IQ of 129. The young man presented himself far from being a dummy in his speech and retention of information.

He simply received many blows below the belt in his early life, experiencing a collection of hardships which mounted, provoking the raw man to lash out violently at everyone and everything which he perceived to be a threat toward him.

Buchanan owned a facet of life growing up, Dobbs lacked in his upbringing. He knew his father well, and he provided for his wants and needs a child required growing up. Buchanan's father did the best he could during the Great Depression as a father mentor in his life. Buchanan's upbringing with a father laid the future foundation for him as a father in his own family. He expressed to Dobbs his father exemplified a hard working blue collar work ethic, edifying to him that hard work in every endeavor of life will cause success for a person whatever he or she might enter. A trait he possessed and attributed to his father instilling in him as an innate, integral spearhead for Buchanan's success in life. Dobbs had no mentor, mother or father, to instill a blue collar work ethic he observed in Buchanan. The young man considered himself lucky to be alive.

The testimony of Chaplain Buchanan in months past touched Dobbs' heart more than any other spiritual influence in his life. Many features of Buchanan's life reflected his own. They shared a history of abusive mothers. The pair suffered the pains of alcoholism. They shared the need to fight people for nothing more, nothing less, but to prove how tough and independent he might be, a smug independence eventually to destroy him.

"I've heard your story of life, sir, in devotions and communion services all these months. And, well....well, I see many parts of my life similar to yours, sir. I've been reading your pamphlets and the Bible you gave me. I thought about how the Lord changed you, sir. I got down on my knees and asked Jesus to change my life. Jesus penetrated your heart like mine." said Dobbs. He spoke with peace and calm in his voice.

"Yes Dobbs, He did. The Grace bestowed upon the both of us came with a price - His sacrifice on the Cross."

Dobbs shook his head, smiling. "As you always say, sir - Amen!"

"Amen!" responded Buchanan. He leans back in his swivel chair and says in jest, "Maybe our similarities are attributed to the two of us being short and skinny. My wife refers to that as the Napoleonic Syndrome."

The two chuckle at the thought.

"Maybe so, sir. Do you know the Scripture that spoke volumes for me? Most penetrating for me?"

"No, what?"

"Matthew 11:28-30. That was it. It was in a pamphlet you handed me."

"Oh?"

"Yes, sir. I've memorized it already." Dobbs said.

"You have?"

"Yes, sir." Dobbs quotes the Matthew passage. "It's 'Come to me, all who labor and are heavy laden, and I will give you rest· Take my yoke upon you, and learn from me; for I am gentle and lowly in heart, and you will find rest for your souls. For my yoke is easy, and my burden is light.'"

Buchanan sat in his swivel chair, awestruck, listening to Dobbs quote Matthew 11:28-30 so eloquently and with conviction. Mesmerized by every word which flowed from his mouth, Buchanan sat listening to a man who had experienced a radical change in his life.

Dobbs, solemn and at peace in front of Buchanan, smiles, lifting his hand up to his heart. "It's all about what's in here, sir."

Buchanan touches his heart and nods with a joyful smile.

Sitting in front of Buchanan sat a young man truly changed and delivered from the bondage of an evil world. A young man discovering rest for his soul, who has taken His yoke upon him and found a new gentleness and joy within his heart. Buchanan, awed by Dobbs' memorization of Scripture, looked over a young man who God indeed had penetrated a hardened and resistant heart. Miracles do happen.

When news of Dobbs' conversion circulated the camp to those who knew him well, including his friends, were overjoyed with the news. More than a dozen men attended the day of the baptism, witnessing the immersion of water in the Tyn Loan River. A day many prayed for the very first day they met Dobbs.

The domino effect kicked in as Dobbs' conversion served as a catalyst for the Lord to speak to the hearts of his friends in his hootch.

Later on the next day, Buchanan reminded Jackson of his prediction of Dobbs and his friends back in October 1968. Indeed, Dobbs' small circle of friends came to know Christ as Savior.

Jackson shrugs his shoulders. "All I can say, sir, is - The Lord hasn't ceased performing miracles."

The spiritual team had come a long way since October 1968, witnessing many deaths and horrific atrocities committed by the NVA and the Viet Cong. But within all the conflict of war, the penetrating, powerful Spirit of God moves about, searching to change men's hearts and minds.

Buchanan considered Michael Dobbs' experience a miracle. In fact, war hardens hearts. The hearts of men strengthen and entrench ten fold, distancing human beings even more so away from God's Grace. The witnessing of man's inhumanity to man and the subjection of hate because of original sin toughens men's hearts even further.

Buchanan rejoiced in the fact that miracles happen, even in the middle of a harsh and dreadful war. Dobbs' conversion experience reinforced Buchanan's conviction of God's omnipotence and omnipresence in the sequence of human beings' lives. Dobbs proved doubting God is futile in effort. No one can doubt the power of God when the impossible becomes the possible. God is everywhere and all powerful, even in the middle of a frustrating and futile war.

All Buchanan can say is, "Glory to God."

Buchanan remembered this night fondly in the years to come. The memory of taking home the Rummy winnings meant nothing compared to Dobbs' day of conversion. The winning night of Rummy dwelled distantly in Buchanan's mind over the years, nearly forgotten, a secondary remembrance. Dobbs' conversion took center stage and reigned dominant in Buchanan's memory.

Dobbs eventually arrived home, found a local congregation in Los Angeles, his home area, and ministered for the rest of his life, witnessing and working for the Lord. His witness for God led others to Salvation in Jesus. Eventually, he achieved his GED, attended a local college, and studied agricultural science, starting his own business.

Eventually, Dobbs met a Godly woman, married and started his own family, raising his children in a Christian home. The fact he raised his children in a Christian home made him very proud. He provided his children a Christian environment growing up in a home of nurturing love he never had.

Indeed, the evening will be a night to remember. A night to remind everyone that miracles never cease.

THE LAST DAYS

SEPTEMBER 28, 1969

Finally, Buchanan enters his last days as a short timer.

Just ten more days and Buchanan will set his feet onto the ground of one of his favorite countries, Japan. Then to Guam. And finally, yes finally, California, the Sunshine state.

Buchanan envisioned his plane landing in Los Angeles, stepping down the airstair, and running to his family waiting patiently on the tarmac.

However, to step foot onto California soil, Buchanan must first survive the next ten days unscathed, praying the horrendous Viet Cong fail in any attempt to take his life. Or any of his friends' lives at that matter. The thought pushed him to loathe the VC.

The concept of hate theologically is far from Christian thought and doctrine. To hate another human being is frowned upon within the Christian tradition, separate from Christian demeanor and living a Christian daily life.

Yet, Buchanan for an entire year in Vietnam battled within himself a spiritual fight between the deep inner despisement of the Viet Cong and how Christians are to treat their enemies in Matthew 5:43-47 - to love and pray for those who hate and persecute you. Living out Matthew 5:43-47 in a war zone was easier said than done.

Entering his tenth day from departing Vietnam, the spiritual battle within Buchanan's inner self surged to a point of boiling over.

Buchanan accompanied Bravo Company to upgrade Route QL-1S sectors in preparation of paving the road, to upgrade and direct maintenance on Route 4 between BT 056589 to AT 968584. The patrol included conducting mine sweeps of Route QL-1S between AT 999707 to BT 042621 in a three and a half day mine sweep with Skawinski's combat engineering team. The spiritual team checked and double checked every step of the way in front of them on this patrol. The Viet Cong set five times as many booby traps in the area, insuring that not only combatants but civilians alike felt terror beyond measure.

The Viet Cong increased terror efforts the past two weeks on Route QL-1S, Route 4, and Route 1, setting a record number of booby traps, not only killing United States servicemen, but maiming civilians, especially children. The dismemberment and disfiguration of children appalled Americans, infuriating United States military chaplains.

Once in the bush, Rockford split Bravo company into a triangular formation with himself and 1st squad at the point, with 2nd and 3rd squads on the company flanks at about 70 feet apart.

Scattered within the point of the triangular formation, Skawinski's team searched and probed the vegetation for booby traps as the formation moved slowly forward.

The first day of the patrol reaped success in disarming literally dozens of booby traps and discovering two Viet Cong tunnels with ammunition caches capable of supplying hundreds, possibly more, of VC and NVA for months to come. A majority of the booby traps were amateur and hastily manufactured. Skawinski and his team had little trouble with most of the devices. None of the less, each booby trap served as a dangerous explosive device.

On the second day of the sweep, Bravo Company patrolled on pins and needles.

From the outset, Rockford felt jittery. Frost of Alpha Company protected Rockford's west flank about a half of mile away, while two squads of Charlie Company protected Rockford's right flank about a half a mile distant.

Most concerning for Rockford dwelt with a new sergeant in Bravo Company heading the point, Sergeant Doug Hanover. Rockford read his service record tallying a spotty report, evidence he owned a high casualty rate leading marines in the bush. In time spent with Hanover in Camp Love, Rockford sensed a marine out to carry out orders and complete a mission - period. He picked up from Hanover he had little concern for the number of casualties to complete a mission. Rockford cared little for a marine sergeant who shunned protecting the lives of fellow marines when out on patrol, as his gut feeling for Hanover perceived a man who cared little for human life. To assert Rockford cared little for Hanover is putting it mildly.

The patrol held some weight, an operation to lift a considerable burden of pressure off the civilian population from Viet Cong booby traps set to intimidate non-combatants. Considerable numbers of casualties of friendly South Vietnamese, especially the elderly and children, mounted, causing much suffering from the deadly mechanisms. Terrorizing pro-American South Vietnamese is unacceptable to Americans, especially the murder of children.

The operation took in dozens of miles, requiring the cooperation with the 3rd Battalion, 11th Marines and 1st Battalion, 7th Marines.

The second day of the patrol, Rockford reconnoitered isolated sectors he found disagreeable. Unfamiliar with the territory, his stomach turned. Skawinski's combat engineering team conducted their sweeps alongside several green unreliable marines, members of combat companies, to protect the engineering team from enemy ambushes and attacks. Skawinski was just as apprehensive of Hanover as Rockford had been. He suddenly felt an urge of 'gun ho' shielding the engineering teams.

Rockford broke out in a cold sweat patrolling in heightened enemy territory, topping his nerves with Hanover at the point for Bravo Company, making him doubly nervous.

Rockford led at the point of the triangular formation with 1st squad, entering coordinate BT 042621. The point of the formation preceded slowly in the jungle, a meticulous motion forward scanning every inch of terrain. B Company prided itself on a first day of success sweeping the area. Leading the patrol the second day with intensity, Rockford wavered minute after minute, trekking deeper and deeper into perilous territory.

The air reeked of danger.

The sense of uncertainty filled the hearts of the patrol as adrenaline ran high. The confident, yet apprehensive patrol, including the spiritual team, accrued a nauseating gut feeling of imminent danger from an enemy presence in the bush. The enemy, as usual, was ready, willing, and able to assault and to deliver evil onto the marines. The horrifying experience in the bush knowing the enemy roamed just ten feet away, but hidden in the jungle, is one the civilian population will never understand. An experience many members of the patrol had felt in the bush.

Rockford feared the enemy imminent, ordering a withdraw. And sure enough, Rockford's gut feeling came quick as the natural buzz of the jungle, accompanied by the silence of the bush, unexpectedly came interrupted with an instant rattling of gunfire - RATATATATATATA!

Type 67 machine gun fire sprayed onto Rockford and the 1st Squad.

RATATATATATATA!

Gunfire erupted right and left of Rockford. The rapid fire of projectiles knocking the earth about in every direction, reflecting mini explosions peppered in and amongst 1st Squad.

Reinforcing the Type 67 machine gun came the firing heat of a Type 24 MG-08 machine gun on Rockford's immediate left - RATATATATATATA!

Then came the repetitive sounds of AK-47's - POP! POP! POP! POP! POP! - projectiles thrown out of the muzzle one after the other.

Horror-struck Rockford in milliseconds, spotting three marines hit from direct frontal fire, who lay dying or dead on his right. Worse came, to his disgust, catching the sight of close to a dozen men near death or killed. Terror struck him like a lightning bolt - in shock. The slaughtered and doomed lie all around him.

And lying in front of him lay Hanover. His uniform ripped to pieces from bullets slamming into his body simultaneously, with his left arm and foot blown to pieces.

All the while, 1st Squad returned fire toward enemy machine gunners. VC machine guns rapidly fired bullets, followed by green tracers searching to snatch the life out of a young marine. Enemy fire seemed to come from all directions.

Rockford returned fire, finding himself pinned down, covered by fallen trees.

The wounded moved about in the open, pushing themselves backward toward cover. All the while, machine gunners picked off wounded marines one after the other, killing all of them, except one. In all the confusion, Rockford, in shock, spotted the last gravely wounded marine straining to crawl for cover - Taxi.

Sims exerted every once of energy within himself to crawl toward cover, screaming in agony. His right arm ripped up, along with many bullet wounds from machine guns throughout his torso and limbs. His friends from cover spotted Taxi pulling himself on his stomach with his left arm and pushing with his legs toward three or four other marines hunkered down behind a compacted mound of dirt with jungle debris all about. Taxi exemplified a man of phenomenal strength. He exhibited exceptional athleticism in high school, and unlimited endurance ran through his veins. Since living a Christian life, though short-lived, he presented himself as a changed man. His heightened desire to push forward and succeed in life reached the greatest inclination to climb to the highest point presented to him in life, and everyone in camp noticed the change. He crawled on the ground for cover, exhibiting all the desire he possessed in the world to push forward and succeed in life to its fullest.

Saturated in his own blood-soaked uniform, Taxi pulled himself toward the safety of the mound.

With just two feet from the knoll, Rockford hears a "Ah!" and catches a glimpse of Sims' legs hit from top to bottom with projectiles, hit in the upper right shoulder and near his lower right abdomen.

His journey comes to an undesired end two feet from cover.

All the while, Buchanan watched Sims through a crevice of a tree, cheering him all the way. "Go, Taxi! Go!"

Buchanan and Rockford caught sight of marines reaching out, including Dobbs, grabbing Sims' arms, pulling him over the mound.

Incredibly, Sims held on to life just a bit longer, despite his wounds.

Just as Dobbs and friends pulled Sims over the mound, Bravo Company heard gunfire from 2nd Platoon, 2nd and 3rd squads of Charlie Company outflanking the two Viet Cong machine gun teams.

Charlie Company disbursed the Viet Cong machine gunners far into the jungle, killing all the members of the VC who refused to surrender.

"Corpsman!" Dobbs yelled. He and his friends leaned Sims upward on the side of the mound.

The spiritual team ran to Sims as the gunfire ceased.

Buchanan dropped himself beside Sims, with Jackson falling to the left.

"Hold on, Taxi!" Jackson declared.

"Yes, John. Hang on. Hang on!" Buchanan said. The spiritual team fought back the emotion, for Sims' sake.

Buchanan holds the back of Sims neck holding his head up, holding his hand, knowing the magic of a corpsman's skills now will never save him, fights back his tears.

Knowing the end is near, Buchanan simply says, "It-It's OK, John. It-It's going to be - OK. OK Taxi."

Buchanan throws a quick glance toward a solemn Jackson, holding his other bloody hand.

By now Sims' friends surround him, emotional, in shock, and saddened.

Sims sustains enough energy to utter, "Home."

Buchanan says, "Yes, John. You're going home. You'll be home soon." He takes a quick glance at all surrounding Taxi, emotions running high. Buchanan comforts Sims. "You'll be home soon. No more pain. No more sorrow. You'll be home soon. With Jesus."

"Pray sir." muttered Sims, fraught to talk, glaring straight at Buchanan. Taxi attempted to smile with all the energy left in his tank, which neared empty.

Buchanan, befuddled, ganders all about from one marine to the next, begging for a miracle, an intervention bypassing Sims' stay. He then lifts a quick prayer.

Gazing back down toward Sims, Buchanan said, "Remember, John - the Beatitudes."

Buchanan stoops down closer on one knee, placing his left arm around Sims, starts quoting the Beatitudes. Buchanan haphazardly quotes but two of the Beatitudes when Sims, with every muscle of endurance left in his broken and torn body, tears his hand from Jackson's grip, lifting his left hand up to his chest, smiling widely.

Sims abruptly stares wide eyed, straight up into the air, taking in his last breath of this life.

Many of Sims' friends were convinced he uttered 'Jesus' as he looked up into the sky.

By now, no one can hold back their emotions. As Taxi's friends gathered around him, they just witnessed their friend endure an incredible feat and who had lived a different way of life his last few months as a believer. A new man transformed living a new life following his conversion. The change had been evident. The studying and absorbing mentally the Bible each and every night, an excavation of sorts to dig deeper and deeper into the Scriptures to discover the truths of Jesus' morals and to live those truths daily. He certainly lived the demeanor of Jesus over the past 150 days of life. Sims died on September 28, 1969, in the presence of his friends who loved him. He now was in the loving arms of his Lord.

The passing of Sims is not the end of the day for the spiritual team.

Ten minutes passed when three marines came running up to Rockford from Alpha Company talking a mile a minute, inaudible to Rockford.

"Captain! Captain!" yelled a corporal, huffing and puffing, struggling to catch his breath from running through the bush.

"Slow down, corporal. Slow down." Rockford insisted.

The corporal again rattled off word after word a hundred miles an hour, undetectable to Rockford.

"Yes, marine. Catch your breath. Now what is it?"

After catching his breath, he audibly said, "Alpha Company was h-hit h-hard. Casualties. Casualties all over the place. Men - wounded, asking for the Padre."

The spiritual team eavesdropped, overhearing the corporal's information delivered.

Before Rockford uttered a word, Buchanan asked, "Can we go, Captain?"

Rockford turns measuredly toward the chaplain. "Of course, Robert." He gawks down toward the ground.

"It's not your fault, Thomas." said Buchanan softly, out of earshot of others.

Buchanan pats Rockford's shoulder. "Did ya *hear* me? I *said* it wasn't your fault."

Rockford nods.

"I'll come visit ya in camp."

Rockford again nods, half smiling.

The spiritual team heads toward Company A with the messengers.

All along, Buchanan's utmost desire for the moment is to collapse and weep, but moved by the Spirit, thinks twice. He bellows out to Jackson and the messengers from Company A, "Hold it a minute!" Realizing Bravo Company had endured a heavy blow, turned a 180 and returned to Taxi.

Sims, whose friends had not left his side, laid motionless, lifeless.

As he marched himself up to Sims' corpse, the deepest sorrow built within, heartbroken from an unexpected loss of a fellow Christian brother Buchanan loved. He stooped down onto one knee. "I'm sorry John. I wanted to enjoy the taxi ride in Los Angeles. I'm sorry."

Taxi's friends fell into a inundated state of complete shock.

Buchanan spoke one last prayer over Sims, promising the men a visit in camp tonight. Turning, he asked the corporal to lead the spiritual team to Alpha Company.

When the party arrived, the spiritual team discovered the corporal hadn't imagined things.

The scene mirrored the familiar aftermath of a battle in Vietnam, the very sight no one wished for, even for the most hated of enemies.

The marines placed the KIAs in ugly black body bags, ready to pickup from Huey helicopters, yet to arrive at the battle sight. Body bags full of what once lived a man full of energy and life. The many wounded located to the right of the body bags lined up ready for pickup in the tall grass.

The crews of the Huey helicopters, MEDVAC type choppers armed with two M-60 machine guns, ever so eager to pick up the KIAs and transport the brave fallen patriots back to a safer spot to begin their trip back home for proper burial. Alpha Company was pleased to see the helicopters were not the unarmed "Dust Off" choppers.

Frost, holding his emotion back, stepped up to the spiritual team, explaining what happened. "They hit us with just maybe five minutes left of darkness. The attack truly came unexpected. It took us by complete surprise, Padre." Turning to Jackson, he said, "Sure wish we had you, Sergeant. Served with you in the past. Ya sure have proven to be a warrior in battles past."

Puzzled, Buchanan glances toward Jackson, pondering once again of his hidden past of his devoted enlisted friend.

"The morning bared out a showing of proven warriors today, though. And one of them asked for y'all." Frost said. He directed the spiritual team to a wounded marine, frantically asking for the Padre and his assistant.

When Buchanan made his way to the feet of the wounded marine, Frost said, glancing down toward the marine, "In fact, he insisted, no - he demanded to see the chaplain and you as well, Sergeant."

"You're here. Y-You're h-h-here!" said the wounded marine, exhilarated by the sight of the spiritual team in front of him, lying in pain and agony.

"Ohhhhh, thank God. T-Thank you God. You're here! Ahhhhh! I-It hurts! " yelled the wounded marine, attempting to lift himself up to greet the chaplain and his assistant.

Two corpsmen rush to the marine to calm his nerves.

The spiritual team gave the wounded marine a thorough look over, discovering the marine is much more seriously wounded as first noted.

Jackson leans down for a closer look, intrigued by the identity of the marine, covered with dirt and a layer of black soot from head to toe. Buchanan follows suit by kneeling down on one knee beside the wounded marine.

Wide-eyed and bowled over, Buchanan, in shock, says, "Corporal Lawrence Patrick Jansen."

"Y-Yes, sir. We-We made amends, sir." Jansen said.

"You - what, son?" asked a perplexed Buchanan.

In seconds flat, Buchanan remembered Jansen and Private John Thomas McElwaney's cowardice moment in the bush, February 7, 1969. Jurgensen, furious the two marines fell asleep on watch, had to be held by many marines from killing the two young marines. Days after the event, Buchanan convinced himself Jurgensen would have beaten the Hades out of them for falling asleep on guard duty, but not killing them. At least he hoped so. But in weeks to come, Buchanan reassessed his conclusion Jurgensen has been anything but an onlooker to marines falling asleep. With incidences of marines falling asleep on watch in the weeks after and the repercussions of marines risking the lives within camp, Buchanan thought differently. A marine falling asleep risked the lives of the entire camp when one failed to stay awake. The retort of marines resulting from a neglectful knucklehead guard convinced Buchanan Jurgensen would indeed have killed Jansen and McElwaney for the deaths triggered from the incompetency on their part on February 7, 1969.

Jansen said, "Made up for our mistakes."

Buchanan and his friends are perplexed by Jansen's comment. For the sake of preventing Jansen from over hearing, Frost motioned for Buchanan to step away from Jansen, still in mild shock from the battle.

Jackson provided Jansen a presence of a friend, to console the man suffering a thorough mental shake up from the battle just ensued.

Frost, followed by Buchanan, stepped far enough away out of earshot of Jansen. "Padre, Jansen and McElwaney fought like they were let out of some sort of time warp from Sparta or something."

Jackson stepped up to the left of Buchanan, curious to hear Frost, along with additional sergeants, including Thomas Childs of Alpha Company and a Sergeant Dennison.

The spiritual team's ears perked up as Frost informed the team of Jansen and McElwaney. "It's like this, sir. We're ambushed with three contingents of Viet Cong. One to our left, one to our right, and one smack dab in front of us."

Sergeant Dennison said, "Our front and right held steady, and actually pushed the VC back, even outflanking Charlie on their left."

A confident Sergeant Childs added, "We were outnumbered at least 2 to 1, maybe even 3 to 1. Yet, we still had the upper hand on the right and the front."

The spiritual team, listening to every word spoken with intensity, became concerned with Jansen's overall wellbeing.

Childs would add to his account of the battle. "But our left, the Sergeant in command, only God knows, gave a command to withdraw a couple of minutes into the firefight."

Frost interjected, "I yelled and directed from the center. Maybe, we figured, he heard me yell an order to withdraw or back down. We don't know. What we know is it was chaotic on our left - everything was in disarray."

With a short pause, Frost conferred, "The left collapsed with great momentum, with the men very confused, Padre."

Dennison said, "If the left had collapsed entirely, only God knows what would've happened to us."

"Yep. Most, possibly all of us, could have perished, chaplain." interjected Childs.

Frost chimed in with a tone of assurance. "1st Platoon, 1st Squad pivoted toward the left to help the 2nd Squad." Sergeant Dennison had an eyewitness account of what occurred next and said, "The VC in front and right of us must not have know what was going on our left or they would've put up more of a fight."

"Question is - how'd the left hold its own?" asked Jackson with intrigue. "What happened next?"

Frost answered Jackson. "Well, Sergeant. After 1st Platoon pivoted, they witnessed, along with myself and others, Jansen and McElwaney save the left flank and the entire company."

The sergeants and Frost shook their heads, fervently affirming everything said held the truth, while the spiritual team stood dumbfounded, awestruck by the news.

Childs attested further and said, "It's true, sir. Wish you could've seen the fight, Jackson." Frost and Dennison shook their heads even more emphatically.

Marines in Vietnam rarely shed kudos on men if tabbed a coward. Describing a marine in Vietnam as ostracized proved to be a yellow-bellied coward, or a bystander is putting it mildly.

Sergeant Childs continued, "Sir. Jackson. True or not, there seemed to be hundreds of VC running toward the 2nd Squad. Once reached, Charlie laid into the 2nd something awful. There was some harsh hand to hand combat something fierce that unfolded...." Sergeant Dennison interrupted himself, sighing. "In the middle of all the chaos fought Jansen and McElwaney. They were grand. Breathtaking." Lifting his hand ardently, Dennison stood in front of the spiritual team, puzzled with disbelief.

"Listen to this." Frost said, "They fought as if they were pushing the Devil's legions back to hell, as drove after drove of Charlie came down on the innocent and good."

"How many did they fight off? Fight back?" Jackson asked.

Childs admitted, "Don't know, Sergeant. But, we know one thing? The dead laid about. Many, many Charlie."

Frost and the sergeants described Jansen and McElwaney fighting the Viet Cong. The Michiganders lifted the VC above their shoulders, slamming them on fallen trees. The Michigan friends stabbed one VC after the other, coming straight at them with knives. The pair flipped the enemy left and right from Karate training received from the Marine Corps. Eye witnesses swore the pair grabbed clubs from the ground double wielding the clubs beating the VC to unconsciousness. The Michiganders used any means necessary to avert the VC from over running the left, outflanking the company. By the end of the succinct battle, the once cowardly marines laid upon the ground covered from head to toe in dirt, debris, and blood, unrecognizable and thought to be dead.

In fact, marines inspected Jansen in the fighting's aftermath, thought of him to be dead, but regained consciousness from exhaustion yelling out from pain. Company corpsmen rushed to Jansen's side, assisting and tending to his wounds. The shocked corpsmen examined the condition of Jansen, bewildered beyond words how a human being could survive such an ordeal as he had gone through.

The immeasurable endurance of a human being in Vietnam baffled Buchanan. By the end of his tour, nothing surprised him more than how durable and resilient body tissue, bone structure, and tendons of a human being could withstand man made weapons and survive a brutal beat down. Only God could know how a human being could survive such a beating upon flesh and bone.

Unfortunately, McElwaney's luck in life had run out. Corpsmen lost count of wounds on what was left of him. Of the vast number of wounds dispersed upon his body, the corpsmen simply cleaned him up a bit and placed him along with the other deceased. Shortly thereafter, marines placed the Michigander's remains inside the grisly body bag to transfer his remains back to the 'Great Lakes State'.

Jansen laid on the ground in great shock, still unaware of McElwaney's demise. Frost explained to Jansen as best he could and with the utmost caution, his friend caught many fatal projectiles taking the life of his beloved friend. And even after coming to his senses, Jansen longed to know his friend's condition remained with the living. Frost reckoned he fell into a condition of early denial. Jansen looked forward with great pleasure picnicking with his family at his favorite park with McElwaney and his family along the water coast of Lake Michigan.

The spiritual team stood stoic, stupefied, hearing the account of the Michiganders' heroism.

Buchanan thought, 'How life changes within minutes.' Grinning, he stepped toward Jansen, kneeling on one knee, placing his hand on his shoulder.

"Chaplain, Padre." said Jansen.

"I'm here son."

An exhausted Jansen smiles up toward his chaplain. Buchanan saw nothing but a beaten, energy drained marine.

"Sir. Larry's looking forward to-to seeing Michigan beat your Buckeyes this year." Jansen said, struggling to talk.

"They just might, Corporal Jansen." Buchanan replied. "Say nothing else, son. Save your energy."

Impressed with the strength Jansen showed forth, Buchanan felt an overwhelming inner sense of pride for Jansen's bravery given on this day.

In just a matter of seven months since February 7, 1969, Jurgensen nearly killed him that day. Today, Buchanan set his eyes on a young man, just in his early twenties, a hero and a proven marine who faced and fought the enemy as if he alone had been all between his fellow Americans and demons unswerving to the Devil himself.

The Hueys indeed arrived, as the marines, emotional and fuming mad at the loss of many friends, laid the remains into the helicopters as reverent and temperate as possible.

Frost put in applications for a silver star for Jansen and McElwaney, posthumously of course, for their actions on September 28, 1969, a day of death and fierce combat. In no time at all, the Navy awarded the Michiganders the prestigious awards for their actions.

When the day arrived for Jansen with the realization that death took his friend away from him, devastation set in, pushing him into a deep depression. Buchanan visited him in the Da Nang hospital on his way home ten days later.

Buchanan's last days were short, but not kind as he witnessed an abundance of death and war. His last days haunted him for the rest of his life, poignant beyond words.

The fact Sims took Jesus in his heart, experiencing genuine joy for the first time in his life followed by his unfortunate demise in Vietnam, haunted Buchanan for the rest of his life, never to be forgotten. The love Buchanan held for the young man is beyond measure. Taxi was special. He led Sims to Jesus. The Lord gave skills and talents of painting and drawing upon Sims, an ability Buchanan longed to possess within himself, but knowing full well he would never gain the skill. Looking forward to Sims painting him a picture of the Ohio River now is forever gone. He is now forever gone. Never will his skillful hands paint the Ohio river for Buchanan. War snatched him away, squelching the life out of him. But Sims professed Jesus as Savior. And Buchanan clung to faith, confidence in the future for believers. A faith convincing those who believe in Jesus will gather together in Heaven one day. The day of Buchanan's passing, Sims will welcome Buchanan home, waiting for him in Paradise with a painting of the Ohio River.

Lieutenant Colonel Lucas' cats welcomed Buchanan with consecutive mornings, consoling him. The visits in the office were most anticipated and expected from Lucas. He visited with Buchanan, distracting his mind from the horrible day of losing Sims.

The scars of war this day were heavy laden upon Buchanan's heart, never to be forgotten. This day set a permanent remembrance, holding Sims in his arms as he inhaled his last breath, a memory for many a Navy chaplain in Vietnam.

Ohio, Here We Come

October 1, 1969

Ecclesiastes 9:12 For man does not know his time. Like fish which are taken in an evil net, and like birds which are caught in a snare, so the sons of men are snared at an evil time, when it suddenly falls upon them.

Buchanan faced six more days in Vietnam. His stay as a short timer neared the end of a year, ministering to marines in the most adverse settings possible.

"Whoo hoo!" Buchanan yelled as he got up this morning! He knew he had but just six days left in his tour.

Buchanan woke up this day thrilled to no end. His departure for home was just around the corner. Burns played Dvorak's *Goin' Home* several nights ago, and the lyrics sunk into the hearts of all the marines and sailors in camp. The words spoke loud and clear in the music: mothers, fathers, and dear friends gather, waiting patiently for their fathers, sons, and brothers to soon come home.

Following a soothing shower and shave, he prepared himself for a one day mining sweep of Route QL-1S and An Hoa road, securing roads for maintenance and upgrading transportation routes.

Sitting at his desk, Buchanan read his Bible, equipping himself with a mental state to step out into the bush just one last time. Anticipation heightened as the moment neared, an unbearable endurance upon his nerves.

The patrol combined Rockford's Bravo Company to accompany Skawinski's combat engineering team. B Company, however, faced a delay because of a logistical problem.

While waiting for the patrol's departure, Buchanan thought of the progress, or lack of, winning the war.

Frustrations stemmed from the war reached a boiling point for Buchanan. He simply grew sick of a conflict of attrition. Reading recent papers Dorothy and his brothers sent him indicated the war is winding down to the point for the United States throwing in the towel and giving up winning the war. A war Buchanan still maintained is winnable, regardless of what politicians and protesters in the streets might have to say. The strategy and tactics necessary to win would now never be implemented due to politics and the new left of the political spectrum. The new left in Buchanan's estimation simply impeded anything worth achieving, politically or socially.

Since the unfortunate day of losing Sims, the past few days brought few casualties and fierce fights.

Buchanan's loyal enlisted friend Skawinski entered the latter stages of a short timer himself, with only 17 days left in his tour. Ecstatic, with less of a month to go, he will find himself back in the United States, at home in Ohio on the family farm.

Finished with his Bible reading and devotion, Buchanan received a knock on the door at 0600 hours in the morning. "Yes, who goes there?" Buchanan inquired.

Buchanan heard a familiar voice say, "Hahaha! Ya say it every time."

"What? I know that laugh anywhere. Ski, it's you." Buchanan said as he stands to welcome Skawinski.

"Of course it's me, sir. Who else could it be?" replied Skawinski, grinning as he enters the hootch. He briskly steps smack dab in front of Buchanan's desk. "Whoo hoo Sir! Your last patrol with us."

Buchanan leans back into his seat, grinning. He rubs it in, saying, "*Yeah.*"

Skawinski noted from the outset a fidgety and nervous Buchanan, fiddling around with papers on his desk. He opened a drawer or two as if looking for something, leafing through his calendar book nervously. Skawinski asked, "Well, are ya excited, sir?"

"Are you kidding me, Ski?" Buchanan exalted. "I, well - yes, I am. Asking me if I'm excited is like asking the hundred million dollar lottery winner if he's happy. Of course I'm excited - thrilled!"

"Good, sir. Good." said Skawinski, grinning. "What are ya so nervous about? This is your last one. Your last patrol - ever!"

"I *know*."

Sensing Buchanan's gloomy mood, Skawinski says, "Sir, there's nothing ya could've done for Taxi. I know it's hard to accept. But this is not my first tour, and I can tell ya - war is not a kind thing. Ya know that yourself now. War takes away things you love. Things you cherish. Snatches friends and loved one's away in a split second."

Buchanan stared intently, listening meticulously at every word Skawinski spoke forth.

Buchanan admits, "It's amazing to me, here in Vietnam, I can count them many times over on my fingers, the instances I had been counseled and given a word of encouragement from others when I needed it the most."

"You're only human, sir."

"*Yeah*. But I'm the one who's a counselor, the chaplain. I'm designated as a source of spiritual and physical support."

Skawinski ponders the results of war on his chaplain. He says sympathetically, "War effects everybody, sir. Even the best and loving people of this world, and that, well - includes you too, sir."

Buchanan shrugs. "Well, all we can do is support one another when we get back home, help each other get through the rest of our years in this life. It'll hurt, but we'll make do. 'Cause we're not getting support from our people in the country, that's for sure."

"Amen to that, sir."

"Ten more days, Sergeant. Ten more days, and I'll be in California. Seven more days, out of Vietnam. Yep. My first and last tour - over and done with." Buchanan said, grinning. "And you've 16 more - short timer."

"Whew! It sure was hard, sir. But I made it." said Skawinski. "You're staying in, right, sir?"

Buchanan paused. "The Navy? If they let me. If not, I'm aligned to enter the reserve program."

"Good. The Navy needs to keep you, even if it's a reserve status." Skawinski added. "There's a reserve center all over Ohio. Columbus. Cincinnati. Portsmouth. Cleveland."

Buchanan agreed. "*Yeah*. And plenty of ministering opportunities in the state."

Skawinski paused, reflecting on what might come in Ohio for both him and Buchanan.

"Sir, remember, you and your family must visit Preble County. The farm, meet my parents. Introduce ya to my dogs."

Buchanan sighs. "I can't wait. Can't wait to see everything."

"Ya promised months ago you would. I'm gonna hold ya to that promise, sir." Skawinski said with eagerness.

"I promised, Ski. And I'm planning on it."

Skawinski, for the umpteenth time, described his breathtaking, beautiful farm. Buchanan listened patiently. Proud of the family homestead, Skawinski paints a mental picture for Buchanan the shudders resembling a Midwestern farm out of a Norman Rockwell painting. The marine sergeant depicted the red barn picture perfect, displaying a faultless chipped cowshed to every visitor laying their eyes upon the barn. His father was undeniably proud of the perfect set of rows of crops laying out various sorts of vegetables. Again Buchanan heard the fun Skawinski experienced growing up rearing the dozens of animals ranging far and wide, including horses, chickens, goats, and pigs. The most lucrative of the farm, of course, comprised the hundreds of dairy cows, employing more than a dozen employees, working diligently every day the daily chores of an influential dairy farm such as the Skawinski's.

"Besides, I can then call ya Robert, without constraints." stressed Skawinski, causing Buchanan to chuckle.

"The truth is, it'll always be Chaplain Buchanan, sir."

Buchanan grins.

"Ohio, here we come!" Skawinski declared.

For a half hour, the Ohioans conversed, longing for time to linger until the day they step onto a plane to lift them out of Vietnam toward the Buckeye state. Fellowship of the men centered in on Ohio State football, the state of Ohio, national politics and religious issues, including Vatican II. The Catholic council convened in the early 1960s, inspiring the mutual Christian friends from Ohio to believe Vatican II is an essential step in laying a foundation to encourage cooperation between two flocks of believers, encouraging a positive spirit amongst Protestants and Catholics alike.

"Ya know, sir. It's true. I never thought in my life I would learn anything good from a Baptist, or any other non-liturgical to guide me in a direction of being a better believer in Christ."

Buchanan nods, smiling. "Well, as I've said many times over, there are believers in all Christian denominations."

Skawinski said. "The military exposed me to many a thing, sir. But one thing's for sure - I've met so many people - truly believers in Christ, many Baptist like yourself. I knew non-liturgicals in school, but surrounded all my life by nothing but Lutherans outside school. My vision wound up narrow, but I guess that came from Mom and Dad." He paused, thinking of his new perspective on religion. "I've learned so much about the other denominations meeting new people."

Grinning, Buchanan nods knowing Skawinski's words rang true.

Skawinski jokes, "When I informed Mom you graduated from the Lutheran seminary in Columbus, she said in a letter you were good for something. I won't tell ya what she said you were worth."

The men chuckle at the thought.

Buchanan glanced at his watch, noticing the time, 0720 hours. Neither the marine nor sailor tolerated a habit of being late for anything. And with the patrol to depart at 0800 hours, the pair enjoyed some eats in the chow hall, secure their gear, and make their way to the main entrance for muster.

Components of the patrol - Jackson, Bravo Company, as well as Skawinski's engineering team gathered for muster.

At 0800 hours, Rockford ordered to saddle up. The patrol finally departed Camp Love for Buchanan's last trip into the bush with the most cherished company he got to know.

Buchanan insisted on a group picture to remember the moment in time, a reminder of the bond which pushed them ahead, protecting and supporting one another. He insisted on taking an additional slide picture of him and Jackson, he and Skawinski, and a final slide picture of three men who had become so bonded in the past year. Skawinski and Jackson posed with Buchanan as if he had won the Medal of Honor. The men were so proud to have served with him. They would cherish the photos in the years to come.

Skawinski had forgotten to deliver in the mail room a letter to his mother. He asked Buchanan to step quickly to his hootch, retrieve the letter, and drop it in the mailroom. Buchanan champed at the bit to retrieve his fellow Ohioan's letter addressed to the Buckeye state, and drop it in the mailbox. He then quickly stepped back to the patrol, who had just departed Camp Love.

The patrol set out three miles north of An Ngai Tay. Travel time reached an hour to the approximate seven and a half miles to the sectors to patrol because of traveling in familiar territory.

Leaving his comfort zone with a perimeter and guards unnerved Buchanan something awful. Stepping into the bush to face the Devil's legions, the Viet Cong, for his last patrol, Buchanan will experience the chilling and terrifying march into a dense, dangerous jungle for the last time.

Now, finally, at the end of his tour, countless thoughts and reflections subjugated Buchanan's mind. One thought in the forefront of his mind stood out as he stepped along with the patrol. His thought begged for an answer - why all the attention in the bush, placing him in the middle of patrols? His position within the patrol to protect and secure his safety had gnawed at him since his very first patrol in October 1968. His life had been saved a time or two by marines throwing themselves as a barrier between him and bullets to take his life. Regardless, he understood. His status given, after all, was the chaplain.

Once Bravo Company arrived north of An Ngai Tay, the sweep begun. The sweep amounted between two to three square miles of terrain north of An Ngai Tay. The Viet Cong increased nocturnal activity in the area to protect Communist supply lines and permeating pathways deeper into South Vietnam. The patrol penetrated three quarters of the three square miles, when combat engineers of Skawinski's team halted the patrol, discovering numerous booby traps. His team set out to disarm the booby traps, which amounted to multiple cartridge traps, one grenade-in-a-can, and one bamboo whip, a menacing contraption Buchanan scorned with revulsion.

By now, Buchanan, in his 18 months' tour, detected booby traps served as a good indicator the enemy is nearer than he desired, but not necessarily in earshot of marines or even in a range of Viet Cong or NVA gunfire. But the danger of the enemy 25 feet away threatening an attack after a booby trap had been tripped off terrified Buchanan.

Skawinski's team disarmed close to a dozen booby traps set by the VC three square miles into the zone to sweep.

The spiritual team, in the middle of the patrol, waited patiently as Skawinski applied his skills as a combat engineer.

Buchanan attentively kept an eye on Skawinski, fascinated with the cool hand of the young marine, and the calm and expertise of his fellow combat engineers defusing the menacing booby traps. Buchanan, envious of the skills displayed, thought of his own skills in his life. His carpentry work passed the grade well, his trouble shooting with automobiles considered average, his art work nothing but amateur, and his knowledge of machinery mediocre. None satisfactory to make a living wage. In the past fifteen years of Buchanan's life, a saturation of book learning filled the days and hours. He made his living with brain power.

With pride, Buchanan laid his eyes on the combat engineers performing their duties, disarming the work of the Devil.

Buchanan whispers to Jackson, "Sure is good at what he does, isn't he?"

"Sure is, Padre. *Sure* is."

With eyeballs glued on Skawinski, the spiritual team admired the combat engineer's work with a fellow marine working on a booby trap to Skawinski's left. Once the booby trap was secured, he moved toward a marine just two weeks into his tour on their right in front of them, to lend a hand to the green marine.

Buchanan, in a soft voice, says, "I've never had the knack to -"

'BANG - KaBOOM!'

'KaBOOM!' came an immediate second explosion in rapid sequence.

The patrol instinctively hit the deck face down. The spiritual team flew into a naturally eroded hole in the front of them. As the aftermath of the blast ceded, Buchanan took a quick peek at the results of the explosions.

Suddenly, two Viet Cong partially exposed themselves on Buchanan's right, firing their AK-47's.

Hunched down behind a small embankment, Buchanan caught in a split second a glimpse of Skawinski in the corner of his eye, running toward him. Preoccupied, Jackson fired his M-16 toward an M73 machine gun, M219 and a FM 24/29 light machine gun in front of him, all the while screaming "STAY DOWN PADRE!"

'POP! POP! POP! POP! POP!'

Just as Skawinski fell on top of Buchanan's faced down torso, projectiles thrust deep into Skawinski's body, shielding Buchanan from the deadly bullets. All taking place in a matter of seconds.

"Ahhhhhhh!" shrieked Skawinski on top of Buchanan.

Jackson swiftly swung his M-16 toward the VC, firing his weapon, ripping to pieces the two VC on their right flank.

Skawinski yelled, "My God, those boys are out in the open!" He spotted a severely wounded combat engineer. Darting out from behind the small embankment toward the marine, Skawinski exposed himself to even more enemy gunfire.

Several marines in the very front of the patrol had ran for cover, along with one combat engineer who survived the initial explosions due to examining a third booby trap and laying on the ground, while marines fired toward the muzzle blasts of AK-47's spotted in the darkness of jungle.

Many marines ran for cover, struck with the excruciating pain of penetrating bullets tearing into flesh and bone. The young marines fell to the ground dying and wounded.

RATATATATATATATA! The nagging machine gun fire came rampant.

As Buchanan takes a gander of what lay in front of him, he searches for his fellow Ohioan.

On his right, he laid his eyes on Skawinski, assisting a fellow wounded marine along the ravine of the discovered booby traps.

'KaBoom!' a third frightening explosion, triggered by a fleeing marine searching for a better secured space of cover from enemy fire.

The sequence of events all occurred in a matter of seconds. All the while, Buchanan hadn't seen hide nor hair of Skawinski following the third explosion.

Buchanan prayed the most sincere request to God in all his life, "Lord, please! Let not the hand of the Devil lay upon Skawinski this day! I pray Death snap up the enemy, not Adolphus."

Buchanan, in all the chaos of the combat, heard the commanding voice of Rockford barking out orders to Bravo Company. The rattling off of weapons, machine guns, AK-47's, M-16's and .45 calibers fired simultaneously, and the horrible screams of the wounded is a fact of combat forever stored in Buchanan's memory banks. The din of combat reverberated echoes for the Americans, a numbing effect disorienting the marines momentarily. The physical stress of combat posed an intimidating and threatening reality, daring the menace of death face to face to take those who dare to mess with fate.

"Chaplain! C-Chaplain!" came a cry within the stridency of clamor.

POP! POP! POP! POP! POP!

"Kiehl, two o'clock! NAIL HIM!" yelled Rockford. "Vet! Shaw! Watch your right! Drop 'em! Drop 'em!"

Jackson screamed into Buchanan's ear - "It's letting up a little, sir! Hold tight! VC getting hit now!"

PING! POP! POP! POP! PING! POP! PING! came more cracks of AK-47's, M-16's and ricochets of projectiles.

"Ahhhhhhh! Mom!" yelled a wounded marine.

"C-Chaplain! Pleeeeeeeease! Oh G-G-God!" came another shriek from yet another marine.

"Corpsmen!" came another yell from yet another wounded marine.

POP! POP! POP! POP!

All the horrific reverberations, resonances, crash and clatter of war, all thrown together in a mesh of the most appalling and atrocious clamor, beyond words to describe. Experiences no civilian would ever understand.

An object thrown out of the bush reflecting a baseball, a grenade, came very near Buchanan, as Jackson threw himself on top of him. Luckily, the fragments were thrown upward in an opposite direction as the grenade landed on an elevated level of higher ground.

In all the clatter, Buchanan seemed to hear one recognizable voice, all too familiar in the rattle and clash of the fighting.

He heard the voice once again - "Chap-! Q-Quick! Ch-Chaplain!"

At this point in the battle, 2nd Squad outflanked the Viet Cong on the left flank, who were killed or on the run.

With fewer weapons fired, a sporadic gunfire made it possible for Buchanan to perceive the voice more clearly. He scanned the terrain in front of him, and no Skawinski in sight.

"Ch-Chaplain! HELP-HELP!" came another call from the familiar voice.

Buchanan verbally prayed, "Please Lord, let it not be so! Please, Lord!"

One last call will be enough for him to know exactly who screamed, a yell calling out his name - "Ro-Robert!!!"

With that, there is no doubt the voice spoken belonged to Adolphus Skawinski. Buchanan darted out of the natural gnarled hole, sprinting toward the direction of the marine.

"Chaplain, GET DOWN!" Jackson screamed, as sparse gunfire from the jungle continued from the Viet Cong toward the Americans.

Buchanan never ran so fast in his life to reach Skawinski. Jackson followed suit, firing his weapon toward the enemy, which in the five seconds spent running toward Skawinski, the few Viet Cong left firing their weapons were slain by Bravo Company.

Buchanan, rushing to Skawinski, froze to a screeching halt, collapsing on his knees. He set his eyes on what was left of his enlisted friend.

"Corpsmen!" Buchanan shrieked, fighting back his emotions.

Jackson runs behind Buchanan, joining him on the edge of the gully Skawinski is lying in, bumping into Buchanan, and having to catch him from being knocked down.

The spiritual team finally heard a jungle silent of unwanted blasts. Weapons ceased throwing projectiles from barreled cylinders with the sole intent of taking another life. The dismay of combat ended.

Caught catching flies, the spiritual team found themselves in shock, awed by the sight in front of them in the gully. What lied in front of them resembled a figure out of a horror film - a blackened human being, almost unrecognizable, from power burns and residue resulting from the booby traps and projectiles. The sight is beyond words, a marine unrecognizable of the young man Buchanan conversed with just hours ago. Lying on his back on the side of the small gully, Skawinski elevated himself with all the energy he could muster, stretching his hands toward Buchanan. Peppered from head to toe with projectiles from AK-47's and shrapnel from three booby traps exploding in front of him, Skawinski ended up blackened and bloodied from the sheer might of metal penetrating his frail human body. Miraculously, the young Ohioan exerted a smile from ear to ear when setting his eyes on Buchanan kneeling on the edge of the gully. Choking up blood, Skawinski fought with all his might to stay alive. He isn't ready to die, though he is mere moments away from being with Jesus for Eternity.

The gully foiled the Viet Cong from killing him when dashing toward the wounded marine, who lay dead from his wounds just a few feet away. The VC, blind from viewing Skawinski as he laid just under the upper edge of the gully, hid him as the VC fired their weapons just above him, just a few feet away from the Viet Cong.

The spiritual team slid down the opposite side of the gully, damp with water on the bottom from the vast amounts of rain Vietnam amasses every year.

When reaching the bottom lay Skawinski's feet. One foot looked as if shredded from shrapnel. Buchanan, on the right, took hold of Skawinski's arm and hand. Jackson held his left arm and hand, awe-struck at the energy exerted in his dear friend's last moments. Knowing his time drew near, the young Ohioan smiled with the last bit of strength available. He spoke with broken words, "I-I-I'm not going....to see m-my farm....a-again, am I?"

Tongue tied, Buchanan glances toward Jackson. Sad. Heartbroken.

The spiritual team, incapable of withholding tears, wept, knowing the end is near.

With the chaplain and assistant alongside Skawinski - Kiehl, Varnes, Rodriquez, Jurgensen, Rockford, Dobbs and others - joined the spiritual team surrounding their friend in his last moments. Skawinski, in great shock and time to end in this life, took one last look at all his friends, with all the remaining strength left in his tank, smiled as wide as he could.

Skawinski, staring at Buchanan, coughed up more blood, pleading, "Pr-Pray."

Shocked at the energy put forth from Skawinski, Buchanan recited the Lord's Prayer as Skawinski exhibited signs of passing quickly into the eternal side of life. With his last stages now set in motion, hallucinations caused him to shout out, "Buckeyes!" "Dog! Dogs!" "Mom!"

The shock of Skawinski's friends looking down upon their friend, glanced left and right toward one another, bewildered at the sight of what remained of their friend, left them in denial. Weeping profusely and uncontrollably, the sudden fact hit the entire group Skawinski is about to die, leaving a void in their Christian hearts.

Grappling with the intense emotion of the moment, Buchanan barely finished reciting the Lord's Prayer.

Buchanan then quoted the Beatitudes. He grasped the back of Skawinski's neck to hold his head up, placing his hand on his shoulder to help hold him up. Jackson held him on the other side, profusely weeping along with his fellow human beings.

As Buchanan neared the middle of the Beatitudes, Skawinski looks straight up in the air and calls out, "Uh! Uh! Uh!"

The men, now spellbound, fixed themselves on Skawinski in his last moments.

"Jesus! Y-Yes!" screamed Skawinski, smiling from ear to ear, panting and shaking. His companions now gazed at their friend inhale one breath after the other, slower and slower. Skawinski seemed to raise his hands toward the sky and once again screamed, "Jesus! King!" His friends, weeping, glared at him, noticing him breathing slower with more space between each exhale. He stretched his head as high as he could, smiling, pushing a last shrill gasp, followed by a slow, deliberate exhale.

The spiritual team, along with Varnes, lent a hand to lay Skawinski gently back onto the side of the gully to rest in peace.

Kneeling at Skawinski's side for time on end mourning the death of their friend, the group fell engrossed with sorrow over the loss of the most capable combat engineer they had ever known.

Skawinski's friends carefully carried his remains up the opposite bank of the gully, laying him gently on the ground to await a body bag.

As helicopters flew into the perimeter to retrieve the remains of the KIA's, including Skawinski, Buchanan's immediate thought is that somewhere in the deep bush of Vietnam, a chaplain in a combat post, along with an identification team, will identify his fellow Ohioan in a detested cooler Buchanan loathes, for an early trip home to Ohio.

The absence of sleep fell upon every member of Bravo Company, the spiritual team, and the combat engineers on the night of October 1, 1969. The next day's early dawn will discover a camp void of the marine vital for the success of the 7th Engineering Marine Battalion and a dear friend.

The incredible strength, spiritually and physically, shown by Skawinski as he perished, impressed his friends, a permanent lifelong memory of a powerful man. The embodiment of strength of a heart, mind, and soul pushing forward to achieve everything in God's Will for his life.

The devastating events encountered in Buchanan's last days in Vietnam - first Sims, and now Skawinski, his fellow Ohioan who will never again see Ohio - forever instilled a dependence upon God to cope with the desolate and piteous sights of young men dying a painful, shocking death.

Buchanan will never see his friend again in this life. It is always said - 'time heals'. But Buchanan never shed the memory of Skawinski's death from his mind, never recuperating from the tragedy of losing Adolphus Skawinski due to war. Just under three weeks in his last tour, on his way home to Ohio, but suddenly, out of the blue, death stole his life away. Buchanan could not and never accepted the fact. Regardless of his Baptist faith.

The Devil delivered a sucker punch below the belt on Buchanan. The Devil seized a man he treasured in life most admirably. Animosity, and yes, hostility festered within Buchanan, increasing a hundredfold toward the Evil One.

Ohio changed forever without Skawinski.

Ohio lost one of its own. One of its proudest citizens.

Skawinski's parents will never see him again.

Ohio will never again feel Skawinski set foot into his homeland.

Hugo and Albert, his dogs, will never experience the hands of their loving owner, Adolphus, groom and pet them again.

His property will never feel the footsteps of Skawinski working the family farm, milking a cow or harvesting crops ever again.

As in the words of Dvorak, Adolphus is not 'goin' home.'

The Buckeye State will never hear the reverberating echoes of Skawinski's voice bellow, "Ohio, here we come." ever again.

A Visit From Adkins

October 2, 1969

2 Corinthians 4:8-12 We are afflicted in every way, but not crushed; perplexed, but not driven to despair; 9 persecuted, but not forsaken; struck down, but not destroyed; 10 always carrying in the body the death of Jesus, so that the life of Jesus may also be manifested in our bodies. 11 For while we live we are always being given up to death for Jesus' sake, so that the life of Jesus may be manifested in our mortal flesh. 12 So death is at work in us, but life in you.

Thursday. A heavy laden day for the spiritual team - one devotional service, one Communion service, and visiting the men - a weekly routine on Thursdays. On many Thursdays, marines dropped by the chaplain's office for

The routine life in camp this Thursday morning lacked the exuberance and excitement of a man who now is gone forever – Skawinski. The enormous void felt throughout this day hit the camp as a sad state of affairs. The void, wide and irreplaceable, cast a dark shadow over the camp. A somber mood held the camp hostage. Scuttlebutt of Skawinski's death spread like wildfire, a sledgehammer blow knocking out the camp stone cold. The spiritual team hurt more, experiencing Skawinski's death more than any other casualty in Vietnam. The pair, for years after the war, consistently asked the question many people ask of God when losing a dear family member or friend: 'Why? Why, Lord?' The pain and anguish coping with the loss of Skawinski never faded away. The men, however, eventually asked God to forgive them for blaming Him for Adolphus' death.

Buchanan spent his last days visiting the men, and keeping Lucas and his cat's company.

The camp grieved, angry at losing their friend. Skawinski had gained a reputation in camp as the most skilled combat engineer they had ever known in the Marine Corps.

As a short timer with only five days to go, Lucas confined Buchanan mostly in Camp Love, traveling in the jeep to the bush with Jackson for Communion services restricting over nights. His pastoral role as chaplain now took center stage.

Lucas rationalized Buchanan accompanying patrols should have been restricted at least a week ago as a short timer, prior to Sims' death. But then again, Lucas pondered. He determined Buchanan's presence with Sims in his last moments reflected the movement of God in Sims' life of sorts. He mulled over the fact the men insisted Buchanan be with them in the field for tense and stressful situations, such as Sims and Skawinski. A duty Buchanan recollected years later as a great personal achievement, providing spiritual and emotional support in marines stressful and nerve-racking period of their lives.

Other than visiting the men, along with today's services and Sunday's services, Buchanan confined himself in his hootch mourning the death of his young friend.

Unexpectedly, Buchanan received a friend at his hootch door in the late morning - Lieutenant Commander John Adkins. The Seabee visited Buchanan the next two days, confining himself to his hootch. The friends reminisced for hours, mourning the death of their enlisted friend.

In the late afternoon, the two ate chow with Jackson, joining the two officers in Buchanan's hootch, before retiring for the rest of the afternoon in his own hootch.

The three joined for Communion service in the camp hall. Buchanan reached deep into his soul for the strength to lead the service, a most laborious task following the tragedy of Skawinski. For an entire year, Skawinski's presence in Communion services enlightened those attending the Buchanan led gatherings of Christ believers. Today, an eerie void felt by all deepened the pain of Skawinski's fate in the jungle.

Adkins and Buchanan returned to Buchanan's hootch following the Communion service. Once again, the men consoled one another, coping with the loss of Skawinski.

Following a period of mutual personal therapy, Adkins returned to his Seabee contingent in camp for the night. Of course, an emotional departure for Adkins from Buchanan's hootch resulted because of the loss of their close enlisted friend. The chaplain and the Seabee simply refused to accept reality. The pair simply yearned for the return of their friend - alive and well.

Buchanan sat alone, isolated.

Loneliness in the hootch this night swelled ten fold.

Distressed, Buchanan knew Skawinski never again will knock on the hootch door at 0230 hours in the morning, requesting Buchanan's presence in the wee hours of the night to cope with an immediate nightmare dream. To make himself feel better, he showered and shaved in the middle of the night.

Buchanan, his whole life, felt totally refreshed following a shower and shave, lifting his spirit when down and out. Though the physical cleansing served as a pick me up, witnessing the sickening death of Skawinski set permanent in the depths of Buchanan's heart.

Time runs rapidly in life, as time met the half hour at 2130 hours. The time set for music.

Burns selected for the night five short pieces by Johann Strauss II. The pieces were waltz's, the first heard in camp was Annen Polka, Op. 117, with the second piece entitled *Schatz Walzer* Op. 418, Treasure Waltz in English. The third, a familiar piece for lovers of music - Op. 314, *On the Beautiful Blue Danube*, while next to the last waltz, though less familiar to most, came an uplifting, joyful piece of music - *Wein, Weib und Gesang* - Wine, Women and Song in English Op. 333. The last waltz Burns saved for the end of the night - *Tritsch-Tratsch* (Chit-Chat) Polka, Op. 214, a piece of music written for a fast pace, with a temper of merriment, and a spirit of elevation.

Burns possessed a knack of selecting appropriate music for the right time and place for the men in times of depression and glum, as well as times of glee and contentment. The knack astonished Buchanan.

Perfect selections of each piece of music took center stage in camp. The music gently placed a hovering canopy of peace and calm in such a desperately needed time with the loss of Skawinski.

'On the Beautiful Danube' injected a sense of soothing emotions the men will remember for the rest of their lives. While men listened, the sense of calm hit hard as the first waltz's theme emerged with recognizable, yet tender intensifying triad motif played by cellos and horns in D major in the popular tonic, joined by a harp. At the end of each 3-note phrase, the famous Viennese waltz beat heightened, building to a warm and amiable mood.

The waltz' themes in 'On the Beautiful Danube' highlighted the evening, and the camp fell solemn and composed, at least temporarily.

Silence fell upon the camp as the last holding note of Tritsch-Tratsch came to a close, the last waltz heard in the camp.

If there had been a night the men craved for music to carry on into the wee hours of the morning until dawn, tonight was the night.

As temporary as an uplift the music granted the men, Buchanan found motivation from the music injecting a necessity for him to dive deep into the Scriptures and to read his nightly devotion. He skipped his nightly routine this night due to the depressed state he found himself in, but thought better of it.

His time with the Lord instilled inspiration, a time which the Lord spoke to Buchanan, consoling him in his time of mourning. His time spent infused a necessity for some shuteye.

Laying out fruit and scraps from the chow hall for Arthur and Churchill, Buchanan said, "Thanks guys for scaring the critters away for me."

In October 1968, Buchanan's boots hit the ground outside the perimeter of Camp Love. The farthest thought on his mind when arriving in the bush was lizards. One year ago, the last thing Buchanan desired to live with in his hootch were reptiles. Today, 2 October 1969, Buchanan would not take a million dollars for his two amphibian friends, as Buchanan has been ever so grateful the two of them added an extra layer of security in the wee hours of night, an added barrier between him and the insects and small snakes of rural Vietnam.

On one hand, the temptation for Buchanan to smuggle his two amphibian lizard friends out of Vietnam and back to California remained high. He knew the rules were to leave all indigenous creatures behind in Vietnam. The military pushed for the rule to be strictly adhered to, but he didn't care. The least he could do to show his appreciation for Arthur and Churchill is to continue to care for them. On the other hand, ripping them away from their home-grown, native habitat might be too much of a stress upon them. Besides, Dorothy would have a cow knowing lizards were running wild in the house, upsetting the Dachshunds, frightening the children. The extra layer of security the lizards provided him during his Vietnam tour had been all good and well, but his lizard friends wouldn't last a minute with Dorothy or his weenie dogs. The humor, however, seeing the expression on Dorothy's face of two lizards walking through the front door of the house is priceless for Buchanan.

Lizards or not, Buchanan dreaded falling asleep. The trepidation and fright of experiencing a nightmare of Skawinski's death tempted him to remain awake the whole night, to read western novels and military history books.

As Buchanan laid on his cot avoiding sleep, his exhaustion overwhelmed him and fell asleep, regardless. Within his first hour of sleep, Buchanan dreamed - none of war or Skawinski.

But as nighttime wore on, the dreams he dreaded being subjected to, Skawinski and the war, emerged in a succession of involuntarily stages of sleep displaying images and similes resulting in emotions and sensations of fear and anxiety due to his relationship with his young friend.

In his dream, Buchanan traveled to visit the Skawinski farm to meet Adolphus's parents in western Ohio. Upon his arrival, he discovered the farm belonged to his brother in southeastern Ohio, not western Ohio. The odd feature in the dream revealed that his brother's farm in the dream is the Skawinski farm. Buchanan kept saying, "Adolphus, this isn't your farm. It's my brother's." Skawinski replied, chuckling as he spoke, "No, sir. It's our farm. Ya know what, sir? I think you're a bit confused." Dorothy and his children were in and amongst the Skawinski family eating, sharing fellowship with one another. The kindred kinfolk interchange amongst families set a pleasant and nice mood. A second oddity in the dream emerged as his brother was absent from the festivities, nowhere in sight, nowhere to be found. None of his family were to be found, his sister-in-law, his nephews or nieces. A painful emptiness is felt in the sequences of the dream, causing a heightened anxiety as he envisioned his wife and kids enjoying the company of the Skawinski family. Suddenly at the end of the dream, the emptiness gave way to elation as his brother and his wife, and their children came speeding over the creek on a wooden bridge, the entrance onto the property of his brother's farm, joining in the family bliss.

Buchanan woke up quickly as his brother crossed the wooden bridge onto his family farm.

Glancing at his watch, he noticed an early time of 0430 hours in the morning.

Far from being a nightmare, the dream had set a melancholy mood. But yet, the images which crossed his mind were daunting. In the first place, the setting of the dream ended up his brother's farm in Meigs County, Ohio, far from the Skawinski home and Preble County. In the second place, the dream reflected the agonizing separation of Skawinski in this life and his family never seeing him again on their farm.

Waking up with a hollow gut, Buchanan is delivered yet another shot below the belt with his realization Adolphus Skawinski is now forever lost in this life.

Buchanan, forever haunted by the death of Skawinski, sat alone in his hootch. Suddenly, a voice spoke deep within himself.

The Spirit spoke to Buchanan. Psalms 9:9 came to mind - 'The LORD is a stronghold for the oppressed, a stronghold in times of trouble.'

Buchanan's isolation diminished significantly in his hootch. The promise in the Scriptures prompted the Lord's presence is forever with him, even in times of melancholy. The Lord's presence never leaves the faithful.

Raising up out of his cot, Buchanan stepped to his desk and flipped his desk lamp on, grasping his Bible on the desk and turned to Psalms 9:9, reading the verse.

He thought of yet another verse. Turning to Psalms 40:1-2, he read, "I waited patiently for the Lord; he inclined to me and heard my cry. He drew me up from the desolate pit, out of the miry bog, and set my feet upon a rock, making my steps secure."

Yet another passage thought relevant for his mental condition was Proverbs 3:5-6. He turned the pages to Proverbs. "Trust in the LORD with all your heart, and do not rely on your own insight. In all your ways acknowledge him, and he will make straight your paths."

Buchanan never claimed he had all the answers to life's questions. He knew, however, the source for answers to the many questions which arise in life can be found only in God's words. Many a marine came searching for answers for questions that materialized in their lives, and Buchanan, the chaplain, would guide them to find answers to their questions the best he could.

The shock of Skawinski's death threw a curve for everyone, a sudden event hardening hearts a hundred fold toward the Viet Cong. Buchanan, now in his own life, faced uncertainty and the need to find answers for Skawinski's death.

As a Baptist, he accepted Skawinski's death as an act of God's permission will. However, his firm conviction lay in the foundation from the words of Isaiah 65:20, 'No more shall there be in it an infant that lives but a few days, or an old man who does not fill out his days, for the child shall die a hundred years old...' One day sin will be removed forever. No more tears. No more pain. No more war.

His death served a purpose in the entire scheme of God's Will, whether he liked it or not. For now, however, Buchanan lived life in denial. In the decades ahead, he searched for a purpose of any sort, evidence for a logical purpose for Skawinski to enter Heaven at such a young age. The purpose undisclosed today, only to be revealed one day, maybe tomorrow, maybe years to come. Possibly not until the day Buchanan meets him in Heaven will he ever know. But as Proverbs 3:5-6 implies, human beings' answers to questions in this life are finite. Human beings will never understand why history runs its course.

Buchanan considered the Hebrew general Joshua, courageous and strong, entering the battlefield in the Old Testament. All the while, Joshua fell into an immersed dependence upon the Lord to swipe away fright and fear. Joshua knew in his heart the Lord entered battle alongside him, protecting him from harm's way. God's presence never left Joshua's side, walking alongside him, never dismayed.

Buchanan then thought of the fourth verse of Psalms 23, a comforting thought this night - 'Even though I walk through the valley of the shadow of death, I fear no evil; for thou art with me; thy rod and thy staff, they comfort me.'

Buchanan's heart led him to New Testament Scriptures. First was John 16:33 - 'I have said this to you, that in me you may have peace. In the world, you have tribulation; but be of good cheer, I have overcome the world.'

"Amen." Buchanan said.

Buchanan found comfort in this one verse in John. What a message spoken in the verse - Jesus wins in the end! War is tribulation, but Jesus' return will end all war someday and peace will reign forever.

Buchanan then remembered possibly the most important verses in Scripture, assuring that nothing can separate the faithful from Jesus. A promise for all believers Jesus wins in the end - Romans 8:38-39. He turned to Romans reading it aloud, "For I am sure that neither death, nor life, nor angels, nor principalities, nor things present, nor things to come, nor powers, nor height, nor depth, nor anything else in all creation, will be able to separate us from the love of God in

Christ Jesus our Lord." The fact Jesus is Savior the evil world denies. Unbelievers deny wholeheartedly and without question the joy in Jesus. The hope and dependence of unbelievers is in this world, in man, and in things of this world.

Buchanan mulled over the fact believers' hope is in things not seen and in powers beyond comprehension.

His reading of Romans 8 turned his thoughts to yet another verse - Psalms 32:10. He leafed over to Psalms, reading the lone verse, "Many are the pangs of the wicked; but steadfast love surrounds him who trusts in the Lord."

The promise in Psalms, Buchanan treasured - the Lord's love is ever present and with those who suffer from the things of this world, while those who serve the Devil will suffer the consequences in future days.

But the last passage thought of this early morning, just days from departure out of Camp Love, is a passage Buchanan shared in Communion after Communion, repeatedly in devotions, and counseling sessions with the men - I Peter 5:6-7. He quickly turned to I Peter and read it verbatim, "Humble yourselves therefore under the mighty hand of God, that in due time he may exalt you. Cast all your anxieties on him, for he cares about you."

Buchanan wept softly as he finished reading I Peter.

Coming to terms with Skawinski's death and realizing his defiance of accepting Adolphus's death, he actually came close to pushing the Lord aside in his time of mourning, denying the Lord any room in his grief. Following the reading of Scriptures, he opened up his heart to God, permitting the Lord to instruct him and to comfort him in his time of need. The Lord ministered to Buchanan, revealing to the chaplain He Himself did not desire Adolphus to perish.

He asked God to forgive him for forgetting about Him and blaming Him for Skawinski's death.

War snuffed the life out of Skawinski. Evil and the sin of human beings, the longing to harm one another for whatever evil intent lay in others' hearts is a great tool for the Devil. War is a tool causing evil havoc and mayhem, a means which the Devil entices men to partake in to achieve selfish goals.

However, Buchanan's hope relied not on this world. His hope did not lie within the knowledge or power of men. Buchanan's hope is in Jesus. He knew Adolphus believed in Jesus, and knowing, without a doubt, he would see him again someday.

Adolphus will wait for Robert in Heaven with his all too familiar smile from ear to ear, which Robert grew to love and hoped to see day after day in Camp Love.

Buchanan longs for the day when Jesus will return and bring peace to this world, the Savior of Adolphus and Robert. One a Lutheran and one a Baptist. Both fellow Buckeyes and mutual harvesters of this world.

Robert looked forward to the day he will see Adolphus again.

His belief in the Second Coming of Jesus filled him with hope, knowing that day will bring Everlasting Peace and no more war.

Major Porch, No Where in Sight

October 6, 1969

The adrenaline ran 100 miles per hour from head to toe within Buchanan. He has but one more day, then his journey for home begins.

In a few days, Buchanan will reunite with his children, and sleep in the same bed with his loving wife. Waiting for the moment is overwhelming. Buchanan jam-packed his two duffel bags and one small ditty bag to the hilt, ready to go home. He left camp humored with the notion, 'you always leave with more than what you came with'. His bags bursted forth with all the possessions he owned and everything he accumulated in Camp Love.

An additional piece of luggage Buchanan departed with since October 1968 is Burns' album case to hold some 25 LPs he had collected. He will never forget the fact Burns' introduction to classical music afforded him a means of soothing the soul in times of peril. The pleasure of listening to classical music enamored him for the rest of his life.

Surrounded by emptiness, Buchanan sat in an empty office hootch waiting for Jackson to visit An Ngai Tay village with the MedCAP and An Ngai Dong school and orphanage for the last time.

Sitting quietly, he waited for 20 minutes, an eternity with the hootch so empty.

Jackson finally arrived, and the spiritual team made their way to the chow hall to eat breakfast together. The team desired a fulfilling breakfast to set out to visit the village and orphanage for the last visit.

A busy day to face, but hopefully a day of glorious reward.

The sentimental trip to the orphanage is exhilarating. The spiritual team recalled the first trip to the orphanage a year ago, and the impressions made upon them. When the team arrived, the new chaplain met them, guiding them on a tour of the new buildings to serve as community centers and classrooms for the children. The Navy Seabees constructed the buildings with expertise.

Following the tour of the new facilities, he led them to the children for one last visit.

The hearts of the spiritual team shattered as children asked of the whereabouts of the tall, skinny one. Neither member of the team possessed enough courage to divulge the truth to the children, who fell in love with Skawinski. He became a statistic, a number, a KIA to those directing the war. The team simply informed the children - "He went on a far away trip. You'll see him again, someday."

The absence of Skawinski spawned a heartrending mood amongst the kids. Even more so with the news the spiritual team's departure from Vietnam is imminent. Gut-wrenching emotion distended from the children.

Chaplain Kensington's rotation tour date was September 16, 1969, and the new chaplain arrived, a Catholic priest from Denver, Colorado. The chaplain replacement exerted cordiality and extended love toward human beings as Jesus expects out of believers. And most important, he showed forth a fervent support for the orphanage and school. The new chaplain extended his hand in support of the spiritual team. The reputation of the chaplain is exemplary. But he isn't Kensington.

The spiritual team lifted Kensington high as an exemplary Christian. The team and Kensington considered each other a brother in Christ, an extremely important trait of a believer for Buchanan. It will be what Buchanan remembers most about Father Kensington. Denominations were not foremost for any of the three men. Most vital is Jesus living in and guiding human beings' hearts, a motivator to exert efforts for the men to minister.

The three men loved Jesus, inspired to serve Him and Him alone.

Following the visit, the spiritual team traveled back to Camp Love.

Conversation is negligible as the team, downtrodden, had little to say.

Hardly a word uttered on the drive back to Camp Love, but the friends thought of reflection, asking poignant questions within themselves. Questions such as, 'What will happen to the Catholic priests and nuns if the area is overrun by the Communists following the departure of the United States along with its military strength?' 'What will come of any Catholics, including the children at the orphanage, if overrun by the Communists?' In the 1950s, the Communists killed tens of thousands of Roman Catholics in North Vietnam. Many Catholics in the in the north fled to South Vietnam in the 1950s. The atrocities committed by the Communists onto Catholics in the 1950s are unfathomable, and would repeat itself if the ARVN collapsed in pushing back Communist advancements, especially if the United States permanently left, which the spiritual team fears is going to happen soon. An event which would infuriate those pitching their tent in the political camp to stop the worldwide spread of Communism.

What angered even more so the spiritual team, anti-Communists, were politicians in Washington, DC and protesters in the streets of the United States who could careless about the safety and security of Roman Catholics in South Vietnam, let alone their religious freedom.

In no time, the spiritual team arrived in Camp Love, in time to receive the best grub of the day in the chow hall for one last lunch together in the bush. The team spent the remaining part of the day in Buchanan's hootch, spending time with one another for the last night in the jungle. The team reminisced, talked sports, discussed politics, and attempted to explain the devastating experiences thrown at them while in Vietnam, barely mentioning to anyone else once they returned home. Pleasant conversation came with a discussion of the successes of ministry to the marines in Camp Love, Porch, playing cards every Tuesday night, the baptisms in Tyn Loan River, and many more talking points that emerged as the evening passed.

Oddly enough, many marines popped in to speak to him. Instead of the spiritual team making the rounds to visit all the departments, the men made their way to him this night. Lucas. McElrath. Varnes. Vickers. Rockford and Frost. Rodriquez. Burns. Burnside. Shaw. Lipstone. Gross. Doc Delaney. Just about everybody and their uncle. Surprisingly, several of Porch's friends dropped by, expressing their appreciation of his short ministry to the marines in Camp Love.

As the day winded down to 1830 hours. Time flew by.

The spiritual team ate supper, retiring once again to Buchanan's hootch. When settling in for a good restful evening, they rattled off each and every name of those who dropped by to visit. It seemed as if everyone who had a part of Buchanan's tour stopped by, expressing a word of appreciation. Everyone and everybody verbally spoken but one - Major Michael Porch.

The spiritual team knew he is nothing but a stinker. But neither one thought he would avoid Buchanan entirely. Besides, it's no secret to the spiritual team he replenished the candy and supplies for the children. The pair is convinced Porch possesses virtues within himself, showing signs of worth, such as searching for Carl Remington. The team knows without a doubt, Porch, deep down in his heart, desired Jesus to direct and guide his life daily.

All the spiritual team could say in response to Porch's absence is - "Oh Well!"

Buchanan invited Jackson to spend the night in his hootch for old time's sake. Jackson, overwhelmed with glee with such an invitation, enthusiastically accepted the invite.

"Always thought I should've bunked with you here in camp, sir. Besides, I *was* your bodyguard." Jackson said with a smug smile.

"I wanted you to stay here." said Buchanan with raised eyebrows.

"Well, why didn't ya ask me?"

"I thought you would feel uncomfortable bunking down with an officer. Fraternization and all. All the talk of the gap between officer and enlisted. All the talk of officers only and all." insisted Buchanan.

"Sir, this is the bush. None of that matters out here." said Jackson.

"Well, if it didn't matter, why didn't ya ask to stay here the whole while, Sergeant?"

Jackson paused. "Well, I guess you're right, Padre."

Buchanan said, "You wondered what some of those stiff-necked officers like Major Michael Porch would have thought, didn't ya?"

Grinning, Jackson shrugs his shoulders, knowing Buchanan stated the truth.

"Uh-huh. That's it. You were just as worried as I was. Weren't ya, sergeant?" Buchanan smiled.

The spiritual team laugh, knowing the two could have bunked together the whole time, but neither one suggested the move.

Time now stood at 2115 hours. The spiritual team conversed into the night with one more night of music to go.

The previous two nights, Burns filled the air with magnificent pieces of music for the men to enjoy while laying themselves down to, hopefully, a good night's rest. He selected Brahms' Hungarian dance number 5, Aram Khachaturian's Sabre Dance from the ballet *Gayane* and suite no 2 from the ballet *Spartacus,* and Respighi's Ancient Airs and Dances No. 1. Burns considered Khachaturian nothing but a Commie and an atheist, but a great musician nonetheless. He considered him one of the great composers of all time.

Knowing tonight is the last evening for Chaplain Buchanan, Burns sought every inch of Vietnam to find a special LP of music to play.

Burns chose, for the first piece of the night, *The Marriage of Figaro* by Mozart. Buchanan requested it occasionally throughout the past year following an officer friend describing the piece of music for the very first time to him in November 1968.

The second piece of music selected, familiar to Buchanan, filled the camp's airways - 'Hoe-Down' from "*Rodeo*" by Aaron Copland. The third and last piece for the evening filled the ears of the camp - Vivaldi's Concerto for Two Violins in A minor, another piece Buchanan had requested from time to time since November 1968.

Jackson lied on the floor on a mattress he borrowed from an officer next door to Buchanan while he listened to the music.

While listening, Buchanan stared straight up into the ceiling lying on his cot, thinking of his entire year in Vietnam. He laughed. He cried. He measured up his ministry in three short pieces of music.

Occasionally looking off to the side near his desk, Buchanan searched for a peek at Arthur and Churchill. He dropped fruit from the chow hall on the floor close to the desk to give them one last treat for the night. In time, the treats disappeared, eaten so quietly he didn't even notice the lizards emerge from darkness, consuming the food.

Burns intentionally picked three pieces of music to lift the spirits of Buchanan.

Vivaldi's concerto ended as silence triumphed over the camp.

As silence settled in, one last piece of music broke the silence. A piece of music Burns searched high and low for this night. The spiritual team didn't recognize the music initially, as it reflected nothing but snare drums and percussion.

"Is this a percussion concert, or what?" commented Jackson sarcastically.

"Sounds like."

"No. Wait, sir. Listen, listen carefully." Jackson said. "Is it so? Is it so!?!"

Just as Buchanan was about to ask what the music might be, the Ohio State Buckeyes' fight song came blaring through the PA system of the camp.

Cheers filled the air throughout the camp from Ohioans and Ohio State fans. Who knows, maybe even from Big Ten fans merely showing support for their conference.

Within the cheers, the spiritual team heard an undertone of boos coming from hootches occupied mostly with Californians. Jackson assumed the heightened volume of the boos rose with the additional number of smug SEC fans in camp.

"Shut up, Californians!" yelled the spiritual team. The team caught an earful of laughter coming from Doc Delaney, the Texas Longhorns fan.

"Ohio State sucks!" shouted the Californians.

"Stick it in your ear!" Jackson yelled. The spiritual team laughs. Doc Delaney again filled the air with laughter.

As the Ohioans quit their jawing with the Californians, the pair laid in Buchanan's hootch listening to the rest of the Ohio State fight song turning their thoughts toward reminiscing of their fellow Ohioan. The spiritual team thought of nothing but of one person listening to the fight song - Adolphus Skawinski. The pair thought of nothing but his love for his home state and the Ohio State football team representing Buckeyes nationwide.

Silence once again filled the air in camp as marines and sailors heard the last notes of the fight song play out. All in camp thought of Skawinski. The foremost Ohio State fan in camp - and everyone knew it. In fact, no one in camp ever knew a bigger Ohio State fan than Skawinski, including Ohio State fans back home.

"I miss him." murmured Buchanan softly in the dead silence.

After a long pause, Jackson whispered, "Me, too."

Saying Goodbye Never Comes Easy

October 7, 1969

"That's the best pancakes I've had in years, men!" roared Buchanan to the cooks in the chow hall.

"Thank you, sir."

"Amen!" Buchanan added. "Keep up the good work, marines."

"We'll try, sir." replied the smiling cooks, knowing full well Buchanan's personality by now.

The spiritual team's last departure from the chow hall carried with them a list of offices and names written at breakfast to visit and bid a last farewell. Lieutenant Colonel Lucas's office would be the last to visit.

At 1030 hours, a Huey helicopter to transport Buchanan to Da Nang Air Base is scheduled to arrive with replacements. The pilot will have the privilege of transporting Buchanan to Da Nang for his plane out of Vietnam.

The time now ticked to 0745 hours. The list of names and officers to visit carried some weight, extensive and precise, so time is of the essence.

Buchanan encountered a most peaceful last night in Vietnam. A satisfied last night full of pleasant dreams and memories of Skawinski. The dreams painted pictures of farming in Ohio, reminiscent of his Ohioan friend. The dreams carried over into the morning as

Skawinski's spirit accompanied the spiritual team to make their rounds visiting friends and colleagues for the last time.

The visits were quick and memorable. Stopping at McElrath's ordinance office first, Burnside's automotive department would follow, along with The Scrounger's office rounding out the first three visits. Buchanan insisted he peek in on his fellow Pike County native Corporal Jones, who himself went home on October 16, 1969. Knocking out two more departments, the spiritual team saved Burns in supply and Doc Delaney and the field hospital for the last of the marine offices. Buchanan thanked Burns a dozen times over for introducing him to classical music, instilling in him a love for the beauty and enjoyment of a new music genre in his life. Buchanan and Burns vowed to meet in West Virginia after the war for their kinfolk to bond with one another. In jest, the men insisted there is no doubt in their minds West Virginia reigned the best state in the Union. Buchanan dearly loved his wife's home state.

The most difficult visit came last - the medical aid station. When Buchanan stepped into the aid station, he envisioned mentally every marine passing him by that he assisted medically and spiritually in the aid station. Too many a wounded marine, Buchanan read Scripture and prayed over him in medical, some succumbing to their ultimate demise. Doc Delaney and the corpsmen will forever be grateful for his ministry, thanking him for the positive influence on the troops. He thanked Buchanan for mentoring him in becoming a better physician.

Buchanan sought to visit Lieutenant Commander Adkins' Seabee office toward the end, knowing the visit

would be time consuming. The two men were brothers in Christ and close friends.

With the list of visits marked through with a pencil, Lieutenant Colonel Lucas's office rounded out the end of visits. The spiritual team briefly walked to the commanding officer's office, stepping through the front entrance.

"Good morning, sir. Jackson, good morning." Sergeant Vickers said.

"Good morning, Sergeant." responded the spiritual team.

"He's here, sir. The Padre."

Lucas said, "Come in. Come in here, Padre. Cats are wondering why the heck you're still out there."

Lucas chuckled.

The spiritual team grin at Vickers, passing by to enter Lucas' office.

Without a moment's notice, the cats are all over Buchanan and Jackson, sensing friends. Lucas, who knows it's useless to speak to the cats, says anyhow, "Leave those men alone. They don't want kitty hairs all over their uniforms."

"It's OK, sir." Jackson said, grinning. "They seem to enjoy receiving the attention."

"I *know,* Sergeant." Lucas replied. He falls back into his swivel chair, grinning, knowing it's useless pushing the cats away from friendly visitors. The spiritual team takes a seat in the two chairs in front of him, as Hans flops himself in Buchanan's lap, insisting on attention, obliging as he pets him.

Ludwig rubs Jackson's leg, as Jackson glances down toward him, grinning. The aggressive Siamese stares back up at Jackson sternly, jumping straight up toward his chest, as Jackson is startled, saying, "Ahhhhh."

Lucas and Buchanan laugh. "He likes ya, Sergeant." said Lucas.

Ludwig lands in Jackson's lap as the cat settles in, looking up at Jackson pleading for some attention. The insistent cat continues to move about in his lap till Jackson pets and grooms him with his hand. He finally, and hesitantly, reaches up and pets Ludwig, who is finally satisfied when the human caves reluctantly to show the feline the attention wanted toward him.

The three men pet and groom the cats, talking of animals and the good animals bring to human beings.

Lucas turns to Buchanan. "Well, it's your last day."

With a pause of silence, enjoying the cats, all men sit and think, with a loss of words, hammering out mentally all that has occurred in the past year - good and bad.

Breaking the silence, Lucas said, "Ya did a great job, Padre."

Grinning, Buchanan shrugs his shoulders, admitting, "I tried, Skipper. I tried."

"Well, I can tell you for a fact, Robert. A fact you influenced the men to be better men." Lucas said with affirmation in his voice. All along Jackson nodding heartily yes the whole while.

"Well, thank you, sir. Ya supported me from the beginning. From the John Wayne Friday socials to the CAPs, with the number of church services and Communion services."

"It's all about the troops, Robert." said Lucas. "It's all about their wants and needs."

"Thanks as well for letting me hang out in the mornings with the cats toward the end of my tour." Buchanan said.

"Well, the cats appreciated the attention. They enjoyed your company, Robert." Lucas said, "Well, ya better get going, Padre. Your bags are waiting patiently in your hootch to be put on the chopper." Looking down at his watch, he said. "It's 1015 hours."

"Yes, sir. You don't want to wait for the next chopper, do ya, sir?" asked Jackson.

"*Nooooo*, Philip. I wouldn't." Buchanan grins. He stares at Hans, intense with thanks. "Thank ya, Hans. Thank you very much for helping me get through it a little better." Hans glares back up at him, purring emphatically, rubbing himself all over Buchanan. He gives him one last petting. "There ya go, my feline friend. One last pet for ya." Buchanan stands up as Hans jumps onto the floor of the office hootch.

Jackson places Ludwig on the floor, purring at the top of his lungs like his brother cat.

Brahms steps onto Lucas' desk from his lap, looking up at Buchanan as if he knows the chaplain is to leave for good. Buchanan takes a quick look at Brahms, petting the most territorial of the three cats.

Turning toward Lucas, he shakes his hand and says, "Thanks, sir."

"Thank you, Robert."

"Take care of my friend here, Sergeant Jackson." said Buchanan.

"You know it, sir." answered Jackson.

The spiritual team say their goodbyes to Sergeant Vickers, making their way to Buchanan's hootch to retrieve his bags. Jackson takes hold of one duffel bag and the small ditty bag, while Buchanan straps on his back the other duffel bag, lighter but still a hefty load for a 37-year-old, reaching down for the LP box full of albums.

On the way to the camp entrance, Jackson glances toward Buchanan. "Sir. Ya really did a great job, sir. Outstanding job. I became a better believer, better follower in Jesus due to you."

As they continued to walk, they reminded each other, humored by those who they thought had the last hope of becoming Christians became followers of Christ, such as Dobbs and Sims.

Buchanan confessed, "Well, I owe my life to you. Many a time here, the Devil threw his weight at me, and ya stepped in between. I appreciate you, Philip. I love ya. You're my brother in Christ. And I thank you."

Jackson, by now smiling from ear to ear, shakes his hand. He concurred, "I love you too, sir." Pausing as he continued to walk, he says, "Jesus is great, isn't he?"

"He's what got me through, Sergeant."

"Amen. Amen to that, sir." replied Jackson, just as they were about to reach the camp entrance. What they saw in front of them astonished the spiritual team.

From what Jackson could estimate by just looking over and counting the marines assembled at the camp entrance, he softly says, "There's at least 80, 90, maybe even 100 men here sir." Jackson, surprised and catching flies, pauses for a moment. "Their here to see ya off, sir."

Buchanan, at a loss for words, whispers, "Amen." His friends are present, many who Buchanan affected spiritually.

Just as the men arrived at the camp entrance, the helicopter delivering the marine replacements turns, rounds the corner of a distant hillside about a mile away from Camp Love. Buchanan looks back up at Lucas standing at his window space, who snapped up the plastic to get a better look at Buchanan's departure, eyed the

Lieutenant Colonel holding Brahms, looking intently at Buchanan as is his owner, staring to say goodbye.

Lucas waves at Buchanan. He returns a solemn wave to the commanding officer.

The men gather around Chaplain Buchanan, shaking his hand, thanking him for all he had done for them in their brief time together in South Vietnam. As the men continue to greet and show their appreciation to their chaplain, the helicopter homes in on the field outside the camp to land and drop off the replacements and to pick up the chaplain. The men continue to thank Buchanan for his ministry, as the spiritual team noticed a man in the corner of their eyes, standing erect and looking eager. The team, shocked, glance toward the marine - for the man standing is no other but Major Michael Porch. He held an envelope in his hand.

Buchanan and Porch step toward one another, while the entire group looked on.

Meeting one another, Porch said, "Robert, the men are going to miss ya."

Buchanan grins. "Well, *yeah*. As the Scripture says, though, there's a time for everything. And it's my time to go."

Porch tilted his head, grinning.

"I've got to go. I can't handle much more of this." avowed a beaten and worn Buchanan.

Porch nods, sympathizing with Buchanan.

Porch acclaimed, "Robert, I just want you to know. You were fantastic - for all the men, Protestant, Catholic, as well as the Jewish personnel."

Lifting an envelope, Porch said, "The rest of what I want to say is in here. Take it, Robert." Long past as adversaries, were now allies, as Porch made amends. The two men displayed nothing but a mood of distress, though the men departed from one another with a heartfelt and forgiving embrace, expressing the warm, genuine love of two Christian brothers.

Buchanan takes the envelope from Porch. "Good bye Michael."

"Good bye, Robert." said Porch as Buchanan turned toward Jackson.

Jackson leads Buchanan out of the gate entrance and he, just outside the entrance, has the notion of looking back at Lucas just one last time. As Buchanan glances back, he sees the last glimpse of Lucas and Brahms in his plastic window frame as Lucas sits down in his chair, out of sight. He guessed Lucas had time enough to show his respects one last time, knowing a downtrodden Lucas is losing a chaplain he valued.

Once through the camp entrance, Jackson leads Buchanan down the long passageway road between the perimeter, then left into the open field outside the perimeter, then to the helicopter.

Once reaching the helicopter, Jackson said loudly because of the helicopter noise, "Well, sir. This is it."

"Yes, Philip. This is the end, I guess."

The two stare for a moment.

Jackson breaks the brief pause, saying, "Thank ya very much, sir. For everything."

Buchanan grins. "Take care, Philip."

Jackson said, "Remember, sir. This war is hell - and you brought a Heavenly presence as best you could for many of us. You gave 'em a slither of Hope within all the hell." He paused. "I'm proud of ya."

Nodding, Buchanan grins.

Embracing, the men can't help but be emotional.

"Good bye, sir."

"Good bye, Philip."

Buchanan turns and climbs into the helicopter with his one duffel bag and his LP box. Jackson places the second duffel bag and small ditty bag into the Huey.

Jackson stoops down, steps back from the helicopter, as Buchanan looks on.

The two say a final verbal "Good bye" from a distance. Buchanan waves to his friends in Camp Love as the helicopter lifts off the ground up into the air.

As Buchanan sits in the Huey, it lifts high for his trip to Da Nang. Jackson jogs back into camp to join the others, as venturing outside the perimeter without weapons makes one's blood run cold.

As Jackson trots up to the others, the marines stare up into the sky toward the helicopter.

Buchanan, sitting in the helicopter, experienced one of the most emotional instances in his life as the pilot turns toward Da Nang.

He pulls the envelope from Porch out of his upper left-hand pocket of his fatigue coat, opens it and reads.

As he is about to read the Porch letter, he noticed the letter written in a formal military format, dated October 7, 1969. The formal writing of the letter humored Buchanan as he grinned. He read the letter silently.

'Robert, Thank you! Thank you for everything! The Lord used you in so many ways! Helping marines become better believers, providing for the wants and needs of the children in An Ngai Dong and An Ngai Tay, lifting the hearts of men coping with the horrors of war. Most of all, thank you for humbling a stiff-necked man, yours truly, who needed to be knocked down a notch or two. It was a pleasure to have known you. God's speed and God Bless!

Sincerely,

Major Michael Porch'

Buchanan slowly smiles at the matter of fact written note of Porch, as his eyes moistened remembering his past year in a matter of seconds.

Sitting in the helicopter, fastened in his seat belt, Buchanan's thoughts take a turn for the worst as he feels the helicopter make a sharp turn for some odd reason.

Buchanan pounds on the divider between the cockpit and passenger hull. He yells to the pilot, "Hey, up there. What-What's going on? Is something wrong?"

The pilot yells inaudible sentences to Buchanan, which does nothing to satisfy him. He now realizes the helicopter is heading back toward Camp Love.

'But why?' thought Buchanan. Sitting in his seat looking over the edge out of the helicopter, his gut reaction proved correct. The helicopter is close to camp. The pilot, though, flew over the usual drop off spot for helicopters.

Instead, the pilot flew to about half way over the perimeter, pivoted the helicopter, exposing the open space where Buchanan is sitting in his seat to give him a straight shot to see the men assembled just inside the main gate. Peering out the side of the Huey helicopter, fixated on the men, Buchanan noticed the marines placed in a special formation, causing him to feel warm inside. In his heart, he's overjoyed with pride. Looking down at the formation of men, he discovered the formation of a cross. He is beyond himself. On top of that, the men placed their right hand near their heart. The men remembered the two most important themes in Buchanan's ministry while at Camp Love - Father Capodanno's sacrifice for marines and Jesus in your heart.

The marines convinced Lucas into surprising Buchanan following his initial ascension. Lucas thought it a superb idea.

Buchanan placed his hand over his heart, then waved for the very last time to the men, emotional all the while.

Many of the men wave their arms, elated the chaplain entered their lives in the most desperate of times.

The helicopter ascends, turns and heads toward Da Nang.

Buchanan, looking out into the foliage of Vietnam as he endured his last bumpy ride in a Huey helicopter, says in his heart, 'Goodbye."

A Rude Awakening

November 23, 1969

Dreams encountered this night were anything but pleasant for Buchanan. Nightmares interrupted any sleep he set out for. Every boy he held in his arms who perished, or those he prayed over after being declared deceased, filled his nightmares. The faces, voices, demeanor of the boys all surfaced in his dreams, as the Devil laughed hideously throughout the dream, mocking Buchanan's efforts in Vietnam. More hidden in the dreams were Vietnamese children playing and enjoying life as a child. The Viet Cong in his dreams killed the children.

Buchanan had trouble putting the dreams in perspective, craving to forget about them for good.

Today, the Buchanan clan engaged in a frequent outing in the Buchanan household - a picnic in the nearby public park after the base chapel service. Possibly the visit in the park would ease his mind, taking the pain of the nightmares away. Dorothy's training as a nurse came in handy the past several weeks, aiding Buchanan to deal with his stress.

In fact, 44 days had passed since he arrived back in southern California from Vietnam. The Tri-state area it is not, but it is home. He and Dorothy chomped at the bit to set their eyes on the banks of the Ohio river once again, whether it be the Ohio, Kentucky, or West Virginia side. The bank of the Ohio of whatever state it might be. He didn't care. He just desired to sit on a bench in the middle of a park in a river town, maybe in Middleport or Gallipolis, Ohio.

The enjoyment of the beauty of the river guaranteed to ease his mind, at least temporarily, of the pain of war. California is nothing but a temporary abode adjusted to until the day the Buchanan clan packs up and moves back to Ohio, though the family enjoyed San Diego immensely. Buchanan's first duty station had been in San Diego. The people were friendly. The city seemed quiet and clean, with an array of places to go with the kids, including the San Diego Zoo, a favorite of the family. The beaches in San Diego, enjoyed by the Buchanan's, seemed less commercial than the Los Angeles beaches, another plus for San Diego. The Los Angeles area, however, mounted a list of grievances for the Buchanan parents. The LA area, dense with residential communities, overwhelmed the Buchanan's rural preferences and people in the LA area were far less friendly than the San Diego folks. Dorothy thought of no other word but 'horrendous' to describe the bumper to bumper traffic in the Los Angeles metropolitan area. The unreal cost of living added a negative for the Buchanan's. Dorothy added yet another detriment living in Los Angeles, to which she failed to feel safe and secure. The horrific crimes committed against a famous actress and her friends, followed by a married couple the next night, early in August, added to the fear she experienced living in an overpopulated area of California. During the months of August and September, living isolated and alone with her children, one of Robert's brothers, who had lived in Anaheim since 1963, popped in on the family from time to time till he returned from Vietnam.

The park is frequently visited by the Buchanan's, in the deep suburbs of Santa Ana, away from the hustle and bustle of the metropolitan Los Angeles area. The public venue sets itself apart as a park oriented and catered toward patrons searching for a family atmosphere. The park catered to military personnel stationed at El Toro base living in the area.

After the worship service in the base chapel, Buchanan drove the family to their suburban Santa Ana home, changed clothes into casual attire, as Dorothy packed lunch food into two large picnic baskets.

Robert and Dorothy once again loaded up the seven kids into the VW bus off to the park, securing the food in the back of the van.

When arriving at the park, the usual Sunday crowd has already occupied their chosen spots for their routine afternoon picnic under the cool shade of the trees. The regular groups, families with kids and the few hippies, were present, enjoying the pleasant afternoon of the California temperature and climate. Buchanan took a panoramic view of the park, taking in a scene of people enjoying life. People laughing. Children playing on the Monkey bars, playing in the grass. Families lounging around on blankets, eating an afternoon lunch. Single couples, enjoying the company of one chosen to love in conversation.

Buchanan relished the family setting from the picnic crowd. Those in the park conferred the appreciation and value of life by relaxing in the public venue. The park felt the vibes of therapeutic seclusion for reflection and a personal touch effecting people's psyche.

Regardless, Buchanan ambled his way from the VW bus, finding a spot to spread out the blankets to prepare for the afternoon picnic with the children. Robert usually searched a spot near, but not on top of, the metal merry-go-round and swings to provide him the space to play with the children after eating lunch. He and Dorothy spread out five blankets onto the ground, plenty of room to relax with their precious children. Seven children in all. Robert James II, the oldest at ten and a half. John Thomas followed him at nine years of age. Next in line were James Dwight and Jacqueline Louise – the seven-year-old twins. Kenneth Charles followed suit aged five, suffering from a serious vision problem, while Joseph Bethel fell next to the last in line at four years old. At two and a half, Johanna Kathleen fell in last of the Buchanan clan.

Since Buchanan arrived home, Johanna Kathleen referred to him as 'man.' Not 'daddy' or 'pop' - just 'man.' Humored, her parents assumed Johanna in her infant mind attempted to make sense why this 'strange' man showed up out of the blue, living with her and the family. Besides, when Buchanan departed for Vietnam in 1968, Johanna's age was just 13 months.

The spot found by Dorothy and Robert to spend the afternoon was near the merry-go-round and the swings, as Robert insisted on every trip to the park. The two of them let the children momentarily play as they retrieved the food from the baskets, which they placed in the middle of the blankets.

"You bring the Ranch dressing for the hot dogs?" Buchanan asked.

"Yes, babe. I did." answered Dorothy. "I think you would eat Ranch dressing on anything." Dorothy throws an intentional smug smile toward Robert.

"Probably so." Buchanan grins.

"I guess I keep the Ranch dressing business in business, huh?" Buchanan chuckles.

"Laughing at your own jokes has always been a flaw in your character." commented Dorothy with a tone of sarcasm.

Buchanan chuckles even louder.

Dorothy rolls her eyes.

In no time, Robert and Dorothy laid the food out on the blankets. Hotdogs, corn dogs, potato salad – a Midwestern tradition, a jar of pickles for Dorothy, coleslaw to top off the hotdogs, and the usual condiments of ketchup, mayonnaise, mustard, and pickle relish. As usual, the colossal pyramid of corn on the cob for the adults and mini corn on the cob for the children, if so desired, laid ready on the oval plate for consumption. And, of course, the family tradition of potato chips and dip. There never had been a picnic without potato chips and dip for a Buchanan outing. The insistence of providing a variety of chips is routine for the Buchanan clan - rippled, barbecue and sour cream and onion – the usual flavors. Potato chips and dip had become a staple for the Buchanan's.

As Dorothy took a panoramic view of the food, a quote came to mind from TV. She said, "The only time to eat diet food is while you're waiting for the steak to cook."

They chuckle.

Dessert for the day is a cake, concealed till the main course is consumed by a hungry clan of Buchanan's. Any sight of the cake before the main course, and the efforts to encourage the children to eat anything else but the cake, will be futile.

Buchanan said grace and blessed the food, and immediately the Buchanan clan dove into the food. Never did Dorothy see the clan eat so much food so quickly. The children obviously were hungry. Time had raced to 1400 hours in the afternoon, past their usual lunchtime.

Following the picnic lunch, Dorothy lifted the plastic cake holder out of the picnic basket, and the children bolted toward the cake, practically knocking the cake out of her hands. Dorothy sliced a small piece of cake for each child, placing the piece on a paper plate. The favorite family flavors – vanilla cake with chocolate icing - filled the tummies of the junior members of the Buchanan clan. In no time at all, the children were a mess, with icing and cake all over them. Robert and Dorothy are handed a tall order to clean up seven faces smeared with icing and cake.

Following 20 minutes, Robert permitted the children to play after time to let their food settle in.

As the older children ran to the merry-go-round and swings along with Buchanan, Dorothy stayed put on the blankets with the younger babies.

Pushing James softly in the swing, Buchanan kept an eye on Robert II, Jacqueline Louise, and John Thomas playing on the merry-go-round. As a kid, Buchanan loved playing in the swing and having fun on the merry-go-round. Even at a young age, though life had been hard in the Depression and receiving the brunt of an abusive mother, Buchanan incredibly sensed a purpose in life. His way of life changed for the better when he followed a life for Jesus. Prior to, life comprised satisfying oneself, a deflating and dilapidating life resulting in nothing but emptiness. Since his conversion experience, pleasing God with a precedence of showing and expressing His love for others ranked as top priority in his life.

One joy in life for Buchanan is family. Loving his kinfolk as God loves His own is the greatest, most fulfilling experience he has had ever since he became a Christian.

Robert, Jacqueline, and John were on the merry-go-round, while Robert and John pushed the merry-go-round with their right foot to go round, while holding onto the interior bars on the ride. Jacqueline, positioned in the middle of the merry-go-round, held on for dear life. Buchanan noticed her, a little frightened.

"Robert, John. Stop pushing the merry-go-round so fast! You know that startles your sister." yelled Buchanan.

"What did ya say, pop?" answered Robert.

"You heard me! The pace of the merry-go-round's too fast. Slow 'er down. Son!" barked Buchanan.

The merry-go-round slowed a bit, but still too rapid, startling Jacqueline. In fact, her expression was nothing but fright. Actually, the boys did little too slow the merry-go-round to an acceptable speed for their father.

"I want off, pop!" yelled Jacqueline.

"Boys, stop! Stop the merry-go-round." said Buchanan, as he ceased pushing James on the swing, walking toward the merry-go-round to console Jacqueline.

Finally, the boys brought to a standstill the merry-go-round, running off to play with their football.

Jacqueline emphatically ran to her daddy, hugging him tight.

"They did it on purpose, pop." Jacqueline said.

"I know they did, babe. They do anything else today, they'll be in trouble. I can assure you." said Buchanan, smiling down toward Jacqueline. She scampered off to the swing sets, while Buchanan stepped toward the boys to throw some football with them. Jacqueline, a favorite of Buchanan, is named after Jacqueline Kennedy Onassis, the president's wife. A favorite of the Buchanan's first ladies.

Robert delivered a good stern glance to the boys as Buchanan sprightly joined his sons to throw the football. The hard-nosed glimpse hit Robert and John abruptly as their father spoke loud and clear. The pestering of siblings has come to an end for the day. The risk of hassling any siblings, including Jacqueline, if caught, would result in landing themselves in serious trouble. Buchanan caught himself scratching his head, constantly asking himself why male siblings insisted on picking and pestering their female siblings as a holy terror. As a minister, he observed it to be true in most families. Brothers were a holy terror to sisters.

"Great pass, Robert." commented Buchanan as Robert II gleamed as he threw the ball. He developed a good arm at an early age. Buchanan noticed it as well, encouraging him to strengthen his skills by throwing the football.

"Ya keep it up, Robert, and you might play in high school. That'd be great." Buchanan commented.

Following a few minutes throwing the football, Buchanan motioned the older children to draw near to play capture the flag, a favorite outdoor game for the Buchanan's. Robert divided the teams determined by fairness grouping himself, Kenneth, James, and Robert for team one. Team two comprised Dorothy, Jacqueline, and John.

Joseph and Johanna were quiet as a mouse, taking their afternoon nap, safe and secure, close to the family lying on the blankets.

Dorothy's team hid their flag, a green handkerchief from Buchanan, while Robert's team turned their backs, covering their eyes.

"Robert, no cheating!" barked Dorothy, as Robert II turned his head slightly, peeking between his fingers to locate the spot of where his mother's team hid their flag.

"Son, show fair play." admonished Buchanan.

Buchanan and Dorothy chuckled quietly at Robert's orneriness.

Dorothy's team located a crevice hole in a tree near the blankets, sticking the handkerchief in the depths of the crevice, as the team moseyed up to the imaginary line to start the game, as Dorothy yelled, "Ready!"

Dorothy's team turned their backs and closed their eyes.

Buchanan's team located a rock with a groove at the base, placing their flag, one of Dorothy's old blue clothes to clean her glasses with, up into the groove concealing Robert's flag for his team.

When Buchanan's team found their hiding place, they walked up to the imaginary line for the game and Buchanan yelled out, "Ready."

Playing Capture the Flag will be a relief from Buchanan's high level of stress. Dorothy is especially gratified Robert's mind will be distracted from the nightmares experienced last night. She is excited the picnic, Robert's favorite park to visit, taking part in the games with the kids, and the children took his mind off the war and the nightmares. The frequent occurrence of dreams last night triggered a terrible night of frightful images, but the day so far eased his mind.

The teams, eager and competitive, were ready to go. With the anticipation of competing, Buchanan is flying high, fired up to win.

Buchanan spread his team into position, followed by Dorothy.

"Go!" hollered Buchanan. Team members bolted into positions of play. Each team crossed the imaginary line into the opponent's side to find the opposing team's flag. Opposing team member's nearly getting caught but running across back over the line just in time. For a few minutes, neither team achieved the upper hand. So far, the game played to a draw. Eventually, one team member ran too deep into the opponent's field, an all too common risk in Capture the Flag, and found himself caught, young James. He misjudged his distance from the imaginary line, extended too far into Dorothy's space, searching for her team's flag, and is caught by John. James ran to go to the captured area on John's side. Kenneth attempted to free James as he ran into Jacqueline, touching Kenneth, capturing him. Buchanan's team now knocked down to him and Robert, hesitant to risk crossing the line of play to search for Dorothy's team flag. A tall order now faced Buchanan and Robert, forced to protect their own flag and to search for an opening to free James and Kenneth. Dorothy's team now had the upper hand to win the game. Deep down inside, Buchanan rooted for Dorothy all the while with a palpable smug grin on his face, long after Robert treated his sister Jacqueline so rudely earlier in the day.

In an ultimate high, the family immersed in the fun.

The last thought in Buchanan's mind up to this point in the day is Vietnam.

As Dorothy and the children ran playing capture the flag, Buchanan froze suddenly in motion. His face turned white as a sheet, stock-still and at a complete loss.

"Mom, look. Pop's face is scary!" yelled out John.

"Maybe he ate too many hot dogs." James said.

Dorothy darted toward Buchanan.

"Robert, help your mother ease your father to the ground." asked Dorothy. She seized his right side as Robert followed on his left, gently helping Buchanan sit on the ground.

As Buchanan quivered slightly, the children heard short soft grunts from him. Catching flies, Buchanan's offspring witnessed for the first time their father experience a serious flashback. The children sprinted to their father, behaving in the most bizarre behavior, mesmerized at the sight before them. His odd behavior displayed is beyond comprehension for such young minds and ages. His flashback challenged their young little minds to understand the about-face of behavior. The sudden change in behavior baffled the children - one minute playing, having a good time - then in a wink of an eye, suddenly, he acts bizarre and strange.

"He's scary looking." Jacqueline said.

"Is pop tired from running?" asked Kenneth.

"No. He ate too much, right mom?" asked James.

"No, no babe." answered Dorothy. Hoping to relieve the children's fear and dismay, she simply said, "He just remembered something in a dream that upset him, that's all."

Dorothy held Buchanan's hand. She said, "It's going to be OK. It's going to be OK." Dorothy glances toward Johanna and Joseph, checking on the young ones.

Dorothy instructs Robert II, "Robert, step over and check on your brother and sister for me."

Robert obliged his mother. Following the assurance his siblings were secure, he returned to his mother and says, "They're awake. Not crying either. At least not yet."

"John, go sit with the babies till I get your father over onto the blankets." Dorothy said.

"Right, Mom." answered John.

Just as Dorothy and Robert were helping Buchanan to his feet, he said, "I need some water."

"He talked, Mom! He talked." James said.

Kenneth and James laugh, unbeknownst to the severity of the situation at such a young age.

"Yes, boys, your father talked." said Dorothy with a slight half grin.

By this time, several families from the base noticed Buchanan's situation, walking over to lend a hand.

"You're Chaplain Buchanan and family, aren't you?" asked a Gunnery Sergeant and Sergeant from the base.

"Yes, that's right. Aren't you Gunnery Sergeant Lyndon Munson? That's right, isn't it?" answered Dorothy.

"Yes, ma'am. I am." answered Munson. "Let us lend a hand to you, chaplain."

"Thank you, men." said Buchanan, as he is composing himself back to reality.

The two marines gently guided Chaplain Buchanan to the blankets, sitting him down. Dorothy poured some water for him to drink. Buchanan showed signs of recuperating from his traumatic flashback. With all the commotion, Joseph and Johanna were wide awake, sitting up beside their father. Johanna, glancing up toward Buchanan, smiled, patted Buchanan on his knee. She innocently says, "Man." Buchanan peeked down toward his child and caressed her head.

"I love you, Johanna." Buchanan said.

The marine wives stepped over, offering a hand of help to Dorothy in stowing away of the picnic baskets and securing the children in the VW bus to make their trip home.

The sergeants chatted with Chaplain Buchanan of what had just transpired in the park, which seemed to console him, at least for the time being. The Gunny, fresh from a recent tour in Vietnam, empathized with Buchanan.

Once again, the Buchanan's loaded up the children in the VW bus, ready for home.

The Buchanan's thanked the sergeants and their wives, setting off for home. Once settled for the evening, the Buchanan's safely secured the children in their beds, said their prayers, and as soon as their precious heads hit the pillow, fell fast asleep. The Buchanan's were thankful the children fell immediately asleep, as they were exhausted from the distressing experience of the flashback. The pair brushed their teeth, read their Bible, and said their own prayers.

Buchanan switched the radio on, turning the knob to the local classical music station. Maybe the music would serve as a stimulant to sleep.

Hush is the word for Dorothy, brushing aside to ask Buchanan what on earth spurred on the eruption of emotions in the park. She learned from the get go one year earlier, if Buchanan sought a need to discuss the war, he initiated the conversation. Forcing the situation made matters worse more times than not. If Buchanan desired to have a conversation to hammer out a war memory, he started the conversation, not her. Otherwise, she left the situation alone.

The long hush of the night lasted deep into the morning hours. Not a peep from Buchanan. Dorothy assumed Robert kept his emotions to himself, wishing not to discuss the point.

All Dorothy heard in the night's stillness is classical music. Dorothy thought it funny, but the music did indeed ease the tension. She herself enjoyed the music immensely.

Attempting sleep ended up futile. Her only thought is – 'What in tarnation caused Robert to experience such a flashback in the park?' She certainly hungered for the root cause of the commotion. She again asked herself, 'What concealed memory lying in the deepest crevices of Robert's memory bank could agitate such a sorrowful response from playing capturing the flag?' But she accepted the fact if he chose not to talk, she would simply never know.

15 minutes passed and still no sleep for Dorothy. But the music soothed her soul as she laid in the bed, staring straight up into the ceiling, taking in every note of the music. Dorothy discovered this night the love of classical music Buchanan took hold of in Vietnam.

Dorothy assumed Robert had been sound asleep.

In the dim light and quietness of the evening, the music played softly. As five minutes passed, Dorothy heard Robert's soft voice whisper, "Dorothy."

Robert, indeed, is wide awake. Dorothy had been certain he zonked out like a light. Especially following the exhausting experience in the park.

"Yes." Dorothy responded.

"The children."

"What children?" asked Dorothy, pausing. "Our children? What about our children?"

"No."

"Then who's children?"

"The children in Vietnam."

Dorothy rolled over to face him. She looked immediately into his eyes to communicate with him directly.

Buchanan said, "The children playing capture the flag today, well, reminded me of children in Vietnam, playing like our children today. They were in my dream last night. One day, I-I was on my way in the bush with Jackson to conduct a service, one of the few instances I witnessed Jackson weep in Vietnam. On our way, we saw children playing like our babies today. We passed out chocolate bars and hard candy. They were just playing. Then the children ran to a truck full of marines, asking, it seemed, for more chocolate bars. But the children didn't go to the truck for more candy. One - one child had explosives strapped on...and-and.."

Buchanan seemed to be ready to yell as loud as he could, enough to have awoken the children. And he knew it. He sought to divulge all to his wife what had occurred, but disciplining himself to compose his emotions from screaming forth his pain from within. He continued to describe the incident with the children in Vietnam and Jackson.

"And th-they blew themselves up with the truck." Buchanan showed much emotion, not quite enough though to disturb the babies restful night. Robert laid in the bed mourning himself to sleep.

As Robert grieved himself to sleep, he felt the loving arms of Dorothy holding him as he achieves the rest so desired.

Dorothy suffered along with Robert. For the rest of her life, she knew in her heart war disturbed his mental state, and war changed her husband's life forever. Her husband returned from war a different person. With the horror of war forever on his mind, a perpetual impression upon his everyday mental state will be forever present. Yet Buchanan loved his country and served with pride. Dorothy was convinced Robert would do it all over again if God called him to go forth. The flag, honor, freedom - symbols and principles the Buchanan clan held high and worth dying for. The Buchanan clan loved the United States and its freedoms. But war is certainly not anything to be dismissive about. War causes pain and suffering.

Questions mounted high in Dorothy's mind the night of November 23, 1969. 'Will his flashbacks ever dissipate?' 'Will he ever compress in his mind his experiences he witnessed in Vietnam?' A simple game of capture the flag triggered a flashback. 'What else stored in his memory bank deemed traumatic enough to trigger a recurrence?' 'Will time heal his pain and soften the suffering?'

Dorothy endured a rude awakening today. Realization hit her this night flashbacks were permanent and ever present in the Buchanan household. Nothing, including classical music and visits to the park, forced the memories of war to dissolve, to disappear from his memory. Only God served as the source of relief for the pain and agony of war and the vivid memories embedded within his mind.

Marriage Counseling

August 7, 1970

Life stateside sunk in for Buchanan on his first day back from Vietnam eleven months ago. Domestic life took center stage, hitting him like a ton of bricks as soon as he stepped off the plane, placing his feet on southern California soil.

Since his return from Vietnam, his calling has been to minister to marines at El Toro Marine Base in southern California, drastically poles apart from his focus in Vietnam. Ministry now zeroed in on aspects of life for marines stateside. Buchanan's ministry now incessantly centered in on visiting troops, a top priority, but also pastoral counseling is now an integral part of ministry. The change of pace for ministry included PTS counseling, marriage counseling, finances, the stress of military life, along with other issues. The most curious component of ministry composed of marriage counseling. Buchanan happened to have a scheduled appointment at 1030 hours this morning with a couple he casually met, an officer and wife, starting his day off with a bang.

Buchanan placed his appointment temporarily on hold, performing a juggling act with his hands, attempting to feed breakfast to his babies.

At 0830 hours in the morning, Buchanan prayed for an extra hand to prepare breakfast for his children, who all woke up early this morning.

"Honey, I need the creamer." Buchanan yelled.

"It's on the table." answered Dorothy, in the infant's room, changing Johanna Kathleen's diaper.

Searching for the creamer on the kitchen table, Buchanan discovers right in front of him his heavy milked flavored cow creamer. Considered one of Buchanan's favorites, he preferred heavy servings of powered creamer in his coffee. Dorothy, humored with Buchanan's creamer addiction, maintained Robert preferred a little coffee with his creamer.

With every immense scoop of creamer dumped into his coffee mug, Buchanan glances at his beautiful children. For 11 months, he lived a domestic life and loved every minute of it. Buchanan stood high upon a familial mountain top, enjoying life with his wife, seven kids, and two dachshunds, Eva and Heidi.

With hard swigs of his medium mountain roast coffee, Buchanan consumes the flavor of the coffee, swallowing hard and firm, and with the undeniable, obvious pleasure of the coffee. "Umm. That's good stuff. Heck of a lot better than that bush coffee."

Buchanan grins at his own jest.

The Dachshunds, Eva and Heidi, are in their usual spot in the early morning, sitting on the kitchen floor, with food on the table, wagging their tails incessantly with energy and ears perked for free food.

"No Eva. No Heidi. No food for ya, girls. Our food's too fattening for your long backs." Buchanan said, laughing.

Their tails wag even faster, relaxing their ears ever so slightly as Buchanan spoke to the canines begging for food. Smiling from ear to ear toward his canine friends, Buchanan speaks a friendly sign of endearment.

As Buchanan found his hands full in the kitchen, Johanna preoccupied Dorothy's time in the baby's room.

James and Robert tugged on his uniform pants legs. "Daddy, Daddy. I need milk!" James yells.

"OK, OK son."

"I want a pop tart." Jacqueline Louise said.

"OK, honey, give me a second."

He rushed to the kitchen cabinet, grabbed two small glasses off the shelf, stepped to the refrigerator, taking hold of the milk from the refrigerator, and poured the milk for James and Robert. All the while, he glanced up at the kitchen counter surface snatching a package of pop tarts for Jacqueline Louise. As Buchanan finished pouring the milk, he tore open a pop tart package, handing a pop tart to Jacqueline.

He stood erect, proud of himself. No milk is split.

Laughing and giggling with food in their hands, making a mess, John and Kenneth were running circles around the kitchen table.

"John! Kenneth! Stop running, you're making a mess." Buchanan said.

Buchanan laughs, attempting to take hold of them next trip around the table near him. His only thought is – 'at this time last year, he had been in the middle of Hell ministering to marines, surviving to stay alive daily. He pondered how people back home in the United States took life so much for granted. He attempted to block those thoughts out of his mind as much as possible, as he mentally fled the possibility of having a major flashback in the middle of the morning while loving his family and caring for his children as a father.

He caught the two little monsters, holding the two ornery brothers in his hands momentarily. "I love you guys so much." He said, chuckling. "I'm going to do my very best to see we give you the best in life."

Buchanan softly hugs them and puts his two sons in their seats. "Now eat."

He stood for a moment, sighing.

As Buchanan continued to provide breakfast for the babies, Dorothy finally enters the kitchen with Johanna from down the hallway.

"Wow! You sure have been busy, haven't ya?" Dorothy said, grinning.

"Well, I don't see how you did it all alone while I was in Vietnam. Ya must have been on the go all day long."

"I was. But, as you know, Chaplain Daniel Anderson from Georgia, his daughters who are graduating from high school this year, Jennifer & Erma, helped with the baby sitting almost every day, especially in the summer. They're nice people." Dorothy said.

"Yes, they are." Buchanan said. "Johanna, all taken care of?"

"Yes, and she sure pooped something awful."

They chuckle.

"Well, she's just healthy." Buchanan said, smiling.

Dorothy placed Johanna in her high chair, for she was as hungry as a wolf, her tummy talking to her. Dorothy prepared some food for Johanna, as Buchanan finished up taking care of breakfast for the rest of the children.

Topping off his travel coffee mug, Buchanan set out for the base.

Dorothy mopped up, dishing out the breakfast to the babies, as the children finished consuming their morning meal.

Buchanan grabbed his cover from the hat rack, taking hold of his briefcase beside the kitchen cabinet, and headed for the side door of the house.

"I've got to go now. If not, I'm going to be late, and ya know how I feel about being late for anything, especially work."

"OK, honey. I'll see ya when you get home."

"Well, I'll be home as soon as I can. There's a rerun of our favorite western show about the secret service members on CBS tonight. I don't want to miss it." said Buchanan.

"I'm looking forward to it myself. Bye, babe. I love ya."

"Bye, Dorothy. Love ya." responded Buchanan.

He kissed his wife goodbye, hugged his kids, and reminding Robert II to resist 'bugging' his siblings, then flew out the side door, into the family VW bus in the driveway.

Buchanan made his way through the suburban streets onto the main highways of the Santa Ana traffic. He sure missed the Tri-State area of southeastern Ohio and Columbus Ohio traffic, much lighter and tolerable. The Buchanan's tolerance of the dense southern California traffic had run out of gas, lacking understanding for the traffic delays. The heavy traffic is for the birds.

Complaining about the traffic from the time he sat behind the steering wheel until he passed through the base gate, he finally arrived after a 55 minute drive to El Toro Marine Base in Irvine, California, near Santa Ana.

Buchanan arrived at the chapel at 0950 hours, and lo-and-behold, sitting right in front of him, is the 1030 hours appointment, waiting for him. He thought to himself, 'Are you kidding me? 40 minutes early?'

He sighed softly to himself.

Striding confidently into the reception room, Buchanan is greeted by Ms. Alice Becker, the chapel secretary, who rose out of her seat to introduce him to the marine couple who had patiently waited for 10 minutes. The couple actually arrived at 0940 hours.

Buchanan thought to himself, chuckling, '*Seriously*, getting to a marriage counseling session 40 minutes early? This couple must have *real* problems!'

"Good morning all." said Buchanan, in his usual energetic Kentuckian accent.

The couple rose out of the coach. "Good morning, chaplain."

Ms. Becker greeted Buchanan. "Good morning, Chaplain, this is Lieutenant Mark Holman and his wife Candy from Dallas, Texas."

"Yes, we've met through department visits and at some officer's briefings. Isn't that right, Lieutenant?" asked Buchanan.

"Yes sir, we've met. And this is my wife, Candy."

"Good to meet you." said Ms. Holman.

'Uh-oh!' thought Buchanan, giving Ms. Holman a head to toe look over. He thought to himself, 'I got one. A cheerleader type to counsel. Oh, boy.' All Buchanan saw in front of him is a good-looking blonde and she knows it, and thinks the world of herself, which means - 'it's all about me.' He despised counseling beauty queens.

Buchanan thought Holman a prize as well. Tall, good-looking male model type. Beach blonde jock sort of male. The dumb jock type Buchanan despised with a passion. He thought they had trouble thinking themselves out of a paper bag. Thinking posed a challenge in and of itself. The only communication they knew was grunting like a Neanderthal. But then again, he remembered Gunnery Sergeant Richard Jurgensen and Sergeant Smith, and how intelligent and forthright the two men were, setting the mold. He remembered them teaching him a lesson back in Vietnam – be careful judging books by covers. In fact, many dumb jock types he met in southern California were well-rounded individuals, intellectually and *spiritually*. He hoped and prayed Holman possessed a well-rounded mentality.

All the while he thought, 'Why does *this* couple need any help from this nerdy chaplain? Only the Lord knows.' Besides, the Holman's ranged between the mid to upper 20s in age and Buchanan is approaching 40. *Why* come to him? Maybe he seemed older and wiser, possibly the father type. Regardless of the age gap, his first impression of the couple, at least on the surface, is the Holmans were good people. Young and inexperienced, the Holmans simply needed help, regardless of Buchanan's cynical frame of mind toward silly cheerleaders and dumb jocks. He took a deep breath and said a silent prayer to the Lord to grant him patience and decided to take a crack to be as positive as possible entering the counseling session.

"Why don't y'all come into my office and we'll get started." said Buchanan.

Motioning with his right hand to enter the office, the Holmans entered ahead of him.

Glancing toward Ms. Becker, Buchanan ambled into his office, grimacing.

Ms. Becker said all she wanted to say in her smile given toward Buchanan - 'Better you than me.'

Entering the office, Buchanan says, "Keep the mountain roast a brewing, Ms. Becker."

"We'll do, chaplain." answered Ms. Becker.

He promptly swiped the frown off his face before entering his office.

"Please, please, sit down. Sit down." said Buchanan.

The Holmans sat in the two cushion chairs with little emotion.

Buchanan stepped confidently around his desk to his huge leather swivel chair and sat. Grinning, he asked, "What can I do for y'all today?"

Staring straight at him, the Holman's were as quiet as a mouse. The stillness of the moment gave Buchanan the heebie-jeebies.

Buchanan broke the ice with a simple question, "Is y'all's problem a financial one?"

Candy nodded her head no.

"Well, uh - um..." said Buchanan, "is it - a spiritual problem?"

Candy again nodded her head no.

"Is it a problem with the, well - stress of military life? Isn't it?"

Again, Candy nodded no.

After a brief pause, Buchanan blurted out, "Well, it-it's got to be a–a family, in-laws problem? Right?"

The nod thrown from Candy toward Buchanan this time around is ever more emphatic.

After asking every possible question he could ask, he ran out of problems to mention to the Holmans. He is now pressed to ask deeper, more intimate questions.

Buchanan, nervous and fidgety in his chair, caught himself staring directly at the Holman's across from his desk who were gazing right at him - stoic. Though Lieutenant Holman attempted a grin to lighten the tense moment for Buchanan.

Buchanan slightly smiles at the couple, looks to his right, and swallows hard.

The only other problem to point out Buchanan dreaded to mention, but pressed to ask.

Buchanan hated facing the inquiry into the Holman's life, but pressured to ask.

Swallowing hard to clear his throat, he asked, "Is it a - physical problem? You know, an-an intimacy problem?"

Buchanan never witnessed a more animated, spirited nod of affirmative from a human being in his life than the nod from Candy. Sitting in his chair, he glanced down toward his shoes nervously, and with two deep breaths in his best Freudian imitation, says "Well, tell me about it."

He certainly did not intend to make them feel uncomfortable, clearing his throat.

The last thing Buchanan looked forward to this morning was to counsel a set of 'Ken' and 'Barbie' concerning their intimate sexual life. Counseling Ken and Barbie types never resulted as a thrill for Buchanan, considering his disparagement of cheerleaders and dumb jocks. In his experience of life, he thought nothing flowed in the veins of Ken and Barbie's but conceit and smug.

The Holmans remained silent, hesitant to be the first to speak on the subject. Buchanan encouraged some initiative to the young couple to speak once again by saying, "Well, let me know what's going on."

Immediately, the Holmans spoke simultaneously. Stopping suddenly, they glared at one another as if the other had interrupted. After a pause, the couple started speaking up yet again, at the same time. The second attempt to speak extended for a drawn-out moment, followed by arguing with one another. All the while Buchanan strived to lead the couple to speak one at a time, but to no avail.

Finally, Buchanan received the Holman's attention, chuckles and says in his strong mountain accent when excited, "Wait, wait a minute, Mark and Candy. Let's hear from y'all one at a time, please. I-I can't understand y'all when you are both talking at once. Candy, ladies first. Tell me, what's wrong?"

Candy spoke, rambling on and on, talking nineteen to the dozen. The jabbering from Candy made time stand still, an eternity for Buchanan, taking a peek or two toward Lieutenant Holman, reflecting a crushed man drained of a reservoir of human emotion.

The staring of Lieutenant Holman straight at Chaplain Buchanan made him as nervous as a cat on hot bricks, forcing a smile or two while his wife rant and raved.

She went on for ten minutes. Whining and complaining she is ignored the whole day long and her husband is too busy for anything, including showing attention to her physically.

The ancient idiom 'patience is a virtue' served little purpose for Buchanan, listening to Candy spill the beans a mile a minute. His tank of patience sat on empty, in no hurry to fill it up anytime soon. Buchanan sat on deaf ears, following just two minutes of Candy's ten minutes of ranting. He barely heard a word of her spouting off complaints. As she rattled off her ramblings, Ms. Holman, weak and distressed, finally broke down emotionally. Buchanan offered her a tissue or two from his box on his desk. Taking a few tissues from the box, she continued as Buchanan, deaf of her voice, acknowledged her with an occasional nod, smiling to show a state of understanding just to be polite. Ms. Holman's marital problem passed far from his mind, as he thought of how the Ohio State Buckeyes season was going to turn out this year. He thought, 'can the Buckeyes reap revenge on Michigan for beating Ohio State the previous year?'

Ms. Holman's mouth ranting reminded him of silent movie actresses and the rapid mouth movements from films when he worked in a movie house in Middleport, Ohio and the owners sponsored silent movie weekends.

When Candy finally finished, Buchanan, oddly humored with her mouth, is buzzed the young lady finally shut up. With the little he heard from her, he realized she is indeed a nice young lady. Sincere and honest, she exemplified the deepest love for her husband. Breaking down emotionally toward the end of her turn to speak, she reached for another tissue.

"Here, Ms. Holman, a tissue." Buchanan said.

Buchanan heard enough to understand Ms. Holman just sought after the Lieutenant to show her some attention physically and sexually.

Lieutenant Holman now stepped up to bat at the plate, taking a turn to express himself.

As soon as Lieutenant Holman opened his mouth, Buchanan convinced himself another rant is coming his way. And sure enough, Holman rambled on for ten minutes. Ranting seemed to run in the family. Again, Buchanan's mind turned to sports and the Cincinnati Reds. As Lieutenant Holman spoke, Buchanan thought to himself,

'How good are they going to be in 1970? Is this young newcomer going to continue to be a great catcher for the Reds?' The catcher, his favorite baseball position, inspired Buchanan to place this young man as the best catcher of all time and to think of him as an outstanding catcher at such an early stage in his career.

But as Holman spoke, Buchanan took notice of him, pushing his baseball thoughts to the side, at least for now. Listening to Holman, he came to grips Holman suffered as Buchanan suffered, a marine in Buchanan's shoes. He perked up, heeding to Holman's words, detecting clues sparking an interest in Holman's mental and spiritual state. Holman experienced combat. An eyewitness of appalling, horrific, and tragic events like himself. He listened to Holman and his problems, which arose following his return home from the war. The nightmares came frequently. When fireworks ignited, they reminded him of weaponry and explosives discharged in the bush. Even television shows triggered a flashback.

Holman revealed he had experienced the war comparable to Buchanan, but a palpable variance is the fact Holman might have taken the lives of enemy combatants, an experience Buchanan is thankful he knew nothing about.

The very little Buchanan heard from Ms. Holman and 'her side' of the story, it hit him she's innocently obtuse of Lieutenant Holman's difficulties coping with war. He wished now he could rewind the clock and listen more to Candy's explanation of her situation. He certainly will not request of her to rehash her account all over again. The thought made him cringe, and oddly enough, humored him. To his regret, he misjudged the prissy couple. He's now sorry for slapping onto the Holman's the dumb jock and 'silly' cheerleader bias he attained, a bad habit he gained over the years.

"It's difficult chaplain to concentrate on the vital parts of life without thinking about combat, sir." Holman said.

"I've the same problem, Lieutenant Holman." responded Buchanan.

In the Holman's spilling of the beans, the young couple revealed the concerns and problems in their lives. Buchanan caught in his ear the couple blurted out they owned a pool in their backyard. He seemed enlightened with an idea he had used prior to counseling couples experiencing intimacy problems and who owned a pool.

Buchanan spoke up. "Well, we've been here a while and I've heard the two of you speak. And I know without a shadow of a doubt the two of you are very much in love with one another. Y'all kind of remind me of the love my wife and I have for each other. So I am going to suggest something to ya I think will work. And I think it will *really* work. After the sun goes down, and just to make you more comfortable, make sure there's none of your neighbors still up, go out to your pool and just - just, well, go ta-take a swim. Go take a swim, but, b-but skinny dipping. You know, with no clothes. With no....," Buchanan clears his throat, "clothes on, as in...naked. Yes....naked. Who knows what might happen after that?" A nervous Buchanan chuckled.

Buchanan shuffles himself in his chair, fidgety, smiles at the Holman's, and re-situates himself. He clears his throat, shifting his eyes left and right, avoiding at all costs direct eye contact with Ms. Holman as he notices her in the corner of his eye.

Ms. Holman turned as red as her sundress she had on, furious.

Lieutenant Holman looked at Chaplain Buchanan with a slight smile on his face, as if to say, 'Yeah, chaplain, that's a great idea.'

Buchanan noticed Lieutenant Holman's smile. He was just about to say something when Candy jumped straight up out of her cushion chair, placed her hands on her hips, and bellowed, "What? How dare you! That is not something I want you, a chaplain, to suggest to me. My sexual life is very private. I am a private person. *You*, a chaplain, advising *me* to do something like that! What kind of chaplain *are* you? I can't believe a man of God would suggest such a thing! I'm leaving. Come on, Mark."

Candy bolted out the office door, at a blink of an eye, past Ms. Becker's desk, and outside in the Chapel hallway.

Lieutenant Holman rose out of his seat, looking down towards the floor, glancing up at the chaplain. "Sorry chaplain. She gets riled up sometimes, ya know."

"I understand." said Buchanan as he rose out of his leather swivel chair.

"Thanks for all your help. Thanks for listening, chaplain."

"I didn't do anything. Besides, I think I made matters worse for ya." said Buchanan, snickering.

"Listen, Lieutenant Holman. If you need to talk - anything, come anytime."

"Thank you, sir?"

"Mark, let's go!" barked Candy.

"I better go now, sir. Again, thank you very much."

Shaking hands with Buchanan, Holman departed with his wife out to their Volkswagen Bug.

Ms. Becker peeked into Chaplain Buchanan's office, smiling sympathetically.

"I'm sorry, chaplain. She seems to have a difficult time adjusting." Ms. Becker said.

"I'm sorry too, Ms. Becker. Me too."

"Want some more coffee, sir?"

"Do I ever!" answered Buchanan.

Ms. Becker walked into the office and topped off Chaplain Buchanan's coffee mug full of mountain roast.

"Thank you very much, Ms. Becker."

"You're very welcome, sir." said Ms. Becker, closing the door behind her to give Buchanan some privacy.

He ambled over to his phonograph player and placed an album of Vivaldi, an album of light pieces of music to listen to. He sat in his chair, relaxing, drinking his coffee. Turning his chair facing the window, he caught sight of the Holmans heading for their Volkswagen Bug. Candy marched herself straight to the car from the side entrance of the chapel, expressing in every step of the way she is not happy with her husband. Her body language said one thing - he failed to confront the chaplain, informing him he was out of place proposing something so suggestive. Candy stood, yapping away, with her hands on her hips. Buchanan sat in his chair, attempting to make out every word spoken, though inaudible, facing a thick pane of glass separating the uppity sorority beauty queen and a deflated, dejected chaplain.

Buchanan smiled, thinking to himself, 'What do these lay people think ministers are? Boring?' He has been humored ever since he entered the ministry of how ignorant lay people are in churches, let alone worldly people, of clergy's intimate relationships with their spouses.

His mind wondered. First and foremost of thoughts is this time last year he stood amid combat and death. Holding boys breathing in their last moments in this life, praying and reciting Scripture with them, and crying with their fellow marines as they entered Eternity. And now here he is one year later, dealing with people's sexual intimacy problems, needing 12 hands to serve breakfast to his seven precious children, and handling dreadful southern California traffic. Candy Holman is clueless. She had no inkling of the devastating memories and mental pictures permanently imprinted on the minds of combatants, including her own husband.

Regardless, Buchanan is well aware of the truth. Trivial matters in this life count least when one has run the gauntlet of combat as Lieutenant Holman and himself had in Vietnam. Prayerfully, Candy Holman will come to terms with her husband's permanent scares of war. Hopefully, time spent with him will be of help just a tad bit. Buchanan can only pray it will. In time, she will understand the emotions of her husband and to discover some means for her husband to cope with the combat fatigue.

Ken and Barbie

August 16, 1970

In a matter of days, the Buchanan clan will cross the Ohio River out of West Virginia and into the Buckeye state.

The triumphant crossing into God's country will come soon. But Buchanan must first fulfill his obligations as chaplain and deliver his last Sunday sermon on the base, drawing to a close the commitment to his commission as chaplain in California.

On this Sunday morning, Buchanan prepared himself mentally and spiritually to deliver his last sermon at the El Toro Marine Base Chapel, and a memorable one it shall be. Protestant chaplains alternated delivering sermons, and Buchanan took his turn in the pulpit. The chapel, a favorite of Buchanan's in his Navy career, reflected the welcoming and tender Spirit of God, most beautiful. The chapel bestowed colorful stained glassed windows, a spacious and gorgeous baptistery with a painting of a mountainous river valley as a background, and many stone walled portions in between a Spanish type wall for the interior provided the perfect ingredients for a place of worship. Laid out next to the chapel, rested a Spanish prayer garden, a spot Buchanan prayed in from time to time, accompanied with an ecumenical ambiance entering the garden, an added plus for Buchanan.

Arriving early as always, Buchanan isolated himself momentarily to mentally prepare for the delivery of the sermon. The five billeted Navy chaplains at El Toro marine base were an array of various denominations, including two Southern Baptist, counting Buchanan, an Episcopalian, a Methodist, and one Roman Catholic priest. The chaplain Buchanan favored most had been the Roman Catholic priest. The homilies delivered from the young priest enlightened Buchanan spiritually, gaining something new to strengthen his faith in his Lord. Besides, Buchanan enjoyed his company and thought of him as a great fellow human being and follower of Christ. The Episcopalian possessed in his arsenal of skills a counseling degree from the seminary. Buchanan considered his repertory of counseling tips a gold mine, immeasurably improving his skills as a counselor. He certainly needed them sitting with the Holmans several days ago.

Sunday services begun at 1045 hours following Sunday School. Chapel services were typically a packed house each and every Sunday full of marines and sailors and their families, officer and enlisted alike. Rarely would Buchanan look over the church pews and notice any deadwood or empty space in the chapel on Sabbath mornings. The days of any deadwood were Sundays scheduled when Buchanan's fellow Southern Baptist chaplain delivered the sermon. The chaplain seemed rather blunt and service personnel were usually uncomfortable listening to a chaplain speak with bias spilling from his mouth. If the slightest notion from a chaplain from the pulpit preached a theology a person is headed to Hell if congregants refused to accept his personal religious convictions became an instant turn off to fellow military personnel, a deaf ear to the chaplain. A truth Buchanan discovered early in his chaplain ministry and one held stronger today than it did three years ago. The truth is, if a Navy chaplain desires to be a successful, a chaplain must take hold of ecumenicalism. If not, Buchanan insisted no one has any business putting on a Navy uniform with a chaplain insignia on it.

1045 hours came fast. The time to deliver the sermon has now come.

Buchanan peeked out the side entrance door into the sanctuary, spotting his clan sitting in the second row in the front left set of pews. All three sets of pews packed shoulder to shoulder in the chapel. Members of the base arriving on this Sunday morning to express their support for Buchanan, with admiration from one end of the base to the other for the devoted Navy chaplain, seeking to attend his last service who will deliver a sermon to marine and sailor personnel and their families. Dorothy and the children caught him peeking out the door, smiling from ear to ear, sending a resounding wave to the patriarch of the family. He dearly loved each and everyone of his family members. He is proud of his family unit.

Though Buchanan stood confident and assured of himself delivering a sermon, an unusual nervousness came over him this particular morning. In the short temporary moments until he stood in the congregation's presence, the size of the congregation caused his gut to wrench. Glancing out at his family, he once again noticed no deadwood in the sanctuary, not an empty seat in the house.

The organist played the prelude to a finish, signaling the beginning of the service. As usual on Sundays, the chaplains filed out of the side entrance along with the Catholic and Protestant lay readers to read the Old and New Testament Scriptures. Navy Chaplains selected permanent Catholic and Protestant Scripture readers of his choice when delivering the sermon to read the sacred text to compliment his message delivered.

The usual order of service begun. The order usually followed a welcome, singing of the hymns, a reading of the Scriptures, a children's sermon led by one of the chaplains, and special music. The music typically rendered a piece of music reflecting the sermon by the chapel choir, a marine or sailor singing a solo, or a service member's spouse provided a special voice to lift the spirit of God. Prior to the special music, a time reserved for prayer requests provided an opportunity to lift El Toro base's prayers and concerns. The chaplain delivering the Sunday sermon led in the prayer time, requiring Buchanan to rise out of his seat this day, step up behind the pulpit ready and willing to lift up the prayer requests in a vocal prayer.

Buchanan said confidently, as he always did, "Let us pray." Just as he spoke, he stood rooted to the spot as he caught a glimpse of a bad dream, a memory repressed in the deepest crevices of his mind. He set his eyes on none other than Ken and Barbie, Mark and Candy Holman.

Buchanan's blood ran cold.

Congregants stared at Buchanan. Caught catching flies, he adjusted himself accordingly, obviously nervous. His demeanor displayed a complete 180, shifting in place, rubbing his chin, glancing left and right.

Buchanan figured the odds were a million to one the Holmans would be sitting in the congregation on his last day to deliver a sermon on the base. Standing in front of a full house, he stood in shock. Internally, his stomach turned 100 miles an hour. He thought he had seen the last of the Holmans on August 7, 1970, never to see them again.

He never felt so uncomfortable in his life. And here, in the midst of an ecumenical congregation, sat the young girl who thinks of him as dirty and vulgar. He simply set out to help the Holmans days ago. Buchanan thought of nothing else but what scuttlebutt Candy might have spread on base about him. He thought - 'Only the Lord knows what scuttlebutt that girl might have spread all over the base about me.' All sorts of thoughts traveled back and forth in his mind of what she might have spread on base - 'Chaplain Buchanan is a pervert.' 'Chaplain Buchanan has a dirty mind.' 'Chaplain Buchanan is a vulgar person.'

Every soul in the congregation, including the Holmans, caught Buchanan catching flies, who stared straight in their direction.

"Uh, well - Let us pray. Oh. I-I've already said that. Didn't I?" Buchanan chuckles.

His fellow chaplains fidget in their chairs, smiling.

The immense admiration for Buchanan on the base spilled over to civilians and families. Befuddled congregants asked themselves, 'What's wrong with Chaplain Buchanan?'

Dorothy knew a problem arose with the sudden change of demeanor in her husband. She takes a gander toward her husband, smiling a message of, 'Whatever is wrong, it will be OK. Just go on, it will be OK.'

Catching a glimpse of his wife's smile interjected a shot in the arm of self-confidence for Buchanan, a boost of self-assurance endorsing

Buchanan to gain his composure to pray. He prayed confidently as usual, followed by the special music. The music, performed by an enlisted marine, sang *How Great Thou Art*, touching the hearts of the congregants as the words flowed from her lips. Dorothy, who possessed a fine voice herself, listened intently to every word, hearing God's omnipotence in the words sung.

Listening to the marine sing her special, Buchanan thought of nothing but Candy and the possible scuttlebutt spread about the base, spreading rumors of their counseling session, informing her best friends Chaplain Buchanan is dirty minded and had no business conducting Christian counseling.

Buchanan sweated, nervous to no end. He felt it was an eternity for the special music to come to a screeching halt. When the music finally ends, Buchanan's time to deliver the sermon had come. Rising out of his chair, he delivered the sermon. It seemed the most difficult 25 minutes of Buchanan's life delivering this Sabbath day's message. As he delivered his words, he regretted the sermon topic chosen ever more, as his message prepared gave an emphasis on the biblical view of a Christian family unit. When addressing the husband and wife's love for one another within a family unit, it is bloody murder attempting to hash through it.

The effort to avoid any sort of a glance toward the Holmans heightened as Buchanan spoke to the congregation. An accidental glance toward the couple came painfully, immediately shifting his eyes in another direction within the sanctuary.

The sermon found its end, as it was the fastest sermon Buchanan ever preached, and for good reason. As the final hymn sung reverberated throughout the sanctuary, the chaplains filed down the center of the sanctuary between the pews, into the vestibule, to shake hands with congregants as they departed from the chapel.

Today, Buchanan wished he had excused himself to go to the head or something such. But he thought, 'I have to face the inevitable'. So Buchanan stood at the end of the chaplain's line to shake hands with the congregants streaming through the line in the vestibule. Buchanan's mind temporarily came distracted from the Holman's presence greeting and meeting people in line he knew on the base. His mind shifted quickly back onto the Holman's in no time.

As minutes passed, the Holmans reached Buchanan in line to shake hands. He simply had the urge to leave and say nothing, shying away from any confrontation. However, he kept saying to himself, 'The Lord's with me,' over and over again.

The Holmans shook the hand of the first chaplain in line, as the couple made their way down the line to Buchanan, last in line. He thought, 'Here she goes. The chewing out!'

Instead of receiving the brunt end of a chewing out or the cold shoulder, the Holman's presented themselves as cheerie, delighted to see Buchanan, greeting him enthusiastically with the broadest of smiles.

"It worked." spoke Candy softly and displaying the friendliest of smiles.

"What?" responded Buchanan, with a bit of curiosity in his voice. "Worked? What worked?" muttered Buchanan as a slow, stretched out smile emerged upon his face.

"Yes. As Candy said, it worked." concurred a thankful and definite Lieutenant Holman.

"Ohhh, yes. *Yes*, indeed. I'm thrilled it worked out for the two of you. Great!" said Buchanan with zeal and with a broader smile, knowing now exactly what worked.

"Hahaha!" laughed Buchanan. "Amen!"

Clueless is the word to everyone standing about who overheard. It is the chaplain and the couple's little secret all their own.

The three smiled from ear to ear.

Candy confessed, "We wanted to come this morning. Let ya know your suggestion worked perfecto and to support your ministry today, it being your last day. We wanted you to know we appreciate you, chaplain. And I am very sorry for my behavior the other day. It was very rude of me."

"No. No. It's OK. Amen! Amen to an answer to prayers."

"Yes, sir. Well, again, thanks Chaplain." said Lieutenant Holman.

"You're very welcome."

"Well, we better go now." said Candy.

"Bye-Bye." said the Holman's.

"Bye-Bye. Have a good day." responded Buchanan.

Buchanan once again watched the couple depart for their Volkswagen Bug, hand in hand and happy as a clam.

Buchanan, ecstatic for the Holman's, stood watching the couple go forth, knowing their love within burst forth toward one another. But at that moment, a moment of joy and laughter, he oddly evoked memories of boys he witnessed die and would never experience love and companionship.

The eternal haunting of war is gnawing, never to pass away. The remembrance of warfare and its long-lasting impact on his life are forever embedded in the corners of his mind.

Buchanan delivered a last heartfelt wave to the Holmans, as the young couple smiled and gestured back toward the man who aided them to discover their even deeper love for one another. The Holmans drove off in their VW as they held a special place in Buchanan's heart. The Lord placed him in the right place at the right time to minister to the Holman's, facilitating the means for them to merge closer as husband and wife, to rediscover their love for one another.

Though Buchanan played a small positive role in the Holman's life, serving them to discover a deeper love for one another still overlooked the fact that many boys in Vietnam died never to experience love.

With his heart permanently scared, the hurt Buchanan experienced in war is never to pass.

Moving Back Home

August 24, 1970

The pounding of Buchanan clan heart beats felt strong, rapid as gushing adrenaline flowed within the Buchanan's veins, and the licking of lips from wrecked nerves, all in anticipation of crossing the Ohio River into God's country, the Buckeye state, only falling in second behind West Virginia and Kentucky. Just another 4 or 5 more hours on the road to the bridge in Huntington, West Virginia, and to cross over the Ohio river. To cross the river from Huntington, West Virginia, the birthplace of Dorothy and partly raised, into the Buckeye state will be special, for the city is where she attended nursing school. From there, on to McArthur, Ohio, in Vinton County for the next ministry position for the Buchanan's, a pastorate and a commission from the Southern Baptist Convention.

Robert craved to travel through Cincinnati, a route Buchanan choose to travel, but to no avail. His simple intent in Cincinnati had been to purchase Cincinnati Reds' attire for the rest of the baseball season. Dorothy sighed heavily, informing Robert there will be plenty of time for spending money on Reds' attire.

The Buchanan's traveled through Louisville, Kentucky at 1630 hours. The kids were utterly exhausted, sleeping.

The fastest route available at this point is best for the children, arriving at their destination tonight. The kids slept most of the night in the VW bus till their arrival in McArthur, Ohio. The Buchanan's had spent the previous night between St Louis, Missouri and the Illinois state line. The day had been long, traveling Interstate 64 for hundreds of miles, with the anticipation building to a boiling over driving to McArthur, Ohio. The day of August 24, 1970, started early for the Buchanan's, in anticipation of launching a new chapter in their lives, a new ministry in southeastern Ohio. The couple is familiar with McArthur, as Dorothy's father moved from one town after another because of his construction work, building many main routes of travel in southeastern Ohio. Her father possessed a robust Protestant work ethic, instilling into his children the value and importance of work, strengthening within a person's inner self a confidence in one's self. Robert knew of McArthur from attending Middleport High School in Middleport, Ohio, who competed against Vinton County High School in sports. Dorothy graduated from Middleport High School and played in the band. The band played two halftime shows when Middleport traveled to McArthur to compete in football games.

Passing through Louisville, Kentucky, triggered many memories for Robert. He attended The Southern Baptist Theological Seminary in Louisville for just one semester. In the middle of his four-year stint at The Trinity Lutheran Seminary in Columbus, Ohio, he transferred to Southern Seminary. The campus is a carbon copy of educational architecture, Kentuckian southern life, and theological training in a classical sense. Buchanan simply described the campus as 'beautiful.' And the reputation of Southern Seminary is held high in the Southern Baptist Convention and well deserved. Though the seminary's reputation held high marks in the historical method, Buchanan missed the biblical and theological training at Trinity. His love of history flowed within his veins, and Trinity rendered a holistic approach Buchanan relished in. And in true ecumenical spirit and raised a Presbyterian, he soaked in all the theology he could absorb from the Lutherans, considered in his estimation firm in their beliefs. And as a sturdy and strapping Baptist, he grew to appreciate Lutheran theological strengths. He credited much of his success as a Navy chaplain for being exposed to so many theological viewpoints. He understood his parishioners in the Navy better than others, he thought, because of his foundation of knowing others' theological convictions and what he agreed with regarding those theological beliefs as well as what he disagreed with. His wide experience entrenched his own Baptist convictions, creating in him an even more devout Baptist, knowing others' theological stances.

The next benchmark of the trip 45 minutes away from Louisville is Franklin, Kentucky, the state's capital. The passing of Franklin measures 60 minutes closer to the Ohio river. Franklin sat in the heart of the bluegrass state and smack dab in the middle of horse country, throwing out further vibes to the Buchanan clan they were finally home and out of California.

They passed Franklin in no time. The town of Georgetown, Kentucky, came next along Interstate 64 down the road from Lexington, the home of the University of Kentucky. Georgetown, a town the Buchanan's knew extremely well, housed Georgetown College where Buchanan earned his Bachelor of Science degree in History and a Bachelor of Arts degree in Biblical Theology with a track in Bible History. Georgetown is nothing but beautiful from the interstate and the Buchanan's wanted to just stop and drive through for old time's sake. But as Dorothy said, in time, they will return to visit.

The next point of the trip slotted Ashland, Kentucky, the farthest city to reach in between benchmarks. Interstate 64 trailed along the cusp of the most eminent mountains in Kentucky. Just 10 to 15 miles south, a person could drive into major mountain ranges. The Buchanan's missed the mountains, especially crossing the river and visiting kinfolk during the holidays and family reunions.

The Buchanan children were plumb tuckered out, zonked out by travel lag. The Buchanan's simply let their children sleep on a seat in the VW bus or lay down in one of the two baby cribs Dorothy placed in the bus. A crowded bus of exhausted children, but all was good and love filled the air through and through.

An hour and a half passed placing the Buchanan's on the outskirts of Ashland, Kentucky. One exit after another painted the letters - Ashland Kentucky. The Buchanan's were ecstatic. Home is nearer and nearer. The children had woken up by now and joined their parents in the anticipation of crossing the Ohio River.

Just 10 or 12 miles to go and the Buchanan clan will be within the city limits of Huntington, West Virginia, the last major city of travel, then hitting the rural roads to McArthur, Ohio. "We need exit 6 for Huntington." Dorothy said, glancing at the AAA route triptik. Exit 6 ran into Route 52, running straight into Huntington, West Virginia, then across the river toward Ironton, Ohio. From there, state route 93 from the Ohio river straight to McArthur, Ohio. The couple simultaneously spotted exit 6.

"Yay!" came a yell, along with the children, clueless of why all the excitement, except maybe for Robert II, but they yelled anyway.

Pulling the VW bus off onto exit 6, Buchanan turned left onto route 52 toward the bridge. The building of fervor in three and a half years to cross the river into Ohio for good overwhelmed the loving couple. The couple teared up, emotional for home, again wrapping themselves around the various, diverse cultures of Ohio, including the Germans and eastern Europeans, the French and Welsh cultures settling in southeastern Ohio. The Buckeye state is just around the corner. The bridge was now just five miles from the exit, five miles that seemed an eternity.

The children were all awake, including the youngest.

Crossing the city limits into Huntington is now only a matter of time, as the five miles turned into a sprint instead of an eternity, driving over the bridge in the VW bus into Ohio as the wheels of the bus hit the pavement of the bridge, elevating the Buchanan's in the bus from the road pavement onto the surface of the bridge. The VW bus traveled an upward slope from the West Virginia side of the bridge until Robert and Dorothy arrived in the middle of the passage, on an even slope with the river. As the descending slope on the Ohio side of the bridge came forth, the Buchanan's took a glimpse onto the hillsides of Ohio. Robert and Dorothy caved to their emotions as they yelled "Yay" and "Woo Hoo!" with the kids joining in along with them, again not really knowing what all the hoopla is about. Dorothy and Buchanan knew. The Buchanan's caught a glimpse of the welcoming sign which read “Ohio Welcomes You.” Rolling into Ohio signaled to the Buchanan’s they were home to stay.

Robert survived a horrific war. The arrival home eased some of the pain, alleviating some of the grief and heartache. The eyewitness experience of war only Robert Buchanan and his fellow veterans can understand.

McArthur, Ohio, measured less than an hour and a half away. A new ministry forth coming for the Buchanan’s, a new start. The pain of war will always haunt Buchanan, but ministering in a familiar place, with familiar people, will assuage his mental and physical being.

The Restaurant

June 19, 1972

In store today for Buchanan, is a day of trepidation and fear. He scheduled a visit to the Skawinski family farm in Preble County. In Vietnam, Buchanan promised Skawinski a visit to the farm, and nothing from the Devil and his legions are going to prevent him from breaking that promise. The trip from McArthur, Ohio, to the Dayton area amounted to a two and a half hour drive, an agonizing and painful journey for Buchanan. The journey amounted to a mental struggle. An attempt to push aside the heartbreaking memory of Skawinski's death. Buchanan's fear of suffering a major terrifying flashback absent from Dorothy in the presence of Adolphus's parents overwhelmed him. She served as an incredible stronghold of support when a sudden recurrence occurred. Everything and anything to mentally focus on other than the war is welcomed, as his efforts to brush aside the thoughts of the war challenged him. Nervous, Buchanan brainstormed for the words to speak to Skawinski's parents.

To help matters, he stuck a copy of the photo taken of the last patrol out with Skawinski in the upper inside pocket of his dress coat for moral support. Taking an occasional glance at the photo motivated him to fulfill his promise to Skawinski.

Buchanan suffered from a guilt-ridden heart, knowing Skawinski sacrificed his life. If not for Skawinski's bravery to save his chaplain's life, he might very well be in Preble County, Ohio today with his parents.

At 0900 hours in the morning, Buchanan prepared himself mentally and spiritually for his visit

Buchanan spoke on the phone with Skawinski's father for directions to the family farm. Dreading the visit, he set out to fulfill his commitment to Adolphus. The Skawinski family lived in Harrison Township, a small community in Preble County, Ohio, north of Dayton.

Buchanan kissed his wife goodbye, followed by hugging his precious children as he stepped toward the side door of the house into his car. Glancing down toward his children, he prayed his babies will never experience war in their lifetime. The thought saddened him. Stepping into his Buick Oldsmobile, Buchanan waved to his family one last time, driving onto the road out of his driveway. Much of the outing traveled on two-lane country roads of southeastern Ohio until driving to a four-lane highway outside of Chillicothe, Ohio for some fifteen miles, a God send to speed the journey forward. Some ten miles past Chillicothe, the windy and curvy roadways returned, slowing the trip back to a creep and crawl. The tedious and nerve racking route made the trip seem endless. The beauty of summer scenery in rural Ohio eased the pain of traveling at a snail's pace, providing at least a pleasant excursion.

Buchanan dressed himself in his usual black suit, white shirt, and a novelty tie, as always. He preferred statement or novelty ties, those which he is immensely fond of, wearing a distinctive, different tie every day. Buchanan relished in the fun of his ties, lightening the mood in precarious situations such as visiting sick parishioners or delivering a eulogy at funerals. Today, he wore a cowboy western tie to lighten the mood visiting the Skawinski's. When visiting parishioners and prospect members for the church, he insisted on presenting himself professional and ministerial, a top priority for him.

Turning onto US Route 50, Buchanan headed for Chillicothe, Ohio, the midpoint between McArthur and Dayton, Ohio. The last building standing on the outskirts of McArthur, Ohio stood The Griddle, a local restaurant the Buchanan family patronized frequently. The restaurant specialized in steaks and roast beef dishes.

Oh, how he longed to stop and eat, avoiding the inevitable face to face visit with Skawinski's parents. The risk of embarrassing himself suffering a serious flashback in the Adolphus's parents living room terrified him, to the point of tempting him of making a u-turn and racing back home. A point of pride Buchanan set as a top priority had been to keep control of one's self, as Buchanan rarely displayed signs of losing control of his emotions, except for coping with flashbacks related to the war. Now three miles past The Griddle, his fear of suffering a flashback at the Skawinski's intensified tremendously, tempting him to turn around and hightail it back home.

Still yet, he made a commitment and promise to God to minister to the marines of the 7th Engineering Marine Battalion, even after the war ended, and that's exactly what he's going to do – minister to the men and their families when called upon. He fulfilled his commitment. An hour on the road, Buchanan thought to himself, 'Please, Please Lord. Give me the strength. Give me the words to say and encouragement to face the Skawinski's.'

Buchanan's thoughts turned to the day Skawinski died in his arms. A vivid, permanent memory. Skawinski's last moments etched into his memory bank, stirring much sadness in his heart and soul.

Occasionally stopping at a 7-Eleven, Buchanan purchased a pop or bottled water to break the monotony of the drive, which did little to ease the boredom. Just a mile or two down the road following the stop, Skawinski's death emerged first and foremost once again.

Following an additional hour of traveling, Buchanan stopped to eat. Time had raced fast to a bit after 1100 hours, just outside of Xenia, Ohio. Closing in on the Skawinski home, Buchanan felt a little food would calm the nerves. In the past, he patronized a local hamburger joint, A-Mayseing Burgers, he favored when traveling to Dayton. When Buchanan stopped to get a bite to eat, he never failed to observe a table empty of patrons. He figured the customers filled the restaurant day-in and day-out for the excellent customer service from the Mayse family, local farmers and owners and proprietors of A-Mayseing Burgers. Beef certainly had been a lifetime favorite of Buchanan's and stopping at a local burger joint is right up his alley.

The hamburger joint catered to locals to hang out and discuss scuttlebutt thrown around town. Stepping into the burger joint, the hostess seated Buchanan comfortably in a back booth close to the corner.

Patrons, all locals, packed the tables and booths, except for several empty tables in the corner. The clanging of pots and pans in the kitchen, voices in the kitchen barking out orders, the clicking of utensils striking plates, coffee brewing, and the various simultaneous conversations resounded the demanding presence of a business full of life and energy.

Hunger hit Buchanan as soon as he stepped through the doors of the restaurant. When nervous, he ate. Glancing thoroughly over the menu, he located exactly what his taste buds were craving for, the restaurant specialty - a double cheeseburger, steak fries, and his favorite drink, a Mountain Dew with extra ice.

Stepping briskly to Buchanan to take his order, his waitress - short, blonde, and very friendly - ran a mile a minute in the crowded, energetic restaurant.

"Good morning. I'm Florence, and I'll be serving ya. Youin's decided what ya want, sir?"

"I sure do, house special with french fries and a Mountain Dew. That sounds great!" replied Buchanan. "And I want extra ice with that Mountain Dew."

"Well, if you're hungry, it'll fill ya up."

"Thank you." As Florence turned to submit Buchanan's order, he took a panoramic view of the restaurant's décor. His guess, noticing the restaurant's framed military documents and pictures, all of Vietnam, the owner must be a veteran.

Following a couple of minutes, Florence returned with his Mountain Dew. "Ice from top to bottom."

"Great! Just the way I like it. Thank you." Buchanan said. "Can I ask ya a question, Florence?"

"Sure thing, honey. What is it?"

Pointing to the framed pictures, Buchanan asked, "Is the owner of this restaurant a Vietnam veteran?"

"Sure is. And *proud* of it."

Florence stepped to an adjacent booth, checked on its patrons, as Buchanan grinned, pleased with the owner's pride in his service.

As five minutes passed, Florence delivered Buchanan's burger.

Following a blessing of his food, Buchanan delighted in the consumption of his flavorsome lunch. As he enjoyed his burger, two male patrons entered through the restaurant door, featuring traits of veterans, such as age and military attire worn to show a pride of service.

As Buchanan enjoyed his lunch, he caught a glimpse of yet another vet enter the restaurant, then a few more. Eventually, 12 to 14 in all. Navy, Air Force, Marines, Army, even a Coast Guard vet, a full representation of all four branches of the military. Buchanan grasped quickly the men functioned as a support group, who met in the burger joint every Saturday for lunch. The men flooded the space in the corner of the burger joint every Saturday, opposite Buchanan at 1140 hours.

The men spent the morning discussing politics, music, sports, the economy. Just about everything and anything, but the war. Buchanan over heard the most interesting discussion debating who is going to win next year's Super Bowl – the Dolphins or the Cowboys. Next came a discussion on the progress of construction of a new highway. He heard next an exchange on the economic effects of the potential trade embargo on China. One vet expressed his excitement about John Lennon's new release of an album. Many conversations, many topics. One subject not discussed, however - the war. The Saturday mornings were their way of coping. Battling with the constant pain and day-to-day misery of war memories, he too suffered from. The weekend morning contributed to a sort of group therapy for the men. The veterans leaned on each other for stability in their lives.

Buchanan lacked a veteran group to cope. Other than spending time with his wife and kids, music served as a source for Buchanan to cope with his war memories. Music calmed his nerves. Listening to classical music topped his favorite to distract his mind from the war.

Buchanan consumed his last bite of his lunch, extending his hand to Florence with his tip. Thanking her for her service, he stepped to the cash register beside the front entrance and paid his bill.

Turning, Buchanan briskly paced toward the entrance with a boasted strut of confidence. Exiting the restaurant, he made his way to his Buick Oldsmobile and stood frozen beside the driver's door. His boast of confidence is short-lived, knowing the day ahead of him will be a towering hurdle to jump over. Suddenly, home seemed the place for security, to run from his fear of facing the parents of a marine he cherished dearly in his heart. Jumping into his automobile and head home laid heavy on his mind. His emotions were a runaway roller coaster. He sauntered around his Buick Oldsmobile, a shuffled direction left and right. The Skawinski farm just a whiff and a whisker away from A-Mayseing Burgers, but he had never been so nervous in his life, a rare overcoming of uncertainty. He suddenly stepped into his Buick Oldsmobile, contemplating for a few moments on what to do at this point in his journey.

Suddenly, something inside of him said, "Go."

Glancing into the burger joint, Buchanan caught a glimpse of the veterans conversing, enjoying each other's company. He reached up into his inside pocket of his dress coat and glanced at the photo of Skawinski.

Again, a voice inside of him said, "Go." This time, a numbing sensation overwhelmed his sense of space and time, as if the voice seemed audible.

Again, what seemed a discernible voice said - "Go."

Buchanan hunched over the steering wheel, leaning with his arms staring out the windshield. Buchanan is no coward, now knowing the Spirit spoke loud and clear to his heart and soul. Glancing once again at the photo, he half grinned, placing the photo back into his coat pocket.

The Spirit spoke loud and clear, encouraging Buchanan, 'The Skawinskis, they're waiting.'

Though a silent, solemn message given to Buchanan, the message echoed off a bullhorn next to Buchanan's ear. The message rang loud and clear - 'the Skawinski's need a visit from you, Chaplain.' God's voice is real. God's voice is powerful. And if anything in Buchanan's life is certain, he is no coward and God's will is sought first in his life.

"Thank you, Lord." acknowledged Buchanan. With that, he set out for Adolphus' home.

A Family Visit

June 19, 1972

Buchanan turned the ignition of his Buick Oldsmobile, eager to continue his journey. He now knew one truth: God's presence is with him.

Turning the radio on to find some music, he turned to the AM dial, which all he heard turned out to be news and talk shows, with little music. He switched to the Cincinnati Reds pre-game on the Number One 1200 WKYV on the AM frequency, catching the starting pitchers for tonight's game, but still longed for music, so he switched to the FM.

With the love of various genres of music, including recent rock and pop, he turned the radio dial to a local station, catching one of his favorite recent hits on living the country life, singing the lyrics along with the tune as if he is the number one pop artist in the country.

He preferred the country life, and that is exactly what he got with the tune on the radio.

Next came a popular tune from a recent western movie that hit the airwaves. Again, Buchanan sang along.

The next track played is yet another song to ease the trepidation, a special song highlighting the beauty of West Virginia, his wife's home state.

Music fell into place on the radio to ease the tension. The music touched his love of country life, the joy of life, and the Tri-State area. Each facet of life was an important feature within Buchanan's inner soul.

Some 25 minutes passed, and getting nearer to the Skawinski farm. The music seemed a God send to calm his nerves, with his mind distracted from the war, at least temporarily. Leaving the radio on the local station, though in heavier Dayton traffic, Buchanan glanced at his directions for the Skawinski farm, noticing he is near his destination.

The directions guided Buchanan to turn onto Interstate 70 north. His heartbeat quickened at a rapid pace unusual for Buchanan's state of health, as his tongue stuck to the top of his dry mouth.

He seemed nervous, uneasy. 'What is he to say to the Skawinski's?' Questions emerged in his mind - 'What am I to say?' 'Where do I begin?' 'What do I talk about?' 'Do I inform them Adolphus saved my life? And he should be home, alive and well? And not me?'

Traffic lightened up once Buchanan drove past downtown Dayton and more into the rural area north of the city. As 20 minutes passed, Buchanan now exited off the interstate, onto US Route 127 as the directions instructed.

Following a couple of unfamiliar tunes, another uplifting song blasted away on the radio. Again, one of Buchanan's favorites, a fun song, though he questioned the theological message in some lyrics. He didn't care. It's a fun song, and like the others, he sang along. Again, the tune momentarily redirected his thoughts elsewhere.

Toward the tail end of the tune, Buchanan noticed the last road in the directions to the farm - McMillan Road, the road of residence for the Skawinski farm.

Turning the volume down almost to mute on the radio, Buchanan turned right, looking for 556 McMillan Road. The farm location is roughly two miles down the road from the turn. Brush and trees had grown all along the edge of the road, making it almost impossible to see road numbers on the mailboxes. With his vision impaired, he drove alongside the edge of the road, catching a glimpse from time to time of fields full of crops on the other side of the brush and trees bordering the road.

Suddenly, the trees and brush ended on the edge of the road, permitting Buchanan to set his eyes for the first time on the farms and abundant fields of crops cultivated by proud Ohioan farmers. Awed with the sight, Buchanan is beside himself, astonished at what laid before him. As Adolphus described in Vietnam, the farms in western Ohio were beautiful, displaying some of the most impressive farms Buchanan had ever laid his eyes on. The homesteads seemed endless, acre after acre of farmland. His eyes sat on barns in perfect condition, painted with precision, and silos reaching endlessly skyward. The family homes spoke of kinfolk pride, complimented with commercial and crop farms of corn, green beans with crisp leaves, and wheat in perfect form. Most notably to Buchanan is the dairy farms occupied by hundreds of dairy cows. The scene reflected a Saturday Evening Post calendar or painting. Adolphus, in Vietnam, depicted the farms perfectly.

Caught up admiring the beauty of the farms, Buchanan lost his sense of direction on McMillan road. Passing 4 or 5 farm addresses, he becomes conscious of the fact 556 McMillan Road might now be in the other direction. Slowing down considerably to view mailbox addresses, Buchanan attempted to read the postal numbers. The thick heavy brush prevented any exposure of address numbers, pushing Buchanan to the point of stopping his Buick and walking directly to the mailboxes to read the address number. Buchanan stepped out of his car to read the next address number, which read in plain sight: 563 McMillan. Turning around in a driveway, he thought - 'I bet the mailman, out of frustration, is pulling out his hair every day delivering the mail on this road. There's probably a high turnover rate for this mail route'. Buchanan chuckles at the thought.

He backed up into the road, heading in the opposite direction, but slower to view the mailboxes.

After driving for a mile, Buchanan noticed a number on a mailbox which read 556 McMillan Road.

Finally, he reached his destination, full of trepidation, at 1255 hours in the afternoon.

Turning left into the Skawinski driveway, Buchanan pulled into a long and winding drive, as he turned the steering wheel with a sharp left, then a keen right. Trees, along with shrubbery growth, filled the edges of the drive, as the tree branches hovered over the paved driveway, creating a tunnel of nature similar to the foliage of Vietnam. The driveway threw Buchanan a spooky, eerie sensation in his insides. He drove slowly as the trees dissipated in the driveway.

As the end of the driveway stretched out linear, Buchanan laid his eyes on the family homestead spread out for acres.

Skawinski used one word to describe his farm back in Vietnam - 'breathtaking.' Buchanan now has seen with his own eyes Skawinski hadn't been bluffing.

Taking a panoramic view of the farm for the first time, the admiration for the farm fell victim to Buchanan's overwhelming sense of an empty space on the farm. The very fact of Adolphus's absence to greet his chaplain, who ministered to him in a horrific experience the men shared of war, he suddenly found himself overcome with angst and depletion.

Buchanan gradually came to a halt in his Buick 20 feet from the family home. To his left stood two barns, impressive and well groomed.

Not a scratch or chip on the house, painted white with forest green shudders. Buchanan adored large, extensive porches, and the Skawinski porch is wide to the edge, stretching all around the back of one corner of the house. The olive green painted porch welcomed every first-time visitor with warmth, as the Roman pillars painted white stretched from one end of the porch to the other.

The flowers planted in front of the porch welcomed visitors to the Skawinski home, stretching from one end of the front of the porch to the other, while mulberry bushes aligned and stretched down to the corner of the north end of the house.

The drive came to a dead end between the house and the main barn, a magnificent structure displayed in front of Buchanan.

The red main barn, as Skawinski described it in Vietnam, presented visitors the Skawinski's possessed a Protestant work ethic prepared to conquer the agrarian world. The barn presented a perfect structure. No cracks. No blemishes. No chips. Perfect condition. The barn became Adolphus's father's pride and joy. For the Skawinski's, they have always set the condition and presentation of the barn as a top priority for the family.

Adolphus's father insisted the barn on any family farm make a great first impression for a lasting memory for visitors, a priority for the Skawinski's.

Suddenly, two brown healthy Labrador Retrievers, Hugo and Albert, came running around the corner of the barn. Two dogs never to see their master, Adolphus, again. The dogs sprinted lively right on top of the driver's door, wagging their tails, grinning, giving Buchanan the most confident barks they could muster. Hugo and Albert flaunted a love of life and the energy of dogs privileged to live on such a farm. Buchanan loved animals, cats and dogs. The thrill to live displayed by the Labradors thrilled his soul.

The dogs distracted his ensuing observations of the farm, most notably the family garden at the back of the house. The garden presented a picture of perfection, an exact description from Skawinski in Vietnam. Squash, corn, cucumbers, potatoes, zucchini, an additional acre of corn, lettuce, all sorts of peppers and tomatoes – Big Ben, cherry, chocolate sprinkles, grape, Big Boy – amongst others.

Everything about the farm inspired Buchanan. He loved the agrarian culture. All the farm required as a topper, an extra layer of icing on the cake, would be a presence of Adolphus - an extra layer of sweets never to come.

The farm is beautiful. The typical Midwestern Ohioan farm, and one in superb, perfect condition.

Buchanan stepped out of his car, still admiring the farm. He set his eyes on Skawinski's way of life. He now knows why Adolphus considered his home Heaven on earth. As soon as Buchanan exited his Buick, the dogs were all over him, immediately greeting the first-time visitor, smiling friendly, showing their teeth, while they wagged their tails emphatically. A dog lover, Buchanan stretched his hands to greet the dogs. Following the sniffing of his hands, his new found canine friends licked his fingers and palms, jumping and briskly pacing themselves around him. Hugo and Albert sensed a new friend. As Buchanan petted the dogs, he continued to admire the farm.

There were hogs, horses, chickens and roosters, a few cats, goats in a pen, and most numerous domestic animal on the Skawinski farm – hundreds of dairy cows. The agrarian community considered the farm the most prosperous dairy farm in western Ohio. In fact, the farm production ranked most lucrative in the Midwest, employing two dozen employees.

The farm, however, fell short of exact perfection – no Adolphus Skawinski. The beauty. The perfection. But no Adolphus Skawinski. He promised to give Buchanan a grand tour of the farm one day, a day which will never come.

Skawinski is dead. Absent from his dogs. Absent from his farm. Absent from his family.

Standing amid Adolphus's farm, Buchanan thought of nothing but the last moments of his life. The memory of his death flashed before him, as he remembered holding Adolphus in his last moments of life. He remembered Adolphus' attempt to smile one last time and to speak to Buchanan as he died in his arms. And now, he stood in the midst of the Skawinski farm, full of melancholy.

The banging of a screen door interrupted Buchanan's thoughts. William Skawinski stepped forth from the front door of his house, down the steps of the front porch, toward Chaplain Buchanan.

Simultaneously, the men immediately walked briskly toward one another, greeting the other with a firm and warm handshake. The men were ecstatic to meet each other.

"Chaplain Buchanan. Adolphus told us all about you in his letters. It's a pleasure to meet ya. I'm William Skawinski." William said. He glanced at Buchanan's tie. "Great tie. I love the western style - the cowboys, cattle, and all."

"Thank you. It's great to meet you, Mr. Skawinski." Buchanan paused for a moment, troubled by what to say next. Buchanan turned a 180 viewing the entire farm. Turning toward William, he said, "As Adolphus described the farm in Vietnam, it's beautiful. Breathtaking."

Mr. Skawinski looked straight at Buchanan. "He loved our farm, chaplain. He was very proud of it."

Skawinski fought back his emotion.

"I loved your son. Like my own son. A great young man. Proud of his family. Proud of the family farm."

Sternly, Mr. Skawinski said, "He became a man in Vietnam. We sensed it in his letters. You were part of him becoming a man. Thank you for guiding him through it all, Chaplain."

Buchanan nodded in the affirmative. At a loss for words and obviously heartbroken, he simply commented, "He served his country well. His country, Ohio, and *his* family."

The men smile.

"Let's go meet Mrs. Skawinski, Chaplain." William said.

"Let's do. I've been looking forward to meeting her."

"Great! Let's go inside the house. Elsa's probably working in the kitchen or in the garden. Chaplain? I, well -"

"Yes?" questioned Buchanan.

"Well, I - ya need to know."

"Yes, Mr. Skawinski. What is it?" inquired Buchanan.

"You'll see, Chaplain."

Puzzled, Buchanan ambled up the front steps to the front door and entered the house, following Mr. Skawinski. Buchanan fell aghast at what laid in front of him. The home mirrored Christmas, ornamented with decorations. He is beyond belief, flabbergasted. The month of June half complete, and still the Christmas season? Buchanan thought, 'there's definitely something odd here?'

A Christmas tree towered toward the ceiling in the corner opposite from the corner fireplace, with imposing collectibles of Santa Claus and Rudolph figures scattered all over the living room, displayed on the end tables and the spacious coffee table. Garland hung festive on the stairwell facing the living room. Garland hung merrily on top of the fireplace. Original works of art of Santa Claus hung on the walls from a prominent painter. One odd sight for Buchanan was the Christmas cards in a basket post marked 1969 on the coffee table. Taking a peek into the dining room, Buchanan spotted Christmas décor in all four corners of the room, as Christmas dinner ware sat on the dining room table ready to serve a Holiday feast, a meal readied for Adolphus in December 1969. But the oddest sight in the house Buchanan laid his eyes on is the unwrapped gifts under the tree, ready for Adolphus to open on Christmas morning back in December 1969. Buchanan, leaning down toward the coffee table, once again noticed the 1969 postmarked Christmas cards. Turning to Mr. Skawinski, Buchanan turned red and teared up. Buchanan quietly asked, "Don't tell me these Christmas decorations have been up since 1969?"

Mr. Skawinski nods yes. He whispers, "She's kept'em up ever since the news of Adolphus's death. She decorated early for his arrival from Vietnam." His voice broke. "She won't take them down. H-He loved Christmas, ya know."

Buchanan sighed heavily. "I know." He lowered his head, sighing heavier. He thought, 'I'm not alone.' He suffered for three years spiritually and emotionally from the scars of war. He has now seen the effects of war second hand. He has discovered a new perspective of the results of combat fatigue, and the Skawinski's revealed to him the results of combat on a family. He's the beaten end of a stick. And now, for the first time, he's witnessed in someone else how severe war affects the mental and spiritual state of a human being.

Suddenly, the bang of a screen door and the sounds of footsteps indicated signs of Ms. Skawinski's presence. The noise of a busy kitchen became apparent. The rattling of pots and pans banged, then heard placed on the stove. Her presence and the necessity of the kitchen on a farm is evident in her work ethic. Placing the pots on the stove to cook vegetables for supper, she engrossed herself in taking pride in preparing the yield retrieved from the family garden.

"You in the living room, William?" inquired Mrs. Skawinski. "Is Chaplain Buchanan there with you?"

"Yes, Elsa. It's Chaplain Buchanan."

"Great! I'm coming."

Mr. Skawinski quickly and softly spoke to Buchanan. "Be patient with her, Chaplain." Grinning, he gave Buchanan a wink.

Her footsteps drew nearer as she walked on the wooden floors toward the living room. Turning the corner from the hallway in the middle of the house into the living room, Ms. Skawinski, smiling from ear to ear, is delighted she is finally meeting her son's spiritual mentor from Vietnam.

Buchanan stood in awe at the first glance of Adolphus' mother. In Vietnam, he described his mother's appearance with one word - 'beautiful.' And that she is, 'beautiful.' Overwhelmed, she impressed Buchanan with her form of beauty. As a Scandinavian blonde with ivory skin, blue eyes, 5'3" and 125 pounds, she is, as Adolphus described, beautiful and magnificent. In contrast to Mr. Skawinski, who stands 6'3", 230 pounds, stout, and strong, he towered over his wife like a mountain. Looking at the couple, the contrast humored Buchanan. Adolphus exemplified the family pride in his Scandinavian and Swedish history, as the Skawinski family epitomized the hard working Midwestern work ethic.

"I'm sorry I wasn't here to greet you, Chaplain. I picked vegetables in the garden for supper and gathered eggs in the chicken coop."

"That's perfectly all right, Ms. Skawinski. I'm all familiar with your family's work ethic."

She wiped her hands on her apron, shaking Buchanan's hand. The apparent avoidance of mentioning Adolphus stood over Ms. Skawinski, nervous and apprehensive.

"Well, I'm Mrs. Skawinski. But I guess ya already know that, don't you?"

The three laugh.

"Very pleased to meet ya, Chaplain. We have so much respect for you. Adolphus thinks of you pretty much as a second father." said Ms. Skawinski, speaking of Adolphus in the present tense.

Buchanan swallows hard, clearing his throat.

"Adolphus hasn't come home yet from the war. We're still waiting for him. When he does come home, we're going to celebrate Christmas with him." Ms. Skawinski smiles broadly. "He loved Christmas. But you already knew that, didn't you?"

"Well, yes. I did." responded Buchanan, grinning.

No one really longed to smile. There wasn't much to smile about. Suddenly, a deep desire to weep and grieve over Adolphus' absence of a Christmas homecoming is all Buchanan and his parents sought to do. Of course, the three thought better of it.

"Adolphus loves Rudolph the Red-Nosed Reindeer. Can't wait to see it on TV again when he gets home." commented Ms. Skawinski.

Buchanan, taken aback, is now convinced Ms. Skawinski suffers from total denial. Mr. Skawinski, shaken and fighting back his emotions, recognizes the shock on Buchanan's face.

Grinning, Ms. Skawinski said, "Listen, Adolphus wants you to have something. Let me go upstairs, get it for ya."

Ms. Skawinski lowered her head, shifting her eyes left and right, avoiding eye contact. Turning curtly, she ran up the stairs to the second floor of the house, obviously distraught.

Buchanan stood bewildered.

Mr. Skawinski steps to his chair, quietly sitting down. Waiting patiently for Ms. Skawinski's return, Buchanan attempted to put his visit into perspective.

Hearing the clatter in an upstairs bedroom come to an end, Ms. Skawinski hurries back down the stairs, returning to present Buchanan with a gift.

"Here it is! Here it is!" she shouted. "Adolphus wants ya to have this Jack Barnes autographed football. One of his prized possessions of Ohio State, very proud of this football. He loves Jack Barnes." Struggling to hold back her emotions, Ms. Skawinski paused for a moment. "C-Coach Barnes signed this football when William and he attended a game a few years ago. They attend games every year, you know. It's yours." Extending the football in her hands toward Buchanan, expecting him to accept the football wholeheartedly, he's overwhelmed with pity and a sense of defeat, gently grinning.

"Well, I - I don't think I need to, well - take this football. It's a family piece of football nostalgia."

Ms. Skawinski, surprised by Buchanan's response, stared with great disappointment.

"*No*. It's *yours*." Ms. Skawinski insisted.

Buchanan glanced at Mr. Skawinski, shaking his head yes toward Buchanan.

"Well, then....I accept." said a complied Buchanan with apprehension.

"Good." said Ms. Skawinski, smiling joyfully.

"Listen, I've got to get back to the kitchen. Again, it was very good to finally meet you. Your ministry to Adolphus is very good. Thanks for taking care of him. When he finally gets back from Vietnam, you - you..." Ms. Skawinski's composure broke a bit, "you need to bring your whole young family over to have dinner, and we can get to know each other better. Well, goodbye."

Ms. Skawinski is closer to facing the truth. The fact Adolphus's return from Vietnam for his triumphant Christmas homecoming will never come for his parents. Their loving son is never to celebrate Christmas at home again.

Ms. Skawinski turns, returning to the kitchen. The confrontation facing the reality of Adolphus' demise in Vietnam has been long in waiting for Ms. Skawinski, the reality he is never coming home. Frequently, Ms. Skawinski faced the certainty of her boy's death, only to discard the truth. It hurt too much to accept.

Silence stifled Buchanan and Mr. Skawinski, speechless with a loss of words. The men say nothing, as Buchanan spoke little for the rest of the visit. In his heart, he wailed in grief and sorrow. Internally, the whirlwind of emotions inundated him. The fact Adolphus saved his life became too much for him to take. He sought to inform them, but he held back. He felt it necessary to apologize time and time again for Adolphus' death, that he sacrificed his life to save his chaplain's life, and that he should be in the living room here today, not Buchanan. He held back, holding the truth inside.

The back screen door flew open, followed by a bang of the screen door closing shut. Ms. Skawinski returned to the garden, set to pick more vegetables.

"Come back to the kitchen with me, Chaplain." Mr. Skawinski said.

The men cautiously made their way down the hallway to the kitchen, heading smartly toward the back kitchen window. They peeked out the back window, locating Ms. Skawinski in the garden. Frantically and anxiously, she picked vegetables. She manifested a mundane, close to a mechanical routine in the garden. Buchanan noticed a trance like behavior out of her. Buchanan was even more convinced now she suffered from total mental denial.

"Every day. The same every day." commented Mr. Skawinski. "Gets up, cooks, then cleans. From dawn to dusk. Never stops. When she first heard of Adolphus's death, nothing but recluse and isolation resulted from the news. She read and reread his letters from Vietnam repeatedly. The only trips away from the house were to church or to the grocery store. She's in total denial."

A hurt Buchanan had never felt before flourished within himself, hammering away at his heart, his body, and his soul. His thoughts raced. One thought stood atop of all the others - that here in Ohio, a family lost their only child, never to see his beloved farm again because of a cruel, wasteful war. Buchanan learned early in Vietnam war did not discriminate. War killed black, white, fat, skinny, rich, and poor. And sometimes, unfortunately, it snatched a family's only child.

Buchanan hated war. He detested war for many a reason, but one fact of war he immensely abhorred more than any other is the truth that war seized children from one's parents. The war embedded the epitome of pain for parents losing a child due to war. In the Skawinski's experience of losing their only son, their pain ate away at them little by little.

"Here she comes, Chaplain." warned Mr. Skawinski.

The pair of newfound friends scampered back up to the front of the house. They certainly did not intend to hurt her feelings by spying on her. Hurrying themselves to the living room, the men hectically sat on the couches.

The men once again heard the swinging of the screen door pulled open, slamming back into place with a clear bang, giving way to a lengthy but nerve-racking silence for Buchanan and Mr. Skawinski. The two thought, 'What's with the silence?' The men peered toward one another with a notion of intrigue. 'Was she standing dormant next to the kitchen table?' 'What was she thinking about?'

Suddenly, the reverberance of an echo rang through the house of a large pail placed on the kitchen table full of vegetables Ms. Skawinski had picked from the garden. Buchanan heard footsteps once again on the wooden floor as she again made her way from the kitchen up to the living room.

Ms. Skawinski turned the corner from the hallway once again into the living room, smiling toward Buchanan. "Chaplain Buchanan, I'm glad you're still here. I have Adolphus's letters for you for keeps. I'll get them for ya. Wait till you read them all." Ms. Skawinski grins as if humored. "He praises you in all of them. You can walk on water, ya know?"

Buchanan smiles at the notion.

Hurrying back upstairs to retrieve the letters, Ms. Skawinski can again be heard causing a clangor retrieving the letters.

Buchanan motions toward Mr. Skawinski, expressing concern.

"Chaplain, I think this is her way of saying thank you. Giving ya the football, the letters and all. I think maybe this is a breakthrough." Mr. Skawinski can no longer fight back his emotions. He weeps.

Ms. Skawinski scampers back down the staircase, stepping toward Buchanan sitting on the living room couch.

"Here they are." Elsa said, handing the letters in a large box to Buchanan.

Over 100 letters, Buchanan stood, receiving the communications from Adolphus.

"Adolphus says you're the reason he-he got through the war. I-I am...really looking forward to seeing the two of you together someday." By now, Elsa fights back tears with every molecule of her body and soul.

Buchanan said, "Ms. Skawinski, please sit. I, uh - I need to say something." Ms. Skawinski sat down, reflecting fright as he clutched her hand, sitting beside her. Mr. Skawinski stepped over toward Elsa and Buchanan, sitting on the other side of Elsa. By now, she exposed a fidgety, anxious demeanor. Mr. Skawinski put his arm around his wife.

Buchanan, clearing his throat, rubbed his chin, swallowing hard before he spoke. He himself nervous and hesitant. The steady voice heard at the restaurant once again speaks decisively to him. The voice encouraged Buchanan, 'Speak.'

With a pause, the voice spoke once again and with affirmation, 'Speak to her.'

Buchanan hesitated, and again he heard the voice within himself, 'Tell her what she needs to hear.'

So Buchanan, with confidence and assurance, boldly spoke. "Ms. Skawinski - *Elsa*. You will never see Adolphus and me together in *this* life."

Pausing, Buchanan glared straight into Ms. Skawinski's eyes. Never had he deemed a pair of eyes so full of hurt and sadness. In Buchanan's heart, he is now convinced no other mother in the country could be more mournful, grief-stricken, and downcast, losing her boy, her only child, due to the war. Her eyes spoke of grief and weariness from the loss in her life.

Buchanan said, "Adolphus. Adolphus is gone. Gone forever in *this* life. I held him as he died in my arms three years ago."

A pause from Buchanan seemed an eternity.

"I prayed and read scripture with him as he died."

The loss of words is evident as silence overcame the living room.

Ms. Skawinski said, "No. No!"

"Yes. I quoted the Lord's Prayer with him, quoted the Beatitudes, and prayed with him. I'm the last person in this life he laid his eyes on. I promised him I would come and visit the family farm that day. And Here I am."

"No." responded Elsa, as she whimpered, holding back her tears, nodding no the whole while.

Buchanan said, "I know he is with Jesus today. The Lord received him. He's farming still, or plowing, or whatever the Lord had in store for him when he passed through the pearly gates into Heaven. He's waiting for us to join him someday. Elsa, I was praying the Lord would reveal to me what purpose I-I had in coming today. And I think I now know. It's to let you know that Adolphus, well - Adolphus, is waiting in Heaven for you and William to join him there someday."

Elsa painfully sobbed, shaking slightly as Mr. Skawinski held her tight.

Buchanan rose off the coach, stooped down and grabbed the letters in the box. He walked toward the front door, stopping momentarily beside the parents of a young man Buchanan briefly new in this life, but dearly loved as a Christian brother and a young man who considered Buchanan a father figure. Touching Mr. Skawinski's shoulder, he silently asked God to bless them, and continued toward the door.

Elsa cried softly, as Buchanan now knew God had sent him to comfort Adolphus's mother, guiding her in accepting Adolphus's death, and to grieve for him truthfully and honestly.

Stepping toward the chair the football sat in, Buchanan glanced down at the ball, picking it up. Second guessing himself, he placed the football back down into the chair. He found it improper to leave with the football in his possession, as he glanced back toward the Skawinski's, observing the suffering of grieving parents before his very own eyes. Glancing back down toward the football, he once again picked it up, grasping the ball permanently. Elsa insisted he leave with it, knowing her gesture means saying goodbye to Adolphus. Leaving the football behind would have hurt her deep inside her heart. So he left the property with the football sitting in the front seat of his Buick Oldsmobile.

"Chaplain. Thank you." wept William, persistent in holding Elsa. Devastated, she is now totally distraught with misery.

Buchanan glanced back toward two parents who, uncontrollably in pain and hurt, can now push forward in life with the acknowledgment Adolphus is waiting for them in Heaven with Jesus. The acceptance of the fact Adolphus, gone forever, will never step onto the farm again. His parents now came to grips with his death. That for three years the two had denied Adolphus' death. His parents fled from the excruciating pain of losing him. The result had been three years of bewilderment and a meandering state of glum. The Skawinskis will never get over losing Adolphus, but with time, life will adjust to losing their beloved son. But even with time, the pain and suffering of losing Adolphus will be ever so present. The hurt will never go away. Over the years, Buchanan never admitted to them Adolphus sacrificed his life to save others, including his own. News of Adolphus saving Buchanan's life certainly would be a devastating blow to the emotional and spiritual wellbeing of the Skawinskis. Never did he admit to them it should be Adolphus home and well, and Buchanan listed as a KIA. The fact would haunt Buchanan for the rest of his life.

Buchanan stepped out the front door, weeping. Making his way to his Buick Oldsmobile, he would climb into his car with the football under one arm and the letters in one hand. Hugo and Albert greeted him from the front door of the house all the way to the driver's door of his Buick. The canines, displaying a love of life, served Buchanan well as a therapeutic means of coping with the pain of losing Adolphus and witnessing the pain from his parents with their devastating loss, losing their only child. He petted the dogs for the last time. "Goodbye Hugo. Goodbye Albert. Take care of things here at the Skawinski farm." Buchanan smiles at the dogs, stepping into his Oldsmobile behind the steering wheel, closing the driver's door.

Buchanan, stunned and exhausted with the visit, thought, 'Should I have come?' 'Did I make matters worse for the Skawinski's?' The answer is yes he needed to come and visit. And no, it did not make matters worse. To hear the truth coming from Buchanan ended up essential for the Skawinski's coming to grips with Adolphus's death and to go on living their lives. The pain will never go away for the Skawinski's, but now the sting of death can subside, knowing Adolphus is in Heaven eternal with Jesus.

Glancing at the box of letters Adolphus wrote from Vietnam, he sifted through the letters out of curiosity, stunned the letters were placed in chronological order according to the post stamp. Adolphus's last letter written, given to the mail carrier delivered by Buchanan in Vietnam, laid as the top letter of the pile. Puzzled with the condition of the letter, Buchanan examined it thoroughly, discovering the torn edge taped up in layers. 'Why tape it up?' Buchanan concluded the denial entrenched in Elsa steered the abnormal behavior.

Buchanan drew out his pocketknife and cut the letter open. Curiosity got the best of him to know the contents of the letter, too antsy to hold back, opening up the communique with his parents.

Drawing out the letter from the envelope, Buchanan unfolded a 2-page letter and read. From the start of the letter, his brokenhearted emotions ran wild all the way to the end of Adolphus's hand written document. Reading silently Adolphus's last letter, he found humor in his formal dating and location of the letter. Finding any humor at all this day, Buchanan welcomed with open arms.

He finally read the letter.

September 27, 1969
Camp Love
7th Engineering Marine Battalion

"Dear Mom,

I'm almost home. Nineteen more days, and out of the bush. Nineteen more days, I'll be in California. Twenty-one more days, home. Home! I'm ecstatic. So much looking forward being with you, Dad, the farm, taking care of the animals, going back to school. I made it. Three tours - and survived. This last tour was the worst, though. Many violent fights, much violence. Need your help when the problems come my way. One thing is for sure, Chaplain Robert Buchanan inspired me. He helped me maintain my sanity. God put him in my path. His ministry encouraged me, let me know God still loved me, though I took another human life in battle. He's always open to marines to talk. He's inspiring - telling stories and uplifting quips. Of all the chaplains in Vietnam I met, he's the best! It was a pleasure to serve with him. Mom, I witnessed him lift the spirits of many. The birthday party for Corporal Rodriquez, he'd never had a birthday party in his life. He was emotional coming through the chow hall door when we yelled, "Happy birthday!" He never experienced a surprise birthday party. If you could have seen his expression. It was unforgettable! And Sergeant McMillan, denied going home when his mother was close to death, but Chaplain Buchanan fought to get him home early so he could see his mother alive before she passed away. And then there was

Lance Corporal Jones, always depressed and down on himself. Buchanan has helped instill confidence in himself. Chaplain Buchanan helped Pokorny, from South Dakota, get accepted into South Dakota University. He was worried his background would prevent him out of the university. Chaplain Buchanan knows a professor in Kentucky who knows a professor at South Dakota University and he intervened on Pokorny's behalf. He will enter college work when he arrives home in South Dakota. And then there's Burnside, who had an outstanding combat record in Vietnam, who Buchanan helped push through an early departure from Vietnam. He was Quaker, and having problems with his faith's stance of killing other human beings. And of course there were Dobbs and Sims, the two unbelievers I've told you about in the past. Two human beings which no other chaplain but Chaplain Buchanan could have led to become believers in Christ. Totally self absorbed human beings and Buchanan led them to turn their lives around. He held Sims in his arms, shot up on patrol in the bush. He died in the arms of the man who led him to a better life, in becoming a Christian. I have a feeling that our sergeant never did like the idea that they became Christians. Sergeant Smith thought that too much religion would make a marine too soft and be a hindrance in combat. Well, they showed him. They became better marines. All these things happened because of Chaplain Buchanan. God used him. He placed Buchanan in our presence for those things to happen. I know it without any doubt. No one else could have done what he did at that moment in time. I prayed for good things to happen for my fellow marines, my friends, and God used Chaplain Buchanan for my prayers to be answered in the affirmative. I can't wait to show him the farm and for you and Dad to meet him. You are going to like him very much. I want to show him the dairy farming business. I am looking forward to meeting his family. Well, I got to go for now. I will see you within three weeks. Can't wait. Letter is a little long, but I have so much to tell ya. Hug Dad for me. We will go to church and sing in the choir together once again. Greet and pet Hugo and Albert for me. Until then, I love you. Looking forward to being home.

With love,
Your son,
Adolphus

Buchanan emptied his tear ducts, incapable of holding back. Sitting in his car, he's stunned and motionless for, it seemed to him, an eternity.

A dose of depression hits Buchanan, for the letter is yet another reminder Skawinski is dead. And now his parents face a forced adjustment for the rest of their lives in the loss of Adolphus. But his parents can now grieve and go on with their lives. No more pretending Adolphus never lost his life to war. The grieving can aid in healing the pain suffered since October 1, 1969. The Skawinskis now have affirmation Adolphus is never coming home. Buchanan now knows his visit had been a necessity to relay the truth to Elsa Adolphus is indeed dead. God led him to Preble County this day.

Buchanan wept with joy, knowing God spoke to the Skawinskis and to marines in Vietnam through him. He once again reached for the photo of him and Skawinski, smiling at the visual reminder of the loving and energetic kid now in the arms of Jesus, forever and ever in Heaven, waiting for his parents to join him. He laid the photo down on the passenger's seat, pondering a bit about his Vietnam experience.

More than that, Buchanan finally came to know God indeed used him in Vietnam and God had been with him. God answered his prayers, not by the Devil. Prayers lifted to God were acknowledged and affirmed by God, prayers lifted up and not always winding up how Buchanan wanted them answered. The war was not going to just stop because he prayed for it to stop. The killing would not stop with simple, lifted up prayers for it to stop. But prayers for God's blessings to be bestowed upon the lives of the marines were prayers God answered in the affirmative. Today, he discovered the truth. Buchanan showed the men of the 7th Marine Engineering Battalion the love of Jesus. Though many scoffed, those who accepted a life for Jesus had been worth all the blood, sweat, and tears Buchanan and Jackson exerted while assigned to the 7th Engineering Marine Battalion.

Placing the letter back into the envelope, Buchanan turned the ignition of his Buick ready to back up out of the driveway. As he is about to back up in the driveway to pull forward toward the road, he noticed through the front window of the living room Elsa sitting on the couch with her head on her husband's shoulder, weeping and holding on to each other, grieving and mourning Adolphus's death.

Buchanan sighed. He lifted up a prayer for the Skawinskis every day of his life.

Backing up in the driveway, he turned the car around, smiled and waved goodbye to Hugo and Albert, and drove down the driveway onto McMillan Road. He drove back toward Dayton, then on to McArthur, Ohio, to continue his ministry in the small but close knit community in southeastern Ohio.

A couple of miles down the road, he flipped the radio on the AM dial to Number One 1200 WKYV to listen to his beloved Reds on his way back home. Listening to the Big Red Machine calmed his nerves.

For the rest of his life, though, he suffered a difficult struggle with the repercussions of war.

His life would never be the same. He experienced a war memory every day of his life.

Adolphus topped the most frequent memory of combat or war experience. Knowing God applied Buchanan's ministerial skills to assist Skawinski through the days of war while he had been alive smoothed Buchanan's emotions through the years as he coped with the memories of his death.

As Buchanan drove into the early evening, he felt God's presence with him. If indeed he had a flashback, with God's help, he would get through it.

God indeed used him for His Glory and planted seeds of God's love in each marine and sailor, using him to assist the marines in the 7th Marine Engineering Battalion during his combat tour at Camp Love.

Buchanan and the Skawinski's learned the truth on June 19, 1972.

The war haunted him for the rest of his life. But God's omnipresence will forever be present with him, speaking to him ever so softly and lovingly.

Buchanan finally knew in his heart God indeed answered his prayers. God never forsakes him. God's presence indeed is forever present to confront the Evil One in his dreams and the never ending memories of the war.

And in the end, one day
...the Father in Heaven will ultimately win
...and someday,
...someday....no more war.

LETTING GOD SPEAK THE TRUTH

OCTOBER 24, 1987

God is God. Because he is God, he is worthy of my trust and obedience. I will find rest nowhere but in His holy will that is unspeakably beyond my largest notions of what he is up to. - Elizabeth Elliot

The early evening reined in a cold, wintry October fall night in southeastern Ohio. The winter came early in the Tri-State area in 1987. The Buchanan's welcomed the cold, a family favorite season. The temperature is anything but cool inside Waverly Baptist Church, Waverly, Ohio. The temperature rose high as 438 people packed into a sanctuary seating only 375, including the choir loft. The Annual Missions and Evangelism Conference for the Scioto Valley Baptist Association began, and Buchanan, one of the main speakers for the evening, exhilarated a gun ho mood for those in attendance. Buchanan's minister position is Director of Missions for the association affiliated with the Southern Baptist Convention, the largest Protestant denomination in the United States. A Director of Missions position reflected that of district priests in liturgical denominations such as Lutherans or Episcopalians. Buchanan, excited with the attendance of the evangelism conference, an annual event, expected great things for the evening, one of the highest attended meetings every year in the association. Buchanan beamed with confidence to deliver his evangelistic sermon, as his family sat in the congregation wholeheartedly supporting him this night, a special annual night in the association. He delivered one of his finest sermons in his life. Though he is fired up to deliver a message on evangelism and starting new Southern Baptist churches in southeastern Ohio, his mind wondered, distracted because of a nightmare he unfortunately experienced the night before.

Finding himself captured by the Viet Cong in his dream, they parade Buchanan through Hanoi, North Vietnam. The Communists force him to endure a gauntlet of jeers, prickling of knives and swords upon Buchanan's body from spectators alongside the streets. Commies ran toward him, throwing stones and rotten food, hitting his body violently. All the while, Commies threw heavy punches into Buchanan's bruised face. At the end of the gauntlet line, Buchanan finds himself pushed mercilessly into a warehouse serving as an arena for the Devil, who is waiting for him to fight to the death in a boxing ring. The Devil armed himself with swords, knives, and hatchets, while the Devil will expect Buchanan to defend himself with his bare hands. Buchanan, shell-shocked, entered the Devil's Lair. The Commies pushed him violently towards the boxing ring, occasionally knocking him to the ground. Hundreds of Viet Cong and Commies in the arena cheered the Devil on as he slayed each prisoner entering the ring. As Buchanan is shoved fiercely, he looked to his left and right, noticing men and women he served with in Vietnam thrown into a heap of corpses all mangled and torn to pieces, killed in the boxing ring by the Devil. Jackson. Porch. Lucas. Skawinski. Burns. Burnside. And many others. Everyone intertwined in the mangled and bloodied mass of lifeless corpses. The dream tops one of the worst, gruesome dreams he's ever experienced. When finally pushed into the ring with the Devil, Buchanan faces the Devil weaponless and openly vulnerable to the Devil's evil self. Obviously, Buchanan is no match for the Devil, as he toys with Buchanan, spinning and twirling his weapons, circling around him and waving his weapons in the face of Buchanan and toward his neck. The futile attempts to protect himself with his fists humored the Commies and the Viet

Cong as fiendish laughter spilled from their wicked mouths. The Devil, bored with taunting and toying with Buchanan, starts the effort of running him through with his sword, but just as the Devil is about to complete the *coup de gras*, Buchanan wakes up just as the Devil is about to finish him.

Buchanan woke up sweating and exhausted. The dream had shaken him up all day. And the night required him to deliver a sermon on evangelism, which he prayed to God he could get through the evangelism conference without a serious flashback.

Usually, Buchanan and Dorothy, as a team, attempted to interpret dreams together if he felt comfortable to divulge his dream with her. Many dreams Buchanan kept secret, but this dream he couldn't hold within his heart and mind, begging Dorothy to help him cope with the violence of the sequence of images and horrors of the dream. The dream presented a difficult task to decipher, however, because of the odd circumstances within the nightmare. The dream ends up foremost on Buchanan's mind as he sets himself mentally to deliver his sermon. He fell fearful a major flashback might spring up in the middle of his sermon. Nonetheless, his presence tonight seemed essential for the people of the Scioto Valley Baptist Association and he certainly will not dishearten them and, more importantly, disappoint the Lord.

Buchanan used the dream as a catalyst to deliver his sermon like no other in his life, sending a heavy blow to the Devil. The dream fired him up ever more so to counter the Devil's victory in his dream, to dispense a heavy blow to the Evil One, the Devil, and to hammer onto the Adversary an ultimate pounding defeat.

Buchanan delivered his sermon on an all-time high. Never had he preached such an inspirational sermon on reaching unsaved people in his life. He spoke to every heart of every person representing churches in the association he dearly loved. After an evening of sermons, the rejuvenation for evangelism in the association will be evidenced by a new height of unbelievers coming to know the Lord in the next year. As the night progressed, he recognized a row of men in the back of the sanctuary. And lo-and-behold, the men were Jackson, Adkins, and a few others from the war. The intent had been to surprise him, and they certainly did. Buchanan surely stood stunned, but pleased. With a closing prayer to end the conference, he rushed to the back of the sanctuary with a fury to greet the men. The reunion served as a therapeutic shot in the arm for Buchanan. The men reminisced. The men laughed. His spirit soared into the night following the reunion.

Many bright spots emerged through the years for Buchanan, including this evening's evangelism service. The years would come and go. And not without an eminent degree of trepidation; falling asleep every night will be nothing but a risky endeavor out of fear of experiencing a nightmare, a strain on his emotions and physically exhausting. Nevertheless, living life for Robert centered in on one and only purpose - fulfilling God's will in his and his family's life. Spending time with fellow military personnel this night from the war served as a secure, mental stabilizer for him.

Sources to provide security in his life to cope with the sufferings of war will be music and his family. And he appreciates both of them.

But only God will get him through his lifelong pain of permanent memories and emotional suffering of witnessing war first hand.

And God *will* help him.

Fate exerted itself for a no ending certainty for Buchanan.

The Devil systematically raised his ugly head in memory. The Devil milled about in his dreams, sneaky and conniving. But God always, without question, rallied around Buchanan and faced down the Devil, shewing his foe away.

By faith Buchanan submitted to the verse quoted to marines frequently in Vietnam, I Peter 5:7, 'Cast all your anxieties on him, for he cares about you.'

By faith, he confronted his anxieties from within, crushing his fright and trepidation time and time again.

But the pain would never cease, nor would it flee from him.

And the nightmares.....never ending, a constant reminder of war.

APPENDIX A

A HISTORY OF FATHER VINCENT ROBERT CAPODANNO

The first inkling I heard in my life of a hero status of Chaplain Vincent Robert Capodanno, a Roman Catholic Priest, came as I eased dropped in on a conversation of Vietnam veterans, Naval Reservist Chaplains serving with my father, on a weekend Navy drill. For reasons forgotten after all these years, I tagged along with Dad on his weekend drill, which was rare because of the rules and regulations of families denied the liberty to come and go as they pleased, as it disrupted the readiness training of the troops. For whatever reason, I was present, and heard the uplifting conversation of Chaplain Capodanno. The Navy reservists threw words about in the room to describe the chaplain. Brave. Sacrifice. A man of God. The 'Grunt' Chaplain. From the start of the conversation, it had enthralled me with the story of Chaplain Capodanno. As a young teenager, the household I grew up in lifted up sacrifice and courage on the battlefield. The awe felt in my gut hearing of Capodanno impressed my young heart and mind. The lasting impressions of Capodanno still live in my heart this day.

I bumped into Chaplain Capodanno's story again in 1985, going through Navy boot camp in Orlando, Florida. While I worked in the Chaplain's office on the weekends in boot camp, I took the valuable time getting to know the Catholic chaplain at the Base Chapel. The chaplain further reinforced my admiration for Lieutenant Capodanno, informing me how high of a special place he has in the hearts of Navy chaplains, lifting the spirits of marines as a conquering sacrifice of will and individual heroism. The chaplain introduced to me for the first time Chaplain Capodanno has had streets and buildings named after him. The Navy has honored the chaplain by attaching his name to chapels and installations to them. He even informed me the Navy honored him naming a Navy ship with his last name and the only ship ever to be blessed by the Pope himself.

Chaplain Capodanno is one of my heroes growing up. I have admired his sacrifice and bravery ever since my teens.

Lieutenant Vincent Robert Capodanno, referred to in *The Devil in My Dreams*, lost his life, killed in action on September 4, 1967. 'The Grunt Padre', defying orders from marine sergeants to remain secure and away from combat, simply said, "I need to be with my marines." The battalion commander laid his eyes on the chaplain for the last time when 'The Grunt Padre' climbed up into a helicopter to transport the devoted, courageous chaplain into the heat of a fiery firefight raging in a battle in the Que Son Valley, 29 miles southwest of Da Nang. Capodanno frowned upon using a weapon, but exposed himself frequently to enemy gunfire to tend to the wounded in a battle. Hundreds of marines were enclosed along an open knoll surrounded by thousands of North Vietnamese Army regulars who had taken cover in an extended tree line, picking off marines in the open one after the other.

Father Capodanno and marine reinforcements disembarked in the afternoon to relieve the trapped marines. Seriously wounded marines were laid all about over the knoll area from the earlier battle, and Chaplain Capodanno wasted no time in tending to wounded marines. Taking hold of whatever he could clutch his hands on to pull marines to safety, primarily armored jackets, Capodanno used the medical training received for combat duty and bandaged the marines' wounds. In a split second, a mortar round hit the ground near the chaplain, delivering several wounds to Capodanno. The battle taking place is the nastiest combat Father Capodanno had experienced in Vietnam.

The chaplain had been ministering to marines in his second tour at 38 years old - a man twice the age of many marines. Father Capodanno consistently sprinted down one end of the knoll to the other for two hours, tending to the wounded. As he physically cared for wounded marines, he carried out his ecclesiastical duties as a chaplain, praying and blessing the wounded men.

Father Capodanno was known to have said to the marines, "You're not alone, marine. God's with you. You'll be all right."

As the reports of Capodanno's last hours spread with the scuttlebutt, the apparent devotion and inspiration he spread to the marines during the battle and that God showed in the course of the few hours a man of tenacity and resolve.

Following Father Capodanno's urgency tending to several marines and one medic, the chaplain glanced in one direction and yet came across additional wounded marines. As he darted toward the marines, the enemy riddled Capodanno with projectiles from an NVA machine gun, 27 bullet wounds in all.

The Lord welcomed him to Heaven with open arms. And as Jesus said, "Well done, good and faithful servant."

Capodanno was born on February 13, 1929 on Staten Island, New York, the 10th child of Italian immigrants. Growing up in a Catholic household, Capodanno's foundation in life stemmed from his Catholic faith, love of country, and a Midwestern work ethic, though he grew up in New York.

His family worked in the shipyards, while his three older brothers served in World War II. Capodanno had not been short of positive male mentors in his life.

He attended Fordham after high school, while working as a clerk at Wall Street, adding to the family income.

His calling to the ministry came from an early age. As God called him to be an evangelist, he became familiar with the Maryknoll missionaries in China, led by a spiritual mentor and Brooklyn born Bishop Francis Xavier Ford. Capodanno applied to become a Maryknoller in 1949, and after nine years of ecclesiastical training, the ordination of Vincent Capodanno came to pass in 1958. Father

Capodanno's ministry began the same year being sent to present-day Taiwan, the island of Formosa.

While visiting the United States on furlough, Father Capodanno had been given the news of a transfer of ministry to Hong Kong after six years of priestly ministry and teaching on the island of Formosa. While ministering in Hong Kong, God called Father Capodanno to enter a new ministry - the United States Navy Chaplain Corps. His calling is to minister to the increasing numbers of United States service personnel in South Vietnam. Following a process of requesting permission from Catholic superiors to enter the Navy Chaplain Corps, Father Capodanno applied for the chaplaincy program and, after attending chaplaincy school, joined the United States Navy Chaplain Corps in 1966. The Catholic chaplain saddled up and joined the 7th Marines in Vietnam to minister to grunts in the field.

While in Vietnam, Father Capodanno accompanied the grunts on patrols in the bush. He carried his own load, and traveled wherever the marines traveled, rain or shine. Capodanno counseled men. He prayed with them all night while in anguish and heartache following the death of a friend killed in action. He lived amongst the marines in the field, in the bush. The chaplain became so bonded with the marines, the men nicknamed him 'the Grunt Padre', a high honor. He adapted to the harsh life ministering with the Maryknollers, which instilled in him the rigors of the bush.

Capodanno visited many combat bases, hospitals, villages and hamlets while in South Vietnam. Going beyond the expectations of Navy chaplains, he wrote letters of sympathy to parents who lost a son from the hands of the dreaded enemy. An open door policy many chaplains maintained in Vietnam had been apparent in Capodanno's ministry. The men were welcome in his hootch twenty-four seven.

In the 16 months of ministry in Vietnam, Capodanno's popularity spread within the Marine Corps population, Protestant and Catholic alike, who longed for his presence in the bush while on patrol.

Chaplain Capodanno set the standard for ministry and the precedent for future chaplains of the United States Navy and Marine

Corps. His actions on September 4, 1967 has been honored for over five decades, leaving a legacy of tribute.

In 1969, Father Capodanno won posthumously the Medal of Honor. The Navy awarded him the Navy Bronze Star, the Vietnamese Cross of Gallantry with a Silver Star, the Bronze Star with Combat V, and the Purple Heart.

A Navy ship commissioned in his honor was named USS *Capodanno* on November 17, 1973 and the first United States ship to receive a Papal blessing when John Paul II blessed the ship on the anniversary of his death.

Memorials in honor of Father Capodanno came with the Saint Vincent Chapel, Taiwan and the San Francisco Bay Naval Shipyard dedicated Capodanno Hall, to provide space for a Bachelor's Officers' Quarters.

Chaplain Capodanno's legacy has been placed throughout the United States with roads, streets, the naming of Navy base chapels, hospitals, and schools.

The most notable memorials are on Staten Island on Capodanno Avenue and the memorial in Fort Wadsworth, New York, in the front of Father Capodanno Memorial Church.

The Catholic Church has declared Father Capodanno a Servant of God, the first step of four towards sainthood.

His greatest legacy lives far beyond self-absorbed accolades, ribbons, medals, or monuments, but lives on in the hearts of men he served.

APPENDIX B

ARMY AND NAVY CHAPLAINS ON THE VIETNAM WAR MEMORIAL IN WASHINGTON DC

Of the 58,000 names inscribed on the black granite walls of the Vietnam Memorial, there are 16 chaplain names chiseled amongst the panels of brave servicemen and women. The list consists of 16 courageous and fearless chaplains on the wall.

1. Major William J Barragy, 101st Airborne Division
   United States Army
   From Waterloo, Iowa
   Killed May 4, 1966
   Chaplain Barragy died while riding on a CH-47 because of mechanical failure.
   Denomination: Roman Catholic Church
   Panel number 7E/22
2. Lieutenant Colonel Don L Bartley, MACV
   United States Army
   From Rockbridge Baths, Virginia
   Killed June 8, 1969
   Chaplain Bartley was assisting a film crew for a television program on Vietnam Chaplains when a hostile mine exploded, killing the chaplain.
   Denomination: United Presbyterian Church
   Panel number 23W/109

3. Lieutenant Robert R Brett, 2nd Battalion, 26th Marine Regiment
   United States Navy
   From Washington DC
   Killed on February 22, 1968
   The Siege of Khe Sanh is the bloodiest battle of the Vietnam War. Chaplain Brett lost his life ministering to the wounded during the siege due to an artillery attack. He had offered ten or more masses a day.
   Denomination: Roman Catholic Church
   Panel number 40E/58
4. Captain Merle D Brown, 1st Battalion, 20th Infantry, AMERICAL Division
   United States Army
   From Columbus, Ohio
   Killed April 11, 1971
   While on call to soldiers of the 1st Battalion, 20th Infantry, the enemy fired onto the helicopter he was in and shot it down. Chaplain Brown died in the crash.
   Denomination: Lutheran Church
   Panel number 4W/118
5. Lieutenant Vincent Robert Capodanno, 3rd Battalion, 5th Marines
   United States Navy
   From Staten Island, New York
   Killed September 4, 1967
   Chaplain Capodanno was an inspiration to many Vietnam chaplains. The day of his death, his actions earned him the Medal of Honor. As Father Capodanno was ministering to the wounded and administering last rites to marines, enemy and mortar fire wounded him. Though wounded himself, he ran to a wounded corpsman and enemy fire ripped through him, killing him. The Navy considered his actions that day an act of heroism. The marines knew him as the 'Grunt Padre'.
   Denomination: Roman Catholic Church

Panel number 25E/95
*Chaplain Capodanno inspired Navy chaplains Catholic and Protestant alike in Vietnam, a mentor and template for ministry to marines in a combat zone. My first introduction to Chaplain Capodanno was from Dad, serving as a United States Navy Reserve Chaplain. Inspired by Father Capodanno's story as a youngster, his story was one of many factors motivating me to join the Navy Reserve to serve in the chaplain's office. His bravery and dedication to the Lord has never been forgotten.

6. Lieutenant Colonel Meir Engel, MACV
United States Army
From Philadelphia, Pennsylvania
Died on December 16, 1964
Born in Israel and immigrating to the United States, Chaplain Engel served in World War II and Korea, a veteran of two wars. He served in a third combat situation in Vietnam. Showing signs of ill health, he entered a hospital in Saigon on December 16, 1964 and died of a heart attack.
Denomination: Jewish
Panel number 1E/77
7. Captain William N Feaster, 196th Infantry
United States Army
From Portsmouth, New Hampshire
Died October 26, 1966
Enemy artillery fire came raining in on Chaplain Feaster and the 196th Infantry on September 18, 1966. As Feaster attended to the wounded, he himself discovered he suffered wounds from shrapnel and projectiles after the artillery fire began. Fighting an infection in the hospital, he died on October 26, 1966.
Denomination: Congregational Christian Church
Panel number 11E/109

8. Lieutenant Commander William J Garrity Jr., USS Oriskany
   United States Navy
   From Havre, Montana
   Died October 26, 1966
   Chaplain Garrity, serving on the USS Oriskany, died while giving last rites and consoling sailors who had been injured and many dying from a fire which overwhelmed the ship, killing 44 sailors and causing injuries on an additional 156. He died from heat exhaustion and smoke inhalation.
   Denomination: Roman Catholic Church
   Panel number 11E/110
9. Major Ambrosio S Grandea, 1st Battalion, 14th Infantry
   United States Army
   From Baltimore, Maryland
   Died June 13, 1967
   On May 25, 1967, while leading troops in church services, which were interrupted by enemy mortar fire, Chaplain Grandea fell victim to serious injuries from the enemy shells. Airlifted to Clark Air Force Base in his native Philippines, he died later from an infection.
   Denomination: Methodist Church
   Panel number 21E/97
10. Major Roger W Heinz, 5th Special Forces Group
    United States Army
    From Coventry, Connecticut
    Killed December 9, 1969
    Traveling in poor weather, the helicopter transporting Chaplain Heinz crashed into a hillside, killing the popular chaplain. His wife and his two daughters survived him.
    Denomination: Lutheran Church (Missouri Synod)
    Panel number 15W/42
11. Captain James J L Johnson, 4th Infantry Division
    United States Army
    From San Francisco, California
    Killed March 10, 1967

Chaplain Johnson died while traveling on a Navy VC-47 airplane with 14 other military personnel when there was a wing failure while in flight.
Denomination: Baptist Church
Panel number 16E/53

12. Major Aloysius P McGonigal, Army
United States Army
From Washington DC
Killed February 17, 1968
In the final attack on the Citadel in the battle for the control of Hue, Chaplain McGonigal accompanied the 1st Battalion, 5th Marines in combat, as many chaplains did in Vietnam. There were many marines killed and wounded during the attack, and Chaplain McGonigal comforted and gave the last rites when enemy small arms fire killed him. He was a former educator, teaching physics.
Denomination: Roman Catholic Church
Panel number 39E/75

13. Captain Phillip A Nichols, 1st Battalion, 52nd Infantry
United States Army
From Kalispell, Montana
Killed October 13, 1970
A deadly booby trap killed Chaplain Nichols while in the bush as he was making his way between units to minister to the troops. Popular and well liked, the soldiers knew him for his sharp kept green uniforms and playing the guitar.
Denomination: Assemblies of God Church
Panel number 7W/133

14. Captain Michael J Quealy, 1st Infantry Division
United States Army
From New York, New York
Killed November 8, 1966
Chaplain Quealy fell victim to enemy bullets while giving the last rites and tending to the wounded from hostile machine gun fire near Saigon during combat. He flew to the site

against leadership guidance to stay put, but his calling and the need of a chaplain for those dying and wounded superseded leadership advice. His ministry came first and foremost for Chaplain Quealy.
Denomination: Roman Catholic Church
Panel number 12E/43

15. Captain Morton H Singer, XXIV Corps
United States Army
From Flushing, New York
Killed December 17, 1968
While on his way to conduct Chanukah ceremonies on December 17, 1968, Chaplain Singer's C-123 plane transporting him to the field crashed after it had taken off. His untimely death in Vietnam came just one month after he arrived in southeastern Asia. He gave his life pursuing a call to preserve the freedom of religion for United States soldiers.
Denomination: Jewish Faith
Panel number 36W/37

16. Major Charles J Watters
United States Army
From Berkeley Heights, New Jersey
Killed November 19, 1967
Chaplains in the Navy and the Army assisted medics and corpsmen in battle. While offering spiritual ministry to the wounded and assisting medics with wounds, enemy shells threw explosive fragments toward Chaplain Watters, killing him. His actions of bravery and courage displayed that day by Watters earned him a posthumous Medal of Honor.
Denomination: Roman Catholic Church
Panel number 30E/36

BIBLIOGRAPHY

Arnold, James R. *Artillery: The Illustrated History of The Vietnam War.* Vol. 7. New York City, New York: Bantam Books, 1987.

Axelrod, Alan. *The Real History of the Vietnam War: A New Look at the Past.* New York: Sterling, 2013.

Bagar, Robert, and Louis Bincolli. *The Concert Companion: A Comprehensive Guide To Symphonic Music.* New York City And London: Whittlesey House, a division of the Magraw-Hill Book Company, Inc., 1947.

Baker, Dr. Th., ed. *A Dictionary of Musical Terms.* New York City: Schirmer Books, a division of Macmillan Publishing Company, Inc. & London: Collier MacMillan Publishers, 1923.

Bates, Milton J., Lawrence Lighty, Paul L. Miles, Ronald H. Spector, and Marilyn Young. "Reporting Vietnam: American Journalism 1959-1975." New York: Literary Classics of the United States, 1998.

Bergsma, CHC, U.S. Navy Commander Herbert L. *Chaplains with Marines in Vietnam 1962-1971.* Washington, DC: History and Museums Division Headquarters, U.S. Marine Corps, 1985.

Boettcher, Thomas D. *Vietnam: The Valor and the Sorrow: From the home front to the front lines in words and pictures.* Tulsa: Trade and Culture Books, 1985.

Bowman, John S. *The World Almanac of the Vietnam War.* New York: Bison Books Corporation, 1985.

Bulone, Philip V. Soul of the Eagle: A Chaplain Assistant's Recollection of the Vietnam War. Denver, Colorado: Outskirts Press, 2014.

Cohen, Steven. *Vietnam: Anthology and Guide to A Television History.* New York: WGBH Educational Foundation, 1983.

Command Chronology: Camp Love, 7th Engineering Marine Battalion. October 6, 1968.

Command Chronology: Camp Love, 7th Engineering Marine Battalion. November 7, 1968.

Command Chronology: Camp Love, 7th Engineering Marine Battalion. December 6, 1968.

Command Chronology: Camp Love, 7th Engineering Marine Battalion. January 7, 1969.

Command Chronology: Camp Love, 7th Engineering Marine Battalion. February 4, 1969.

Command Chronology: Camp Love, 7th Engineering Marine Battalion. March 11, 1969.

Command Chronology: Camp Love, 7th Engineering Marine Battalion. April 11, 1969.

Command Chronology: Camp Love, 7th Engineering Marine Battalion. May 20, 1969.

Command Chronology: Camp Love, 7th Engineering Marine Battalion. June 20, 1969.

Command Chronology: Camp Love, 7th Engineering Marine Battalion. July 20, 1969.

Command Chronology: Camp Love, 7th Engineering Marine Battalion. August 20, 1969.

Command Chronology: Camp Love, 7th Engineering Marine Battalion. September 20, 1969.

Command Chronology: Camp Love, 7th Engineering Marine Battalion. October 20, 1969.

Command Chronology: Camp Love, 7th Engineering Marine Battalion. November 20, 1969.

Conboy, Ken, Ken Bowdra, and Simon McCouaig. *The NVA and Viet Cong.* Vol. 38. London: Osprey Military, 1991.

Cross, Milton. *Encyclopedia of the Great Composers and their Music: Volume I and II.* Garden City, New York: Doubleday & Company, Inc., 1953.

DiGiovanni, Stephen M. *Armed with Faith The Life of Father Vincent R. Capodanno, MM.* 2018

DK Smithsonian. *The VIetnam War: The Definitive Illustrated History.* New York: Dorling Kindersley Limited, 2017.

Ezell, Edward C. *Personal Firepower: The Illustrated History of The Vietnam War.* Vol. 15. New York: Bantam Books, 1988.

Falabella, J. Robert. *Vietnam Memoirs: A Passage to Sorrow.* Annapolis, Maryland: Naval Institute Press, 1971.

Forbes, John, and Robert Williams. *Riverine Force: The Illustrated History of The Vietnam War.* Vol. 8. New York City, New York: Bantam Books, 1987.

Foster, Randy E. *Vietnam Firebases 1965-73.* Vol. 58. Oxford, United Kingdom: Osprey Publishing, 2007.

Gilbert, Ed. *The US Marine Corps in the Vietnam War: III Marine Amphibious Force 1965-75.* Battle Orders 19. Oxford, United Kingdom: Osprey Publishing Ltd, 2006.

Hammond, William M. *The U.S. Army in Vietnam: Public Affairs The Military and The Media: 1962-1968.* Washington, D.C.: Center of Military History, 1990.

Hearden, Patrick J., ed. *Vietnam: Four American Perspectives.* West Lafayette, Indiana: Purdue University Press, 1990.

Herring, George C. *America's Longest War: the United States and Vietnam, 1950-1975*. New York City, New York: John Wiley & Sons, Inc., 1979.

Hutcheson, Jr., Richard G. *The Churches and the Chaplaincy*. Atlanta: John Knox Press, 1975.

Jamieson, Neil L. *Understanding Vietnam*. Berkeley, California: University of California Press, 1993.

Jones, Ian. *Booby Traps! The History of Deadly Devices from World War I to Vietnam*. New York: Skyhorse Publishing, 2004.

Kamien, Roger, ed. *The Norton Scores: An Anthology for Listening*. New York City: W.W. Norton & Company, 1997.

Karnow, Stanley. *Vietnam: A History: The First Complete Account of Vietnam at War*. New York: The Viking Press, 1983.

Libbey, Ted. *The NPR Guide to Building a Classical CD Collection*. New York City: Workman Publishing, 1994.

Longyear, Rey. *Nineteenth-Century Romanticism in Music*. Second ed. Englewood Cliffs, New Jersey: Prentice-Hall, Inc., 1973.

Machlis, Joseph. *The Enjoyment of Music: An Introduction to Perceptive Listening*. New York City: W.W. Norton & Company, 1970.

Maga, Ph.D., Timothy P. *The Complete Idiot's Guide to The Vietnam War*. New York: Alpha Books A Division of Penguin Books, 2010.

McMahon, Robert J., ed. *Major Problems in the History of the Vietnam War*. Belmont, California: Wadsworth Cengage Learning, 2008.

Melson, Charles. *Vietnam Marines 1965-73*. Elite 43. Long Island City: Osprey Publishing Ltd., 1992.

Melson, Charles D., and Ramiro Bujeiro. *US Marine in Vietnam 1965-73*. London: Osprey Military, 1998.

Mode, Father Daniel L., author and Gerald H. Turley, foreward. *The Grunt Padre*. CMJ Marian Publishers, 3rd edition, June 1, 2000.

Mooney, James W., and Thomas R. West, eds. *Vietnam: A History and Anthology*. St. James, New York: Brandywine Press, 1994.

Olson, James S., and Randy Roberts. *Where the Domino Fell: America and Vietnam, 1945-1995*. New York City, New York: St. Martin's Press, Inc., 1996.

Palmer, Dave R. *Summons of the Trumpet: US - Vietnam in Perspective*. Novato, California: Presidio Press, 1995.

Parade Rest: Protocol and Social Customs for Marine Officers and Spouses. N.p.: Marine Corps Association.d.

Patterson, Thomas G. "Major Problems in American History Series." In *Major Problems in the History of the Vietnam War*, edited by Robert J. McMahon, Belmont: Wadsworth Cengage Learning, 2008.

Pimlott, John. *Vietnam Decisive Battles*. London: Barnes and Noble, Inc with Marshall Editions, Ltd., 1999.

Rosen, Charles. *The Classical Style: Haydn, Mozart, Beethoven*. New York City And London: W.W. Norton & Company, 1997.

Rottman, G. *Viet Cong and NVA Tunnels and Fortifications of the Vietnam War*. Fortress 48. Oxford, United Kingdom: Osprey Publishing, 2006.

Sadie, Stanley, ed. *The Norton/Grove Concise Encyclopedia of Music*. New York City and London: W.W. Norton & Company, 1994.

Sorley, Lewis. *Westmoreland: The General Who Lost Vietnam*. New York, New York: Houghton Mifflin Harcourt Publishing Company, 2011.

Sutherland, Jon, and Diane Canwell. *The American Experience in Vietnam: American Women in the Vietnam War*. Milwaukee, Wisconsin: World Almanac Library, 2005.

The Marines in Vietnam 1954-1973 An Anthology and Annotated Bibliography. Washington, DC: History and Museums Division Headquarters, U.S. Marine Corps, 1985.

"The Vietnam War: A Comprehensive and illustrated history of the conflict in Southeast Asia." edited by Ray Bonds, London: Salamander Books Limited, 1999.

Tucker, Spencer C. *The Encyclopedia Of the Vietnam War: A Political, Social and Military history*. New York: Oxford University Press, 1998.

Verrone, Richard B., and Laura M. Calkins. *Voices from Vietnam: Eyewitness Accounts of the War, 1954-1975*. Cincinnati: David and Charles, 1988.

Vietnam War Memorial: The Names, www.vvmf.org

Waugh, Alexander. *Classical Music: A New Way of Listening*. New York City: MacMillan, 1995.

Wells, Jack. "The Battles of Firebase Six-Shooter." *Vietnam Vol. 30, No. 4*, December 2017., 22-29

Westheider, James. *Fighting In Vietnam: The Experiences of the U.S. Soldier*. Mechanicsburg, PA: Stackpole Books, 2007.

Whitt, Jacqueline E. *Bringing God to Men: American Military Chaplains and the Vietnam War*. Chapel Hill: The University of North Carolina Press, 2014.

Wiest, Andrew. *Rolling Thunder in a Gentle Land: The Vietnam War Revisited*. Oxford, United Kingdom: Osprey Publishing, 2006.

Wiest, Andrew. *Vietnam: A View From the Front Lines*. Oxford, England: Osprey Publishing, 2013.

Wiest, Andrew. *The Vietnam War 1956-1975*. Essential Histories 38. Oxford, United Kingdom: Osprey Publishing, 2002.

Willbanks, James H. *Vietnam War Almanac: An In-Depth Guide to the Most Controversial Conflict in American History*. New York: Skyhorse Publishing, 2009.

Wright, James. "The Capture of Hamburger Hill." *Vietnam Vol. 32, No. 1*, June 2019., 24-31

Notes

War is An Ugly Thing

* Mill, John S. *Principles of Political Economy*. Prometheus Books, 2004.

Preface

* Junger, Sebastian. *Principles of Political Theory*. Grand Central Publishing, 2011.

Traits of a Chaplain

* *True Grit*, 1969. Directed by Henry Hathaway, starring John Wayne, Paramount Pictures.
* *A Prayer Book for Soldiers and Sailors*. 1st ed., The Church Pension Fund, 1941.
* Howard, Vernon. *https://thequotesforlife.com*, Powered by WordPress, 5 July 2017, thequotesforlife.com.

The Veterinarian

* Howarth, David. *Waterloo: A Near Run Thing*. 1st ed., London: Phoenix, 1968.

No News is Good News

* Worcester Cathedral Choir. "Once in Royal David's City." *The Choir Of Worcester Cathedral – Christmas Carols from Worcester Choir*, Polydor: UK, 1972.
* St. Paul's Cathedral Choir. "In the Bleak Mid-Winter," *St. Paul's Cathedral Choir - Christmas Carols from St. Paul's Cathedral*, Music for Pleasure: UK, 1967.
* Hinton, J. Alban. *Rejoice and be Merry*. 1960. Oxford University Press, 1960.

The Navy Officer

* U.S. Congress. (1951) United States Code: Uniform Code of Military Justice, 10 U.S.C. [Periodical} Retrieved from the Library of Congress.

The "Super Sophomores"

* Chandler, David G. *The Campaigns of Napoleon*. 1st ed., MacMillan Publishing Company, 1966.
* MacDonell, A. G. *Napoleon and His Marshalls*. London. 1950.

Kentucky

* Waldo Emerson, Ralph. *quotepark.com*. Powered by Beautiful Quotes. 3 June 2021, adopted from Wikiquote.

A Full Day of War

* Bret Maverick aired on television between 1957-1962. The show starred James Garner, Jack Kelly, and Roger Moore and was created by Roy Huggins. The show centered on a gambler, Bret Maverick, and his travels from town to town gambling and running into trouble from time to time. IMDB provides a thorough description of each episode of the series.

* A television show Bat Masterson aired on television between 1958-1961 starring Gene Barry. The dandy character of Masterson used his innate intelligence and humor to bring justice to the old west. His reputation of using his shrewdness instead of a gun showed throughout the series. The show reflected the real life Army scout, lawman, and gambler William "Bat" Masterson. IMDB lists and describes all the episodes.

The Birthday Party

* Patton, George S. *Finestquotes.com.* Link from Quote of the Day.

No More Cease Fire

* Coolidge, Calvin. *Brainyquote.com.* Link from Quote of the Day.

The Death of a Hero

* Puller, Lieutenant General "Chesty". Rusavskiy, Vitaliy. 'Face of Defense: Navy Corpsman Serves to Help Others.' *defense.gov*, U.S. Department of Defense, 13 July 2018, defense.com.

The Sacrifice of Men

* Roosevelt, Franklin D. *Goodreads.com.* Goodreads Inc.

The Dumb Jock

* Oman, Charles. *Revival: Studies in the Napoleonic Wars (1929), The Battle of Maida*. 1st ed., Routledge, 1929.
* Glover, Richard. *Peninsula Preparation: The Reforms of the British Army, 1795-1809*. Cambridge University Press,1963.

Hating the Enemy

* Tolstoy, Leo. *Goodreads.com*. Goodreads Inc.

John Wayne Visits the Friday Night Social

* Anderson, Patrick. (1969, June 27). The Vietnam Nam Timetable 1969. *Time, Vol. 93 No. 26*, 3-4.

Letting God Speak the Truth

* Elliot, Elizabeth. *Through Gates of Splendor,* Spire Books, January 1970.

All Scriptures taken from the Revised Standard Version.

Printed in the USA
CPSIA information can be obtained
at www.ICGtesting.com
CBHW030858210324
5564CB00003B/8

9 798218 238346